Electronic
Fundamentals
and
Applications

Prentice-Hall Series in Electrical Engineering

William L. Everitt, *Editor*

ANNER   *Elements of Television Systems*
ARMINGTON AND VOLZ   *An Introduction to Electric Circuit Analysis*
BALABANIAN   *Network Synthesis*
BARTON   *Radar System Analysis*
BENEDICT   *Introduction to Industrial Electronics*
CHANG   *Parametric and Tunnel Diodes*
DAVIS AND WEED   *Industrial Electronic Engineering*
DEKKER   *Electrical Engineering Materials*
DE PIAN   *Linear Active Network Theory*
DUNN AND BARKER   *Electrical Measurements Manual*
EVANS   *Experiments in Electronics*
FETT   *Feedback Control Systems*
FICH   *Transient Analysis in Electrical Engineering*
FICH AND POTTER   *Theory of A-C Circuits*
FLORES   *Computer Logic: The Functional Design of Digital Computers*
FOECKE   *Introduction to Electrical Engineering Science*
GOLDMAN   *Information Theory*
GOLDMAN   *Transformation Calculus and Electrical Transients*
HERSHBERGER   *Principles of Communication Systems*
JORDAN   *Electromagnetic Waves and Radiating Systems*
KUO   *Automatic Control Systems*
LECROISSETTE   *Transistors*
LEGROS AND MARTIN   *Transform Calculus for Electrical Engineers*
LO, ET AL.   *Transistor Electronics*
MALEY AND SKIKO   *Modern Digital Computers*
MARCUS   *Switching Circuits for Engineers*
MARTIN   *Electronic Circuits*
MARTIN   *Physical Basis for Electrical Engineering*
MARTIN   *Ultra High Frequency Engineering*
MOSKOWITZ AND RACKER   *Pulse Techniques*
NIXON   *Handbook of Laplace Transformation; Tables and Examples*
NIXON   *Principles of Automatic Controls*
PARTRIDGE   *Principles of Electronic Instruments*
PASKUSZ AND BUSSELL   *Linear Circuit Analysis*
POTTER AND FICH   *Theory of Networks and Lines*
PUMPHREY   *Electrical Engineering*, 2nd
PUMPHREY   *Fundamentals of Electrical Engineering*, 2nd
REED   *Electric Networks Synthesis*
REED   *Foundation for Electric Network Theory*
RIDEOUT   *Active Networks*
ROBICHAUD, ET AL.   *Signal Flow Graphs and Applications*
RUSSELL   *Modulation and Coding in Information Systems*
RYDER, F. L.   *Creative Engineering Analysis*
RYDER, J. D.   *Electronic Engineering Principles*, 3rd
RYDER, J. D.   *Electronic Fundamentals and Applications*, 3rd.
RYDER, J. D.   *Networks, Lines and Fields*, 2nd
SHEDD   *Fundamentals of Electromagnetic Waves*
SKODER AND HELM   *Circuit Analysis by Laboratory Methods*, 2nd
SOOHOO   *Theory and Application of Ferrites*
STOUT   *Basic Electrical Measurements*, 2nd
THOMSON   *LaPlace Transformation*, 2nd
VAN DER ZIEL   *Noise*
VAN DER ZIEL   *Solid State Physical Electronics*
VAN VALKENBURG   *Network Analysis*, 2nd
VON TERSCH AND SWAGO   *Recurrent Electrical Transients*
WARD   *Introduction to Electrical Engineering*, 3rd
WARFIELD   *Introduction to Electronic Analog Computers*
WEED AND DAVIS   *Fundamentals of Electron Devices and Circuits*

Electronic Fundamentals and Applications

THIRD EDITION

John D. Ryder

Dean, College of Engineering
Michigan State University

Prentice-Hall, Inc.

Englewood Cliffs, N. J.

PRENTICE-HALL INTERNATIONAL, INC., LONDON
PRENTICE-HALL OF AUSTRALIA, PTY., LTD., SYDNEY
PRENTICE-HALL OF CANADA, LTD., TORONTO
PRENTICE-HALL OF INDIA (PRIVATE) LTD., NEW DELHI
PRENTICE-HALL OF JAPAN, INC., TOKYO

Fourth printing..... September, 1965

Printed in the United States of America.
Library of Congress Catalog Card Number 64–14393
C—25131

Preface
to the Third Edition

This third edition is intended to provide an integrated treatment of solid-state devices and the older vacuum and gaseous forms of active electronic devices. Much of the fundamental phenomena underlying both types has been consolidated into a joint treatment, since both areas are based on a knowledge of electron energies, charge movements, and conduction in solids, gases, or vacuums. Where the individual device forms are studied, the theory of the transistor and other solid-state types has usually been given first prominence, after which the vacuum devices can be more briefly treated because of similarities in the concepts and methods involved.

Much of the specialized vacuum and gas tube material has been reduced in treatment. The subject of amplifiers has been expanded by further study of pulse response, and the chapter on modulation now includes an introduction to pulse forms of modulation and to information capacity of channels. The text also includes coverage of the newer forms of amplifiers and generators reaching prominence in the uhf field.

The quantitative treatment of previous editions has been retained, and emphasis is given to the basic properties of an analytic method or process rather than to the particular electronic device, since so many of the processes employed are applicable to fields other than electronics. This is particularly true with such subjects as oscillation, modulation, frequency conversion, and feedback.

J. D. Ryder

Table of Contents

Four-Terminal Active Networks | 6 147

Control Devices: The Transistor | 7 164

Control Devices: | 8
The Vacuum Tube

Linear Small-Signal Amplifiers | 9

width of the parallel-resonant circuit. 9–22. Singly-tuned amplifiers. 9–23. Transistor singly-tuned amplifiers. 9–24. Doubly-tuned amplifiers. 9–25. The overcoupled circuit. 9–26. Design of overcoupled circuits. 9–27. Butterworth and Chebyshev responses.

Feedback; Direct-Coupled Amplifiers | 10

10–1. Feedback in amplifiers. 10–2. Input conditions. 10–3. Effects on distortion; feedback in decibels. 10–4. Gain stability with feedback. 10–5. Effect of feedback on input impedance. 10–6. Effect of feedback on output impedance. 10–7. Inverse feedback circuits. 10–8. Stability of inverse-feedback circuits. 10–9. Gain and phase margin. 10–10. Direct-coupled amplifiers. 10–11. Chopper amplifiers. 10–12. Transistor choppers. 10–13. The operational amplifier. 10–14. Transistor operational amplifier. 10–15. Voltage regulators using d-c amplifiers.

Class A and B Amplifiers With Large Signals | 11

11–1. Output circuits. 11–2. Power relations. 11–3. Determination of amplitude distortion. 11–4. Intermodulation distortion. 11–5. Maximum power output—pentodes and triodes. 11–6. Transistor power performance. 11–7. The push-pull Class A amplifier. 11–8. The Class AB push-pull amplifier. 11–9. The Class B push-pull amplifier. 11–10. Cross-over distortion. 11–11. Transistor amplifiers with complementary types. 11–12. Phase inversion for push-pull input. 11–13. Amplifiers with reactive loads.

PHYSICAL CONSTANTS

e = charge on the electron = 1.602×10^{-19} coulomb.

m = mass of the electron at rest = 9.106×10^{-31} kilogram (kg).

e/m = charge to mass ratio for the electron at rest = 1.759×10^{11} coulombs/kg.

c = velocity of light = 2.99776×10^8 meters per second $\cong 3 \times 10^8$ meters per second.

h = Planck's constant = 6.624×10^{-34} joule-second.

k = Boltzmann's constant = 1.380×10^{-23} joule per °K.

N = Avogadro's number = 6.024×10^{23} molecules per mole.

Å = Angstrom unit = 10^{-10} meter.

ϵ_0 = space permittivity = $10^7/4\pi c^2$ = 8.85×10^{-12}.

ev = electron volt = 1.602×10^{-19} joule.

One atomic weight = 1.65×10^{-27} kilogram.

Atomic weights on the physical scale are relative to the weight of the oxygen isotope O^{16} taken as equal to 16.

Electronic
Fundamentals
and
Applications

Behavior of Charged Particles in Fields 1

Electronic devices operate by control of electric charges moving through semiconductor materials, gases, or vacuums. By utilization of these electronic devices in various types of circuits it is possible to control or convert electric energy, or to process electrical signals to yield useful information which may be conveyed by those signals.

Included in the electronic family of devices are the newer solid-state types, the diode and the transistor which employ either electrons or positive charges (holes) to convert energy or to process information. Also included in the family are the array of vacuum and gaseous electron tubes.

This text will treat much of the fundamental theory of both classes of devices. It will also emphasize the characteristics of the circuits in which they are employed, and the fundamental processes of energy transfer or information reduction which can be achieved by linear or nonlinear operation of the active electronic circuit elements.

1-1. Early history

Modern electronic science is usually considered as having been born in 1883 with the discovery of the Edison effect. Edison, in his search for improvements in incandescent lamps, had sealed into one of his lamps a small metal plate in addition to the usual filament. During one of his experiments with this lamp, Edison discovered that when the metal plate was made positive with respect to the heated filament, an electric current would flow in the wire leading to the plate, as was indicated by the deflection of a galvanometer as in Fig. 1-1. When the polarity of the applied potential was reversed, the flow of current through the space inside the lamp ceased.

Interested only in improving his lamp, Edison reported on this unilateral phenomenon and then passed on to other matters which appeared more important to him at the time.

J. A. Fleming (circa 1897) applied the Edison effect to the rectification, or detection, of radio signals, achieving increased sensitivity and stability over the crystal or electrolytic detectors then used. In 1906, Lee de Forest added the grid or control element to the Fleming diode, making a highly sensitive electrostatic relay, the triode tube. In so doing, he started the science of electronics on its present path.

It has been known for many years that certain natural crystals possess rectifying properties, and galena, silicon, and iron pyrites were used as detecting devices in early radio reception. The use of crystals for radio signal detection went into eclipse when the triode vacuum tube became available, but crystal rectifiers were revived as detectors during the development of radar equipment prior to World War II because they gave better performance than vacuum tubes at extremely high frequencies. This led to much research in semiconductor or crystalline materials, and in 1948 a semiconductor triode, the transistor, was announced by Bardeen, Brattain, and Shockley. This further accelerated the research in semiconductor materials, and the transistor has now superseded the vacuum tube in many applications.

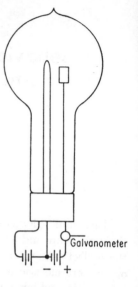

Fig. 1–1. Device used to show the Edison effect.

1–2. The atom

In the late nineteenth century, the atom was believed to be the smallest indivisible particle of matter. Lord Rutherford suggested that an atom might consist of a core of positive charge (*nucleus*) surrounded by a cloud of negative charges sufficient in number to render the atom electrically neutral. Working from Rutherford's conception of the atom, Niels Bohr later proposed an atomic model much like the solar system, dynamic in nature and contrasting with the previously held static theories of the atom. The negatives charges were placed in motion in orbits about a central nucleus of positive charge, and no more than one negative charge was permitted to occupy any given orbit. Bohr's atomic theory was successfully used to explain line spectra, X rays, and electric current conduction through gases.

However, certain other experimental phenomena could not be well explained by the Bohr theory. Efforts to employ the Bohr atom model in explanation of these phenomena have led to modifications in the definiteness of the geometry of the Bohr model. Thus, the negative charges have been assigned wave as well as particle properties, energy values have been substituted for the orbits, and the mathematical formulation of wave mechanics has been developed.

Although much of the positive physical picture supplied by the original Bohr model has been lost, these recent developments have provided a more satisfactory conception of an atom, and of its function in electric conduction in solids, liquids and gases.

1–3. The electron

Later experiments showed that the current passing between the electrodes in the Edison effect was due to a procession of negatively charged particles. Sir J. J. Thomson discovered similar small charges during early research on "cathode rays" and it was proposed that they be named *electrons*, a term invented by G. Johnstone Stoney. This name has been accepted and applied to the negatively charged particle of electricity now considered the basic element in the science of electronics.

The electron is the smallest indivisible unit of electricity, since no smaller charge has ever been detected. Although its configuration is unknown, it may be assumed as spherical whenever it is thought of as a particle. In certain situations the electron also appears to possess wave properties, but no satisfactory explanation of this duality of particle and wave properties is yet available. The concept utilized for discussion of particular phenomena is usually that which leads to the most satisfactory explanation of the experimental results.

Thomson's early measurements showed that every electron carried exactly the same charge per unit of mass (e/m), and when, about 1910, Millikan measured the electric charge on the electron and found it constant, it became apparent that all electrons were identical. The charge on the electron is now believed to be 1.602×10^{-19} coulomb, and since e/m has been measured as 1.759×10^{11} coulomb per kilogram, the mass of an electron is seen to be 9.106×10^{-31} kg.

It is thought that electric current in solids, gases, and vacuums is due to the movement of electric charges, frequently negative electrons. Benjamin Franklin was one of the first to propose that an electric current be thought of as an electric-fluid flow from positive to negative in a metallic circuit external to the source. The technique of electrical engineering has been built on this concept, which is now known to be reversed for negative electrons that actually flow from negative to positive in the external circuit. The customary usage is too well established to be overcome and, although unfortunate, need cause no difficulty. In this text, when electric currents are referred to, the customary direction is meant; when the reference is to electronic currents, then the flow of electrons from negative to positive is to be considered.

1–4. Neutrons, protons, photons

As now postulated, all atoms are made up of electrons moving in orbits around a group of particles compressed into a central nucleus. In this nucleus are concentrated the mass and positive electric charge of the atom. The number of negative electrons is equal to the atomic number of the element, and, for a normal atom, the negative charge of these electrons is exactly balanced by the positive charge of the nucleus. A hydrogen atom has an approximate outer diameter of 10^{-8} cm. and a nucleus of nominal diameter of 10^{-13} cm.

The nucleus is composed of protons and neutrons in varying numbers. The _proton_ is a particle carrying a positive electrical charge which is numerically equal to the negative charge of the electron, and has a mass approximately equal to that of the hydrogen atom H^1, whose nucleus consists of only one proton. The _neutron_ carries zero electrical charge and has a mass 0.08 per cent larger than that of the proton. Neutrons are present in the nuclei of all atoms except hydrogen H^1, and together with the proton they constitute the building blocks of nuclei.

The _photon_, although not a unit from which matter is constructed, is important as a fundamental particle. It is a bundle of radiant energy; and although it cannot be considered as having a material substance or mass, it may be considered as having a radiation mass equivalent to its energy as given by the Einstein relation

$$E = mc^2$$

The amount of energy carried by a photon is dependent on the frequency or color of the radiation. Visible light, heat, radio waves, and X rays are all composed of photons. It has become necessary to think of radiant energy coming in the form of particles as well as in waves in order to explain satisfactorily many of the phenomena encountered in modern atomic physics. This is the same sort of dual viewpoint which must be employed in discussing the properties of the electron.

1–5. Acceleration of an electron in an electric field

Electronic devices operate through motion of electrons or other charged particles under the action of electric and magnetic fields. The basic principles are simple, stemming from the ordinary laws of dynamics, modified in a manner to account for accelerations other than that of gravity.

Since the concept of a confining conductor is frequently absent in electronic paths, it is convenient to consider the actions of individual electrons or other charges in understanding the operation of electronic devices. Restricting the discussion to electrons, it is usual to assume that the number of electrons per unit volume, or *charge density*, is so low that the repulsion of one electron on another is small enough to be neglected. Also, the electrons move in such a high vacuum that there will be no collisions with gas atoms or ions, and the electronic mass is so small that gravitational forces are negligible compared with the effects of fields.

The field intensity in an electric field, equal to the negative of the voltage gradient, is defined as the force acting per unit of positive charge, or in general

$$\varepsilon = -\frac{d\mathbf{v}}{dx} = \frac{\mathbf{f}}{q} \qquad \text{v/m} \qquad (1\text{-}1)$$

if **f** is in newtons and q in coulombs. The positive direction of the field intensity is taken as the direction of the force on the positive charge. Since a positive charge will be attracted to the negative electrode, then the force **f** and field intensity are vector quantities directed from positive to negative electrode as in Fig. 1-2. Rearrangement of Eq. 1-1 yields for the force **f**,

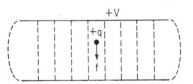

Fig. 1-2. Force **f** on a positive charge q in a uniform electric field.

$$\mathbf{f} = q\varepsilon \qquad \text{newtons} \qquad (1\text{-}2)$$

An electron carries a negative charge of 1.60×10^{-19} coulomb, a *magnitude* known as e. Since the charge is negative, as will be indicated by a negative sign on e, the force exerted on an electron in an electric field will be directed toward the positive electrode, or opposite to the defined positive direction of the field intensity.

The force $\mathbf{f}_e$ on an electron in an electric field is then

$$\mathbf{f}_e = -e\varepsilon \qquad (1\text{-}3)$$

Owing to the action of this force the electron will be accelerated, and Newton's second law allows this acceleration to be determined as

$$\mathbf{f} = m\mathbf{a}$$

or

$$\mathbf{a} = \frac{d\mathbf{v}}{dt} = -\frac{e\varepsilon}{m} \qquad \text{m/sec}^2 \qquad (1\text{-}4)$$

This acceleration is directed along the field flux lines and toward the positive electrode. Equation 1–4 is of fundamental importance in predicting the motion of electrons in electric fields.

1–6. Velocity of an electron in an electric field

In order to establish the direction of motion of bodies, it is customary to treat the vector quantities—force, acceleration, velocity, and so forth— by use of their components along the axes of reference. The resultant motions are then the vector sums of the components.

Assume that an electron is released at point $P(x_0, y_0)$ with an initial velocity v_{0x} wholly in the $+x$ direction. Acting in the region is a uniform electric field directed in the $-y$ direction and of magnitude $\mathcal{E}_y$, due to a potential difference which is positive toward $+y$. The equations of motion of the electron may then be stated from Eq. 1–4 as

$$a_x = \frac{dv_x}{dt} = 0 \tag{1-5}$$

and

$$a_y = \frac{dv_y}{dt} = -\frac{e\mathcal{E}_y}{m} \tag{1-6}$$

Since no force acts in the z direction, $a_z = 0$. The velocity in the y direction at any time t is given by

$$v_y = -\int \frac{e\mathcal{E}_y}{m}\, dt + C_1 \qquad = \frac{e\mathcal{E}}{m} t + C$$

If $\mathcal{E}_y$ is not a function of time, then

$$v_y = -\frac{e\mathcal{E}_y t}{m} + C_1 \tag{1-7}$$

and $C_1 = 0$, since v_y was zero at $t = 0$.

Upon integration of Eq. 1–5, provided that $v_x = v_{0x}$ at $t = 0$, it follows that $v_x = C_2 = v_{0x}$. The resultant velocity at any time t is given by

$$v = \sqrt{v_x^2 + v_y^2} \tag{1-8}$$

The y position at any time t can be obtained by integration of Eq. 1–7, and if $\mathcal{E}_y$ is not a time function then

$$y = -\frac{e\mathcal{E}_y t^2}{2m} + y_0 \tag{1-9}$$

if $C_3 = y_0$. The negative sign indicates a direction opposite to the positive direction of the field.

Similarly, from Eq. 1–5

$$x = v_x t + x_0 \qquad (1\text{--}10)$$

is the x coordinate of position at time t.

If the potential difference applied to the electrodes is a function of time, for example $e = E_m \sin \omega t$, the field intensity will likewise be a time function. This function may be substituted in the expression for acceleration, and the resulting equations integrated.

1–7. Energy acquired by an electron

When an electron is accelerated in an electric field, work is done upon it, and its kinetic energy is increased. The work done to move the charge between two points, A and B, in a field of intensity $\mathcal{E}$ is equal to the kinetic energy acquired by the electron. From Eq. 1–3

$$\mathbf{f}_e = -e\mathcal{E}$$

and the work done on the electron by this force will be given by

$$W = \int_A^B f_e \cos \alpha \, ds = -\int_A^B e\mathcal{E} \cos \alpha \, ds \qquad (1\text{--}11)$$

where α is the angle between the direction of the force $\mathbf{f}_e$ and the positive direction of the movement $\mathbf{ds}$. For the case in which the movement $\mathbf{ds}$ of the negative electron is in the direction opposite to the field intensity or is in the direction of the force (the electron is being attracted toward a positive electrode), the angle α is zero. The work is then equal to the kinetic energy acquired by the electron, or

$$W = \frac{m(v^2 - v_0^2)}{2} = -e\int_A^B \mathcal{E} \, ds \qquad (1\text{--}12)$$

The integral of the field intensity is equal to the negative of the potential V between A and B, so that Eq. 1–12 may also be written as

$$W = \frac{m(v^2 - v_0^2)}{2} = Ve \qquad \text{joules} \quad (1\text{--}13)$$

Equation 1–13 states the energy acquired by an electron in moving or "falling" through a potential V. It makes no difference in what length of time the passage from A to B occurs or over what path the electron moves. If a potential difference exists between A and B, then the energy received by the electron in moving from A to B is given by Eq. 1–13, since in a conservative field the work integral is independent of the path.

By solving Eq. 1–13 for the velocity term,

$$v^2 - v_0^2 = \frac{2Ve}{m}$$

and if the initial velocity $v_0 = 0$, then the final velocity can be calculated as

$$v = \sqrt{\frac{2Ve}{m}} \qquad \text{m/sec} \quad (1\text{–}14)$$

This is the velocity gained by an electron in starting at rest and moving to a point at potential V volts above that of the starting point, when V is not a time function.

1–8. The electron volt

If an electron travels through a potential rise of one volt, it acquires an energy given by

$$Ve = 1.60 \times 10^{-19} \times 1 = 1.60 \times 10^{-19} \text{ joule} = 1 \text{ ev}$$

This amount of energy is known as an *electron volt*, abbreviated ev. If an electron falls through 500 v potential, the energy acquired is 500 ev. It is the convenience of this numerical equivalence that has made the electron volt popular as an energy unit.

The electron volt is much used in stating the energy of high-speed particles. Through popular usage, the word "electron" is frequently omitted, so that we read such statements as "a certain particle has an energy of 10,000 v." This seemingly inconsistent use of units is explained if we remember that electron volts are meant. The abbreviation Mev and Bev are also used, meaning "million electron volts" and "billion electron volts," respectively.

1–9. Sources of energy; current

When a change is made in the velocity of an electron in transit, its kinetic energy is changed, and the energy converted must be supplied by, or be delivered to, the external circuit or electrodes. During the movement of an electron in space toward a positive electrode, as in Fig. 1–3, the electron is accelerated and increases its kinetic energy. The moving electron induces a changing charge on the positive electrode and an oppositely changing charge on the negative electrode. An electron approaching a positive electrode forces a free electron from the electrode into the external circuit. This effect is felt by the electrons in all the circuit conductors as the electrons are given a slight movement in the direction of the negative electrode. The movement of this induced charge

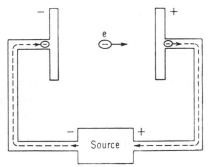

Fig. 1–3. Current induced in a circuit by motion of an electron between electrodes.

is a current throughout the entire circuit. If the movement is viewed as an electric current, it is seen that it flows out of the positive source terminal and represents a flow of energy out of the source.

As the electron comes very close to the positive electrode, it has succeeded in forcing a charge redistribution in the external circuit, prepared a place for itself on the positive electrode, and filled the hole left on the negative electrode when it migrated therefrom. When the electron strikes the electrode, the forces are neutralized, the system is in electrical balance, and current and energy transfer stop. Even if the electron never reaches the electrode, a current and energy transfer have still taken place.

While the electron is in flight in the field, a current flows in the external circuit and supplies energy to, or takes energy from, the electron. However, as soon as the electron strikes an electrode, the current ceases. The amount of this current may be calculated from consideration of the energy transferred. The change in energy of the electron in Fig. 1–3, which is computed from $m(v^2 - v_0^2)/2$, must be derived from the external circuit. The external source of potential V has given up or contributed energy of amount

$$W = Vq = - V \int_{t_0}^{t} i \, dt = \frac{m(v^2 - v_0^2)}{2} \tag{1–15}$$

By taking the time derivative

$$mv \frac{dv}{dt} = mva = - Vi$$

Since $a = - e\mathcal{E}/m$, then

$$i = \frac{ev\mathcal{E}}{V} \text{ amp}$$

For the field of Fig. 1–3, $\varepsilon = -V/d$, so that

$$i = -\frac{ev}{d} \qquad\qquad \text{amp} \quad (1\text{–}16)$$

This is the instantaneous current in the external circuit and out of the positive source terminal when the electron is accelerated by the field ε. The concept that the electron, on striking the electrode, continues on into the external circuit as a current is obviously untrue, considering the energies involved.

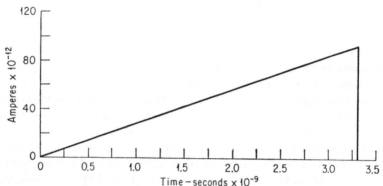

Fig. 1–4. Instantaneous current value due to electron traveling 1 cm through 100 v.

Figure 1–4 is a plot of instantaneous current in the external circuit for an electron traveling between two plates separated 1 cm and with a potential of 100 v between them. The single electron represented a current of 92.9×10^{-12} amp when it struck the positive plate.

For currents due to movement of large numbers of electrons it is convenient to think in terms of charge density ρ in the space, with a velocity of charge movement v. The charge passing a point per second per unit cross-sectional area is equal to the current density J, and

$$J = \rho v \qquad\qquad \text{amp/m}^2 \quad (1\text{–}17)$$

If $\rho = -ne$ for electrons, where n is the number of electrons per cubic meter, then

$$J = -nev \qquad\qquad \text{amp/m}^2 \quad (1\text{–}18)$$

This result could also have been obtained by generalizing Eq. 1–16.

Although the discussion above has been in terms of transfer of energy to an electron, it is equally possible to transfer energy from an electron to an external circuit by "shooting" a moving electron into a retarding field, or causing it to approach and be decelerated by a negative electrode.

The induced current is then found in such a direction as to represent energy *into* the external circuit. In this way certain electronic devices extract energy from beams of moving electrons.

On impact with an electrode, the kinetic energy of the electron is given up and is changed to heat. If the amount of energy per electron is great enough, some of this delivered energy may also appear as electromagnetic radiation or X rays.

1–10. Initial velocity perpendicular to the electric field

The case of motion of an electron in an electric field at right angles to an initial electron velocity of v_{0x} is important in the cathode-ray tube and other electron-deflection tubes. Assume the initial position of the electron to be at the origin, as in Fig. 1–5, and that $v_{0y} = v_{0z} = 0$, and that the field has a magnitude $\mathcal{E}_y$. Then

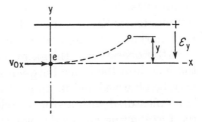

Fig. 1–5. Path of a moving electron in a uniform electric field.

$$a_y = \frac{dv_y}{dt} = -\frac{e\mathcal{E}_y}{m} \tag{1–19}$$

$$a_x = \frac{dv_x}{dt} = 0 \tag{1–20}$$

From Eq. 1–20 it is apparent that $v_x = v_{0x}$. If $\mathcal{E}_y$ is assumed constant with time, then Eq. 1–19 leads to

$$v_y = -\frac{e\mathcal{E}_y t}{m}$$

from which

$$y = -\frac{e\mathcal{E}_y t^2}{2m} \tag{1–21}$$

assuming the initial position at the origin. Since $t = x/v_{0x}$, then it follows that

$$y = -\frac{e\mathcal{E}_y}{2mv_{0x}^2} x^2 \tag{1–22}$$

which shows the path of the electron to be a parabola in the x, y plane.

1–11. Millikan's measurement of the electronic charge

During the years 1910 to 1916, R. A. Millikan, then at the University of Chicago, performed his classic oil-drop experiment and obtained a value of 1.590×10^{-19} coulomb as the charge on the electron. This result was very close to the now-accepted value of 1.602×10^{-19} coulomb, which has been obtained by X-ray methods. The apparatus, shown diagrammatically in Fig. 1–6, consisted of two parallel plates separated a distance d and connected to a battery through a reversing switch. There was a small hole in the upper plate and, above this, a chamber containing an atomizer for producing an oil spray. The space between the plates was illuminated with a strong light, and an observing telescope having crosshair markings was focused on the space below the hole in the upper plate.

After operation of the atomizer, an oil droplet may find its way through the hole into the space between the plates. The movement of the droplet may be observed and its time of fall between certain of the telescope cross hairs measured with a stop watch. If no potential is placed on the plates, the force acting on the droplet will be that of gravity, which will be proportional to v_d, the downward-measured velocity:

$$\text{force} = f = mg = kv_d \qquad (1\text{–}23)$$

During the fall, the droplet may acquire an electric charge from free charges in the air, or, if no charges are initially present, they may be set up by passing X rays through the space for an instant. If a potential with the proper polarity is then applied to the plates, the droplet may be caused to rise in the field. The net force existing then is proportional to the upward-measured velocity v_n, and

$$\mathcal{E}q_n - mg = kv_n \qquad (1\text{–}24)$$

where q_n is the charge acquired by the droplet.

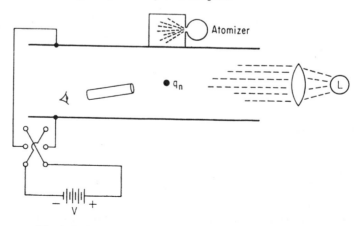

Fig. 1–6. Apparatus for Millikan oil-drop experiment.

Use of these two equations allows q_n to be written as

$$q_n = \frac{mg}{\mathcal{E}v_d}(v_n + v_d) \qquad (1\text{--}25)$$

If the time of movement of this droplet is measured with a different value of acquired charge q_m, another equation similar to Eq. 1–25 may be obtained:

$$q_m = \frac{mg}{\mathcal{E}v_d}(v_m + v_d) \qquad (1\text{--}26)$$

and, when Eq. 1–25 is subtracted from Eq. 1–26,

$$\Delta q = q_m - q_n = \frac{mg}{\mathcal{E}v_d}(v_m - v_n)$$

After this process is repeated for a great many droplets, it becomes apparent from study of the data that the values of Δq obtained are always integral multiples of some smaller number and that none of the values of Δq is ever smaller than this number; that is,

$$\Delta q = ne \qquad (1\text{--}27)$$

The least common multiple of all the ne's is obviously the value of e, the smallest indivisible unit of electricity, or the charge on the electron.

Millikan obtained the value of the mass m of the droplets from Stokes' law. For small spherical droplets falling freely in space, Stokes' law gives for the radius

$$r = \sqrt{\frac{9\eta v_d}{2g\delta}} \qquad \text{m}$$

where η is the viscosity of the medium and δ is the density of the liquid of the drop. The mass of the droplet is then

$$m = \tfrac{4}{3}\pi r^3 \delta \qquad \text{kg} \quad (1\text{--}28)$$

1–12. Electron in a magnetic field

The force on an element of conductor of length ds in a magnetic field, carrying a current i and oriented as in Fig. 1–7, is

$$f_m = Bi\,ds\,\sin\theta \qquad \text{newtons}$$

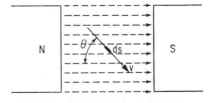

Fig. 1–7. Force on a moving electron in a magnetic field.

and, since current is rate of movement of charge through ds,

$$f_m = B\frac{dq}{dt} ds \sin\theta = Bdq\frac{ds}{dt} \sin\theta$$

Certainly the electronic charge e is an elemental charge and may be considered as a negative dq, in which case ds/dt is the velocity of movement of this charge and

$$f_m = - Bev \sin\theta \qquad\qquad \text{newtons} \quad (1\text{-}29)$$

This is the force on an electron moving with velocity v meters per second in a magnetic field of strength **B** webers per square meter, where θ has meaning as the angle between the direction of ds or of the velocity, and the magnetic flux lines. In the case of an electric motor, the force $\mathbf{f}_m$ is at right angles to the plane containing both **B** and **v** and in the direction of a right-hand screw rotated in the direction **v** to **B**. For negatively charged particles, such as the electron, this direction will be reversed. An electron moving in the direction indicated in Fig. 1–7 will be acted upon by a force perpendicular to and into the paper.

Since this force is always perpendicular to the motion and velocity, *no work can be done on the electron by the magnetic field,* and its velocity remains unchanged except in direction. If **v** and **B** are constant, then $\mathbf{f}_m$ is constant and will produce a constant acceleration at right angles to the velocity. A motion of this sort with constant accelerating force is circular motion. The path described by an electron moving in a plane normal to a magnetic field is, therefore, a circle, as shown in Fig. 1–8.

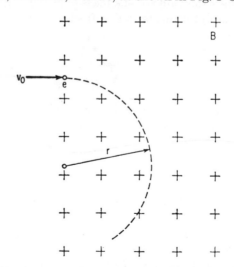

Fig. 1–8. Path of an electron moving in the plane of the page and in magnetic field B normal to and into page.

The properties of this circular motion can be easily discovered by use of the laws of dynamics. The centripetal force toward the center is

$$f_c = \frac{mv^2}{r}$$

But this is the force created by the motion of the electron in the magnetic field owing to the velocity component normal to the field, or

$$\frac{m(v \sin \theta)^2}{r} = Bev \sin \theta$$

Solving, the radius r of the circular path is

$$r = \frac{mv \sin \theta}{eB} \qquad\qquad \text{m} \quad (1\text{–}30)$$

The velocity $v \sin \theta$ is the peripheral velocity of the circle. The angular velocity then is

$$\omega = \frac{v \sin \theta}{r} = \frac{eB}{m} \qquad\qquad (1\text{–}31)$$

The time T required to pass once completely around the circle is available from

$$Tv \sin \theta = 2\pi r$$

and substituting for r,

$$T = \frac{2\pi m}{eB} \qquad\qquad \text{sec} \quad (1\text{–}32)$$

It is interesting to note that the time of one revolution by the electron is independent of velocity, being dependent only on B. This is so because the radius increases directly with velocity, a high-velocity electron traveling around a circle of large radius and taking the same time for the circuit as a low-velocity electron in traveling around a circle of small radius.

1–13. Thomson's measurement of e/m

The factor e/m has appeared frequently in the equations of electronic motion. This ratio of charge to mass, has for the electron the value 1.76×10^{11} coulombs per kilogram. Sir J. J. Thomson, in 1897, using an evacuated tube such as shown in Fig. 1–9, proved that the ratio e/m is the same for all the particles in the so-called "cathode rays." These particles are now known to be electrons. A beam of electrons is obtained by the acceleration of electrons leaving the cathode K by means of a positive potential on

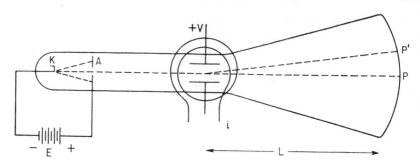

Fig. 1–9. Demonstration of the Thomson measurement of e/m.

an anode A. In the center of the anode is a small hole, and some of the electrons pass through this hole to form a small pencil of electrons. With no electric or magnetic fields applied, these electrons pass straight on to the fluorescent screen, where their impact at P is indicated by flashes of light given off by the material of the screen.

If a potential difference V is given to the deflection plates indicated, then a field of magnitude $\mathcal{E} = -V/d$ is set up, and a force

$$f = -e\mathcal{E} \tag{1–33}$$

deflects the beam of electrons upward to a new spot P' on the screen.

A magnetic field of strength B is now applied by coils mounted on each side of the tube and connected so as to produce a downward deflection of the electron beam. This gives a downward force f_m on the electrons of

$$f_m = -Bev = \frac{mv^2}{r} \tag{1–34}$$

since θ is 90°. If the strength of the field is adjusted so that the beam of electrons returns to the initial spot P, then the two forces must be equal and

$$e\mathcal{E} = Bev \quad \text{or} \quad v = \frac{\mathcal{E}}{B}$$

From Eq. 1–34,

$$\frac{e}{m} = \frac{\mathcal{E}}{rB^2} \tag{1–35}$$

Since the deflection radius can be determined from the geometry of the tube, Eq. 1–35 allows direct computation of the ratio of charge to mass of the electron.

1-14. Parallel electric and magnetic fields—focusing

Let an electron with velocity v_0 be released at P into parallel electric and magnetic fields, of magnitudes ε and B, directed in the negative x direction as shown in Fig. 1-10. The velocity v_0 makes an angle θ with respect to the x axis and with the alignment of the fields, as defined by the figure.

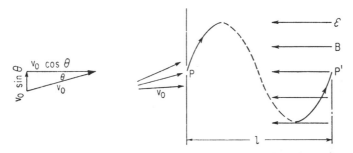

Fig. 1-10. Path of a moving electron in parallel electric and magnetic fields.

The initial component of velocity parallel to the field alignment is $v_0 \cos \theta$, and this will not be changed by the magnetic field. The acceleration due to ε will, however, add to this velocity such that the velocity in the x direction will become

$$v_u = v_0 \cos \theta \pm \frac{e\varepsilon t}{m} \qquad (1\text{-}36)$$

The sign is determined by the direction of ε and will be negative for the conditions of the figure. The component of velocity perpendicular to the fields is $v_0 \sin \theta$, and this component will produce a force

$$f_m = - Bev_0 \sin \theta \qquad (1\text{-}37)$$

leading to a circular motion in a plane perpendicular to the magnetic field. The resultant of the two motions is a helix. From Eq. 1-30 the radius r of the circular motion is

$$r = \frac{mv_0 \sin \theta}{eB} \qquad (1\text{-}38)$$

In the time taken to complete one revolution, the electron will also have moved longitudinally a distance l parallel to the field to P', owing to v_u. Consequently, since the time of a revolution is

$$T = \frac{2\pi m}{Be}$$

and the average velocity acting over this period is $v_0 \cos \theta \pm \pi \mathcal{E}/B$, the distance traveled during the period of one revolution is

$$l = \frac{2\pi m}{Be}\left(v_0 \cos \theta \pm \frac{\pi \mathcal{E}}{B}\right) \qquad (1\text{--}39)$$

If all electrons reaching the point P have equal initial velocity v_0, and if θ is small so that $\cos \theta \cong 1$, then the distance l will be the same for all electrons. If point P is considered as being a small area over which the electrons are scattered in arriving, then at P' there will be an exactly equivalent area, or image of P. This method is capable of focusing at P' a bundle of electrons arriving at P with dissimilar directions, provided that all electrons with θ large are removed by a diaphragm device, as shown in Fig. 1–10. If there is no parallel electric field, or $\mathcal{E} = 0$, then the path is that of a helix of constant pitch.

The method is used for *magnetically focusing* a beam of electrons.

1–15. Effect of the relativistic change in mass

Newton's second law states that

$$f = \frac{d(mv)}{dt}$$

If mass is given the possibility of varying as a function of velocity, then

$$f = m\frac{dv}{dt} + v\frac{dm}{dv}\frac{dv}{dt} \qquad (1\text{--}40)$$

If mass is not a function of velocity, then the right-hand term drops out, leaving the familiar form

$$f = ma$$

The theory of relativity requires, and it has been experimentally proven, that the masses of all bodies vary with velocity. The actual mass of a moving body can be expressed as

$$m = \frac{m_0}{\sqrt{1 - v^2/c^2}} \qquad (1\text{--}41)$$

where m_0 is the so-called "*rest mass*," or mass at zero velocity; v is the velocity of motion; and c is the velocity of light $= 3 \times 10^8$ m/sec. This result shows that the mass is not much different from the rest mass until the velocity becomes appreciable with respect to that of light. The difference is less than 1 per cent for electrons that have energies of less than

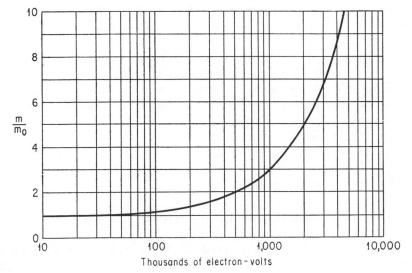

Fig. 1–11. The relativistic mass variation of an electron.

2500 ev. Figure 1–11 is a plot of m/m_0 or the value of $1/\sqrt{1 - v^2/c^2}$ for various values of energy.

Applying Eq. 1–41 to the expression for force in Eq. 1–40 and taking dm/dv as required,

$$f = \frac{m_0}{(1 - v^2/c^2)^{3/2}} \frac{dv}{dt} \tag{1–42}$$

Now, by the laws of dynamics,

$$W = \int_0^t f \, ds = \int_0^t fv \, dt = \int_0^v \frac{m_0 v}{(1 - v^2/c^2)^{3/2}} \, dv = Ve$$

$$Ve = \left[\frac{m_0 c^2}{\sqrt{1 - v^2/c^2}} \right]_0^v = m_0 c^2 \left(\frac{1}{\sqrt{1 - v^2/c^2}} - 1 \right) \tag{1–43}$$

which relates the velocity reached to the accelerating voltage on the charge. Solving Eq. 1–43 gives

$$v = c\sqrt{1 - \frac{1}{(eV/m_0 c^2 + 1)^2}} \tag{1–44}$$

This equation permits the calculation of the actual velocity reached when the electron falls through a potential V.

As V increases the second term in the denominator decreases, and the equation then states that c, the velocity of light, becomes limiting and will not be exceeded, since the mass becomes infinite at that velocity.

$$\sqrt{\frac{2eV}{m_0}}$$

Electrons have been accelerated to velocities above 99.9 per cent of the velocity of light; the energy of an electron at such a velocity is above 100 Mev.

The variation of m may be neglected in most engineering applications, since the voltages are relatively low. In high-voltage cathode-ray tubes and X-ray tubes the variation of m may be appreciable, and this is particularly so in large particle accelerators. In the latter case the increase in mass becomes an important design factor.

Figure 1–11 allows estimation of the mass variation. Unless otherwise stated, the relativistic change in mass will be neglected in this text.

1–16. Metric system magnitudes

In stating the magnitudes of many physical quantities in electronics it is often found that very large numbers of a small unit, or very small portions of a large unit are required. Since the m.k.s. system of metric units is now universal in electrical engineering, it is convenient to also adopt the principle of identifying each of the major orders of magnitude with distinctive names, which is a characteristic of the metric system.

The International Committee on Weights and Measures adopted a set of unit prefixes in 1958, and it is therefore appropriate to use that set in this text. The complete table is:

10^{12}	tera—	T	10^{-12}	pico—	p
10^9	giga—	G	10^{-9}	nano—	n
10^6	mega—	M	10^{-6}	micro—	μ
10^3	kilo—	K	10^{-3}	milli—	m
			10^{-2}	centi—	c

We will frequently employ the prefixes mega, kilo, centi, milli, micro, nano, and pico.

Problems

1-1. If unit atomic weight represents 1.65×10^{-27} kg, calculate the velocity reached by the following after acceleration by a potential of 100 v: (a) electron, (b) singly charged hydrogen ion, and (c) singly charged mercury ion.

1-2. Two large parallel metal plates are horizontal and are separated a distance of 0.5 cm, with the upper plate being 150 v positive with respect to the lower plate. An electron with initial velocity of 10^6/m per second upward is released at the center of the lower plate.

(a) What will be the velocity of the electron upon striking the upper plate?

(b) Calculate the length of time consumed by the electron in flight.

(c) How much energy is conveyed to the upper electrode?

1-3. In the preceding problem at the instant the electron is 0.3 cm above the lower plate, the potential on the plates is reversed in sign.

(a) Determine which electrode will be reached by the electron.

(b) Find the velocity of arrival.

(c) Determine the total time of flight.

(d) Calculate the energy of the electron at the instant of potential reversal and the energy given to the electrode upon impact. Account for the difference.

1-4. An electron with zero initial energy leaves the negative plate [(a), Fig. 1–12], passes through a small hole in a parallel electrode at +100 v and distance 2 cm, and strikes a second parallel electrode at +300 v and distance 4 cm from the starting point. Find the time of transit to the second electrode. Assume that the small hole has no effect on the distribution of the electric field.

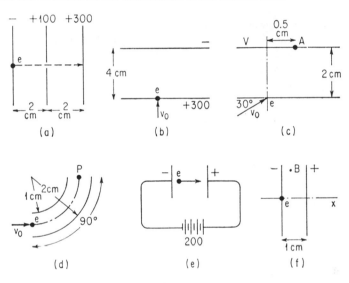

Fig. 1–12.

1-5. (a) Considering the electron of Problem 1-4, plot curves of current flow in the external circuits of both electrodes as a function of the time of flight.

(b) Find the net energy contributed by the first electrode during the flight of the electron.

(c) How much kinetic energy is dissipated as heat on the second electrode?

1-6. An electron with initial velocity due to 250 ev, and directed upward and perpendicular to the plates, enters the field [(b), Fig. 1–12].

(a) After how much time will the electron strike an electrode?

(b) How far does the electron travel?

(c) How much energy, in joules, is delivered to the plate on impact?

(d) Plot a curve of current flow in the external electrode circuit vs. the time of flight of the electron.

1-7. An electron with energy of 75 ev enters an electric field at an angle of 30 deg to the plate [(c), Fig. 1–12].

(a) What value of potential V will be required between the plates to make the electron hit the point A on the upper plate?

(b) How much energy will be delivered to the plate by the electron?

(c) Find the average value of current flow from the source V during the flight of the electron.

1-8. An electron of 300 ev energy enters a magnetic field at the origin of axes. If its initial velocity is directed along the y axis:

(a) Find the flux density in webers per square meter and the direction of the magnetic field required to make the electron reach the point $x = 2$ cm, $y = 0$, $z = 0$.

(b) How long a time does it take for the electron to reach the above point?

1-9. In (d), Fig. 1–12, an electron is released as shown, with $v_0 = 0.5 \times 10^6$ m/sec, and with the inner electrode positive.

(a) Find the value of electric field intensity required along the indicated path midway between the electrodes to make the electron reach P.

(b) If the electric field is replaced by a magnetic field, specify its magnitude and direction to make the electron reach P.

1-10. In (c), Fig. 1–12, the potential V is removed and a magnetic field substituted. Find the magnitude and direction of the field which will force the electron to reach point A, other conditions being as in Problem 1–7.

1-11. An electron of 100 ev energy directed in the plane of the page, enters a magnetic field of 0.05 weber per sq m directed normal to the plane of the page. Find the radius of the electron path and the rpm it makes in the field.

1-12. In copper, it is usually assumed that there is one conduction, or free electron, per atom. It has been established that there are 5×10^{22} atoms per cu cm of copper. If a piece of No. 10 B and S copper wire supplies current to a 100-w, 115-v lamp, find the average drift velocity of the electrons in the wire.

1-13. The circuit of (e), Fig. 1–12, is connected by the No. 10 B and S copper wire of Problem 1-12. Assuming that the electron in the space between the electrodes had zero initial velocity:

(a) Find the value of current flowing in the external circuit at the instant just before the electron strikes the positive plate. The plates are separated 0.1 cm.

(b) Compute the drift velocity of the electrons in the copper wire of the circuit at the instant of (a), and compare with the velocity of the electron in the space. Why is there such a difference in velocities?

(c) Show that the *rate* of energy output by the battery at this instant is equal to the *rate* of increase of energy by the electron.

1-14. An electron with an energy in the horizontal direction of 100 ev enters the field between two horizontal plates 2 cm long and separated 2 cm. The upper plate is at $+100$ v.

Find the direction and flux density, in webers per square meter, of a magnetic field required to prevent deflection of the electron from its path between the plates. Neglect fringing of the electric field.

1-15. An electron at time $t = 0$ is released from the left-hand plate with zero velocity. It is acted upon by the electric field due to 1000 v, and by a uniform magnetic field B perpendicular and out of the paper [(f), Fig. 1–12].

(a) What value of flux density B will be required just to prevent the electron from reaching the positive plate?

(b) Sketch the path of the electron.

1-16. Two electrons, of energy 100 ev each, enter at the same point a magnetic field of strength 0.05 weber/sq m with initial velocities making angles of $10°$ and $15°$, respectively, with the magnetic field.

(a) After completion of one revolution of the helical path, how far apart are the electrons?

(b) Compute the respective radii of the paths.

1-17. An electron with 100 ev energy enters at $t = 0$ the field between two parallel electrodes at an angle of $40°$ to the lower plate. The plates are separated 1.0 cm, and the potential between the plates varies as $e = 10^8 t$, with the upper plate positive.

(a) Find the time taken by the electron in reaching the upper plate.

(b) Compute the velocity and energy upon arrival at the upper plate.

1-18. The potential across a certain X-ray tube is 1 megavolt.

(a) If an electron starts from rest on the negative electrode, what will be its velocity on arrival at the anode?

(b) What is the mass of an electron when it strikes the positive electrode?

(c) If the total electron current through the tube is one ma, find the power delivered to the tube anode.

Use relativistic mass corrections.

References

1. Boast, W. B., *Principles of Electric and Magnetic Fields*. Harper & Row, Publishers, New York, 1949.

2. Crowther, J. A., *Ions, Electrons and Ionizing Radiations*, 7th ed. David McKay Co., Inc., New York, 1939.

3. McArthur, E. D., "Determining Field Distribution by Electronic Methods," *Electronics*, **4**, 192 (1932).

4. Millikan, R. A., *The Electron*. University of Chicago Press, Chicago, 1917.

The Cathode-Ray Tube | 2

The cathode-ray tube is an important application of electron ballistic principles. It is the modern counterpart of the Crookes tube of 1879 in which the electron first made its presence known in the cathode rays, by use of which X rays were discovered, and in which Sir J. J. Thomson first measured the e/m ratio of the electron. The cathode-ray tube is now extensively used as a laboratory and production tool to investigate and visualize electric-circuit phenomena, and as a viewing device for the reception of television images and radar signals.

Adequate study of many other electronic devices and circuits would be impossible without the cathode-ray tube.

2–1. Focusing of electron beams

In an electric field, the electrons tend to accelerate along the flux lines or to move parallel and opposite to the field, since this is the direction of the force acting on them. If a configuration of electrodes is set up (as in Fig. 2–1, which is a cross section of a set of cylinders) and voltages are applied, the equipotentials between the cylinders A and B will appear as sketched. Electrons, entering through a small hole at A with small angles of dispersion, will be given a small inwardly-directed force on first entering the field between

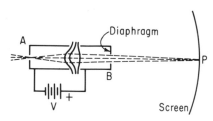

Fig. 2–1. Electric-field focusing of an electron beam.

24

the cylinders. Upon emerging through the curved field on the far side of the lens section, the electrons will be given a small outwardly-directed force due to the opposite curvature of the flux lines. In passing through the field the electron has been accelerated, the initial inward force acts on the electron for a longer time than the final outward force, and the net result is an inward component of velocity which will cause the electrons to emerge in a bundle at B, with final convergence of their paths at point P. By variation of the potential V, the curvature of the field can be shifted and the distance to the point of convergence or focus P, altered. The electron lens is not perfect near the edges, and a diaphragm is placed at point B to cut off all wide-angle electrons. Designing an electron lens of this nature is more difficult than designing an optical lens because, although light travels in straight lines, the paths of the electrons are curves.

In electron optics, it becomes desirable to think of an electron as having wave properties and wave length. This wave length has been found to be related to the velocity of the electron by

$$\lambda = \frac{h}{mv}$$

where h is Planck's constant. The higher the velocity, the shorter the wave length. The range of wave lengths at usual velocities falls below that of visible light and into the X-ray region.

In optical systems, lens corrections are required to prevent chromatic aberration if the light rays do not all have the same wave length (color). The electron lens likewise suffers in sharpness of focusing if λ is not the same for all electrons. Since λ is a function of the voltage through the velocity reached by the electron, changes in voltage may cause defocusing. The effect may be minimized by making the final velocity as large as possible with respect to the initial velocity. This variation of electron wave length is one of the fundamental limitations of sharpness in electron lenses.

Other forms of lenses, using magnetic fields in accordance with the theory of the preceding chapter, are also used for focusing electron beams. They suffer from aberrations similar to those of the electric field type.

Magnification of the image is possible in such lens systems just as for optical systems. An application of this feature is made in the electron microscope in which electrons replace the visible light of the ordinary microscope. Since the electron wave length is considerably less than that of visible or ultraviolet light, much smaller objects may be resolved with the electron microscope than by any instrument using conventional optical systems.

2–2. The cathode-ray tube

The complete cathode-ray tube, as shown in Fig. 2–2, consists of an evacuated space in which are an electron gun, a set of plane electrodes positioned around the beam, and a fluorescent screen. In tubes designed wholly for magnetic deflection, the plane electrodes may be omitted. The interior surface of the screen is coated with a translucent layer of a material which fluoresces when hit by high-speed electrons, so that the location of the electron beam can be seen as a lighted spot.

The electron gun contains a heated cathode or source of electrons K. These electrons pass through a hole in grid G and are accelerated by a potential on the focusing anode A_1. The beam of electrons is further accelerated by the potential on the second anode A_2, and is focused on the screen by the electron lens set up by the fields between the first and second anodes. On leaving the second anode a diaphragm cuts off electrons which passed through the outer edge of the lens and were not properly focused.

The number of electrons, and, therefore, the brightness of the spot, may be controlled by the potential on grid G; the focus, or sharpness of the spot, may be controlled by proper shaping of the electron lens by adjustment of the anode potentials. Magnetic focusing may also be used in certain applications.

If one pair of the deflection electrodes is so positioned as to produce a horizontal electric field when a voltage is impressed across them, then a deflection of the beam horizontally, or along the x axis, is possible if potentials are placed on this pair of electrodes. A deflection of the beam vertically, or along the y axis, is possible by application of potentials to plates oriented to produce a vertical field. If the screen is considered as lying in the x, y plane, the simultaneous application of suitable potentials to both pairs of plates gives complete control of the spot of light in both x and y coordinates.

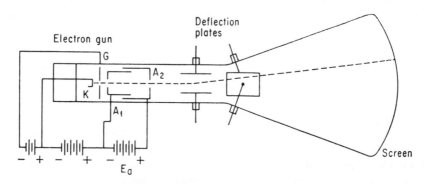

Fig. 2–2. The cathode-ray tube.

Since the masses of the electrons are so small, alternating potentials may be applied to the plates and the spot caused to oscillate over the screen without inertia effects at all frequencies up to those of the order of 10^8 cycles per second. Since an a-c voltage is a time function, to be seen in its true wave form it must be plotted against time. A voltage which may be applied to the x-axis plates to produce such a deflection is called a *saw-tooth wave*, or *sweep voltage*, and is shown in Fig. 2–3. If, at the same time, an a-c voltage is placed on the y-axis plates, then the wave form of this a-c voltage will be seen traced out against time, as in Fig. 2–4.

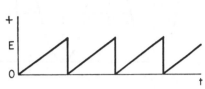

Fig. 2–3. Wave form of a saw tooth sweep voltage.

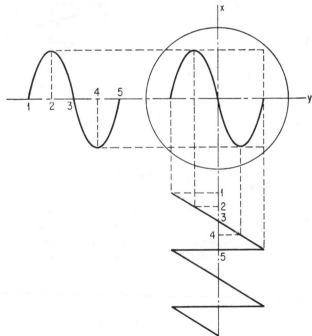

Fig. 2–4. A sine wave traced as a time function by a sweep voltage.

It might be supposed that at high frequencies the movement of the spot of light would be too fast to follow with the eye; but owing to a slight amount of phosphorescence in the screen material and to persistence of vision in the human eye the spot develops a tail, and at high rates appears as a solid-line plot of the phenomena.

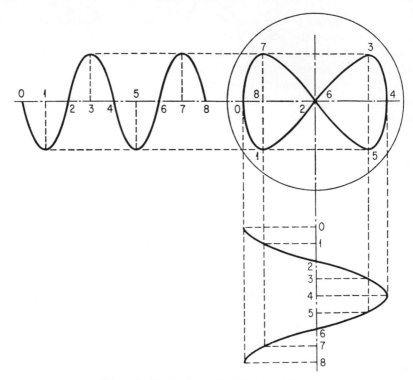

Fig. 2–5. Production of a Lissajous figure.

2–3. Electric deflection of the electron beam

Before deflection the electron beam will be raised to a high velocity v_0 by the accelerating potential V_a. It may then be assumed that the time in traveling the distance l_d along the deflecting plates, in Fig. 2–6, is short with respect to a cycle of the deflecting voltage V_d, or that V_d is a constant during a particular electron's flight time.

The path of the electron in passing through the deflecting plates is parabolic according to Eq. 1–22. From this equation, the slope of the parabola at $x = l_d$ and, consequently, the slope of the straight line o'-P' tangent to the parabola at $x = l_d$ is

$$\frac{dy}{dx} = -\frac{e\mathcal{E}_y}{mv_{0x}^2} l_d = \tan\theta \qquad (2\text{–}1)$$

The location of o' is determined by

$$x - o' = \frac{y}{\tan\theta} = \frac{\frac{1}{2}at^2}{\tan\theta} = \frac{l_d}{2} \qquad (2\text{–}2)$$

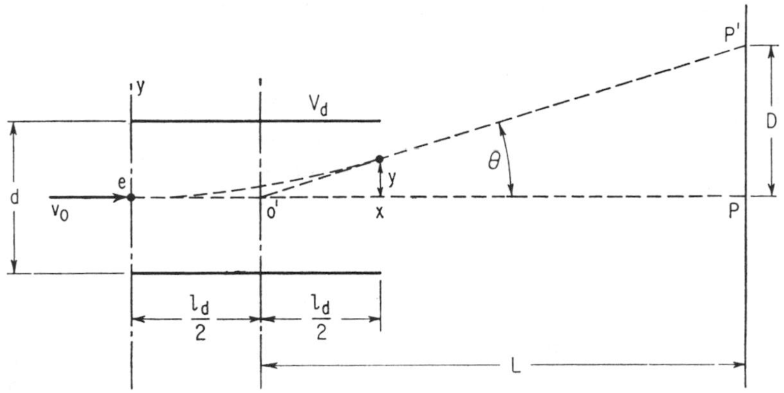

Fig. 2–6. Electric field deflection of the cathode-ray beam.

since $t = l_d/v_{0x}$. Consequently, point o' is at the center of the deflecting plates and distant L meters from the screen.

The deflection D is then given by use of Eq. 1–14 and the definition of $\mathcal{E}_y$ as

$$D = L \tan \theta = \frac{LV_d l_d}{2dV_a} \tag{2-3}$$

The deflection sensitivity is defined as the deflection per volt deflecting potential V_d, so that

$$S_e = \frac{Ll_d}{2dV_a} \qquad \text{m/v} \tag{2-4}$$

The length l_d and spacing d are limited by the beam striking the plates for large deflections, and L is set by desirable mechanical size. The accelerating voltage should be high for maximum spot brightness, so that any given tube is a compromise. Customary sensitivities for laboratory tubes are of the order of 0.2–0.5 mm per volt. It should be noted that since V_d was assumed constant during the time of flight of one electron, V_d partakes of the nature of an instantaneous voltage. If a sinusoidal a-c voltage is applied, the maximum deflection will be that produced by the double peak voltage.

Fringing of the electric field has been neglected above, so that actual deflections will differ slightly from the theoretical values of Eq. 2–3.

The total energy is given up by the electron upon impact with the screen. Part of the energy is transferred to the atoms of the screen material and is emitted as light; the remainder is dissipated as heat in the screen. The cathode-ray spot should not be left stationary on the screen because of the danger of overheating the screen material.

2–4. Magnetic deflection of the electron beam

Current-carrying coils mounted on the sides of the tube, as in Fig. 2–7, cause a magnetic field transverse to the beam direction. Assuming that the magnetic field acts over the axial distance l_m in Fig. 2–8, with B uniform, the beam will be deflected in a circular path of radius $r = eB/mv_0$. From the geometry of Fig. 2–8, it can be seen that

$$\sin \theta = \frac{l_m}{r} = \frac{eBl_m}{mv_0} \qquad \text{ERROR} \qquad (2\text{–}5)$$

Distance L is measured to the point of intersection of a line tangent to the final deflection of the beam and the line of the original velocity v_0. The point o' is not at the center of l_m, as in the electrostatic case, but the error introduced by assuming it to be at the center of the field region

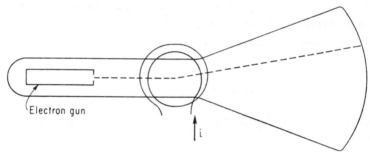

Fig. 2–7. Position of coils for magnetic deflection of the beam.

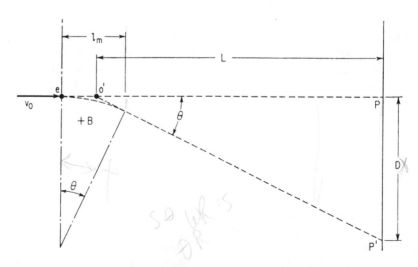

Fig. 2–8. Magnetic deflection of the cathode-ray beam.

is negligible for small angles of deflection where $\cos \theta \cong 1$. Then

$$\tan \theta = \frac{D}{L}$$

so that by use of trigonometric identities

$$\tan \theta = \frac{eBl_m/mv_0}{\sqrt{1 - (eBl_m/mv_0)^2}} \qquad (2\text{-}6)$$

For small values of B, or large values of r, the second term under the radical may be neglected with respect to unity. Consequently, to a good approximation

$$D = \sqrt{\frac{e}{m}} \frac{Bl_m L}{\sqrt{2V_a}} \qquad \text{m} \quad (2\text{-}7)$$

The magnetic-deflection sensitivity is defined as meters deflection per weber per square meter, so that

$$S_m = \sqrt{\frac{e}{m}} \frac{l_m L}{\sqrt{2V_a}} \qquad \text{m/weber} \quad (2\text{-}8)$$

For air-cored coils, B is directly proportional to the current flowing, and the deflection is a direct function of the coil current. Magnetic deflection cannot be used for direct observation of the wave form of an applied voltage since the coil current which sets up flux density B is a function of the time integral of the voltage.

It should be noted that the factor $\sqrt{e/m}$ appears in the expression for magnetic deflection but is not present for electric deflection. In that type, stray negatively charged gas atoms are deflected to the same extent as equally charged electrons, but in the electromagnetic type the deflections are smaller when the mass is greater. Since the atoms have large masses relative to that of an electron, the deflections will be small and the charged atoms will fall at or near the undeflected position of the beam. Continued bombardment of this nature is damaging to the screen, resulting in a brownish appearance near the center. Use of a very thin aluminum coating on the inner surface of the fluorescent screen has made tubes less sensitive to ion spotting. The coating is so thin that the small, high-velocity electrons are able to pass through it and excite the fluorescent material to visibility, whereas the much larger ions are caught by the aluminum. This coating also serves as a reflector of light and returns to the front of the tube a considerable portion of the light which would otherwise be lost into the tube interior.

Since the magnetic deflection sensitivity is less affected by changing V_a, therefore the accelerating potential can be increased to give greater spot brilliance with a smaller decrease in sensitivity for magnetic tubes than for electric-deflection tubes.

Although the sensitivity is stated above in terms of flux density, it is more convenient for circuit design to state the sensitivity in terms of ampere turns required on the exciting coils placed against the neck of the bulb. In such terms average sensitivities may be stated as 0.5–1.0 mm deflection per ampere turn.

2–5. Fluorescent screens

The fluorescent-screen material must be coated on the inside of the glass bulb thinly enough for the light from the electron impacts to pass through the screen and be viewed from outside the tube. For normal laboratory observation, zinc orthosilicate is used in the P-1 phosphor. It gives a yellow-green color of good visual and photographic properties. The spectral characteristics are such as to give peak response at about 5200 Å, which is near the maximum sensitivity of the human eye.

In the P-5 screen, calcium tungstate gives a screen with a bluish trace of excellent actinic characteristics. This screen has a very short persistence time and may be used with a special camera for recording the phenomena. In this application, the spot moves in one axis only, and the film moves continuously on an axis at right angles to that of the spot. The film movement supplies the time axis, and the need for short persistence of the trace is apparent because persistence blurs the film image.

A list of standard screen designations and characteristics is given in Table 1. A *long*-persistence screen may retain a visible image from a few seconds up to several minutes, a *medium-short* persistence indicates that the useful image is retained for 20 to 30 milliseconds, whereas the *very short* persistence of the P–5 phosphor indicates a retention of less than 30 μsec. Over 25 different phosphors are used to provide various special screen characteristics.

Since the electron beam striking the screen is carrying negative charge and the screen is insulated by the glass, the removal of this charge is necessary; otherwise the potential of the screen would fall to such a negative value as to repel the beam. Fortunately, as the electrons strike the screen they not only cause the screen to give off light but also to emit other electrons. This effect, known as *secondary emission* (see Chapter 3), may result in an average of more than one secondary electron being emitted per electron in the beam. The secondary electrons are attracted to a graphite coating placed over the interior bulb walls and connected to the second anode. As a result, instead of the screen acquiring a negative potential, it may be a few volts positive with respect to the second anode.

TABLE 1. CATHODE-RAY TUBE FLUORESCENT SCREENS

Phosphor No.	Color	Persistence	Application
P-1	Green	Medium short	General-purpose oscillograph
P-2	Blue-green	Long	Transient visualization
P-4	White	Short	Television
P-5	Blue	Very short	Fast photographic oscillography
P-7	Blue-white; then yellow	Very long	Radar screens
P-11	Blue	Short	Photographic oscillography
P-12	Orange	Long	Radar
P-16	Bluish purple	Very short	Television pickup
P-19	Orange	Long	Radar indicators

2–6. Anode voltages

For high spot brightness the accelerating potential should be high, but for high sensitivity the accelerating potential should be low, and any tube design is a compromise of these requirements. A trace registered at high spot velocity must carry high beam energy if the trace is to be seen, and thus high accelerating potentials must be used for such tubes. Actual voltages in use range from 500 to 80,000 volts, with usual laboratory equipment with 5-in. screen diameters employing 1500 to 5000 volts.

Another solution to the problem of obtaining a brilliant spot with high spot velocity is furnished by a tube with one or more intensifier electrodes around the glass bulb between the deflection plates and the screen. These electrodes operate at positive potential above that of the accelerating anode and further accelerate the beam after deflection. The resultant effect is that of a tube with low accelerating voltage with respect to deflection sensitivity but with high spot energy by reason of the acceleration received by the beam after deflection.

The cathode-ray tube is ordinarily operated with a power supply in which the positive potential connected to the second anode is grounded. The cathode of the tube is then negative, or below ground. The deflection-plate circuits are connected to the second anode, so that no axial acceleration of the beam will occur during deflection. Since the deflection-plate connections are frequently handled, grounding of the anode is a safety measure as well as a convenience in the avoidance of isolating capacitors.

2–7. Frequency limitations

The capacitance of the deflection-plate electrodes to each other, or to the other electrodes, is usually of the order of 2 to 5 pf. The reactance represented by this capacitance is large except for the very highest frequencies, so that the shunting effect of the deflection-plate system on circuits being investigated is usually negligible. The major items affecting the input impedance of the deflecting plates are the currents due to stray electrons and to gas ions produced by collision of atoms with the electrons.

At very high frequencies the deflecting voltage may not be a constant during the time of transit of one electron between the deflecting plates. This irregularity will produce an improper deflection of the beam. To prevent this aberration, the velocity of the beam may be raised.

These factors limit the common laboratory cathode-ray tube to frequencies of the order of 10^7 cycles and if amplifiers are used to increase the deflection-plate voltages, the frequency limits will be set by amplifier design and may be much lower. However, special techniques in which the periodic wave is sampled at repetitive intervals, allow frequencies as high as 10^9 to be accurately portrayed on the screen.

2–8. The complete oscillograph

The cathode-ray tube is usually used in an assemblage of apparatus called a *cathode-ray oscillograph*, arranged for easy and flexible operation.

A power unit to supply the high d-c accelerating potential and voltages for amplifiers is included. Amplifiers are provided so that voltages of value in millivolts may produce usable screen deflections on both x and y axes. These amplifiers must be well designed and must transmit all necessary harmonic components of the highest frequencies used without distortion of wave form or change in phase angles. An oscillator is incorporated to generate the sawtooth linear sweep voltage, so that voltages or currents may be seen on the screen plotted as functions of time. This oscillator must also be variable in frequency, so that single or multiple waves of varying frequency may be observed. Circuits are also supplied to start or trigger the sweep wave at a desired time in the input cycle, for ready observation of portions of input waves.

Means for focusing and varying the intensity of the spot, and of shifting the axes to different screen positions are also supplied. These controls result in a flexible and rugged instrument, usable over a wide range of currents, voltages, and frequencies. Direct-coupled amplifiers may be used to avoid losing d-c components in the observed signals.

Problems

2-1. A cathode-ray tube has applied to the y deflection plates a sinusoidal 60-cycle voltage of 35 rms value. The observed deflection is a vertical line 1.76 in. long.

(a) Calculate the electric deflection sensitivity.

(b) If the accelerating voltage on this tube were increased to double value, what would be the observed deflection for the above voltage?

(c) If the magnetic field is assumed to act only over the region of the deflection plates, which are 0.3 in. apart and 1.0 in. long, and the accelerating potential is 2000 v, calculate the peak value of B necessary to give a magnetic deflection equal to that for (a).

2-2. The x deflecting plates of a certain cathode-ray tube are 1.0 cm long and separated 0.4 cm. The distance L is 15 cm, and the accelerating potential is 800 v.

(a) Find the screen deflection produced by a d-c voltage of 200 v.

(b) Find the flux density required over the area of the deflecting plates to produce an equal deflection magnetically.

(c) Voltage fluctuations cause the accelerating potential to drop to 720 v. Calculate the deflection for the voltage in (a) and the flux density used in (b).

2-3. The cathode-ray tube of Problem 2-2(a) has applied to the deflecting plates a sinusoidal voltage of 100 v peak and frequency of 3×10^9 cycles. If an electron enters the deflecting plates at the voltage zero, find the deflection of this electron on the screen. What does this indicate as to a possible limiting frequency for this particular tube?

2-4. (a) Find the velocity of the electron of Problem 2-2 on entering the deflecting plates with $V_a = 1800$ v.

(b) The beam current totals 500 μamp. If the spot is 0.5 mm in diameter, find the watts per square centimeter delivered to the screen by the beam.

2-5. A voltage of $e_y = 100 \sin (2\pi 1000t)$ is applied to the y plates of a cathode-ray tube. On the x plates is $e_x = 120 \sin (2\pi 250t)$. If the deflection sensitivity of both sets of plates is 0.23 mm/v, what are the x and y coordinates of the electron spot on the screen at $t = 0.0005$ sec? The origin is the spot position at $t = 0$.

2-6. A 40-cycle sine voltage is applied to the x plates and a 60-cycle sine voltage of equal amplitude to the y plates of a cathode-ray tube. The two waves are zero and going positive at $t = 0$. Graphically construct the complete path of the fluorescent spot on the screen.

2-7. Two equal 100-cycle sine voltages are applied to the plates of a cathode-ray tube. Construct the pattern seen on the screen when:

(a) The two voltages are in phase.

(b) y-plate voltage lags x-plate voltage by 30°.

(c) y-plate voltage lags x-plate voltage by 45°.

(d) y-plate voltage lags x-plate voltage by 150°.

(e) Develop a formula by which the phase angle between two waves can be computed from measurements on the pattern.

2-8. Repeat Problem 2-6 if the voltage on the x plates is a 200-cycle sine wave and that on the y plates has a frequency of 50 cycles.

2-9. Repeat Problem 2-6 if the voltage on the x plates varies as $e_x = 140\epsilon^{-10t}$ and that on the y plates as $e_y = 80 \, \epsilon^{-4t}$, over a period from $t = 0$ to $t = 0.1$ sec.

References

1. Feldt, R., "Photographing Patterns on Cathode-Ray Tubes," *Electronics*, **17**, 130 (February 1944).

2. Haas, A., and R. W. Hallows, *The Oscilloscope at Work*. Philosophical Library, Inc., New York, 1956.

3. Nelson, R. B., R. P. Johnson, and W. B. Nottingham, "Electrical and Luminescent Properties of Phosphors under Electron Bombardment," *Jour. Appl. Phys.*, **10**, 335 (1939).

4. *The Cathode-Ray Tube and Typical Applications*. A. B. DuMont Laboratories, Clifton, N. J., 1948.

Solid-State Conduction; The Semiconductor Diode | 3

Most types of electronic devices are now available using either semi-conductors or vacuum-tubes. Study of both forms will be integrated in this text, since they utilize related circuitry, but the relative importance of the solid-state forms dictates that they be given prior and major treatment.

A desirable starting point for study is the simple unilateral rectifier or two-element *diode*. In its semiconductor form it depends on conduction in solid materials, with careful control of material composition and methods of deposition. To study the movement of electric charge or the conduction process it is desirable to adopt the particle viewpoint of the electron as discussed in Chapter 1. Conduction can then be considered as a directed flow of charges through the material, superimposed on the usual random thermal motions.

The conduction properties of materials are strongly dependent on the number of free or unbonded charge carriers available, as well as on the sign of the carriers. In good conductors there is always a sufficiency of free carriers, usually electrons, and conduction properties are largely a result of interaction between the electrons and the metal crystal lattice. Properties created by control of the number and type of carrier are of particular interest in the semiconductor materials. Because of this control of the number and sign of the available charge carriers, and the avoidance of crystal boundary imperfections by using single crystal material, certain properties are developed which lead to electronic solid-state devices.

3-1. Electrons in metals

The Bohr atom theory, discussed briefly in Chapter 1, supposes a positively charged nucleus surrounded by a group of electrons, established in definite states, orbits, or *energy levels*. The number of negative electrons is assumed equal to the atomic number of the element, and for a normal atom the negative charge of these electrons is balanced by a positive charge in the nucleus attributable to the presence there of an appropriate number of protons.

The positive charge on the atomic nucleus sets up an electric field inside the atom. Since work is done by movement of a charge through a field, then work would be done in moving an electron from the position of the nucleus to a particular orbit. This establishes the energy level of an orbit, and shows that the farther an orbit is from the nucleus, the higher the energy associated with that orbit. Consequently the outermost electrons are the high-energy electrons. It is also these outer electrons that are most easily affected by external influences. The inner or lower-energy electrons are effectively shielded from external influences by the fields of the outer electrons, and are considered as bound in shells or bands in which all possible electron energy levels are filled with electrons. In copper, of atomic number 29, there are four such shells, three completely filled with 2, 8, and 18 electrons, respectively, and a fourth or outer shell having only one electron and being only partially filled thereby.

This outer electron is called a *valence* electron, since this external electron will be fixed in a valence bond with a neighboring atom when they are incorporated in a crystal or compound. These outer-shell or valence electrons determine the chemical properties of the element. When the outer shell of electrons has all available electron energy levels filled, it is no longer possible for these electrons to contribute to the external properties of the element, and it is reasoned that a filled shell is an indication of a stable condition.

In a metallic crystal there will be many more high-energy levels than will be occupied by the electrons at a particular instant. An electron can exist in an atom, however, only if it is at an assigned energy level, and no more than one electron can occupy a given energy level at any instant. In order to occupy a given level, an electron must possess an exact amount of energy.

If the electron is given additional energy, it can take up only the exact amount required to raise its total energy to that of another discrete level, and it then exists there. If it loses energy, it can lose only the exact amount which will allow it to drop back to a lower-energy level. The energy level differences in isolated atoms, as in a gas, are relatively great, and it is difficult to give electrons the additional energy required to permit a step up to a higher-energy level. Under normal conditions most of the electrons in a gas atom will be found grouped in the lowest possible energy states, and the atom is then said to be in the *normal, or unexcited,* state.

In a liquid, since the atoms are forced much closer together, interacting forces between atoms are greater, and the number of allowable energy levels per atom is greatly increased. The energy difference between levels is correspondingly reduced, and it is easier for some of the electrons to acquire thermal or other energy sufficient to permit them to be raised to levels above normal.

In metals a great many atoms are forced very close together in a regular pattern, called a *crystal lattice*. The interatomic forces are very great due to the close spacing between the nuclei, and it is these forces which give a metal its great physical strength. As a result of the inter-atomic reactions, each of the original electron energy levels is split into a great number of energy levels. Thus, the energy required for an electron to move up from one level to the next may be very small, and the possible energy levels represent almost a continuous band in a metal.

When an electric field is applied to a metal by connecting a potential across it, some of the electrons will take up slight amounts of energy from the field (measured as i^2R losses), and the field will produce a component of electron motion in the direction of the positive electrode. This slow *drift*, superimposed upon the random thermal motions of the charges, constitutes an electric current. The ability to take up this additional energy implies that there are empty higher-energy levels available in which the electron can exist. This is the case with good conductors, there being many additional energy levels available to these so-called "free" electrons.

The reverse case, in which no empty higher-energy levels exist leads to a basic principle of quantum mechanics: when an energy-level band is completely filled with electrons, the electrons in the band cannot contribute to electrical conduction. There is no open energy level to which the electrons can rise if they absorb energy from the small electric fields associated with conduction, and therefore they cannot absorb such energy and cannot take part in conduction.

3–2. Semiconductor materials

Copper, with a resistivity of 10^{-8} ohm-meter is considered as one of the best electrical conductors. Quartz is typical of the nonconductors or insulators at the other extreme, with a resistivity of about 10^{12} ohm-m. There are a number of materials with useful properties which have resistivities intermediate to this range, and are therefore given the name of *semiconductors*. Of major importance are germanium, with a resistivity of about 0.60 ohm-m in the very pure state, and silicon having a resistivity of 1.5×10^3 ohm-m. Of lesser importance at present are lead sulfide, selenium, other metallic oxides and sulfides, as well as certain intermetallic compounds to be mentioned later.

Germanium and silicon are from Group IV of the Periodic Table, comprising carbon, silicon, germanium, tin, and lead. These elements crystallize in the cubic form, as does carbon in the diamond state, and hold their electrons in shells or groups of energy levels having the following number of electrons:

	Atomic number	Electron shells
C	6	2, 4
Si	14	2, 8, 4
Ge	32	2, 8, 18, 4
Sn	50	2, 8, 18, 18, 4
Pb	82	2, 8, 18, 32, 18, 4

The inner shells of 2, 8 or 2, 8, 18,$\cdots$, are completely filled shells, have no excess energy levels, and are stable and unaffected by outside influences. It is the four outer or valence electrons of each of these elements which are affected by external influences and cause these elements of Group IV to have similar chemical and physical properties.

Of the above elements, carbon in diamond form is an insulator, silicon and germanium are semiconductors, and tin and lead are good conductors. Germanium and silicon are the members of the family which possess the desired range of properties. However, it is the possession of four valence electrons which makes the elements interesting.

In the crystal lattice each atom of silicon or germanium utilizes these electrons in four covalent bonds with four neighboring atoms, each bond having two electrons, one from each atom, as in Fig. 3–1. Each atom is thus surrounded by a complete and stable shell of eight electrons, all electrons being rigidly bound at 0°K. Since no charges are free to move, the materials do not conduct electrically at that temperature.

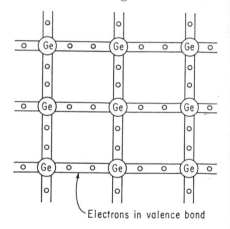

Electrons in valence bond

Fig. 3–1. Symbolic representation of pure germanium at 0°K.

3–3. The Fermi-Dirac energy distribution

In order to demonstrate that there are higher energy levels available for conduction in metals, it is necessary to study the energies of the electrons in the metal in greater detail. As the temperature of a metal is raised above absolute zero (0°K), the atoms begin to vibrate about their lattice positions in an arbitrary manner because of increased thermal energy. Many of the outer orbit or high-energy electrons obtain additional energy from these thermal vibrations, and are broken free of their valence bonds to the neighboring atoms of the crystal. These electrons are then free to drift through the crystal lattice. They suffer collisions with the vibrating atoms, receiving and losing energy, and the direction of the resultant motions is completely random. Since the number of collisions between atoms and electrons is very great, the problem of determining the energy held by the electrons at a given temperature is a statistical one. That is, some average or mean energy will be transferred in each collision, a mean distance or *mean free path* will be traveled by the electrons between collisions, and an average or *mean free time* between collisions may also be determined. There will, of course, be a statistical variation of the individual electron motions around the mean values.

The statistical manner in which the thermal energies are distributed among the different electrons of a metal at a given temperature has been studied extensively, and the function which most satisfactorily meets the physical requirements is known as the *Fermi-Dirac distribution*. This function allows us to determine the number of electrons dN per unit volume, which may be expected to have a value of energy in the range E to $E + dE$ at a temperature T. Actually, wave mechanics tells us that the figure obtained is a *probability* that this number of electrons will be in this energy range, but for our purposes it is sufficient to consider that they do have the computed value.

The Fermi-Dirac function is of the form

$$dN = \frac{C E^{1/2} dE}{1 + \epsilon^{(E-E_F)e/kT}} \tag{3-1}$$

where the proportionality constant is

$$C = \frac{8\pi (2m^3)^{1/2}}{h^3} = 6.82 \times 10^{27} \tag{3-2}$$

The symbols in the equations are

E = energy level, volts.
E_F = Fermi energy level, to be defined.
m_e = electron mass. *At Rest* $= 9.11 \times 10^{-28}$ g
e = electron charge magnitude.
k = Boltzmann's constant = 1.38×10^{-23} joule/°K.
T = temperature, degrees Kelvin, or Centigrade absolute.
h = Planck's constant = 6.62×10^{-34} joule-sec.

$C = 2.998 \cdot 10^{10}$ cm/sec

$e/m = 1.759 \times 10^{11}$ coul/kg $\sqrt{\frac{CU_A}{zm}} = V_R$

It should be noted that the term kT/e has dimensions of joules per unit charge, or volts. It is often called the *voltage equivalent of temperature,* and will recur frequently in many following discussions.

The numerator of the Fermi relation may be considered as determining the energy of a given state or level. The denominator is a dimensionless number which gives the probability that any particular energy level E will be occupied by an electron. The overall expression may then be considered as giving the distribution of electrons in the various possible energy levels.

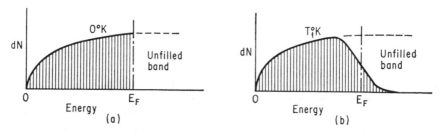

Fig. 3–2. Fermi-Dirac energy distribution of electrons in a metal (a) at 0°K., (b) at temperature T_1.

The curve of Fig. 3–2 is plotted from the above relation for $T = 0°$ K, and shows that in a metal at absolute zero temperature all possible energy levels may be expected to be occupied by electrons up to a certain value of E_F. That is, the probability of electrons existing in such levels is unity. The probability of electrons existing at any energy level above E_F is likewise shown to be zero. Absolute zero is then the condition of lowest possible energy for the electrons.

The E_F level appears as the maximum energy that any electron may have at absolute zero; it is also called the *Fermi characteristic energy.* If $E = E_F$, then the denominator of Eq. 3–1 takes on the value of two, or the probability that a level at E_F is filled is one-half. This reasoning provides another definition for the Fermi energy: it is that value of energy at which the probability of occupancy of a level is one-half.

For finite temperatures and $E > E_F$ the function approaches zero as a limit; that is, the probability of there being electrons in the very high energy levels decreases to zero, as shown by the curve for temperature T_1. Because of the large effect of the exponential term, the change from the parabolic curve to the zero asymptote occurs for values of energy which depart from E_F by only a few multiples of kT/e beyond E_F. Physically this suggests that only the outermost or high energy valence electrons are affected by increased temperature, or can acquire energy by impact with the thermally vibrating atoms.

For metals there are many energy states above E_F into which electrons are free to move if given sufficient additional energy, as by heat or an electric field. Since the existence of such higher unfilled states is a wave-mechanical requirement for electrical conduction, it follows that metals are conductors of electricity.

The value of E_F at 0°K can be found by integration of Eq. 3–1 for values of $E < E_F$, when the expression reduces to $dN = NE^{1/2}\,dE$. Then

$$E_F = \left(\frac{3N_V}{2C}\right)^{2/3} = 3.64 \times 10^{-19} N_V^{2/3}$$

where N_V is the valence electron density in the metal. For copper this figure is taken as 10^{29} per m³. Since N_V is a function of the material, then E_F will likewise vary for different metals.

3–4. Intrinsic conduction

The electron energy distribution discussed in Sec. 3–3 applies to good conductors such as silver, copper, iron and similar metals. The electron energy distribution in insulators and semiconductors differs from that for metals, and accounts for the differences in magnitude and behavior of the electrical conductivity. The distribution takes the form of Fig. 3–3 (a) and (b), and shows a valence-electron band in which all available electron energy levels are completely filled by electrons at 0°K, separated by a normally empty and higher energy band by an energy gap, ΔE wide. This energy gap covers a region of energy levels which are forbidden or

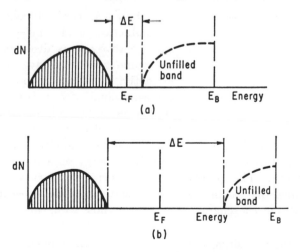

Fig. 3–3. Density of electron states at 0°K in (a) a pure semiconductor; (b) an insulator.

unallowed for electrons. No electrons are able to contribute to electrical conduction through charge movement, and at 0°K the conductivity of a pure semiconductor is zero.

This view may be reconciled with that of the previous section by noting that to free an electron from a valence bond requires an amount of energy equal to ΔE. Smaller amounts of energy will not break the valence bond and cannot be accepted by the electron; such smaller amounts of energy are therefore forbidden or fall within the energy gap.

This situation contrasts with that in a good metallic conductor where the electron energy band is not filled, and additional higher levels are always available for electrons to fill, with only small increments of energy required. Numerous valence electrons (approximately one per atom) are easily broken from their bonds, are more or less free, and are able to drift under an applied electric field and contribute to conduction.

As the temperature of the semiconductor is raised, some electrons receive thermal energy from the thermally excited lattice atoms in amounts equal to or greater than the gap energy ΔE, and these are able to break their valence bonds and transfer to energy levels in the upper band. Since these electrons are then in an incompletely filled band, they may accept additional energy from an applied electric field in small amounts, drift under the urging of this field, and contribute to electrical conduction. As the temperature rises further the conductivity of a semiconductor increases, or the resistivity decreases, because of the increased numbers of free charge carriers reaching the upper band, and these materials have negative temperature coefficients of resistance.

When an electron receives greater than ΔE energy, breaks its valence bond, and transfers to the upper or conduction band, an electron vacancy or *hole* is left in the lower band. The electron energy distribution is then as illustrated in Fig. 3–4. The hole, while fixed to a given atom in the crystal lattice, as in Fig. 3–5, is attractive to electrons and can be filled by passing an electron from a neighboring bond, after it is in turn broken loose by the furnishing of sufficient thermal, electrical, or radiant energy. It must be recognized that when the first electron was broken loose from its valence bond, it absorbed energy. When such an electron again enters a hole in a valence bond, it releases this energy as a quantum of light or thermal energy. The quantum may in turn be reabsorbed by another electron to break its valence bond, creating a new *electron-hole pair*, and effectively moving the charge deficiency or hole along in bucket-brigade style.

The hole has a positive charge of absolute value equal to that of an electron, but it appears to move more slowly than an electron. If an electric

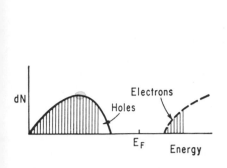

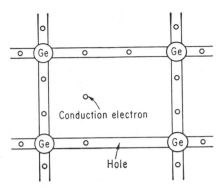

Fig. 3–4. Formation of holes in the lower band.

Fig. 3–5. Result of formation of an electron-hole pair in germanium.

field is applied to superimpose a drift component on the random thermal movement of electrons and holes, then the action represents conduction by the positive charges or holes, as well as by the negative electrons which have been broken free, and this is called *intrinsic conduction.*

At room temperature very pure germanium, one of our most useful semiconductors, may have an intrinsic resistivity of about 0.60 ohm-m (copper has 10^{-8} ohm-m), and such a resistivity value requires the release of only about one electron-hole pair for every 10^{10} germanium atoms. The resistivity of a pure semiconductor is related to its gap energy ΔE in ev, as

$$\rho = A\epsilon^{\Delta Ee/kT} \tag{3–3}$$

where A is a coefficient.

Insulators differ from semiconductors in the magnitude of ΔE, this gap energy running up to 15 ev for some insulators. Very high temperatures are needed to make insulators conduct appreciably, as shown by the relation above. The gap energy of carbon in diamond form as an insulator is 7 ev, whereas silicon and germanium are considered semiconductors with gap energies of 1.12 ev and 0.72 ev respectively, and germanium has the lowest resistivity at usual ambient temperatures. Intrinsic conduction increases rapidly with temperature and is not desired in diode or transistor operation since the intrinsic currents mask the operating currents carried largely by either holes or electrons. Thus, operating temperature limits of approximately 85°C for germanium and 180°–200°C for silicon will be set by the intrinsic conduction. The higher permissible operating temperature for silicon is a logical result of the larger gap energy of this material.

3–5. N and P conduction

In the usual ranges of temperature, impurity atoms present in the semiconductor lead to conduction considerably greater than that due to intrinsic conduction. However, in order that the characteristics of the semiconductor be suited to the requirements and controllable, it is first necessary to prepare germanium or silicon of extreme purity and then add tiny and controlled amounts of the desired impurity atoms. Germanium and silicon have 4.5×10^{22} and 5.2×10^{22} atoms per cu cm, respectively, and addition of only one impurity atom per 10^6 or 10^7 semiconductor atoms is sufficient to yield the desired characteristics, and to reduce the resistivity for germanium from about 0.60 ohm-m to the range of 0.04 to 0.10 ohm-m.

Desired impurities are chosen from Group III of the Periodic Table, with three valence electrons, or from Group V with five valence electrons. A very small amount of an element from Group V, such as phosphorus, antimony, or arsenic, may be caused to diffuse into the high-purity germanium as the crystal is grown from the melt. Since there may be only one impurity atom for about 10^7 semiconductor atoms, the lattice is essentially undisturbed and the impurity atoms are forced to accept a position in the germanium lattice, and only four of their five valence electrons can enter the valence bonds with other germanium atoms.

The fifth electron has an energy value which lies below but near the level of the upper conduction band. At usual temperatures it will readily acquire sufficient thermal energy to move into the conduction band, and contribute to conduction. In fact the number of available charge carriers will be practically equal to the number of impurity atoms, or it may be assumed that all the excess impurity electrons are raised to the conduction band. The situation is symbolically represented in Fig. 3–6(a), and the conduction will be by electrons or of N-type, the impurity atoms which supplied the electrons being called electron *donors*.

Even though there is only one impurity atom per 10^7 germanium atoms, this means that there will still be 10^{15} impurity atoms per cu cm contributed by the impurity. While the impurity atom becomes a positive ion upon losing one electron, it is not attractive to electrons because the valence bonds are filled.

Likewise, hole-rich or P-type material may be formed by causing atoms from a Group III element, such as boron, aluminium, gallium, or indium, to diffuse into the crystal as it is grown, or by later processes. These atoms have only three valence electrons for the bonds, and when they are forced into the germanium lattice there is one electron vacancy, or a hole left for every impurity atom. The missing electron may be supplied by a nearby germanium atom, and the movement of the resultant

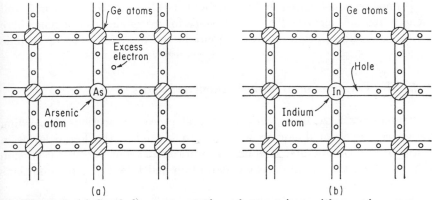

Fig. 3–6. (a) Symbolic representation of germanium with arsenic as an N impurity; (b) Same with indium as a P impurity, showing a hole.

hole from one atom to another constitutes conduction by positive charges. Impurities of this type are known as electron *acceptors*, and the situation is symbolically shown in Fig. 3–6(b).

The energy-level diagrams for N and P materials appear in Fig. 3–7. This demonstrates that the energy level of the extra electron associated with a donor atom is only a little below the bottom of the conduction band, and a slight addition of thermal energy will activate this electron to the conduction band. Likewise, the level of energy of the hole in the lattice created by the presence of the acceptor atom is only a little above the energy of the top of the filled band. Thus, a small amount of thermal energy will make possible the jump of an electron from one of the valence bonds into the acceptor level, leaving an unfilled lower band.

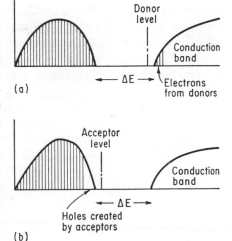

Fig. 3–7. Energy level conditions in (a) N materials; (b) P materials.

N-type conductivity indicates free electrons available for conduction, whereas P-type material indicates conduction by electron deficiencies or holes. Desirable properties, dependent on controlled conduction by one predominant or majority type of charge carrier, are thus produced in the semiconductor materials.

It must be remembered that throughout the above processes the material actually remains electrically neutral, since for every electron or hole there is an equal and opposite charge present in the material or in an atomic nucleus.

3–6. The Fermi level in intrinsic semiconductors

Statements have been made in several preceding sections concerning the energy levels of donor or acceptor atoms, and of the Fermi levels in N and P semiconductors. It is now appropriate to continue the discussion of Sec. 3–3 on the Fermi energy distribution and to apply it to conditions in semiconductors.

We shall assume and later prove, that the Fermi level lies midway in the forbidden energy gap for intrinsic semiconductors. The various bands are then distributed as in Fig. 3–8, for a temperature sufficient to cause thermal generation of holes. A measure of the variation of electron density with energy in the conduction band can be obtained by study of the Fermi expression, as modified by the presence of the forbidden energy gap in semiconductors. If the bottom energy level of the conduction band be designated E_C, then Shockley has shown that the numerator of Eq. 3–1 becomes $N_i(E - E_C)^{1/2} dE$, as the function describing the energy associated with a given state. The density of occupied states or energy levels in the conduction band at a given temperature T can be obtained by integrating the modified Fermi expression between E_C and ∞.

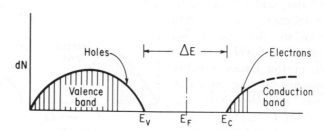

Fig. 3–8. Fermi level in an intrinsic semiconductor at temperature T.

The Shockley expression is valid only in the region near the bottom of the conduction band, but the electrons will most probably be in the bottom or lower-energy levels of the band, and thus the expression is usable even though the upper limit of integration be made ∞.

Then

$$n = N_i \int_{E_C}^{\infty} \frac{(E - E_C)^{1/2} \, dE}{1 + \epsilon^{(E-E_F)e/kT}} \tag{3-4}$$

The symbol n indicates electron or negative carrier density in the intrinsic material. Energy E, stated in ev, will be above E_C, and E_C at the bottom of the conduction band will be several kT/e above E_F, so that it is appropriate to say

$$\epsilon^{(E-E_F)e/kT} \gg 1$$

and thereby neglect unity in the denominator.

Rewriting the integral in view of this assumption

$$n = N_i \int_{E_C}^{\infty} (E - E_C)^{1/2} \epsilon^{-(E-E_F)e/kT} \, dE$$

and if a substitution of $x = (E - E_C)e/kT$ is made, it is possible to write the expression as

$$n = N_i \left(\frac{kT}{e}\right)^{3/2} \epsilon^{-(E_C-E_F)e/kT} \int_0^{\infty} x^{1/2} \epsilon^{-x} \, dx \tag{3-5}$$

which has as a solution[1]

$$n = N_i \left(\frac{kT}{e}\right)^{3/2} \frac{\sqrt{\pi}}{2} e^{-(E_C-E_F)e/kT} \tag{3-6}$$

Combining the constants

$$N_N = \frac{2(2\pi mkT/e)^{3/2}}{h^3} \tag{3-7}$$

and then

$$n = N_N \, \epsilon^{-(E_C-E_F)e/kT} \tag{3-8}$$

which states the density of electrons in the conduction band of an intrinsic semiconductor as a function of temperature. The constant N_N has the value $1.76 \times 10^{22} T^{3/2}$ for germanium and $4.74 \times 10^{22} T^{3/2}$ for silicon.

It can be shown that the variation of energy in the states at the top of the valence band is given by $N_p(E_V - E)^{1/2}$, where E_V is the energy at the top of the valence band, in ev. This expression is accurate only near the top of the band, but it is to be expected that the holes will lie there, since they will have been created by the most energetic electrons. Thus, the expression is usable as was the one for the conduction band. By a method analogous to that employed in the development above, it is possible to arrive at an expression for p, the density of holes in the valence band, after integrating from E_V to ∞, as

$$p = N_p \left(\frac{kT}{e}\right)^{3/2} \frac{\sqrt{\pi}}{2} \epsilon^{-(E_F-E_V)e/kT} \tag{3-9}$$

[1] Pierce, B. O., "A Short Table of Integrals." No. 496.

The constants may be combined, giving

$$N_P = \frac{2(2\pi m_p k T/e)^{3/2}}{h^3} \tag{3-10}$$

with m_p representing the effective mass of the hole. Then, as before

$$p = N_P \epsilon^{-(E_F - E_V)e/kT} \tag{3-11}$$

as the hole density in the valence band, as a function of temperature.

In an intrinsic semiconductor $n = p = n_i$. Equating Eqs. 3–8 and 3–11 gives the Fermi energy, stated as E_{Fi} for intrinsic material, as

$$E_{Fi} = \frac{E_C + E_V}{2} + \frac{kT}{e} \ln \frac{N_P}{N_N}$$

The ratio N_P/N_N is a function of the masses of the hole and the electron. For our purposes these may be assumed essentially equal, and so

$$E_{Fi} = \frac{E_C + E_V}{2} \tag{3-12}$$

or in an intrinsic semiconductor the Fermi level is located at the middle of the unallowed energy gap.

Multiplication of Eqs. 3–8 and 3–11 leads to

$$np = n_i^2 = N_N N_P \epsilon^{-(E_C - E_F)e/kT} \tag{3-13}$$

Noting from Eqs. 3–7 and 3–10 that

$$N_N = K_1 T^{3/2} \qquad N_P = K_2 T^{3/2}$$

and that $E_C - E_V = \Delta E$, the energy gap in ev, then Eq. 3–13 can be written as

$$np = n_i^2 = K_1 K_2 T^3 \epsilon^{-\Delta E e/kT} \tag{3-14}$$

This result shows the product of hole and electron densities in an intrinsic semiconductor to be an involved function of temperature. The effect of the particular material is apparent only in the gap energy in the exponent, and the result supports the earlier reasoning that materials of large gap energy would have few carriers. The value n_i is often called the *intrinsic carrier density*.

3–7. The Fermi level in N and P semiconductors

The Fermi level serves as a measure of relative electron energy in materials, and knowledge of its value is of later importance. In *N* and *P* materials the Fermi level can be shown to be displaced from the center of the unallowed energy gap, where it was for intrinsic materials.

Assuming an N material, but with a few acceptor impurities, it will be found that at $0°K$ some of the excess electrons in the donor level will have dropped down and filled the acceptor states. The donor states will then be only partially filled, and the conduction band will be empty. The Fermi level must then be at or near the donor energies, since these are the only partially occupied states, and only at the Fermi level can the probability of occupancy be between zero and one. As the temperature rises the Fermi level must drop slowly, to account for the reduced occupancy of the donor levels as donor electrons are excited to the conduction band. With continuing temperature rise the Fermi level drops still more, until it reaches the midgap position when thermal generation or intrinsic conduction begins.

While the Fermi probability for occupancy of a given conduction band level is less than the probability of occupancy of a donor level, there are so many more conduction levels than donor levels that it is to be expected that all the donor electrons will be found in conduction bands at usual temperatures. In this situation the donor levels are said to be fully activated or the donor atoms all ionized.

With donor levels fully activated, and if intrinsic conduction is negligible or thermally-generated holes and electrons are not present in significant numbers, then the density of electrons in the conduction band approximates the donor atom density, or $n \cong N_D$. It follows from Eq. 3–8 that

$$n \cong N_D = N_N \, \epsilon^{-(E_C - E_F)e/kT} \qquad (3\text{--}15)$$

from which the Fermi level E_{FN} in an N semiconductor can be written as

$$E_{FN} = E_C - \frac{kT}{e} \ln \frac{N_N}{N_D} \qquad (3\text{--}16)$$

Since kT and N_N are both functions of temperature, it can be seen that the Fermi level should progressively sink below E_C as the temperature increases.

The donor level may be taken as 0.04 ev below E_C in a given N silicon sample. Since the gap energy in silicon is 1.12 ev, then the donor level is 3.5 per cent of the gap width below E_C. In silicon $N_N = 4.7 \times 10^{22} T^{3/2}$ per m³, and a particular sample may be assumed as having $N_D = 5 \times 10^{15}$ impurity atoms per m³ (one impurity atom per 10^7 silicon atoms). Then the second term of the equation has the value of 0.20 ev at $100°K$, and at that temperature the Fermi level in this N sample is about 18 per cent of the gap width below the E_C level.

In a similar manner, and assuming that all acceptor levels are filled, it is possible to determine the Fermi level in a P semiconductor as

$$E_{FP} = E_V + \frac{kT}{e} \ln \frac{N_P}{N_A} \qquad (3\text{-}17)$$

where N_A is the density of acceptor atoms, or of filled acceptor levels. The Fermi level will lie at the acceptor level just above the valence band at $0\,°K$, and will rise with temperature, reaching the half-gap value under conditions of intrinsic conduction.

3–8. The preparation of the semiconductor materials

Germanium is a hard, dense element obtained as a byproduct of zinc refining in the United States, and from the flue dust of certain coals in Europe. It is available commercially in the dioxide form (GeO_2) and this is heated to about $650\,°C$ in an atmosphere of hydrogen, resulting in a reduced germanium powder. Heating above the melting point ($937\,°C$) in an inert gas atmosphere then allows the material to be obtained in the form of bars of uncertain purity and of polycrystalline form.

Purification to semiconductor standards is carried out by the process of zone refining or zone melting in inert gas atmospheres. Most impurities present tend to remain dissolved in the liquid state rather than to freeze into the solid form, so if a short section of a germanium bar is melted and the melted region caused to move slowly from right to left along the bar, the impurities will tend to remain in the liquid zone and ultimately concentrate at the left end of the bar. Such heating of small sections is most easily carried out by the induction process. By repeating the zone melting a number of times over the length of the bar, the germanium can be raised to a purity represented by a resistivity of the order of 0.60 ohm-m, where theoretically pure germanium is calculated to have a resistivity of 0.65 ohm-m at $20\,°C$.

Metals usually solidify in polycrystalline form, and the crystal boundaries introduce inconsistencies or imperfections in conduction properties. For consistent conductive properties it is customary to grow the useful semiconductor materials into large single crystals.

The desired single crystals may be grown by dipping a small seed crystal into a bath of molten germanium and withdrawing the seed uniformly as the crystal grows and cools. The seed is a small single crystal, and must be properly oriented in the holder to obtain growth along the desired crystal axes. Rotation of the crystal as it is withdrawn serves to give more uniform characteristics. The bath is usually heated to an accurately controlled temperature by induction heating, and an inert atmosphere maintained over the melt.

Since pure germanium has a resistivity higher than desired for semi-conductor devices, controlled amounts of N or P impurities are added to the melt during the crystal-pulling process. Final crystals may be several inches long and of the order of an inch in diameter. These are sliced by diamond saws into small wafers, usually several millimeters on a side and a fraction of a millimeter thick. Surfaces are etched by various acids, and extreme cleanliness is practiced at all times in the manufacture of semiconductor devices.

Silicon is a hard, light element, appearing much like graphite, and melting at 1420 °C. Because of the great solubility of other materials in silicon, it is difficult to purify silicon to the level required by semiconductor practice. The tetrachloride can be readily obtained by the action of chlorine on a heated mixture of sand and carbon. Silicon of about 99.9 per cent purity is then obtained by reduction of the tetrachloride with zinc, followed by use of hydrogen and other reducing agents.

Zone melting is finally employed for purification, but since silicon dissolves quartz and reacts with carbon and other materials, it cannot be melted in the usual laboratory boats or crucibles. Melting of a small zone in a vertical rod clamped between supports and enclosed in an inert atmosphere is possible, the short molten zone being held in place by the surface tension of the liquid. The impurities rise to the surface of the liquid zone and can be swept to the upper end of the silicon bar. A great many passes of the induction heating coil are required, and very close temperature control is also needed to avoid flow of the molten slug. Purities represented by resistivities of about 1500 ohm-m are obtained.

The single crystal is drawn by methods similar to those for germanium, although extreme care must be used to avoid contamination, and temperature control is made more difficult by the higher melting point of silicon. The higher gap energy and the possible higher operating temperatures for silicon semiconductor devices make all this care worthwhile, however.

By alternate doping of the crystal melt with N and P impurities, or by other post-melting processes, it is possible to form alternate regions of N and P material in the same crystal. A *junction* is then produced where two such regions come together in a crystal, and this junction is found to have the unilateral conductivity characteristic of a rectifying diode. The theory and properties of such diodes as well as the transistor will be discussed in later sections.

3–9. Conduction by drift of charges

Conduction in semiconductor materials occurs by reason of two mech-anisms: (1) drift under the effect of an applied potential, and (2) diffusion or charge motion from a region of high density to a region of lower charge density. The first mechanism will be considered here.

With thermal energies acting alone, the charge carriers move in random directions and with statistically varying velocities. When an electric field is applied to the material, a slow drift component in the direction of the field attraction is added to the random motions. The motion of each charge thus consists of a series of random displacements, but with a statistical average velocity component owing to the field action.

The current density due to electron motion through a region has been shown in Section 1–9 as

$$J_n = \rho v = -nev_n \qquad \text{amp/m}^2$$

where n is the electron density per m³, and v_n is the electron drift velocity component induced by the applied electric field. For holes this may be written as

$$J_p = pev_p \qquad \text{amp/m}^2$$

where p and v_p are density and velocity values for the holes.

It is convenient to define as the *charge mobility*

$$\mu_n = \frac{v_n}{\mathcal{E}} \quad \text{and} \quad \mu_p = \frac{v_p}{\mathcal{E}} \qquad (3\text{–}18)$$

as velocity per unit field intensity, or in units of meter/second/volt/meter, i.e. m²/v-sec. Then the total current density can be obtained as

$$J = e\,\mathcal{E}(n\mu_n + p\mu_p) \qquad \text{amp/m}^2 \quad (3\text{–}19)$$

for charge movement of both electrons and holes. The negative sign disappears from the J_n element because v_n is opposite to v_p.

Rearrangement of the above leads to

$$\sigma = \frac{J}{\mathcal{E}} = e(n\mu_n + p\mu_p) \qquad \text{mho/m} \quad (3\text{–}20)$$

for the conductivity, or current density per unit field intensity.

The velocity which enters into computation of mobility is a statistical mean given by

$$\text{mean velocity} = \frac{\text{mean free path}}{\text{mean free time}}$$

Mean free path and mean free time are average values measured between collisions of the charges and the thermally vibrating atoms of the lattice.

For metals, the value of n is very large and not a function of temperature in the usual ranges. However, temperature rise affects the mean free path, reducing it by more frequent collisions due to the greater amplitude of lattice atom vibration at elevated temperatures. The mean free time between collisions is also reduced. They do not vary identically, however, and as a result the velocity and mobility fall slowly with rising temperature. This accounts for the rising temperature coefficient of resistance of metals.

In semiconductors at low temperatures, there are few charges free to move and conductivity is very low. At higher temperatures the donor or acceptor levels come into action and provide carriers, and the conductivity rises. At some temperature all donor or acceptor levels may be considered as activated, and n and p become constant. The conductivity then depends on the mobility which decreases somewhat with temperature, and as a result the conductivity falls. At a still higher temperature, carriers become available by thermal generation and intrinsic conduction begins. The conductivity rises rapidly with increasing temperature owing to the increase of n or p, even though mobility may be falling slowly.

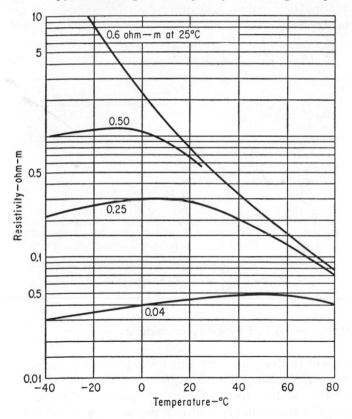

Fig. 3–9. Variation of resistivity of germanium with temperature and purity.

Figure 3–10, which is the curve for 0.04 ohm-m germanium of Fig. 3–9 replotted in terms of conductivity, illustrates the effects described above in a semiconductor. At −40° all acceptor or donor levels may be considered as activated, and from −40° to +50° the conductivity falls slowly because of a small reduction in mobility with temperature. Above 60° thermal generation of carriers starts to be appreciable and the curve ultimately approaches

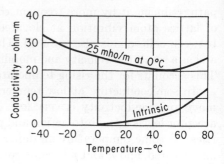

Fig. 3–10. Variation of conductivity of germanium with temperature.

that for 0.60 ohm-m material, which represents essentially intrinsic conduction in pure germanium.

Typical mobility values and other data for germanium and silicon appear in Table 2.

TABLE 2. PROPERTIES OF GERMANIUM AND SILICON*

	Germanium	Silicon
Atomic number	32	14
Atoms/m³	4.4×10^{28}	5.0×10^{28}
Melting point	937°C	1420°C
Resistivity, ohm-m	0.60	1.5×10^3
Energy gap, ev, 0°K	0.75	1.15
Dielectric constant, ϵ_r	15.8	11.7
μ_n, m²/v-sec.	0.39	0.13
μ_p, m²/v-sec.	0.19	0.048
n_i, at 300°K/m³	2.4×10^{19}	1.5×10^{16}
D_n, m²/sec.	0.0095	0.0033
D_p, m²/sec.	0.0045	0.0013

* E. M. Conwell, "Properties of Silicon and Germanium; II," *Proc. IRE*, 46, 1281, (1958).

3–10. Measurement of mobility of minority carriers

The minority-carrier mobility can be measured by a simple transit-time experiment. By Eq. 3–18, μ is defined as the velocity per unit electric field intensity, and the circuit of Fig. 3–11 provides the necessary data.

A rod of N germanium has a current passed through it which provides a field measurable by the voltmeter V and the distance A_2, as $\varepsilon = V/A_2$,

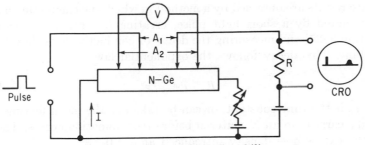

Fig. 3–11. Measurement of mobility.

v/m. Two additional pointed wires are placed on the rod as emitter and collector and the distance A_1 measured accurately. An input pulse of possibly 1 μsec duration is applied to introduce holes at the emitter, and this pulse may be given a repetition rate of possibly 100–500 pulses per second. The pulser may also be used to synchronize the CRO sweep, and the input pulse will appear on the screen near the start of the sweep, due to its application across the bar and resistor R in series.

The holes drift down the bar, under the action of the applied field, and reach the collector t seconds after the injection time. The pulse of charge is also acted upon by diffusion processes, and so the received signal on the CRO, as measured across R, will not be an image of the applied pulse, but will be smeared somewhat in time, as indicated in the figure.

By use of the sweep-time calibration, and measuring between the center of the applied pulse and the maximum of the received signal, the time t can be calculated, and the velocity v follows by use of the distance A_1 between the probes. Since both v and ε have been determined then the hole mobility follows as

$$\mu_p = \frac{v}{\varepsilon}$$

Material of P characteristics may be used, with electron mobility being determined by reversal of applied voltage polarities.

3–11. Lifetimes of the charges

In the experiment of the previous section, as the holes migrate along the bar some of them will recombine with the excess electrons present in the N material, and therefore the received pulse will decrease in amplitude along the bar. The average lifetime of the holes could be determined by varying the transit time and measuring the received pulse height. More accurate results are obtained by a method in which the conducting material is illuminated by a short light pulse, creating free carriers as explained in Section 3–25, and measuring the decay of conductivity as these carriers recombine. This decay follows the exponential law

$$p = p_0 \epsilon^{-t/\tau_p} \qquad (3\text{–}21)$$

where τ_p is the time constant, or can be taken as the mean lifetime of the minority carriers in an N material before recombination occurs. The term p_0 is the excess hole density introduced at $t = 0$.

Usual lifetimes are in the range of 1 to 1000 μsecs, but depend on temperature and impurity concentration. However, lifetime in the bulk crystal may be considerably longer than the surface lifetime, which the illumination method essentially measures. Minority electrons in P material will be found to have essentially the same lifetimes.

The *diffusion length* or the average distance travelled before recombination is given the symbol L_p or L_n. It can be shown that

$$L_p = \sqrt{D_p \tau_p} \qquad (3\text{–}22)$$

For germanium L_p is in the range of 0.007 to 0.2 cm, and this has important implications for the thickness of the base of a PNP transistor, for instance. It is ordinarily assumed that recombination is negligible in hole flow through this electrode, and so the base thickness must be small with respect to L_p.

3–12. Conduction by diffusion

In a homogeneous field-free region, under equilibrium conductions, the charge movement is due to thermal energies and is completely random, and the net flow of charge or the current across any given boundary is zero. However, materials exist in which the distribution of holes or electrons may vary in some manner throughout a region. In such cases it may be expected that, given time, the charges would tend to redistribute themselves so that a condition of charge homogeneity would exist; in this process of charge *diffusion* through the material, net values of charge may be found to flow across reference planes, representing currents across them. That is, in a region with a charge density gradient, more carriers of a particular type are available to move away from the region of high density than are available to move toward the high-density region, under thermal actions. A net movement away from the high-density region thus occurs.

Diffusion may result in a redistribution of charge which will lead to potentials arising between portions of the material. If this occurs, then we may expect that drift currents will be set up, and under final equilibrium the potential established will be just sufficient to create a drift current equal and opposite to the diffusion current, resulting in a net flow of zero.

For further consideration, assume pieces of N and P material as in Fig. 3–12(a). The N material is, of course, electrically neutral, but it does have high-energy electrons in the conduction band, supplied by the electron-donor impurities. At the right the P material has holes in the valence band, produced by the acceptor atoms, although the material is also electrically neutral. Now assume the two blocks to be pushed tightly together so that at the boundary x the two become unified in an atomic sense. We thus have a material in which there is an inhomogeneity in distribution of charge carriers.

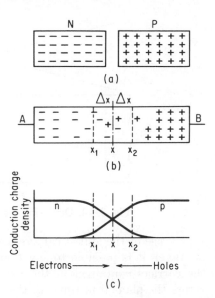

Fig. 3–12. A PN junction: (a) electron and hole distribution before joining; (b) same after joining; (c) variation of charge density.

In the N material there is a much higher electron density than in the P material, and there will be diffusion of electrons from N to P. Similarly, there is a hole density gradient across the junction, and there will be diffusion of holes from P to N. Actually these effects are limited to a narrow region between x_1 and x_2, as in Fig. 3–12, (b) and (c), which is known as the *depletion* or *barrier layer*, and is of the order of 10^{-4} cm thick.

For further study of diffusion, let Fig. 3–13 represent a much expanded view of the charge distribution in the barrier region. Only one-dimensional charge movement will be considered; thus the electron density increases from right to left, and the hole density increases from left to right. At the junction plane at x the electron density has a value of n per m³, while the corresponding hole density is p per m³. Distances Δx are laid off at each side of x, equal to the mean free paths of the respective carriers, or the mean distance which will be travelled by holes or electrons per mean free time Δt. It is also assumed that Δt is small with respect to charge lifetimes, so that the effects of recombination may be neglected. Since no external field is acting, the charges will continue their random thermal motions, but a diffusion component will also appear.

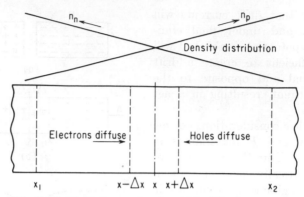

Density distribution

Electrons diffuse   Holes diffuse

x_1 $x - \Delta x$ x $x + \Delta x$ x_2

Fig. 3–13. Depletion region in which diffusion occurs.

By use of the statistical averages or mean values of distance and time of travel, it is possible to say that owing to random motions, one-half of the carriers contained in the region x to $x + \Delta x$ will move to the left across the plane x in time Δt, the other half of the carriers having x components moving them to the right and are not of interest to our problem. This statement can be made because of the assumption that Δx was the *mean free path* of the charges. Likewise, one-half of the carriers in the region $x - \Delta x$ to x will cross the plane x in the same time while moving to the right, the other half traveling to the left and out of the problem. Since the density of holes at x is p, and the density gradient of holes is dp/dx, then Fig. 3–14 shows that the hole density at $x + \Delta x$ is

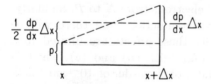

$$p + \frac{dp}{dx} \Delta x$$

and the average density throughout the region of thickness Δx is

Fig. 3–14. Computation of number of charges in the space Δx.

$$p + \frac{1}{2} \frac{dp}{dx} \Delta x \qquad (3\text{–}23)$$

The number of holes per unit volume in the region x to $x + \Delta x$ is then available as

$$\Delta x \left(p + \frac{1}{2} \frac{dp}{dx} \Delta x \right)$$

and the number of holes expected to pass across the plane at x in time Δt is

$$P_{\leftarrow} = \frac{1}{2} \Delta x \left(p + \frac{1}{2} \frac{dp}{dx} \Delta x \right) \qquad (3\text{–}24)$$

Reference to Figs. 3–13 and 3–14 shows that the number of holes per unit volume in the region $x - \Delta x$ to x can be written as

$$\Delta x \left(p - \frac{1}{2} \frac{dp}{dx} \Delta x \right)$$

and the number of holes crossing x to the right from this region will be one-half the above, or

$$P_{\rightarrow} = \frac{1}{2} \Delta x \left(p - \frac{1}{2} \frac{dp}{dx} \Delta x \right) \qquad (3\text{--}25)$$

Thus, we have established the fact that there are more holes available to move to the left than there are to move to the right, or that a density gradient will produce carrier flow. Therefore the net hole flow to the left is

$$P = P_{\leftarrow} - P_{\rightarrow} = \frac{1}{2} (\Delta x)^2 \frac{dp}{dt} \qquad (3\text{--}26)$$

This charge flows in the mean free time Δt, and the net hole flow per unit time then is

$$P_{\leftarrow} = \frac{1}{2} \frac{(\Delta x)^2}{\Delta t} \frac{dp}{dx} \qquad (3\text{--}27)$$

A *hole diffusion constant* D_p can then be defined as

$$D_p = \frac{1}{2} \frac{\Delta x}{\Delta t} \Delta x \qquad (3\text{--}28)$$

in m²/sec units. Physically D_p is proportional to the mean thermal velocity and the mean free path.

As a result of the above it is now possible to write the diffusion current density, or charge flow per unit time, for holes as

$$J_p = - eD_p \frac{dp}{dx} \qquad \text{amp/m}^2 \quad (3\text{--}29)$$

representing conventional current to the left across the junction. The negative sign appears because the current is in a direction opposite to the positive gradient of holes.

A similar process may be followed for the assumed electron density gradient, showing electron flow to the right. The diffusion current due to electrons may then be written as

$$J_n = eD_n \frac{dn}{dx} \qquad \text{amp/m}^2 \quad (3\text{--}30)$$

which also represents a conventional current to the left. The positive sign appears because the current is in the direction of increasing electron gradient.

In semiconductors the drift and diffusion currents can be simultaneously present. It is possible to combine Eqs. 3–19, 3–29 and 3–30 to yield expressions for total electron and hole currents as

$$J_p = e\mu_p p\mathcal{E} - eD_p \frac{dp}{dx} \qquad \text{amp/m}^2 \quad (3\text{–}31)$$

$$J_n = e\mu_n n\mathcal{E} + eD_n \frac{dn}{dx} \qquad \text{amp/m}^2 \quad (3\text{–}32)$$

Diffusion current is proportional to the space gradient of charge density, or a charge inhomogeneity must exist. Drift current is a function of electric field, whereas diffusion may occur in regions essentially free of external electric fields, a condition which may exist in many semiconductor devices.

At voltage differences approximating 0.25 v both types of current may exist. When the potential has values significantly less than 0.25 v then the diffusion action will predominate, and when potentials greatly exceed this level the drift currents will occur.

3–13. The *PN* junction as a diode

A single crystal may be grown from germanium which has been doped with a small amount of *N* impurity, and then at an appropriate instant in the growth process a *P* impurity may be added in sufficient quantity to override the effect of the *N* material. The excess *N* electrons simply fill some of the holes added by the *P* impurity, the result being as if less *P* material had been added. In this way a crystal with a *junction* between *N* and *P* material is formed. This process yields a crystal in which the change between *N* and *P* is relatively gradual, although the complete discontinuity may occur in 0.001 mm.

An alloy junction may be formed by placing a dot of *P* impurity, such as indium, on an *N* germanium wafer, and causing the indium to fuse onto the germanium by heat. At the interface a layer of *P* material, only a few atoms thick, is formed by the diffusion of indium atoms into the germanium lattice. The remainder of the indium serves as an ohmic contact to the *P* germanium layer. Such a junction is abrupt in nature, since the change from *N* to *P* characteristics may occur in only a few tens of atom diameters.

The result has a large density of electronic carriers in the *N* material, since the donors will be assumed fully activated. There will also be a small density of holes present due to thermal pair generation. In the P material there will be a large hole density, due to activation of the acceptors, as well as a small density of electrons from pair generation. In each case, at normal and usual operating temperatures, the excess of the majority carriers over the intrinsic charges, is very great.

There is now a charge inhomogeneity, and some of the electrons in the N material and near the junction, will diffuse across the junction and fill holes on the P side, and some holes will diffuse across the boundary and occupy positions on the N side. There will be an excess of electrons on the P side, a deficiency on the N side, and a potential will exist across the junction with N positive to P. The region of the junction itself is thus depleted of excess or majority charges, and only the fixed atomic charges are left. This accounts for the use of the name _depletion layer_. It will be assumed in all that follows that this depletion region is so thin that recombination can be neglected in the transit of charges across the region.

Under equilibrium, with no external potential applied, the internal potential or barrier voltage V_B will be just sufficient to make equal to zero the algebraic sum of the diffusion current which would be set up by the nonuniform charge distribution, and the drift current which would occur due to V_B. The potential V_B will appear across the junction layer, but the total semiconductor remains electrically neutral since no net charge has been added or subtracted.

Energy-level diagrams for the N and P materials, unjoined, will be as in Fig. 3–15 (b). As discussed in Section 3–7, the Fermi level of the N material will lie near the conduction band level E_C, and the Fermi level of the P material will be close to the top of the valence band edge E_V. There will be electrons excited to the conduction band of the N material from the donor levels, and holes in the valence band of the P side created by the acceptor levels of the P impurity.

After junction there will be an adjustment of charges as discussed above, and as a result the Fermi levels will adjust to equality much as water levels in connected tanks, the barrier potential V_B will appear, and the energy-level diagram will change to that at Fig. 3–15 (c).

By Eq. 3–15,

$$n = N_N \epsilon^{-(E_{CN}-E_{FN})e/kT} \tag{3–33}$$

in N material. Similarly, the intrinsic electron density in P material can be written by analogy with Eq. 3–8 as

$$n_i = N_N \epsilon^{-(E_{CP}-E_{FP})e/kT} \tag{3–34}$$

If these N and P materials form a junction, and under equilibrium conditions, then the Fermi levels must be equal across the junction, or

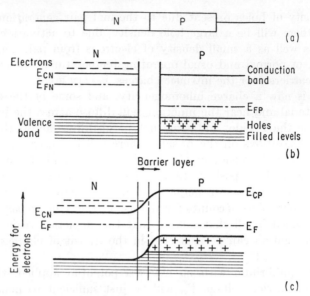

Fig. 3–15. (a) Junction PN diode; (b) Electron energy levels in N and P materials; (c) Energy levels under thermal equilibrium after joining.

$E_{FN} = E_{FP}$, and

$$\frac{n}{n_i} = \epsilon^{(E_{CP} - E_{CN})e/kT} \tag{3-35}$$

From Eq. 3–32,

$$J_n = e\mu_n n \mathcal{E} + eD_n \frac{dn}{dx} \tag{3-36}$$

but under the assumed equilibrium conditions the net current must be zero, or the drift and diffusion currents must be equal and opposite, for both holes and electrons. Setting $J_n = 0$, and separating variables

$$-\frac{\mu_n}{D_n} \mathcal{E} \, dx = \frac{dn}{n} \tag{3-37}$$

Integration of this expression across the width of the depletion or barrier layer, or between x_1 and x_2 of Fig. 3–16(a), provides

$$-\frac{\mu_n}{D_n} \int_{x_1}^{x_2} \mathcal{E} \, dx = \int_{n}^{n_i} \frac{dn}{n}$$

It has been shown that the P material is negative to the N, and accordingly the integration of $-\mathcal{E}$ from x_1 in N to x_2 in P will yield V_B as a rise from P to N, and the barrier potential of the equilibrium junction. Also

$$\frac{n}{n_i} = \epsilon^{(\mu_n/D_n)V_B} \tag{3–38}$$

Comparison of this result with Eq. 3–35 leads to two conclusions: that the barrier potential is equal to the displacement of the conduction levels, or

$$V_B = E_{CP} - E_{CN} \tag{3–39}$$

and that

$$\frac{\mu_n}{D_n} = \frac{e}{kT} \tag{3–40}$$

Equation 3–39 allows Eq. 3–35 to be written as

$$n = n_i\epsilon^{eV_B/kT} \tag{3–41}$$

which relates the barrier potential to the electron densities on the two sides of the junction. A similar expression governs hole densities.

Equation 3–40 could have been obtained for holes, as well, and so in general it may be said that

$$D = \frac{kT\mu}{e} \tag{3–42}$$

and this result is known as the Einstein relation. It permits the ready interchange of junction relations from those in terms of mobility and diffusion constants, to situations where it is preferable to study the phenomena in terms of potentials and temperature.

By applying an external potential V of small magnitude with positive to P, or opposing V_B, the junction equilibrium is upset, the diffusion process creates a current from P to N, and this is called the *forward direction*, or the direction of low resistance. The energy-level diagram will be as in Fig. 3–16(c). The current will be found to depend on carrier density or material conductivity, and the applied potential.

Figure 3–17(a) further illustrates the carrier changes which occur in

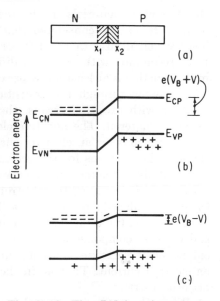

Fig. 3–16. The PN junction energy pattern: (b) with reverse voltage ($+V$ to N); (c) with forward voltage ($+V$ to P).

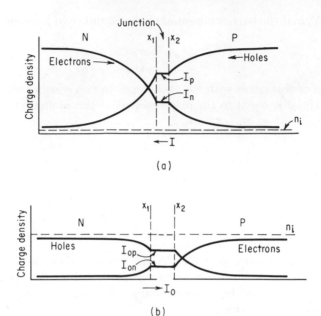

Fig. 3–17. (a) Currents near the junction, forward potential; (b) Same, reverse potential.

the N and P materials in the regions near the junction, with current flowing. It may be considered that positive V on the P electrode injects holes which diffuse to the left, or toward the junction. Some of these holes recombine with electrons diffusing across the junction, and so I_p in the junction is at least a few per cent less than the injected hole current. After passing through the transition layer these holes progressively recombine with excess electrons, the hole current decaying exponentially in the N material. The negative electrode on N, however, has been supplying electrons, or an electron current flows in N to the right, and this supplies the electrons for the recombination process. A few of these electrons will diffuse across the barrier as I_n, and will then rapidly recombine with excess holes in P, the electron current decaying exponentially until the electron density reaches the n_i level.

Obviously, the total current through the device, or the sum of the hole and electron components, must be constant. The total current I, which enters the P electrode as a hole current, emerges from the N electrode as an electron current. That is, in the forward direction, current flow is by majority carriers.

When the applied potential is reversed, as in Fig. 3–17(b), with P negative to N, the carriers on each side tend to be attracted away from the junction, or the depletion layer is thickened, and only thermally-generated intrinsic charges are available to carry the small reverse current

I_o. This is the high-resistance direction, and the junction represents a high resistance, shunted by a capacitive component owing to the dielectric effect of the depletion layer, which contains the fixed atomic charges.

Figure 3–17(b) shows the carrier flow under reverse potential. Such movement is due to intrinsic carriers, swept out of the junction region by the applied potentials. This reverse current is carried by minority carriers, and is a function of temperature due to its intrinsic nature. The reverse current will be of small magnitude, due to the scarcity of carriers at usual temperatures.

The material with the larger μn product will have the lower resistivity, and in general the material of lower resistivity will supply the majority carriers through the transition region. In Fig. 3–17(a) the major current in the transition or junction region is due to holes.

3–14. Current-voltage relations for the *PN* diode

It is now possible to quantitatively determine the barrier potential and the currents which will flow through the junction under applied external potentials. In the following the transition layer will be assumed very thin, and the time of transit short with respect to the charge lifetimes, so that recombination effects may be neglected. It should also be noted that since kT/e is equal to 0.026 v at 300°K, then the voltages appearing in exponents combined with this voltage-equivalent of temperature will be of comparable magnitudes, or small by usual standards. In fact, most typical potentials appearing across the junctions of diode devices will be only a few tenths of a volt in the forward direction.

As shown by Fig. 3–17, there are four components to be considered in deriving an expression for the total current through the transition region. These are I_n and I_p existing with external voltage applied, and intrinsic components I_{on} and I_{op}. The algebraic sum of these components will predict the diode current under all conditions.

By Eq. 3–41 the current I_{on} can be obtained, starting with

$$n = n_i\,\epsilon^{-eV_B/kT}$$

and noting that the defined direction of positive potential has been reversed in Fig. 3–18. The area of the junction may be taken as A square meters, and multiplying by ev, the particle charge magnitude and average velocity to obtain nev, a current, we find for the I_{on} current component through the transition region

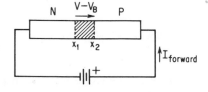

Fig. 3–18. Junction with applied forward potential.

$$I_{on} = An_iev_n\epsilon^{-eV_B/kT} \tag{3–43}$$

By analogy

$$I_{op} = A p_i e v_p \epsilon^{-eV_B/kT} \tag{3-44}$$

after noting that $v_p = -v_n$.

Equations 3–31 and 3–32 must be used to obtain the current components existing with applied potential, since both drift and diffusion elements may be present. By use of Eq. 3–42 these may be written as

$$-\mathcal{E}\,dx = -\frac{I_n\,dx}{e\mu_n n} + \frac{kT}{e}\frac{dn}{n} \tag{3-45}$$

$$\mathcal{E}\,dx = \frac{I_p\,dx}{e\mu_p p} + \frac{kT}{e}\frac{dp}{p} \tag{3-46}$$

An external potential V in the forward direction or with P positive, is applied as in Fig. 3–18. It is assumed that the crystal material has good conductivity, and the potential then appears across the junction region, tending to inject holes into P, or opposing the barrier potential V_B which has made N positive to P.

The potential across the junction may be obtained by integration of the field across the junction, or between x_1 and x_2, and for the electron component of current this is

$$-\int_{x_1}^{x_2}\mathcal{E}\,dx = -\frac{1}{e\mu_n n}\int_{x_1}^{x_2}I_n\,dx + \frac{kT}{e}\int_n^{n_i}\frac{dn}{n}$$

The term on the left represents the total potential across the junction, which must be $-(V - V_B)$ in accordance with the symbolism of Fig. 3–18. The first term in the right contains the term $e\mu_n n$ which is recognizable as the electron conductivity of the material from Eq. 3-20. This term is then the iR drop through the junction and will ordinarily be small. The remaining term is the potential due to electron movement. Thus

$$-(V - V_B) = \frac{kT}{e}\ln\frac{n_i}{n}$$

This can be written as

$$n = n_i \epsilon^{(V-V_B)e/kT} \tag{3-47}$$

which is of the same form as Eq. 3–41 for the junction without external potential.

If Eq. 3–46 is treated similarly, there results for the hole current

$$p = -p_i \epsilon^{(V-V_B)e/kT} \tag{3-48}$$

Again multiplying by Aev, we find for the current *through the transition region*, with a forward emf applied:

$$I_n = Anev_n = An_iev_n\epsilon^{-eV_B/kT}\epsilon^{eV/kT} \tag{3-49}$$

$$I_p = Apev_p = Ap_iev_p\epsilon^{-eV_B/kT}\epsilon^{eV/kT} \tag{3-50}$$

The total current through the transition region of the PN junction is then given by the algebraic sum of the four current components, or

$$I = I_n + I_p - I_{on} - I_{op} = A(n_iev_n + p_iev_p)\epsilon^{-eV_B/kT}(\epsilon^{eV/kT} - 1)$$

The intrinsic components may be combined and defined as I_o, which gives

$$I_o = A(n_iev_n + p_iev_p)\epsilon^{-eV_B/kT} \tag{3-51}$$

so that finally the total current through the PN diode may be expressed as

$$I = I_o(\epsilon^{eV/kT} - 1) \tag{3-52}$$

In the forward direction $(+V)$ the exponential term will quickly become large with respect to unity and the current then increases exponentially with V. Likewise, with reverse potential $(-V)$ the exponential term reduces to a negligible value and the current I_o then flows, due to the intrinsic charges generated by thermal energies. In fact, at 300°K the value of $kT/e = 0.026$ v, and for appreciably greater reverse voltages the diode reverse current will be constant at the value I_o. Since thermal generation of pairs is constant at a given temperature, then the reverse current is theoretically independent of applied potential. The current I_o, known as the *reverse saturation current*, is the only factor in Eq. 3–52 affected by the constants of the materials. It is proportional to conductivity, and is therefore a function of temperature, as shown in Fig. 3–19.

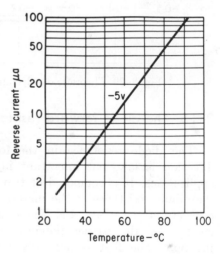

Fig. 3–19. Variation of reverse current with temperature.

Equation 3–52 is the semiconductor diode volt-ampere relation. It is apparent that the relation is nonlinear in general, and that such a device is unilateral or a rectifier. The theoretical volt-ampere relation plotted in Fig. 3–20 confirms this conclusion. The device has great value because of the low forward voltage drop which permits the attainment of high power efficiency.

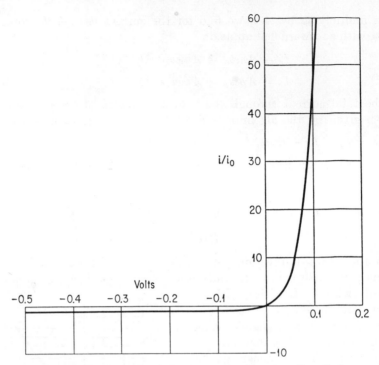

Fig. 3–20. Theoretical volt-ampere curve for a junction diode.

3–15. The diode forward resistance

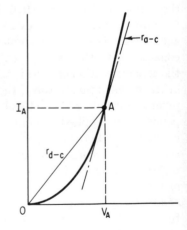

Fig. 3–21. Resistance of the diode.

The diode resistance in the forward direction is low, but important in some applications. It is composed of two parts, the ohmic resistance of the materials and contacts of the diode, and the resistance created by the barrier potential of the junction. The first is desirably but not always small, and the second can be calculated.

Using the forward quadrant of the diode volt-ampere curve of Fig. 3–21, the d-c resistance of the device at a point A is given by $r_{\text{d-c}} = V_A/I_A$. Using Eq. 3–52, then

$$r_{\text{d-c}} = \frac{V}{I_o(\epsilon^{eV/kT} - 1)} \qquad (3\text{--}53)$$

For a-c or variation of current around an operating point as at A, it is the slope of the curve that represents the effective a-c resistance. At A this is $r_{\text{a-c}} = dV_A/dI_A$. For the diode

$$\frac{1}{r_{\text{a-c}}} = \frac{di}{dv} = I_o \frac{e}{kT} \epsilon^{eV/kT} = \frac{e}{kT}(I + I_o)$$

At 20°C (293°K) this becomes

$$r_{\text{a-c}} = \frac{0.025}{I + I_o} \cong \frac{0.025}{I} \qquad \text{ohms} \quad (3\text{–}54)$$

where the current is in amperes. This result neglects the internal ohmic resistances, which are often appreciable.

3–16. Capacitance of a gradual junction

With reverse potential applied, the depletion region of a PN junction is swept free of mobile charges but the fixed impurity ions remain. That is, on the P side of the junction there will be hole-forming impurity atoms with the holes filled with electrons, and the net charge in this small area will be negative. On the N side of the depletion region there will be donor atoms that have lost electrons, and the space charge here will be positive. It is evident that the depletion region around the junction has a stored charge and will represent a capacitance.

At greater distances from the junction the mobile charges will not have been withdrawn and equilibrium conditions will prevail. The density of donors and acceptors on the two sides of a gradual junction made by crystal growth techniques is indicated in Fig. 3–22(a), as a result of a change from N to P impurity in the growth process. The apparent junction might be considered as located at 0, where the density of donors, N_D, and the density of acceptors, N_A, are equal or $N_A - N_D = 0$. There will then be a separation of charge in the depletion layer which extends across the junction and the potential $V - V_B$ arises, where V is negative for reverse potentials. The potential distribution across the junction appears in Fig. 3–22 (b).

As the reverse voltage is increased, the width W of the transition region increases, and more charge appears there. Because of this increase of dielectric thickness with potential, it is found that the change of charge with applied potential is not a linear relation, and the resultant capacitance is a function of applied voltage.

The actual distribution of charge through the graded junction approximates that of Fig. 3–22(c), and this will be assumed modified to Fig. 3–22(d), to provide a form of variation which is more suited to use in mathematical analysis. It is also desirable to assume that the area of the junction is large, so that field changes occur along the x axis only.

From Fig. 3–22(d), the charge density is assumed to vary linearly with distance inside the transition or depletion region, so

$$\rho = - ax \qquad (3\text{-}55)$$

where

$$a = \frac{e(N_D + N_A)}{W} = \frac{1}{W}\left(\frac{\sigma_n}{\mu_n} + \frac{\sigma_p}{\mu_p}\right)$$

where W represents the distance over which the composition of the N and P materials is graduated. Equation 3–55 applies for the distance where $-W/2 < x < +W/2$, in accordance with Fig. 3–22(d). Equation 3–20 is also used, with full activation of donors and acceptors assumed. The subscripts apply in the respective materials.

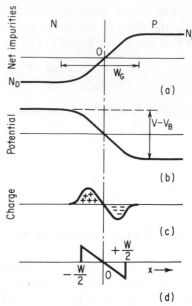

(a)

(b)

(c)

(d)

Fig. 3–22. Conditions in the graded junction.

Now consider an infinitesimal cube of sides dx, dy, dz, located in the region between $-W/2$ and $+W/2$, as in Fig. 3–23. The charge enclosed by these volumes is

$$dq = \rho \, dx \, dy \, dz$$

Under the assumption of large area of junction in the y, z plane, the electric flux will be directed only along x. Defining inward electric flux as negative, then passing in through the right-hand face of the cube is a total flux $-D_2 dy \, dz$, D_2 being the flux density at the point. Passing out of the left face is a flux $D_1 \, dy \, dz$, so that the net outward flux, by definition equal to the enclosed charge, is

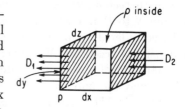

Fig. 3–23. Development of Poisson's equation.

$$(D_1 - D_2) \, dy \, dz = \rho \, dx \, dy \, dz \qquad (3\text{-}56)$$

But $D_1 - D_2$ is the change of flux density in length dx, so that dividing by dx, the rate of change of flux density in the region can be written as

$$\frac{dD}{dx} = \rho \qquad (3\text{-}57)$$

Also by definition $D = \epsilon \, \mathcal{E} = -\epsilon \, dV_x/dx$, so that

$$\frac{d^2V_x}{dx^2} = -\frac{\rho}{\epsilon} \tag{3-58}$$

where ϵ is the absolute dielectric constant $= \epsilon_r \epsilon_v$, and V_x is the potential at a point x in the depletion layer. This result is recognizable as *Poisson's equation*, specialized to one dimension. Use of Eq. 3–55 leads to

$$\frac{d^2V_x}{dx^2} = \frac{ax}{\epsilon} \tag{3-59}$$

It will be assumed that the conductivity of the N and P materials is good, so that there is negligible voltage drop in the equilibrium regions outside of the junction thickness. Then $dV/dx = 0$ at $x = \pm W/2$, and $V = 0$ at $x = 0$. After double integration of Eq. 3–59, we have the potential at any point x in the depletion region as

$$V_x = \frac{ax}{2\epsilon} \left(\frac{x^2}{3} - \frac{W^2}{4} \right) \tag{3-60}$$

This expression indicates a variation of potential as at Fig. 3–22(b).

The total potential across the junction is $V - V_B$, and this represents the difference between Eq. 3–60 evaluated at $x = +W/2$ and $x = -W/2$. Thus

$$V - V_B = V_x]_{x=W/2} - V_x]_{x=-W/2} = \frac{aW^3}{12\epsilon} \tag{3-61}$$

The effective width W of the depletion layer is then found to be a function of applied voltage, as

$$W = \left[\frac{12\epsilon(V - V_B)}{a} \right]^{1/3} \tag{3-62}$$

The maximum charge density on one side is at $x = W/2$ or $\rho_{max} = aW/2$. Using this as the height of the triangle of charge density, the total charge on one side of the junction, equal to that on the other, is

$$Q = \frac{aW^2}{8}$$

and use of Eq. 3–62 gives

$$Q = \frac{a^{1/3}}{8} \left[12\epsilon(V - V_B) \right]^{2/3} \tag{3-63}$$

The capacitance associated with a charge separation is defined as $C = Q/V$. However, in this case the capacitance is a function of the applied potential, and so it is the change of capacitance as the voltage changes which is of interest with a-c voltages across a junction. Then the *space-charge, transition, or depletion region incremental capacitance* is

$$C_T = \frac{\partial Q}{\partial(V_B - V)} = \frac{\epsilon^{2/3} a^{1/3}}{[12(V_B - V)]^{1/3}} = \epsilon^{2/3} \left[\frac{\sigma_n/\mu_n + \sigma_p/\mu_p}{12W(V_B - V)} \right]^{1/3}$$

$$\text{f/m}^2 \quad (3\text{-}64)$$

The capacitance equation might also be written as

$$C_T = \frac{\epsilon A}{W} \qquad \text{farads}$$

where A is the area in square meters. This is the form of expression normally expected for a parallel-plate capacitance of dielectric thickness W and absolute dielectric constant ϵ. It differs from the usual capacity in that W is a function of applied potential. The larger the reverse voltage $(-V)$, the larger W and the capacitance drops. If a be considered a measure of the steepness of gradation of the junction, then the capacity increases with the abruptness or steepness of the junction. Usually the acceptor density $N_A \gg N_D$, or the P region is of higher conductivity materials, and as σ_p or N_A is increased the capacity rises.

A typical value for C_T is in the order of 10–50 picofarads at usual voltage biases.

3–17. Capacitance of an abrupt junction

The previous section considered the capacitance created in a junction where the change of material characteristics was relatively gradual, as in a grown junction. By use of diffusion or alloying techniques, it is possible to alloy a P-forming impurity, such as indium, onto an N germanium base wafer. Some of the indium diffuses shallowly into the germanium, converting it to P material, and the remainder of the indium serves as a contact electrode. The concentration N_D of the ions in the N material is relatively constant up to the diffusion limit. Here the impurity changes rapidly to P type. The P region will have a conductivity higher than the N region, or $N_A \gg N_D$.

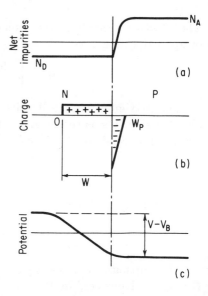

Fig. 3–24. Depletion layer charge and potential in an abrupt junction.

The resultant impurity distribution is shown in Fig. 3–24(a), with the assumed fixed charge distribution under reverse bias at Fig. 3–24(b), the origin being arbitrarily selected as shown. The constant charge density in the N material is

$$\rho = eN_D = \sigma_n/\mu_n \qquad (3\text{–}65)$$

in the region $0 < x < W$. The total charge in the P material must, of course, equal that on the N side. Poisson's equation may again be used

$$\frac{d^2 V_x}{dx^2} = -\frac{\rho}{\epsilon} = -\frac{\sigma_n}{\epsilon\mu_n} \qquad (3\text{–}66)$$

Integration of this expression, and use of the conditions that $dV_x/dx = 0$, $V_x = 0$, at $x = 0$, gives

$$V_x = -\frac{\sigma_n x^2}{2\epsilon\mu_n} \qquad (3\text{–}67)$$

The ohmic drop in the material can be neglected, or the total potential is assumed to appear across the junction, and actually appears across the N side since the P material is so thin and its conductivity is much higher then the N material. Thus, the total junction potential $V - V_B$ where V will be negative, can be determined as before

$$(V_B - V) = V_x]_{x=W} - V_x]_{x=0} = \frac{\sigma_n W^2}{2\epsilon\mu_n} \qquad (3\text{–}68)$$

The effective width of the depletion layer under the assumption that the P side is very thin, is

$$W = \left[\frac{2\epsilon\mu_n(V_B - V)}{\sigma_n}\right]^{1/2} \qquad (3\text{–}69)$$

This again indicates that the width W of the transition layer increases as a nonlinear function of the reverse voltage.

The total charge on one side of the junction is given by

$$Q = \sigma_n W/\mu_n = \left[\frac{2\epsilon\sigma_n(V_B - V)}{\mu_n}\right]^{1/2} \qquad (3\text{–}70)$$

As before, it is the incremental capacitance, or the change in capacity as the applied voltage changes, which will be important in circuits operating with a-c voltages across a junction. The transition region incremental capacitance, per unit area of the abrupt junction, is

$$C_T = \frac{\partial Q}{\partial(V_B - V)} = \left[\frac{\epsilon\sigma_n}{2\mu_n(V_B - V)}\right]^{1/2} \quad \text{f/m}^2 \quad (3\text{–}71)$$

This result is also that of a parallel-plate capacitor if it is written as

$$C_T = \frac{\epsilon A}{W} \qquad \text{farads}$$

where W is shown as a function of applied voltage by Eq. 3–69. This result is similar to that of Eq. 3–64 for the gradual junction except for the value of the exponent, and the dependence on N conductivity instead of both conductivities. This is, of course, a result of the assumptions which came from the thinness of the P side of the junction.

A typical value for C_T in the abrupt junction is in the range of 30–100 picofarads at -5 v bias.

3–18. The diffusion or storage capacitance

For forward bias, as will be encountered in usual diodes, or in the emitter junction of the transistor, a larger capacitance appears. This is called the *storage* or *diffusion capacitance, C_D.*

In the theory of the PN junction it was explained that under forward bias the potential barrier is lowered, and holes from the P side enter the N side, and electrons from the N side diffuse across the junction to the P material. These charges diffuse away from the junction and progressively recombine, the respective minority charge densities decaying exponentially as was indicated in Fig. 3–17(a). It may be considered that this charge is stored upon application of forward potential, and the amount of stored charge varies with applied potential, as for a true capacitor.

The effective capacitance C_D can be shown to be related to the diffusion constant and the diffusion length, as might be expected from the physical action which occurs. That is

$$C_D = \frac{\partial Q}{\partial V} = \frac{L_n^2}{D_n r_n} + \frac{L_p^2}{D_p r_p} = \frac{\tau_n}{r_n} + \frac{\tau_p}{r_p} \qquad (3\text{–}72)$$

The resistances r_n and r_p are the electron and hole components of the diode a-c resistance of Eq. 3–54.

This storage capacitance may have values of several hundred picofarads, and will be considered when high-frequency equivalent circuits are derived for the transistor. For the ordinary junction diode, this capacitance serves to limit its usefulness to relatively low frequencies, and the point-contact diode takes over at higher frequencies.

In certain switching circuits, where the applied emf is abruptly changed from forward to reverse, this capacitance must discharge and the flow of displacement current after the potential has changed tends to put "tails" on pulse response. Considerable study has gone into the development of special switching diodes in which this storage effect has been minimized.

The transition capacitance was effective under reverse bias, and is a creation of the majority carriers. Conversely, the storage capacitance is effective under forward potential and is created by the minority carriers.

3–19. The Zener diode

That practical junction diodes do perform as predicted by Eq. 3–52 is illustrated by the typical volt-ampere characteristic of Fig. 3–25. However, at large reverse voltages, about −140 v for the example, the reverse current increases rapidly, and this is known as the *breakdown level*. The diode there appears to have a very low dynamic resistance, and the current is almost entirely a function of the external circuit resistance. The voltage at which the breakdown occurs is stable, and choice of material conductivity permits design of units in which the breakdown occurs at reverse voltages from about three volts to several hundred volts.

The breakdown phenomenon is reversible and not damaging to the junction, provided that the power loss is limited and a safe operating temperature maintained. Such units are used to accurately regulate voltage sources, and are known as Zener diodes, after the man who first explained the phenomenon.

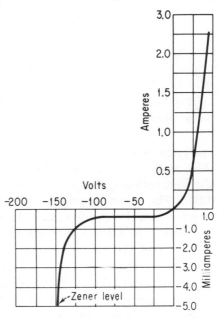

Fig. 3–25. Junction diode characteristic, showing Zener level.

In a very thin barrier layer, as in Fig. 3–26(a), the reverse voltage creates a high field intensity, of the order of 10^7 v/m. This is a sufficiently high field that some electrons are able to jump across the gap, from the filled valence levels in P to some of the unfilled conduction levels in N. The process is known as *tunneling* of the barrier, and is related to the wave properties of the electrons.

In some thicker junctions there is an *avalanche* breakdown caused by bombardment of the atoms by the electrons in the reverse saturation current. At a critical field level the moving electrons acquire sufficient

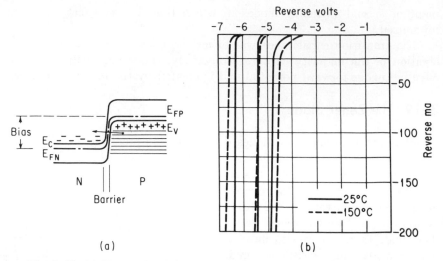

Fig. 3–26. (a) Energy levels in Zener breakdown; (b) Temperature characteristics of Zener diodes.

energy to break the valence bonds upon collision; after each such collision there exist two electrons and two holes, each creates two more pairs after the next collision, and rapidly the discharge goes into an avalanche condition. The critical requirement is that the field intensity be high enough to permit an electron to obtain the required energy in less than one mean free path. The voltage at which the avalanche occurs is a function of the resistivity of the material.

Figure 3–26(b) shows an enlarged section of the breakdown characteristic of several diode regulators using these phenomena. The regulating or steep current characteristic is somewhat a function of temperature, but with a zero temperature coefficient obtainable at some current value near the five volt level. For precision control of voltage applied to a circuit, the temperature relation may be important.

Regulators of Zener type are usually employed in a shunt circuit as in Fig. 3–27. A diode will be rated in terms of maximum current $I_{z\,max}$, and ordinarily the operating current I_z will be about 20 per cent of the maximum rating. The value of R may be found by

$$R = \frac{E - E_d}{I_L + 0.2I_{z\,max}}$$

The current may then shift back and forth between the load and the diode, the total of the two currents remaining constant, the voltage being constant at E_d.

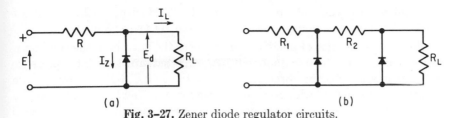

(a)   (b)

Fig. 3–27. Zener diode regulator circuits.

The dynamic internal resistance of the diode is that shown to changing internal currents, and over the near-vertical portion of the diode curve, will be very low. Diodes regulating at five volts may have dynamic resistances of the order of an ohm or less, which may be increased to one hundred ohms or more for units regulating at the level of several hundred volts.

3–20. The Hall effect

Since conduction theory was scant and holes unknown, observation by Hall in 1879 of phenomena due to the flow of holes in a conductor in a magnetic field could be reported only as a conduction anomaly. Now known as the *Hall effect*, and explainable by modern theories, it provides a basic method of measurement of charge mobility and carrier density, and is applied in several electronic devices for measurement of magnetic intensity.

In Fig. 3–28 a cross-section of a conductor is diagrammed, in which holes are assumed to flow axially in the x direction, constituting a current J per unit cross section, with current density uniform across the conductor section. A magnetic field of density B is now introduced perpendicular to the section, so that by the usual symbolism the dots indicate the magnetic lines in the positive z direction. Positive charge or hole movement through the magnetic field creates a force on the holes which causes them

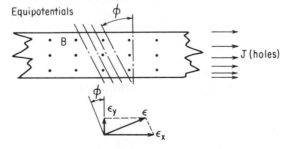

Fig. 3–28. Cross-section of a conductor illustrating the Hall effect in hole conduction.

to crowd toward the bottom surface of the conductor, and the current distribution becomes nonuniform as indicated by the arrows for J.

The greater density of positive charges near the bottom of the conductor creates an electric field component, $\mathcal{E}_y$, directed upward. The presence of $\mathcal{E}_y$ creates an electric force upward on the holes, and an equilibrium situation is reached in which the magnetic force downward on the moving holes is balanced by an equal electric field force upward on the displaced holes.

The resultant electric field in the conductor is $\mathcal{E}$, inclined upward at an angle φ. Equipotentials in the conductor will be orthogonal to the electric field and therefore will be inclined to the x axis by the angle φ. By use of probes on the upper and lower surfaces it is possible to locate the equipotentials and to measure φ with accuracy.

If the carriers were electrons the electric field and the slope of the equipotentials would be reversed, and it is thus possible to classify a material immediately as being N or P in nature. It was the occasional measurement of a material with the hole-caused slope which Hall noted but could not explain.

Since

$$\sigma = pe\mu_p$$

it is possible to write the electric field as

$$\mathcal{E}_x = \frac{J}{\sigma} = \frac{pev_p}{pe\mu_p} = \frac{v_p}{\mu_p} \tag{3-73}$$

and this applies here if it is assumed that the nonuniform distribution of charge density created by the magnetic field is not large.

The forces on charges in fields were studied in Sections 1–5 and 1–12. The force on the holes due to the magnetic field is

$$f_m = BJ = Bpev_p$$

if unit dimensions are assumed. The counter force set up by the electric field is

$$f_e = pe\,\mathcal{E}_y$$

and equating these forces for equilibrium gives

$$\mathcal{E}_y = Bv_p \tag{3-74}$$

From Fig. 3–28

$$\tan \varphi \cong \varphi = \frac{\mathcal{E}_y}{\mathcal{E}_x} = B\mu_p$$

from which

$$\mu_p = \frac{\varphi}{B} \tag{3-75}$$

This expression shows how the Hall effect may be used to measure the mobilities of the majority carriers.

If the conductivity of the material is available, then

$$\frac{\sigma \rho}{pe} = \frac{\varphi}{B}$$

$$p = \frac{B}{e\varphi} \tag{3-76}$$

and this allows the same data to be used in the determination of the density of the carriers.

Similar expressions will result from N type conduction. It is evident that the Hall effect measures the characteristics of conduction due to the majority carriers.

3–21. Other semiconductor materials

It has been previously pointed out that each atom of silicon or germanium has four valence electrons, which form covalent bonds with their four neighbor atoms in a tetrahedral configuration, or in which each atom is at the center of a triangular pyramid with four other atoms at the corners. These factors: valence electron to atom ratio of four, the covalent bonds, and the tetrahedral structure are found to serve as criteria in the search for and prediction of additional semiconducting compounds.

A gallium atom (Group III) has three valence electrons, arsenic (Group V) has five valence electrons, and these may form gallium arsenide, GaAs. The material has a four to one valence electron to atom ratio, on average, forms tetrahedral crystals, and is found to be a semiconductor. Other III-V group compounds can be formed and many are semiconductors, with characteristics as given in Table 3. It is possible to extend the search by similar reasoning to compounds of the II–VI groups, or to multiple combinations involving atoms from three or more groups, many of which occur in nature as minerals. Such multiple combinations are illustrated by Cu_3AsS_4, $CuSbS_2$, $AgSbTe_2$, and $AgAsSe_2$.

In general, replacement of an atom by a heavier atom of the same group will reduce the energy gap, the melting point, and the thermal conductivity, and will increase the mobility of the carriers.

TABLE 3. INTERMETALLIC COMPOUNDS

Material	E (ev)	μ_n (m²/volt-sec)	μ_p (m²/volt-sec)
CdS	2.4	0.02	...
AlSb	1.52	>0.04	>0.04
GaAs	1.35	0.40	0.025
InP	1.25	0.34	0.065
GaSb	0.68	0.40	0.070
InAs	0.35	3.00	0.02
PbTe	0.27	0.12	0.048
PbSe	0.22	0.118	0.087
InSb	0.18	7.70	0.12
For comparison:			
Si	1.12	0.12	0.05
Ge	0.72	0.39	0.19
Te	0.32	0.083	0.054

TABLE 4. ELEMENTS USEFUL IN SEMICONDUCTING COMPOUNDS

I	II	III	IV	V	VI	VII
Cu	Zn	Al	C	P	S	F
Ag	Cd	Ga	Si	As	Se	
		In	Ge	Sb	Te	
			Sn	Bi		
			Pb			

Table 4 lists many of the elements which join in compounds which may crystallize according to the above criteria. After a new compound has been prepared, and found to be stable, various measurements determine whether it is a semiconductor, and provide data which may be useful in appraising its potential application. The thermoelectric power, the thermal conductivity, the Hall coefficient, and the rectification properties are all easily measured and contribute useful information, looking toward possible application in thermoelectric cooling or power generation, or in high temperature diodes or transistors.

3–22. The tunnel diode

The Zener diode disclosed certain reverse characteristics not in accord with general diode theory, and Esaki discovered in 1957 that certain other diodes displayed tunneling effects in the forward direction as well.

In heavily doped materials, with very abrupt junctions of the order of 100 Å in thickness, the volt-ampere characteristic at low forward voltage

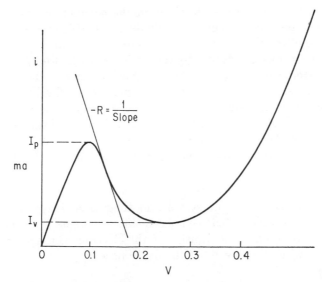

Fig. 3–29. Volt-ampere curve of a tunnel diode.

takes the form of Fig. 3–29. The curve
shows a negative internal resistance, or a
decreasing current for an increasing voltage, in the region from about 0.1 to 0.2
applied volts, and this is an interesting
circuit property. For reasons which well
follow, the device is known as the *tunnel
diode*.

These diodes may be made from
gallium arsenide, because of the high
electron mobility and reasonable gap
energy. Because of the heavy doping of
donors and acceptors in the N and P
regions, the donor and acceptor energy
levels broaden and merge with the conduction and valence bands. The Fermi
level as given by Eq. 3–14 for N material
with N_d so large as to exceed N_N, now is
above E_C. In a similar manner the Fermi
level in the P material, as given by Eq.
3–15 with N_A exceeding N_P, moves into
the valence band. The energy level situation in such a diode, unbiased, is shown
in Fig. 3–30(a).

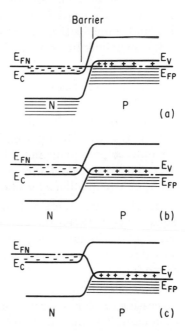

Fig. 3–30. The tunnel diode:
(a) zero bias; (b) small forward
bias; (c) large forward bias.

In Fig. 3–30(a) there are electrons in the conduction band of the N side, but these face filled electron levels on the P side across the barrier. Net tunneling of the thin barrier is then zero. As a forward bias is applied, the N levels are raised relative to the P levels as in Fig. 3–30(b), and conduction band electrons face valence band holes across the barrier, and tunneling occurs in great numbers, as explained in the section on the Zener diode. As further forward bias is applied, the conduction band electrons face the forbidden energy gap as in Fig. 3–30(c), and tunneling ceases. For bias beyond the I_V level of Fig. 3–29 the current follows the normal diode law, and is due to charges urged over the barrier by the applied potentials.

The current I_P is called the *peak current,* and I_V the *valley current.* These are two stable current states and their ratio may reach 15 to 1 in some diodes. Switching between these stable currents is extremely fast, due to the wave-mechanical transfer of the electrons through the barrier. The time of switching may be of the order of a few nanoseconds.[2]

The negative resistance existing for certain forward biases adds an additional simple circuit element to the usual R, L, C combinations. Oscillation and amplification are also possible in addition to the switching function of the tunnel diode.

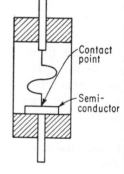

Contact point

Semi-conductor

3–23. The point-contact diode

Early diodes were of the point-contact form, as in Fig. 3–31. The semiconductor wafer is only a few millimeters square and a fraction of a millimeter thick, and the contact wire or cat-whisker is usually of one or two mil diameter phosphor bronze.

Fig. 3–31. Point-contact semiconductor diode.

In the usual junction diode the barrier is very thin, and represents a capacitance between the two electrodes. This capacitance tends to shunt out the rectifying action at high frequencies. The point-contact form provides a low capacitance diode suitable for operation up to 10 gc or more.

Such a semiconductor is usually manufactured of N material, and during processing, a high-current pulse is passed between contact and semiconductor. This appears to form a P region around the contact. The theory of operation then follows that given above for the junction unit.

[2] Metric system magnitude designations were discussed in Sec. 1–16.

For point-contact diodes, the general shape of the volt-ampere charac-teristics is the same as for the junction unit, but with lower possible currents. The junction diode has lower forward resistance, lower reverse current, greater possible peak currents, and a larger *rectification ratio*, or the ratio of forward to reverse current at a given applied voltage, than does the point-contact unit.

3–24. Large-area rectifiers

Older forms of semiconductor rectifiers employ the barrier-layer properties of cuprous oxide, selenium, and magnesium to copper sulfide. These consist usually of a layer of semiconductor bonded onto a metal base, with electric contact being made to the semiconductor surface and the base. The forward direction of current flow is with the semiconductor positive; this implies that the electron flow is from the contacting metal, or that the operation is explained if the semiconductor is considered of P properties.

In the copper-cuprous oxide cell, developed by Grondahl in 1926, the cuprous oxide is formed on a copper washer by controlled oxidation at high temperature. The washers are stacked on an insulated bolt as part of a sandwich of copper, cuprous oxide, and a lead washer, as in Fig. 3–32(b) Each disk is limited to about 8 v in the reverse direction, so that for higher voltages it is customary to stack units in series. Cells may be paralleled

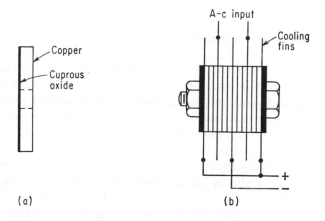

Fig. 3–32. (a) Single copper-cuprous oxide disk; (b) complete rectifier with three disks in series in each arm.

for higher currents. The back current is a function of temperature, and operating temperatures are limited to about 45°C.

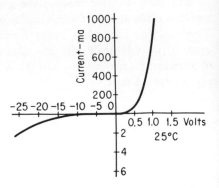

Fig. 3–33. Selenium volt-ampere characteristic.

The selenium rectifiers used in many small radio receivers are similar in construction, the selenium being deposited on either iron or aluminum. It will withstand up to 26 v back emf per disk, and may be operated up to 100°C. A typical volt-ampere curve is shown in Fig. 3–33.

The properties of several types are summarized in Table 5. As germanium and silicon are further developed, the use of these materials will decline.

TABLE 5. RECTIFIER PROPERTIES

Material	Current Density		Inverse Volts	Leakage
	amp/in.²	temp. °C		
CuO	0.10	40	8	Low
Selenium	0.25	40	26	Very low
Mg-CuS	15	35	3.5	Large

3–25. Photoconductive diodes

It has been previously mentioned that intrinsic conduction can be created in semiconductors by absorption of light quanta. This phenomenon is called *photoconduction*, and assumes the absorption of radiant energy to raise an electron from the top of the filled band, across the unallowed gap, and into the conductivity band. A hole is also left, and this may migrate as described in previous sections.

The minimum energy which must be supplied by the radiation must be equal to the width of the unallowed band, or the gap energy, and this is of the order of 0.7 ev for germanium. The quantum of energy required to produce photoconductivity is smaller in amount than that required for photoemission, wherein usual work functions approximate 1 ev or more. Hence photoconductivity can be excited by light of longer wave length than that needed for photoemission.

Assume that the gap energy for germanium is 0.7 ev; then, since a photon carries a quantum of $W = hf$ joules and

$$\lambda_0 = \frac{c}{f_0} = \frac{hc}{e\Delta E} \qquad\qquad m, \quad (3\text{–}77)$$

the longest exciting wave length or minimum energy threshold is

$$\lambda_0 = \frac{6.62 \times 10^{-34} \times 3 \times 10^8}{1.60 \times 10^{-19} \times 0.7} = 17.7\mu = 17{,}700 \text{ Å}$$

This wave length is in the infrared. A curve of relative output vs. wave length for germanium is given in Fig. 3–34.

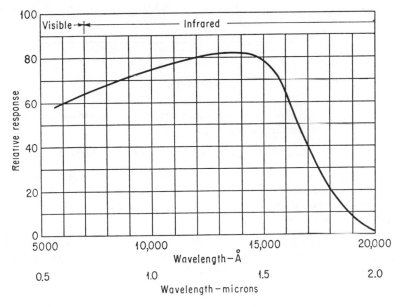

Fig. 3–34. Response of germanium in photoconduction.

Very small photodiodes are made utilizing this principle. The light energy is made to strike the junction area of an appropriate PN diode, thus creating the necessary carriers by photon radiation.

Large area junctions are also made, with the junction as close to the surface as possible. These cells are useful for conversion of solar energy directly to electricity in satellite and other service. In gallium arsenide efficiencies of 11 per cent have been obtained, and in silicon an efficiency of 15 per cent has been reached. The design problem in such cells is to have the photon absorption occur in the junction region, without appreciable reflection and without deeper penetration. Ninety five per cent of the photons will be absorbed in three microns of gallium arsenide, so that very thin cells are used. Characteristics of such cells are given in Table 6.

TABLE 6.

	Comparison of solar cells		
	Open-circuit volts	Short-circuit current ma/m²	Internal resistance ohms
Silicon	0.6	2700	10
GaAs	0.9	1700	30

Problems

3-1. Compute and plot the energy distribution of the electrons for germanium at $0°K$, for intrinsic germanium $N_v = 4.5 \times 10^{22}$.

3-2. Repeat Problem 3-1 for a germanium temperature of $500°K$.

3-3. A sample of germanium has intrinsic resistivity of 0.10 ohm-m at $85°C$. If the mobility of electrons is 0.36, m^2/v-sec and that of holes is 0.17 m^2/v-sec, compute the number of germanium atoms per cu cm having broken valence bonds at this temperature. $30./ \times 10^{13}$ $1.18 \cdot 10^{14}$

3-4. A germanium wafer has a cross section of 3 mm $\times$ 1 mm. If the mobility of electrons and holes is as in Problem 3-3, and if there is one antimony atom per 10^7 germanium atoms, compute the conductivity of the material, neglecting intrinsic conductivity. $./2 / \cdot / 0^{-4}$ $7.8 \cdot 10^{-2}$ mul/cm

3-5. A silicon wafer with P-type resistivity of 100 ohm-m has dimensions of 3 mm $\times$ 0.5 mm. If the mobility of electrons is 0.12 $m^2/$volt-sec, and that of holes is one-third as much, compute the number of silicon atoms present per gallium atom, neglecting intrinsic conductivity.

3-6. Phosphorus of atomic weight 31 is added to a pure sample of silicon in the amount of 10^{13} atoms per cc. If all donor atoms are activated, what is the resistivity at $20°C$?

3-7. Repeat Problem 3-6 for germanium.

3-8. Why does silicon absorb light of wave length shorter than a certain critical value, and become transparent for light of longer wave length? What is this critical wave length for silicon? For germanium?

3-9. Compute the rectification ratio (ratio of forward to reverse current at same voltage) for a germanium diode at 0.15 applied volts. The inverse saturation current is 25 μamps.

3-10. Plot the forward and reverse volt-ampere curves for the diode of Problem 3-9, over the range of 2 v forward to 200 v reverse.

3-11. With germanium of characteristics of Table 2, calculate the intrinsic resistivity at 300°K.

3-12. Intrinsic germanium has $n_i = 2.4 \times 10^{19}$ carriers / m³ at room temp. Find the number of grams of indium which must be added per kg of germanium to reduce the resistivity to 0.04 ohm-m, assuming complete activation.

3-13. Calculate the rectification ratio (see Problem 3-9) at bias voltages of 0.02, 0.1 and 0.5 v for a theoretical P–N germanium junction, at 300°K.

3-14. With germanium of 0.54 ohm-m resistivity intrinsic value, an impurity concentration of one antimony atom per 10^8 germanium atoms is added. Calculate the Fermi energy level after the impurity addition.

3-15. With $N_N = 5 \times 10^{22} T^{3/2}$ per m³ in silicon, and one impurity atom per 10^7 silicon atoms, plot a curve showing the variation of the Fermi level as a function of temperature, using E_C as 100 per cent, and the intrinsic level as 0 per cent.

References

1. Bardeen, J., and Brattain, W. H., "Conductivity of Germanium," *Phys. Rev.*, **75,** 1216 (1949).

2. Breckenridge, R. G., "Semiconducting Intermetallic Compounds," *Phys. Rev.*, **90,** 488 (May 1953).

3. Conwell, E. M., "Properties of Silicon and Germanium," *Proc. I.R.E.*, **40,** 1327, (1952).

4. Cornelius, E. C., "Germanium Crystal Diodes," *Electronics*, **19,** 118 (February 1946).

5. Esaki, L., "New Phenomenon in Narrow Ge PN Junctions," *Phys. Rev.* **109,** 603, (1958).

6. Gobat, A. R., et al, "Characteristics of High-Conversion-Efficiency Gallium-Arsenide Solar Cells." *I.R.E. Trans. PGME*, Mil-6, 20, (1962).

7. Hall, R. N., "Germanium Rectifier Characteristics," *Phys. Rev.*, **83,** 228 (July 1951).

8. Keck, P. H., and Golay, M. J. E., "Crystallization of Silicon from a Floating Liquid Zone," *Phys. Rev.*, **89,** 1297 (1953).

9. Lark-Horovitz, K., and Johnson, V. A., "Theory of Resistivity in Germanium Alloys," *Phys. Rev.*, **69,** 258 (1946).

10. Middlebrook, R. D., *An Introduction to Junction Transistor Theory.* John Wiley & Sons, Inc., New York, 1957.

11. Pfann, W. G., "Continuous Multistage Separation by Zone-melting." *J. Metals,* 7, 297, (1955).

12. Ramsey, G., "The Selenium Rectifier," *Elec. Eng.*, **63,** 425 (1944).

13. Seitz, F., *The Physics of Metals.* McGraw-Hill Book Co., Inc., New York, 1943.

14. Shockley, W., *Electrons and Holes in Semiconductors.* D. Van Nostrand Co., Inc., New York, 1950.

15. Shockley, W., "Theory of P-N Junctions in Semiconductors and P-N Junction Transistors." *Bell Syst. Tech. Jour.*, 28, 435, (1949).

16. Special Transistor Issue, *Proc. I.R.E.*, 46, 947–1346, (1958).

17. Torrey, H. C., and Whitmer, C. A., *Crystal Rectifiers.* McGraw-Hill Book Co., Inc., New York, 1948.

Electron Emission; The Vacuum Diode | 4

In the previous chapter the distribution of energy among the valence electrons of a metal conductor was discussed. It will now be shown that if sufficient additional energy be supplied, it is possible to cause some of the electrons to pass through the metal surface and emerge into the surrounding space. The process is called *electron emission,* and is basic to the operation of most types of vacuum and gaseous electron tubes.

Basically all forms of electron emission appear to be similar, but they are differentiated by designation of the manner in which the additional emission energy is supplied. Thus, if the emission is produced by application of heat or thermal energy, the process is known as *thermionic emission;* application of strong electric fields to the surface produces *high-field* or *autoelectronic emission;* use of radiant energy or light causes *photoelectric emission;* and bombardment by a primary beam of electrons or other particles results in *secondary emission.*

4–1. Emission of electrons

To determine whether the kinetic energies possessed by electrons in metals are sufficient to overcome surface forces and cause emission, it is necessary to determine the work done in such emission. This amount of work, or the energy given up in the emission of an electron through a surface, is designated E_B, or the *surface barrier energy.*

For discussion, it is convenient to consider the emission energy as consisting of two parts—E_1, the energy given up in overcoming forces near the surface, and E_2, the work required to overcome other forces at greater distances from the surface. Then

$$E_B = E_1 + E_2$$

In the study of E_1, it is discovered that the location of the surface is not exact, that the atoms are not laid up like bricks, and there will be a surface roughness of the order of atomic diameters. Many of the surface atoms will have unfilled valence bonds because of the absence of neighbor atoms, and this will create surface charges and forces. The electron must have sufficient kinetic energy to overcome these rather irregular forces owing to the surface atoms. Consequently, E_1 is a function of the particular metal and of its surface condition, including the effects of deposited layers of other metals or of adsorbed gases.

The additional energy E_2 is required to move the electron through the force fields existing at distances from the surface which are large with respect to atomic diameters. At such distances the forces due to charges associated with individual atoms will cancel or compensate, and the force field existing is due to the attraction from the so-called *image* or induced surface charge. When an electron leaves a metal surface, the surface will have a positive charge, and an electric field will exist between the electron and the surface, as at Fig. 4–1(a). Since the metal surface is an equipotential in the field, the electron will note no difference in field distribution if the field of Fig. 4–1(a) is changed to that at Fig. 4–1(b). The position of the metal surface is taken over by an equipotential in the field between the two opposite point charges, and the electric flux lines (by means of which the electron comes in contact with the outside world) remain unchanged. Since the field is unchanged, the force on the electron must be the same. The positive charge at the left is called the *image charge*.

From Coulomb's law it is possible to calculate the force between the negative electron and the positive image as

$$f_x = \frac{(+e)(-e)}{4\pi\epsilon_v(2x)^2} = \frac{-e^2}{16\pi\epsilon_v x^2} \tag{4-1}$$

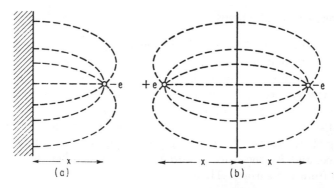

Fig. 4–1. The image principle.

where the charge is in coulombs, and $\epsilon_v = 10^7/4\pi c^2$, the permittivity of space. The negative sign indicates the force is to the left, or in the negative x direction. As explained, the expression holds only at a distance where the surface can be considered as a true equipotential plane, or for x greater than a few atomic diameters.

If now the electron is entirely removed from the surface, theoretically to an infinite distance, the work done against the force of Eq. 4–1 is

$$E_2 = -\int_x^\infty f_x \, dx = \frac{e^2}{16\pi\epsilon_v x} \qquad \text{joules} \quad (4\text{--}2)$$

indicating that the work done is an inverse function of distance in the field of the image charge, as shown in Fig. 4–2.

Energy E_B is dependent on the particular metal and its surface condition, and on the image forces, and is the total work done by the electron in freeing itself from the binding forces of the metal. To secure emission the individual electrons must possess this minimum value of energy. Any excess over E_B will appear as kinetic energy of the electron after emission.

4–2. The work function

Since it has already been shown by the Fermi-Dirac distribution that even at absolute zero many electrons in metals possess an energy near the value E_F, it is only necessary to supply an additional energy E_W, where

$$E_W = E_B - E_F \qquad (4\text{--}3)$$

in order to secure emission of an electron. The value of energy E_W is known as the *work function*.

The work function is the value of energy that must be supplied to an electron at absolute zero to overcome the surface forces and cause emission. As shown above, the work function depends on the material, its surface condition, adsorbed films, and metal impurities. Since surface conditions enter into the determination of the work function by experimental means, it is not surprising that values from the work of various experimenters may differ considerably. Those given in Table 7 are believed to be representative.

4–3. The thermionic emission equations

The Fermi distribution for the electrons in metals, as shown in Fig. 3–2, indicates total energies, regardless of the directions of the electron velocities. If an electron is to be emitted, its velocity must have a sufficiently large component toward the surface to overcome the surface forces. When only electrons having outward-directed velocities are considered, the

TABLE 7. VALUES OF THE EMISSION CONSTANTS*

Element	A_0 (amp/m²/deg²)	b_0	E_W (ev)	Melting Point (°K)
Calcium...............	60.2×10^4	37,100	3.2	1083
Carbon................	60.2×10^4	54,500	4.7	....
Cesium................	16.2×10^4	21,000	1.81	299
Copper................	$65 \ \ \times 10^4$	47,600	4.1	1356
Molybdenum...........	60.2×10^4	49,900	4.3	2895
Nickel................	26.8×10^4	58,000	5.0	1725
Tantalum..............	60.2×10^4	47,600	4.1	3123
Thorium...............	60.2×10^4	39,400	3.4	2118
Tungsten..............	60.2×10^4	52,400	4.52	3643

* Becker, J. A., *Rev. Mod. Phys.*, 7, 95 (1935).

electron energy distribution becomes like that of Fig. 4–3 for absolute zero T_0 and for a higher temperature T_2. Since the curve for T_2 approaches the axis asymptotically, there will be some electrons with high energies. If these energies exceed E_B it will be possible for these high-outward-velocity electrons to pass through the surface and be emitted.

To find the current represented by these electrons per unit area of the surface, it is necessary to determine the equation of the distribution for a temperature T_2, integrate this equation from E_B to infinity to obtain the number of electrons passing through the surface, and multiply by the average velocity of the electrons and the charge carried per electron. An equation of the form

$$J = A_0 T^2 \epsilon^{-(E_B - E_F)e/kT} \qquad \text{amp/m}^2 \quad (4\text{–}4)$$

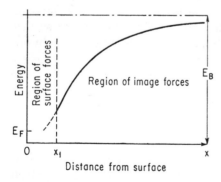

Fig. 4–2. Energy conditions near a surface.

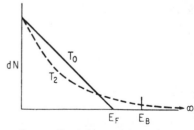

Fig. 4–3. Energy distribution among electrons having velocity components normal to a surface.

is the result. The term $E_B - E_F$ can be recognized as the work function E_W.

Combining terms, and introducing the surface area of emission S in square meters, leads to the form

$$I = A_0 S T^2 \epsilon^{-b_0/T} \qquad \text{amp} \quad (4\text{-}5)$$

where

T = temperature of the source, °K.
$A_0 = 4\pi m e k^2/h^3$ = proportionality constant, amp/m²/deg².
$b_0 = e E_W/k = 11,600 E_W$.
S = surface area, sq m.

An equation of this form, but having the exponent of T as $\frac{1}{2}$, was developed by O.W. Richardson in 1914. The form of Eq. 4-5 is believed to have a better theoretical basis, and is known as *Dushman's equation*, since it was developed by S. Dushman in 1923. Because of the major effect of the exponential term, experiment cannot show which form is correct.

Theory indicates A_0 as a universal constant of value 120×10^4 amp/m²/deg², but experimental values cover a wide range. This is explained by the theory that many electrons are reflected by surface atoms, thus the emission is less than the theoretical value.

Equation 4-5 may be written in the form

$$\log_{10} I/T^2 = \log_{10} A_0 S - 0.4343 b_0/T \qquad (4\text{-}6)$$

If the left-hand side of this equation is plotted against $1/T$, the result should be a straight line with an intercept of $\log_{10} A_0 S$ and a slope of $-0.4343 b_0$. By such a plot, values of A_0 and b_0 may be determined experimentally, although results depend greatly on the surface condition and the impurities present.

The asymptotic form of the T_2 curve of Fig. 4-3 shows that some of the electrons will have energies greater than E_B, and will have velocities after emission. It can be shown, however, that the mean of these energies is given by kT/e, in ev, which has a value of only 0.24 ev for a metal at 2800°K. Thus, although the electrons do have energies and velocities after emission, these velocities and energies will be quite small compared with the velocities developed by the electrons in their movements in electron tubes, and these velocities of emission will usually be neglected.

4-4. Photoemission

Light is a form of radiant energy, and experimentally it is found that electrons may be emitted when light of suitable wavelength strikes prepared

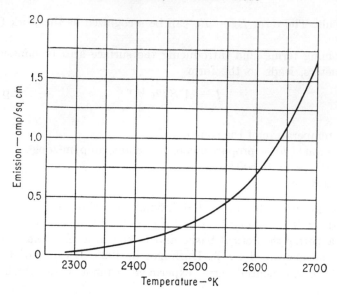

Fig. 4-4. Emitted current density for tungsten.

metal surfaces. Such *photoelectric emission* differs from thermionic emission only in that the work-function energy is supplied by light rather than by heat.

As was mentioned, light or radiant energy, while having wave properties, also is conceived as consisting of corpuscles or bundles of energy called *photons*. The energy carried by each photon is a variable and dependent on the frequency of the light or radiant energy as

$$W = hf \qquad\qquad \text{joules} \quad (4\text{–}7)$$

where h is Planck's constant.

Einstein explained photoelectric emission on an energy basis. That is, the energy hf is available from each photon as it strikes a particular surface atom of the emitting cathode. To produce emission the photon must contribute the work function energy eE_W, with any excess energy from the photon available to supply kinetic energy for the emitted electron. Then

$$hf = eE_W + \frac{mv^2}{2} \qquad\qquad (4\text{–}8)$$

and the photon has given up all its energy and disappears.

Although some of the light (photons) is reflected, as the light intensity increases the number of photons increases also, so that the emission rises linearly with light intensity. This can be easily demonstrated experimentally. The maximum available kinetic energy $mv^2/2$ is a function of frequency, and this is also experimentally supported. Since any particular photon may produce emission of an electron, then emission may begin immediately on light impact, and experiment shows emission actually occurs in less than 10^{-9} sec. Thus, the Einstein equation, based on the corpuscular theory of light, is supported experimentally.

The dual concept of light as both wave and particle is similar to the theory of the behavior of an electron. The final integration of the particle and wave theories into a unified whole has not yet been accomplished, so that each is employed in cases where it seems to most adequately explain the phenomena.

Since eE_W is a constant for a particular surface, it is obvious that at some frequency f_0 given by

$$f_0 = \frac{eE_W}{h} \tag{4-9}$$

the current will become zero. This is a *threshold* frequency, no lower frequency having sufficient energy per photon to overcome the work function and cause emission.

Equation 4-9 furnishes a method of measuring the work functions of various materials by measurement of their threshold photoelectric frequency. If surfaces of high cleanliness are used, good checks can be obtained between values obtained by this method and those from thermionic methods. This agreement furnishes support for believing that the emissive phenomena are similar in the two cases.

Usual photoelectric cathode materials are those having small work functions, such as cesium and rubidium.

4-5. Secondary emission

It has been shown that if sufficient energy is transferred to an electron in an atom, the electron may be emitted. If the source of this energy is from mechanical impact of an electron or ion, then the electrons emitted are called *secondary* electrons and the phenomenon is *secondary emission*. The original electrons, or other particles such as gas ions, are called *primary electrons, primary ions,* and so forth.

To produce secondary emission, a surface of a conductor or non-conductor is bombarded by electrons or other particles. The secondary electrons, which are emitted by reason of the energy contributed to the surface atoms in mechanical form, will find their way to any electrode of higher potential in the region, and will constitute a flow of charge away from the bombarded surface, in contrast to the primary beam which forms a charge flow to the surface.

The ratio of the average number of secondary electrons emitted to the number of primary electrons, or equivalent charges, striking the surface per unit time is called the _secondary-emission coefficient_ δ. The energy of the emitted secondary electrons is small, usually of the order of 10 to 20 ev.

Measurements of secondary emission may be made with a special tube indicated diagrammatically in Fig. 4–5. The beam of electrons passes through a hole in the shield S, and strikes the test surface A_2. Secondary electrons emitted from the surface are attracted to the more positive shield, and constitute a current to that electrode. Measurement of shield current and A_2 current permit calculation of the ratio δ.

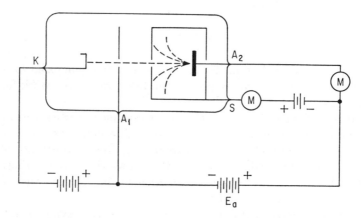

Fig. 4–5. Measurement of secondary emission coefficient.

As the primary electron strikes the surface, it may free one or more electrons before its energy is dissipated. As the primary beam energy is increased, more energy is available to emit electrons and the curve of δ in Fig. 4–6 rises. Still greater primary energies cause the primary electrons to penetrate deeply, possibly to 100 or more atom diameters. Many of the electrons to which energy has been given are recaptured by other atoms on their way to the surface, and are never emitted. The curve then has a maximum around 400 to 500 ev in the primary beam.

Any material is capable of secondary emission, but high-emission surfaces have low values of work function. Surface condition and composition contribute greatly to emitting ability since secondary emission is primarily a surface function. The presence of impurities or gases on the metal surface may raise the emission factor severalfold.

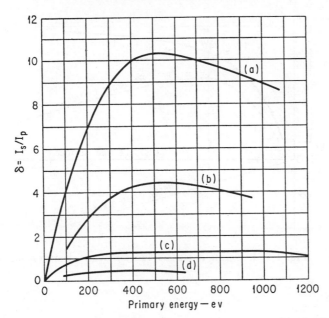

Fig. 4–6. Secondary emission ratio: (a) Cs-Cs$_2$O-Ag surface; (b) Na-Na$_2$-Ag surface; (c) nickel; (d) carbonized nickel.

4–6. The Schottky effect

A positive potential on an electrode near an emitting cathode may aid in accelerating the emission electrons. At a distance x from the cathode in the resultant electric field an electron will have received an energy of eV joules to urge it away from the cathode, where V is the potential of the point. This accelerating force opposes the image forces near the cathode surface, and reduces the surface barrier energy by a slight amount. This reduction is represented as ΔW at a distance x_o in Fig. 4–7, where x_o is the point at which the field force equals the image force from Eq. 4–1, or

$$e\mathcal{E} = \frac{e^2}{16\pi\epsilon_v x_0^2}$$

$$x_o = \frac{1}{4}\sqrt{\frac{e}{\pi\epsilon_v\mathcal{E}}} \qquad (4\text{--}10)$$

The reduction of work function ΔW is equal to twice the field force at x_o, so

$$\Delta W = 2e\mathcal{E}x_o$$

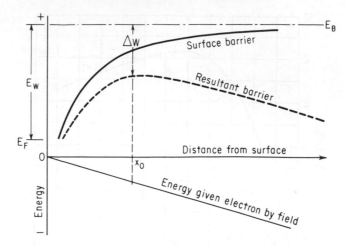

Fig. 4–7. Lowering of surface barrier by an electric field.

so that

$$\Delta W = \frac{e^{3/2}}{2} \sqrt{\frac{\mathcal{E}}{\pi \epsilon_v}} \tag{4–11}$$

As an example, choose a field of 100,000 v/m. The reduction ΔW due to the field $\mathcal{E}$ can then be calculated as 0.012 ev. This is a very small reduction in the work function, but it is responsible for a noticeable increase in emission current as the applied voltage is increased.

The lowering of the work function by an applied accelerating field is called the *Schottky effect*, after the man who first calculated its magnitude. As a result of the Schottky effect, the temperature saturation current predicted by Dushman's equation is to a small extent a function of the field intensity applied to the cathode surface.

4–7. High-field emission

If the applied accelerating field at the cathode surface were increased indefinitely, a value might be reached at which the exponential in Eq. 4–4 would disappear as a result of the reduction of E_B by the Schottky effect. Also, as the field intensity at the cathode is increased and the energy barrier height is lowered by ΔW, the distance to point x_0 is reduced. At some small value of x_0 the barrier becomes so thin that it is possible for electrons to tunnel through the barrier as well as travel over it, and the emission current may reach high values at fields approximating 10^8 v/m. The result is called *high-field emission*.

Such fields may be obtained between two closely spaced plane electrodes, a point and a plane, or between a coaxial wire and a surrounding cylinder, and all may reach high values without unusually high applied voltages. For this reason, design precautions are required in very high-voltage tubes, usually taking the form of rounded corners and the elimination of sharp points on the electrodes.

4–8. Thermionic cathodes

The emitter electrode of a tube is called a *cathode*, since it is the negative electrode. In *thermionic* emission, cathodes are divided into two classes, (1) filamentary and (2) equipotential, or indirectly heated.

In the filamentary construction a wire is heated by passage of electric current through it, and electron emission takes place directly from the wire. Such a filament is shown at Fig. 4–8(a). Since the heating current flows directly through the wire, a potential drop of a few volts is uniformly distributed along the wire; that is, all points of the filament are not at the same potential.

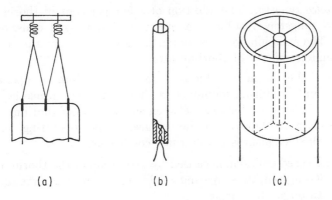

(a)　　　　　(b)　　　　　(c)

Fig. 4–8. Cathode construction: (a) filamentary; (b) equipotential; (c) heat-shielded.

In the equipotential construction a loop of tungsten wire insulated with a refractory material is inserted in a thin, hollow cylinder, usually made of nickel. The outside of the cylinder is coated with emitting material, and the passage of current through the heater wire causes the cylinder to reach emitting temperature. Since the emitted current is small and no heating current flows in the cylinder, it is equipotential. Such a cathode appears at Fig. 4–8(b). Owing to heat storage, cathodes of this type require a short heating time, but this thermal storage also reduces cyclic variations of temperature which might appear when the cathode is heated by alternating current.

A *heat-shielded* construction is illustrated in Fig. 4–8(c). Inside a small central cylinder is a heater wire, and radiating from the cylinder are metal fins within an outer cylinder of polished nickel. The fins and inner cylindrical surfaces are coated with emitting material. The heater raises the structure to proper temperature, and because of the radiation shield provided by the polished outer cylinder, the power needed to maintain operating temperature is reduced.

The range of materials for thermionic emitters is fairly narrow. Desirable qualities are low work function and a high melting point, so that T in Dushman's equation may be as high as possible. Many materials with low work functions, such as cesium, have very low melting points, and the attainable thermionic emission is too small to be useful.

Tungsten is desirable as an emitter because of its high melting point of 3643°K. This value allows tungsten filaments to be operated at temperatures of 2500° to 2600°K without an excessive rate of evaporation of tungsten. Tungsten is susceptible to reduction of emission by adsorbed layers of oxygen, so that high vacuums must be maintained.   •

Thoriated tungsten. The addition of a few per cent of thoria (thorium oxide) to tungsten, results in a material of improved emission characteristics. The emission depends on partial coverage of the tungsten surface by a monatomic layer of thorium atoms.

Some of the thoria is reduced to metallic thorium by operation at a high temperature during manufacture. The emitting surface layer is then the result of a delicate balance between evaporation of thorium atoms and diffusion of more thorium to the surface. Proper operating temperature of about 1900°K insures equilibrium conditions.

The increased emission is caused by attraction of the thorium electrons toward the tungsten, thus creating a field in a direction to urge the emission electrons through the surface.

Oxide-coated materials. The oxide-coated cathode has a metal base of nickel, on which barium or strontium carbonates are deposited. During evacuation these compounds are broken down to the oxides and to some pure barium and strontium. The pure metals increase the conductivity of the emitting layer and also reduce the work function by setting up a field to aid the electrons, much as in the case of thoriated tungsten.

The *relative emission efficiency*, defined as milliamperes of emission per watt of heating power, is a comparative figure. As a result of the low value for tungsten indicated in Table 8, this metal is rarely used at the present time. The other emission constants are somewhat variable, but the table presents representative data.

TABLE 8. CHARACTERISTICS OF CATHODE MATERIALS

Material	A_0	b_0	E_w (ev)	Emission Efficiency (ma/w)	Operating Temperature (°K)
Tungsten	60.2×10^4	52,400	4.52	4–20	2500–2600
Thorium on tungsten	3.0×10^4	30,500	2.6	50–100	1900–2000
Oxide-coated	0.01×10^4	11,600	1.0	100–1000	1000–1200

Over 95 per cent of all radio tubes employ oxide coatings because of the low operating temperature, 900° to 1100°K, which requires small amounts of power for heating.

4–9. The diode volt-ampere curve

Since the thermionic diode or two-element rectifier is the simplest of the vacuum-tube types, many phenomena associated with all can be studied conveniently in the diode. This is particularly true for the effect of the space charge in controlling the space current, or in determination of the volt-ampere relation for vacuum electronic tubes.

A vacuum diode consists of a thermionic cathode and an anode sealed into an evacuated envelope. If, with the cathode heated to temperature T_1, a positive voltage is applied to the anode and a plot made of the potential across and the current through the device, a curve as for T_1 in Fig. 4–9 is obtained. The current increases as the voltage is raised, but eventually levels off or *saturates*, after which large potential changes produce only small current increases.

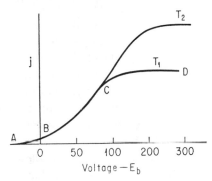

Fig. 4–9. Volt-ampere diagram for a vacuum diode.

The volt-ampere curve consists of three regions. The toe from A to B indicates that some electrons are emitted with sufficient energy to reach the anode without aid of an accelerating field. From B to C the current received at the anode is less than the emitted current value predicted by the Dushman equation. In the region C to D all the electrons emitted are attracted to the anode, and no further current increase is possible at temperature T_1. If the temperature is raised to T_2, a higher current value is emitted and can be attracted to the anode by a higher voltage, until saturation is again reached.

It is shown that the current increases at a slow rate in the saturation region even though the Dushman equation gives only one possible current value. This slight current increase is due to the reduction of the work function by the Schottky effect as the applied field at the cathode surface rises. For thoriated-tungsten or oxide cathodes the current increase is quite large and these cathode types show little saturation.

4–10. Field conditions at the cathode surface

When electrons are emitted from a thermionic cathode in a vacuum, they possess a considerable spread in excess energy values. This accounts for region A-B of the volt-ampere curve. To explain the action in the region B–C, consider a diode without positive anode voltage. A cloud of electrons has been emitted, filling the space around the cathode with negative charge. The electrons at the cathode surface are faced with a repelling electric field owing to the charges of the electrons already in the space. Equilibrium conditions will be reached when the negative space charge provides a repelling electric field at the cathode surface sufficient to prevent further electrons from leaving the cathode region.

If the anode is made positive to the cathode, electrons will be attracted from the space cloud to the anode. This flow reduces the space charge and the repelling field at the cathode surface, and allows some of the highest-energy electrons to leave the cathode and enter the space. Equilibrium of the cathode surface field will be reached at some new value of space-charge density at which the number of electrons able to leave the cathode is balanced by the number taken by the anode.

Equilibrium at any other value of surface field leads to unstable conditions: if equilibrium allowed a current value leaving the cathode momentarily greater than that reaching the anode, then the space charge would grow until the field at the cathode reduced the number of electrons leaving; if the equilibrium allowed a current leaving the cathode below that reaching the anode, the space charge would decrease until more electrons were permitted to leave the cathode to replenish the space charge.

The space-charge cloud of electrons acts as a velocity filter, permitting only electrons with velocities or energies above a certain minimum to leave the cathode region. The emission of electrons from cathodes is quite erratic with time, and the space-charge reservoir acts as a surge tank to smooth out the electron flow to the anode, reducing noise or erratic anode currents.

Assume two large parallel plates separated by a distance d. If a potential is applied between the plates, the potential distribution in the space d would be as the straight line in Fig. 4–10. The slope of this line is the potential gradient $= dV/dx$. If now the left-hand, or negative, electrode is raised to a high temperature, electrons are emitted from it and enter the space. The presence of the electrons in the space lowers the potential at all intermediate points, as is shown by curve (b) for space charge. The concentration of electrons near the cathode produces a negative gradient, or repelling field (negative slope of curve), at the cathode

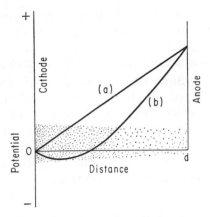

Fig. 4–10. Potential variation in a diode: (a) no space charge; (b) with space charge.

surface. As the potential minimum of curve (b) is raised or lowered by changes in electron density or by anode potential, the repelling field at the cathode surface changes and more or fewer electrons are enabled to leave the cathode region. The potential minimum established by the space charge is usually close to the cathode and is referred to as a *virtual cathode* because it may be regarded as the virtual source of the electrons moving to the anode.

4–11. The space-charge equation

Assume two very large (theoretically infinite) parallel plates positioned as in Fig. 4–11. Let the left-hand plate be heated to a very high temperature so that the emission will always be larger than any demands for electrons,

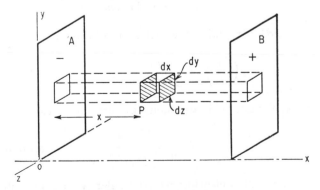

Fig. 4–11. Analysis of the parallel-plane diode.

or the current will never be temperature-saturated. The right-hand plate, or anode, is left cold and a positive potential E_b is applied with respect to the left-hand plate, or cathode. These two plates exist in a vacuum sufficiently high that no collisions of electrons with gas atoms need be considered.

Since the surfaces are large, fringing of the electric field may be neglected, and the field will be uniform and everywhere perpendicular to the surfaces. Electrons that are emitted from A pass across the space under the influence of the positive potential on B and represent a current density of J amp/m^2 of electrode area. If ρ is the density of charge per unit volume at a point in the space P, and v is the velocity with which the charge is moving, then for electrons

$$J = -\rho v \qquad\qquad \text{amp/m}^2 \quad (4\text{--}12)$$

Considering a volume of charge as indicated by the infinitesimal cube of sides dx, dy, dz, at a distance x from the cathode, it is possible to relate the charge density to the potential by use of Poisson's equation from Chapter 3. Because of the infinite dimensions in the y, z plane, the flux is everywhere x-directed, and so the one-dimensional form may be used, as

$$\frac{d^2V}{dx^2} = -\frac{\rho}{\epsilon_v}$$

Neglecting emission energies as small, the velocity of the electrons is also a function of the potential, as

$$\frac{mv^2}{2} = Ve \qquad\qquad (4\text{--}13)$$

Substitution of Eqs. 4–12 and 4–13 into Poisson's equation leads to

$$\frac{d^2V}{dx^2} = \frac{J}{\epsilon_v\sqrt{2Ve/m}} \qquad\qquad (4\text{--}14)$$

Multiplying by $2dV/dx$ and integrating, a solution can be obtained as

$$\left(\frac{dV}{dx}\right)^2 = \frac{4JV^{1/2}}{\epsilon_v\sqrt{2e/m}} + C_1$$

Neglecting C_1 as a small field, and again integrating gives

$$J = \frac{4\epsilon_v}{9}\sqrt{\frac{2e}{m}}\,\frac{V^{3/2}}{x^2} \qquad\qquad \text{amp/m}^2 \quad (4\text{--}15)$$

since $V = 0$ at $x = 0$. Selecting as particular values of potential and distance those at the anode, E_b and d, the equation for current density reaching the anode is

$$J = 2.34 \times 10^{-6} \frac{E_b^{3/2}}{d^2} \tag{4-16}$$

where d is the anode-cathode separation in meters.

This result is known as the *Langmuir-Child law*, after the two investigators who independently developed it. It is also known as the *three-halves power law*, or the *space-charge equation*. The equation shows the current proportional to the three-halves power of the applied voltage, and indicates that a vacuum diode is a nonlinear, as well as a unilateral, circuit device.

This equation predicts the value of current obtained in the region B–C of Fig. 4–9, and explains how the charge existing in the space limits the current to a value less than the possible emission. The Dushman equation predicts the number of electrons that *may* be emitted from a given cathode at temperature T; the Langmuir-Child law establishes the number of electrons *actually* emitted and which reach the anode. Most vacuum-tube operation is in the region of space-charge limitation of the current.

Langmuir also obtained an expression for the space-charge-limited current of a diode with long concentric cylindrical electrodes. This expression is

$$i = 14.7 \times 10^{-6} \frac{lE_b^{3/2}}{r_a\beta^2} \qquad \text{amp} \tag{4-17}$$

where l is the length of the cylinders and r_a is the anode radius in consistent units. Note that this equation is for total current flow and not current density.

The factor β is a function of $\log_e r_a/r_k$ (r_k being the cathode radius), which appears as a result of integrating the field differential equations in cylindrical coordinates. Values of β^2 have been calculated for ratios of r_a/r_k, and are presented in Table 9. It may be noted that for $r_a/r_k > 10$ the term β^2 may be assumed as equal to unity with small error.

TABLE 9.* VALUES OF THE CONSTANT β^2

r_a/r_k	β^2	r_a/r_k	β^2
1.00	0.000	20.00	1.072
3.00	0.517	50.00	1.094
5.00	0.767	100.00	1.078
10.00	0.978	∞	1.00

* From Langmuir, I., and Blodgett, K., *Phys. Rev.*, **22**, 347 (1923).

The current density J may be obtained from Eq. 4–15 in terms of V and x, and equated to the result in Eq. 4–16, since the current density at all points in space must be equal for the parallel-plane case. Solution for V gives the potential at any distance x as

$$V = E_b\left(\frac{x}{d}\right)^{4/3} \qquad \text{v} \quad (4\text{–}18)$$

This potential distribution does not reflect the potential minimum (due to the electron concentration near the cathode) because the constant C_1 was dropped in the derivation. Had it been determined, the potential distribution predicted would be of the form of the space-charge distribution of Fig. 4–10.

4–12. Determination of the exponent

No tube can be built to meet exactly the assumptions set up—some fringing of fields is unavoidable, deviations from plane or cylindrical shapes are necessary, and values of the exponent of E_b may be found in the range from 1.3 to 1.8. This result neither invalidates the basic theory nor changes the important fact that the vacuum tube is a nonlinear device. In general, the Langmuir-Child law may be written for a particular tube as

$$i_b = KE_b^a \qquad (4\text{–}19)$$

where the values of K and a will center about the theoretical values, and i_b is the tube current. Taking the logarithm

$$\log i_b = \log K + a \log E_b \qquad (4\text{–}20)$$

and data taken on a particular tube and plotted on log-log paper should yield a straight line. Determination of the slope of this line will yield a value for a, and K may be found by substitution of the coordinates for one point.

4–13. Power loss in the diode

If the velocities of emission are neglected as small, an electron will arrive at the anode of the diode with an energy given by

$$W = eE_b \qquad \text{joules}$$

As the electrons are stopped by the impact with the anode, the energy conveyed by the electrons is converted into heat. In the use of voltages above about 50,000, a minor amount of energy is also converted into X radiation.

The power delivered to the anode by n electrons in t seconds is

$$P = \frac{E_b e n}{t} \qquad\qquad \text{w}$$

The term en/t is the current, so that

$$P = E_b I_b \qquad\qquad \text{w} \quad (4\text{--}21)$$

By use of the space-charge law $I_b = K E_b^{3/2}$, then

$$P = K E_b^{5/2} \qquad\qquad (4\text{--}22)$$

This is the power loss in the tube due to space-current.

In most tube designs this total power must be removed from the anode largely by radiation, which requires choice of anode area and material to withstand a considerable temperature rise. This temperature rise is limited by anode melting point, loss of vacuum because of release of internal anode gas at high temperature, and the melting point of the glass envelope. In receiving tubes the design limits the temperature rise to that at which the anodes do not show color. In higher power radiation-cooled transmitting tubes the anodes of molybdenum, tantalum, or graphite operate at much higher temperatures. Another class of tubes employs water or forced air for conduction cooling, utilizing water jackets or copper fins.

The performance of a tube is definitely limited by maximum operating temperature, and tubes used for appreciable power output are rated in terms of allowable anode loss or *plate dissipation.* In this respect they differ from other types of electrical apparatus, which more usually are rated in terms of power output than in terms of allowable losses.

Problems

4-1. An electron in tungsten has an energy equal to E_F at 0°K. It is given an additional energy directed outward of 12×10^{-19} joule. If it is able to leave the tungsten surface, what will be its velocity after emission?

4-2. A certain tube has the following emission data taken:

I-amp	$T°$K	I-amp	$T°$K
0.000382	1900	0.0694	2300
0.00169	2000	0.1952	2400
0.00665	2100	0.5037	2500
0.0219	2200	1.169	2600
		2.75	2700

Determine by graphical means the values of the emission coefficients A_0 and b_0, if the emitting area is 1.8 cm^2.

4-3. (a) To what value must the work function of a tungsten surface be changed to raise the current density to 20,000 amp cm^2 at a temperature of 2600°K?

(b) What value of field intensity could provide this reduction of work function?

4-4. A large oxide-coated cathode is to have an emission current of 100 amp when operated at 1050°K.

(a) Determine the surface area needed.

(b) Find the surface area of tungsten needed if operated at the same temperature as the oxide-coated cathode.

4-5. At 2400°K a tungsten filament is observed to increase its emission periodically by amounts up to 5 per cent. What change in value of work function E_W is required to explain this change?

4-6. If secondary electrons are emitted with average energy of 10 ev and δ for a particular surface is 9, find the ma emission per input watt, if the primary beam has fallen through 300 v and the surface work function is 0.85 ev.

4-7. A cesium photoemissive surface has a work function of 1.81 v. Find the threshold wave length for this surface; also the maximum emission velocity if electrons are emitted when this surface is struck by light of 5300 Å wave length.

4-8. (a) Calculate the energy carried by photons of red light of $\lambda = 6439$ Å; yellow light of 5890 Å; and ultraviolet light of $\lambda = 3302$ Å and 2537 Å.

(b) Each of the photons of (a) strikes a sodium surface of 1.9 v work function. If electrons are emitted, find their velocities.

4-9. Threshold wave lengths are measured for platinum at 2570 Å; potassium 7000 Å; cadmium, 3140 Å; and magnesium, 3430 Å. Compute the work functions.

4-10. A flash of light from the ultraviolet line of mercury at 2537 Å, lasting 0.1 second strikes a sodium surface of 1.5 cm^2 in a phototube. The surface has a work function of 1.9 v, and the light has a power density of 0.5 w/cm^2. If half the photons cause the emission of an electron, find the current flowing during the flash.

4-11. (a) For a vacuum diode with parallel electrodes, spaced 0.5 cm and with $E_b = 250$ v, plot the variation of potential across the space under the assumption of space-charge conditions and negligible emission velocities of the electrons.

(b) Make a similar plot of charge density, and of velocity of the electrons. What relationship between v and ρ is indicated? Why is this true?

4-12. The tungsten filament of a cylindrical-plate diode has a diameter of 0.023 cm. and a length of 5.1 cm. The anode diameter is 1.90 cm. If the filament operates at 2570°K, at what anode potential will the current become temperature-limited?

4-13. A parallel-plate diode with spacing of 0.20 cm has an anode-cathode voltage of 200 v. The cathode is capable of emitting an infinite number of electrons.

(a) How much heat in w/m^2 will the anode have to dissipate?

(b) What will be the power dissipated per unit area if the anode-cathode voltage is doubled?

(c) If the anode surface emissivity is 0.4, find the anode temperature for both (a) and (b). Assume that the surrounding temperature is 20°C and that the heat is radiated from only one side of the anode.

4-14. The tungsten cathode of Problem 4-12 is at a temperature of 2500°K.
(a) Will the current be temperature- or space-charge-limited at $E_b = 100$ v?
(b) What value of current density reaches the anode?
(c) How much power will the anode have to dissipate per unit area?

4-15. A cylindrical-plate diode, with a thoriated-tungsten filament of length 2.5 cm and diameter 0.04 cm, has a filament temperature of 1950°K. The anode diameter is 2 cm.

If the current through the tube is to be one-eighth of temperature saturation value, what anode-cathode voltage should be used?

4-16. A certain vacuum diode on test shows that 25 v is required to cause 180 ma anode current.
(a) How much voltage is required if the anode current is to be increased to 325 ma, assuming sufficient emission?
(b) What is the maximum current which can flow without causing the anode loss to exceed 25 w?
(c) If the anode area is 4 cm² and emissivity 0.6, what will be the anode temperature rise above a 20°C ambient, for part (b)?

4-17. A vacuum diode is to be built with cylindrical anode and thoriated-tungsten filament, to give a saturation current of 250 ma at an anode voltage of 105 v. The anode must be large enough to radiate the input under this condition at a rate of 1.3 w/cm² Find the diameter and length of the anode, if $\beta^2 = 1.0$.

4-18. A certain vacuum diode was used to obtain the following data:

E_b (v)	I_b (ma)	E_b (v)	I_b (ma)
5.0	0.34	20.0	2.77
10.0	0.96	25.0	3.98
15.0	1.75	29.7	5.02

Determine graphically the values of the constant K and the exponent a for this tube.

4-19. Derive the relation for space-charge density as a function of distance in the space between cathode and anode. How is this related to the velocity?

References

1. Becker, J. A., "Phenomena in Oxide-Coated Filaments," *Phys. Rev.*, **34,** 1323 (1929);**38,** 2193 (1931).

2. Coombes, E. A., "Pulsed Properties of Oxide Cathodes," *Jour. Appl. Phys.*, **17,** 647 (1946).

3. Dushman, S., "Electron Emission from Metals as Functions of Temperature," *Phys. Rev.*, **21**, 623 (1923).

4. ———, "Thermal Emission of Electrons," *International Critical Tables*, VI, 53. McGraw-Hill Book Co., Inc., New York, 1929.

5. Glover, A. M., "A Review of the Development of Sensitive Phototubes," *Proc. I.R.E.*, **29**, 413 (1941).

6. Langmuir, I., "The Effect of Space Charge and Initial Velocities on the Potential Distribution and Thermionic Current between Parallel Plane Electrodes," *Phys. Rev.*, **21**, 419 (1923).

7. ———, "The Effect of Space Charge and Residual Gases on Thermionic Currents in High Vacuum," *Phys. Rev.* **2**, 450 (1913).

8. ———, "The Electron Emission from Thoriated-Tungsten Filaments," *Phys. Rev.*, **22**, 357 (1923).

9. Reimann, A. L., *Thermionic Emission*. John Wiley & Sons, Inc., New York, 1934.

10. Richardson, O. W., Emission of Electricity from Hot Bodies, 2nd ed. David McKay Co., Inc. New York, 1921.

11. Woolridge, D. E., "Theory of Secondary Emission," *Phys. Rev.*, **56,** 562, (1939).

12. Spangenberg, K. R., *Vacuum Tubes*. McGraw-Hill Book Co., Inc., New York, 1948.

Power Supplies and Filters | 5

A large percentage of electronic equipment is supplied with direct current from the a-c lines by use of vacuum or semiconductor diodes as rectifiers. This chapter will consider the circuits in which either type may be employed for such applications. The use of the diode in large power rectifiers will be discussed in Chapter 18.

5–1. Diode internal resistance

It has been shown that the volt-ampere curve for a semiconductor diode is predicted by an exponential relation, that for the vacuum diode

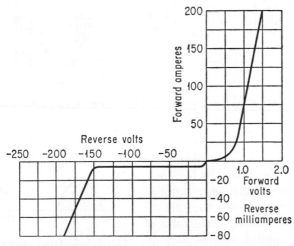

Fig. 5–1. Characteristic of 1N412A silicon power diode.

by the three-halves power law. Examples of the curves for actual devices,
whose volt-ampere curves approximate
the theoretical relations, are drawn in
Figs. 5–1 and 5–2.

At point A on the vacuum diode
curve, the internal resistance is less
than 150 ohms. The internal iR drop of
a semiconductor diode will usually be
less than a volt. The low resistance of
the vacuum diode, compared to most
loads of several thousand ohms, and
the small voltage drop of the semiconductor diode make the consideration of diode resistance in rectifier
circuit analysis unnecessary. This is
equivalent to considering the diode
as "lossless" or electrically perfect.

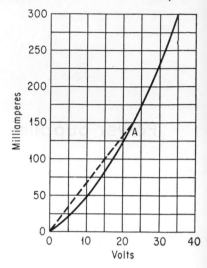

Fig. 5–2. Characteristic of 5Z3
vacuum diode.

When the resistance of the rectifier must be considered for more accurate analyses, the methods of Section 5–14 may be used.

5–2. The half-wave rectifier with resistance load

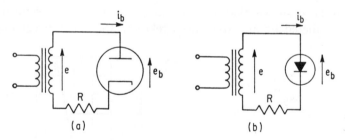

(a)   (b)

Fig. 5–3. Half-wave diode circuits: (a) vacuum diode; (b) semiconductor
diode.

The circuit of a *half-wave rectifier*
using a diode is shown in Fig. 5–3.
If an alternating voltage is applied
the wave form of current through the
load and diode will be of the form of
the positive applied voltage, as indicated in Fig. 5–4, and the currents

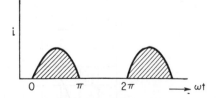

Fig. 5–4. Current pulses in the load of
a half-wave rectifier.

will be given by

$$i_b = \frac{E_m}{R} \sin \omega t \qquad 0 \le \sin \omega t \le 1 \qquad (5\text{–}1)$$

$$i_b = 0 \qquad -1 \le \sin \omega t \le 0 \qquad (5\text{–}2)$$

The ultimate object in the use of a rectifier is to obtain direct current from an alternating source. A d-c ammeter in series with the load will read the d-c or average value as

$$I_{\text{d–c}} = \frac{1}{2\pi} \int_0^{2\pi} i_b \, d\omega t = \frac{1}{2\pi} \int_0^{\pi} \frac{E_m}{R} \sin \omega t \, d\omega t + \frac{1}{2\pi} \int_{\pi}^{2\pi} 0 \, d\omega t \quad (5\text{–}3)$$

$$= \frac{E_m}{\pi R} = \frac{I_m}{\pi} \qquad (5\text{–}4)$$

from which the d-c load voltage is

$$E_{\text{d–c}} = I_{\text{d–c}}R = \frac{E_m}{\pi} \qquad (5\text{–}5)$$

The total power input into the circuit is

$$P_{\text{a–c}} = I_{\text{rms}}^2 R \qquad (5\text{–}6)$$

where I_{rms} is the effective value of the current pulses through the diode, or by definition of the rms value, is

$$I_{\text{rms}} = \sqrt{\frac{1}{2\pi} \int_0^{2\pi} i_b^2 \, d\omega t} = \sqrt{\frac{1}{2\pi} \int_0^{\pi} I_m^2 \sin^2 \omega t \, d\omega t} = \frac{I_m}{2} \qquad (5\text{–}7)$$

This is the value of current read by an a-c ammeter in series with the diode.

A Fourier analysis of the half-sinusoid voltage pulses applied to the load of Fig. 5–3 yields

$$e = \frac{E_m}{\pi} + \frac{E_m}{2} \sin \omega t - \frac{2E_m}{3\pi} \cos 2\omega t - \frac{2E_m}{15\pi} \cos 4\omega t \cdots \qquad (5\text{–}8)$$

as the harmonic series. The first term on the right is the average or d-c voltage. The lowest frequency and the only odd harmonic is that of the supply frequency. With these emf's applied to a resistance load, corresponding frequency terms appear in the current series.

A rectifier may be considered as fundamentally a frequency converter in which one input frequency is changed to a large number of frequencies, only one of which is the desired output. This is the zero-frequency term or d-c component. It should be noted, however, that $P_{\text{d–c}}$ is not all the power dissipated in the resistance load but is merely the portion due to the d-c component of rectifier output. This is the power which would be effective in charging a battery or in an electrolytic process. Consideration of the terms of Eq. 5–8 indicates that currents of harmonic frequencies will flow through the load, representing power which is unavailable as direct current. This power loss lowers the efficiency. Circuits which prevent the a-c components from flowing through the resistive load are therefore desirable. Such circuits are called *filters* and are discussed later in this chapter.

The *peak inverse voltage* is the maximum voltage appearing across the diode during the time of nonconduction. Insulation strength of the diode determines the allowable magnitude of this voltage. From the circuit of Fig. 5–3 it is apparent that during the nonconducting period, the voltage e_b across the tube is equal to the applied voltage $e = E_m \sin \omega t$, and the peak inverse voltage for a half-wave rectifier is

$$P.I.V. = E_m$$

5–3. The full-wave circuit with resistance load

It appears from Section 5–2 that if the load could be supplied with current during the inactive cycle, the efficiency might be raised. The full-wave or biphase circuit of Fig. 5–5 accomplishes this. It consists of two half-wave circuits connected to serve a common load resistance. The additional circuit is connected so that the polarity of the a-c voltage applied to the dipole is opposite to that of the first circuit. Consequently, since conduction occurs only during the half cycle in which the anode of the diode is positive, the diodes will conduct on opposite half cycles, resulting in a current wave as shown in Fig. 5–6, consisting of successive sine pulses, each

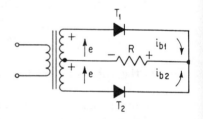

Fig. 5–5. Full-wave or biphase circuit with resistance load.

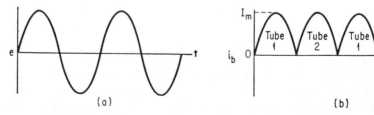

Fig. 5–6. Applied voltage and load current of a full-wave rectifier.

of 180° duration. Assuming identical diodes, the currents can be written from the mesh equations as

$$\left. \begin{aligned} i_{b1} &= \frac{E_m}{R} \sin \omega t \\[2mm] i_{b2} &= 0 \end{aligned} \right\} \qquad 0 \le \sin \omega t \le 1 \qquad (5\text{–}9)$$

$$\left. \begin{aligned} i_{b1} &= 0 \\[2mm] i_{b2} &= -\,\frac{E_m}{R} \sin \omega t \end{aligned} \right\} \qquad -1 \le \sin \omega t \le 0 \qquad (5\text{–}10)$$

with the positive directions used on e as indicated in Fig. 5–5. The voltage $e = E_m \sin \omega t$ is the input for each diode, or half of the transformer secondary voltage. Each diode operates independently and under exactly the same conditions as in the half-wave circuit, only the load currents and voltages being combined.

By taking the average of the current wave in the load, the d-c current is obtained as

$$I_{\text{d–c}} = \frac{2E_m}{\pi R} = \frac{2I_m}{\pi} \qquad (5\text{–}11)$$

which is twice the value of the half-wave circuit, since it is the sum of the diode currents. The output voltage is

$$E_{\text{d–c}} = I_{\text{d–c}}R = \frac{2E_m}{\pi} \qquad (5\text{–}12)$$

The a-c power input to each diode is the same as for the half-wave circuit, so that the total a-c input is

$$P_{\text{a–c}} = \frac{E_m^2}{2R} \qquad (5\text{–}13)$$

by reference to Eqs. 5–6 and 5–7.

The voltage wave form applied to the load, causing the current wave forms of Fig. 5–6 to flow, may be analyzed as

$$e = \frac{2E_m}{\pi} - \frac{4E_m}{3\pi} \cos 2\omega t - \frac{4E_m}{15\pi} \cos 4\omega t - \frac{4E_m}{35\pi} \cos 6\omega t \cdots \qquad (5\text{–}14)$$

In the full-wave case, the lowest frequency present is double the supply frequency, which makes removal of the harmonics with filter circuits easier. That fact, plus increased output voltage, makes the full-wave circuit more desirable than the half-wave circuit.

By writing an instantaneous voltage equation around the outside loop of the circuit of Fig. 5–5 during the interval in which T_1 is nonconducting, it is found that

$$e_{b1} = -2E_m \sin \omega t.$$

The maximum value for e_{b1} occurs when $\omega t = 3\pi/2$; then

$$\text{P.I.V.} = 2E_m \qquad (5\text{–}15)$$

5–4. Ripple factor

In many applications, any residual pulsation in the output direct current is considered undesirable. The pulsations, or ripple, are caused by a-c harmonic components present in the load current, and can be reduced by selection of rectifier circuit or by filtering of the rectifier output. The current in the rectifier load consists of two components: I_{d-c}, or the average value, and I_{a-c}, or the effective value of the a-c components. A measure of the purity of rectifier output is called the *ripple factor*, and is stated as the ratio of the two current (or voltage) components:

$$\gamma = \text{ripple factor} = \frac{\text{effective value of a-c harmonic components}}{\text{average, or d-c component}}$$

The effective value of the total load current is

$$I_{\text{rms}} = \sqrt{I_{d-c}^2 + I_{a-c}^2}$$

from which

$$I_{a-c} = \sqrt{I_{\text{rms}}^2 - I_{d-c}^2}$$

Use of the above value in the ripple factor definition gives

$$\gamma = \sqrt{(I_{\text{rms}}/I_{d-c})^2 - 1} \qquad (5\text{–}16)$$

The form factor F of any recurrent wave is defined as the ratio of the effective to the average value, and the ripple then may be expressed as

$$\gamma = \sqrt{F^2 - 1} \qquad (5\text{–}17)$$

Use of the values of I_{rms} and I_{d-c} for the half-wave rectifier in Eq. 5–16 gives the value of 1.21, or 121 per cent, for the ripple factor of the half-wave rectifier with resistive load. The full-wave rectifier under similar conditions has a ripple factor of 0.48.

5–5. The shunt-capacitor filter

As a power source for many types of electronic equipment, a rectifier must provide direct current having a ripple factor much smaller than is

obtainable directly, and filter circuits are employed. While reducing the
ripple, filter circuits also improve the power efficiency because they prevent
the alternating harmonic components from flowing in the resistance load,
and dissipating undesired power therein.

A simple filter is obtained by shunting a capacitor across the resistance
load of a rectifier. If the capacitance is so chosen that $X_c \ll R$, then the
alternating currents find a low reactance shunt path through the capacitor,
and only a small alternating current flows in the load to produce a ripple
voltage. Such a filter appears at Fig. 5–7(a), as applied to a half-wave
diode rectifier.

The presence of the capacitor causes a considerable change in the
operating conditions of the diode, as compared with those existing when
supplying a simple resistance load. During the time the rectifier output
voltage is increasing, the capacitor charges to a voltage equal to the rectifier output, and stores energy. When the rectifier output voltage falls,
the capacitor delivers energy to the load, maintaining the load voltage
at a higher value over a period than if the capacitor were not present.
The diode, therefore, delivers a pulse of current with each cycle to charge
the capacitor, and then acts as a switch to disconnect the source and permit
the capacitor to discharge through the load. If the time constant of the
filter and load circuits is long with respect to the time of a cycle, the discharge will be slow, and the voltage nearly constant over the cycle. The
diode conducts for short pulses, rather than over the whole positive half
cycle, and the circuit is excited by repeated current transients, as illustrated by Fig. 5–7(b) and (c).

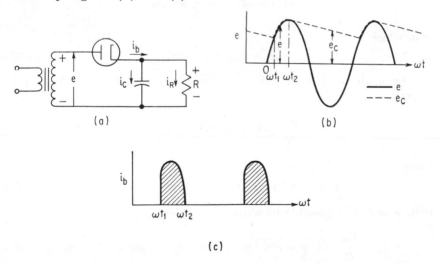

Fig. 5–7. (a) Half-wave diode rectifier with capacitor filter; (b) voltage
wave forms; (c) diode current wave forms.

Referring to Fig. 5–7, the voltage across the capacitor during the charging interval, ωt_1 to ωt_2, is equal to the supply voltage, or

$$e_C = e = E_m \sin \omega t \qquad \omega t_1 < \omega t < \omega t_2 \qquad (5\text{--}18)$$

By inspection of the circuit, it can be seen that during this same time interval

$$i_b = i_C + i_R \tag{5--19}$$

Since

$$i_R = \frac{E_m}{R} \sin \omega t \qquad\qquad \omega t_1 < \omega t < \omega t_2$$

and

$$i_C = C \frac{de_C}{dt} = \omega C E_m \cos \omega t$$

then the diode current during the conduction interval is a pulse having a form given by

$$i_b = E_m \left(\frac{1}{R} \sin \omega t + \omega C \cos \omega t \right) \qquad \omega t_1 < \omega t < \omega t_2 \qquad (5\text{--}20)$$

At ωt_2, when diode conduction ends, or $i_b = 0$, then $i_C = i_R$ from Eq. 5–19, and

$$\omega C \cos \omega t_2 = - \frac{1}{R} \sin \omega t_2$$

from which

$$\omega t_2 = \tan^{-1} (-\omega R C) \tag{5--21}$$

The angle ωt_2 lies in the second quadrant. Equation 5–20 may be written as

$$i_b = \frac{E_m}{R} \sqrt{1 + \omega^2 R^2 C^2} \sin (\omega t + \phi)$$

where

$$\phi = \tan^{-1} (\omega R C) = \pi - \tan^{-1} (-\omega R C) \tag{5--22}$$

from which it is possible to write

$$i_b = \frac{E_m}{R} \sqrt{1 + \omega^2 R^2 C^2} \sin (\omega t_2 - \omega t) \qquad \omega t_1 < \omega t < \omega t_2 \qquad (5\text{--}23)$$

as a simplified expression for the current pulse through the diode.

Equations 5–21 and 5–23 introduce the term ωRC, a dimensionless parameter occuring frequently in the analysis of rectifier circuits with capacity filters, and representative of the circuit conditions. Large values of ωRC may mean large capacitance or large load resistance (low current), whereas small values of ωRC mean small capacitance or low load resistance (large current). Much of the information to be obtained concerning capacitor filters will be presented in terms of ωRC.

At ωt_2 the voltage output of the diode is falling faster than the capacitor can discharge, and the diode output voltage becomes less than e_C. The diode then has a positive cathode and ceases conduction, disconnecting the source from the load. For the period between ωt_2 and $2\pi + \omega t_1$, it can be seen that $i_R = -i_C$, or that

$$\frac{e_C}{R} = -C\frac{de_C}{dt}$$

from which

$$\frac{de_C}{dt} + \frac{e_C}{RC} = 0 \qquad\qquad (5\text{–}24)$$

Equation 5–24 is the circuit differential equation for the interval ωt_2 to $2\pi + \omega t_1$, and has a solution

$$e_C = A\epsilon^{-t/RC}$$

At $\omega t = \omega t_2$, $e_C = E_m \sin \omega t_2$, so that, after A is evaluated,

$$e_C = E_m \sin \omega t_2 \, \epsilon^{-(\omega t - \omega t_2)/\omega RC} \qquad \omega t_2 < \omega t < 2\pi + \omega t_1 \qquad (5\text{–}25)$$

is the expression for the capacitor voltage during the interval when the capacitor is supplying the load current. For large ωRC— that is, for large C or large R (light current load), the exponential term will approximate unity, and the voltage during the interval will not drop greatly below the value at ωt_2. This leads to small ripple. For small ωRC— or heavy current loads (small R), the exponential term has greater effect and the voltage during the interval drops considerably below its value at ωt_2. Thus, *the ripple with a capacitor filter increases with increase in load current.*

At $\omega t_1 + 2\pi$, Fig. 5–7(b) shows that

$$e_C = E_m \sin (\omega t_1 + 2\pi) = E_m \sin \omega t_1$$

and from Eq. 5–25 this becomes

$$E_m \sin \omega t_1 = E_m \sin \omega t_2 \, \epsilon^{-(\omega t_1 - \omega t_2 + 2\pi)/\omega RC}$$

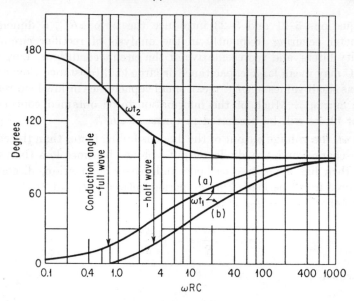

Fig. 5–8. Conduction angles for the shunt-capacitor filter: (a) full-wave; (b) half-wave.

from which

$$\sin \omega t_1 = \sin \omega t_2 \, \epsilon^{-(\omega t_1 - \omega t_2 + 2\pi)/\omega RC}$$

$$(5-26)$$

This is a transcendental equation which can be solved graphically, and curves of ωt_1 and ωt_2 as functions of ωRC are plotted in Fig. 5–8.

Having values for ωt_1 and ωt_2 as functions of ωRC, it is possible to plot typical diode-current wave forms from Eq. 5–23, as in Fig. 5–9. Note that since ωt_2 decreases and ωt_1 increases with ωRC, the conduction angle is short for large values of capacitance. At the same time, Eq. 5–23 shows that the peak amplitude of i_b increases with the value of C.

The direct voltage across the load may be obtained by averaging the voltages given by Eqs. 5–18 and 5–25

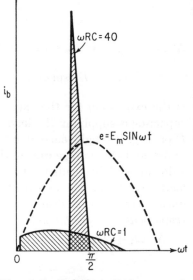

Fig. 5–9. Relative diode current waves in a half-wave circuit with shunt-capacitor filter for two values of ωRC.

over a cycle. That is,

$$E_{d-c} = \frac{1}{2\pi} \int_{\omega t_1}^{\omega t_2} E_m \sin \omega t \, d\omega t + \frac{1}{2\pi} \int_{\omega t_2}^{2\pi + \omega t_1} E_m \sin \omega t_2 \, \epsilon^{-(\omega t - \omega t_2)/\omega RC} \, d\omega t$$

$$(5\text{-}27)$$

After integration and substitution of Eqs. 5–21 and 5–26, this reduces to

$$E_{d-c} = \frac{E_m}{2\pi} \sqrt{1 + \omega^2 R^2 C^2} [1 - \cos(\omega t_2 - \omega t_1)] \qquad (5\text{-}28)$$

which relates the d-c output voltage to the peak a-c input for various values of ωRC. The ratio E_{d-c}/E_m is plotted in Fig. 5–10(a) as a function of the parameter ωRC. The curve shows that for low values of C the ratio approaches $1/\pi$, which is the value with resistance load. At large values of C, the ouput voltage approaches the peak value of the input voltage. For good regulation with varying load, sufficient capacitance should be used to ensure operation on the upper plateau of the curve. Because of the high value of ωRC needed for small ripple, the half-wave rectifier with capacitor filter is ordinarily used only for applications requiring small average currents at high voltage (R large).

On the inverse half cycle, the capacitor voltage will add directly to the a-c supply voltage. Since the capacitor voltage for large ωRC is nearly equal to E_m, the peak inverse voltage on a diode at light current loads may approach $2E_m$.

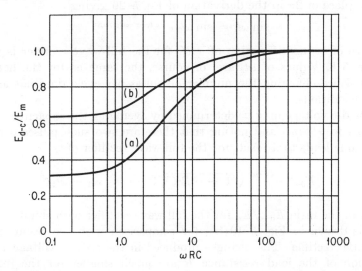

Fig. 5–10. Variation of E_{dc}/E_m with ωRC, shunt-capacitor filter: (a) half-wave; (b) full-wave.

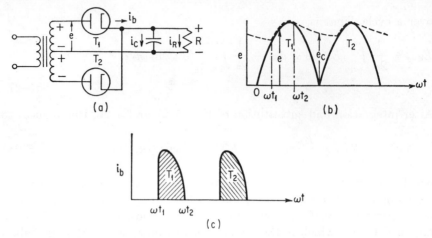

Fig. 5–11. (a) Full-wave circuit with shunt-capacity filter; (b) circuit voltages; (c) diode current.

The full-wave circuit may also be used with the shunt-capacitor filter, as illustrated in Fig. 5–11. The operation is similar to that of the half-wave circuit, with the discharge time of the capacitor running only to $\pi + \omega t_1$ instead of to $2\pi + \omega t_1$, and with improved regulation and lessened ripple.

With the above change in limits of operation, the equations for i_b, i_C, and i_R still apply. The cut-in angle ωt_1 may be redetermined by the use of π in place of 2π in the derivation of Eq. 5–26 giving

$$\sin \omega t_1 = \sin \omega t_2 \, \epsilon^{-(\omega t_1 + \pi - \omega t_2)/\omega RC} \tag{5–29}$$

A curve of ωt_1 as a function of ωRC for the full-wave rectifier is plotted in Fig. 5–8. Values of ωt_2 are, of course, the same as for the half-wave circuit, since changing the number of pulses per cycle does not alter the cutoff conditions.

The d-c voltage may be determined by averaging the capacitor voltages from ωt_1 to $\pi + \omega t_1$ and noting that there are two such pulses per cycle. This value leads to a result for the full-wave rectifier of

$$E_{\text{d-c}} = \frac{E_m}{\pi} \sqrt{1 + \omega^2 R^2 C^2} [1 - \cos (\omega t_2 - \omega t_1)] \tag{5–30}$$

A plot of the ratio $E_{\text{d-c}}/E_m$ for the full-wave rectifier with shunt-capacitor filter is drawn in Fig. 5–10(b), for comparison with the results for the half-wave rectifier. The changes produced in the output voltage $E_{\text{d-c}}$ by variation of the load resistance R are much smaller for the full-wave rectifier than for the half-wave circuit—that is, the voltage regulation is better for the full-wave circuit.

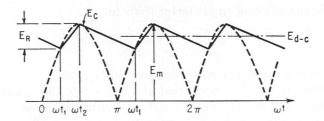

Fig. 5–12. Output wave approximation, full-wave circuit.

Because of the complex wave forms, it is difficult to calculate ripple factor from the above results. However, if the output voltage wave form is approximated by the solid curve of Fig. 5–12, simplified and reasonably accurate expressions can be obtained. The wave form is assumed to be made up of straight lines with a peak of E_m and a peak-to-peak ripple magnitude of E_R. The average of such a wave, or the d-c value, is

$$E_{d-c} = E_m - \frac{E_R}{2} \qquad (5\text{–}31)$$

During the discharge interval, ωt_2 to $\pi + \omega t_1$, the capacitor is assumed to lose charge at a constant rate with a current I_{d-c}. The rate of loss of potential is

$$\frac{dE_C}{d\omega t} = \frac{E_R}{\pi + \omega t_1 - \omega t_2} = \frac{1}{\omega C}\frac{dq}{dt}$$

and the rate of loss of charge is

$$\frac{dq}{dt} = I_{d-c}$$

so that

$$E_R = (\pi + \omega t_1 - \omega t_2)\frac{I_{d-c}}{\omega C} \qquad (5\text{–}32)$$

where ω applies to the supply frequency.

For an axis along E_{d-c} it can be found by standard methods that the rms value of the ripple component is

$$E_{a-c} = \frac{E_R}{2\sqrt{3}} = \frac{(\pi + \omega t_1 - \omega t_2)I_{d-c}}{2\sqrt{3}\,\omega C} \qquad (5\text{–}33)$$

Use of the definition of ripple factor leads to

$$\gamma = \frac{E_{a-c}}{E_{d-c}} = \frac{(\pi + \omega t_1 - \omega t_2)}{2\sqrt{3}\omega RC} \qquad (5\text{-}34)$$

for the full-wave rectifier with shunt-capacitor filter.

Reference to Fig. 5–8 shows that at $\omega RC = 100$, the conduction angle $(\omega t_2 - \omega t_1) < 0.2$ radian, or $10°$, and neglecting this angle with respect to π in the numerator of Eq. 5–34 will introduce only small error in computation of the ripple. This can be verified from the ripple plot in Fig. 5–13, which shows less than one per cent ripple for $\omega RC > 100$. Figure 5–10 also shows that substantially $E_{d-c} = E_m$ for such large ωRC values.

At reasonably high d-c load resistances, and with semiconductor diodes, it becomes practical to use rectifier designs with $\omega RC > 100$. Vacuum diodes could not safely supply the high peak currents needed by such ωRC values and short conduction angles, but semiconductor diodes have larger allowable ratios of peak to average currents. Using electrolytic capacitors of 40 to 100 mfd it then becomes possible to design rectifiers with excellent regulation and very low ripple values, using the shunt-capacitor filter circuit and the full-wave rectifier.

Equation 5–33 may be used in Eq. 5–31 to yield

$$E_{rms} = \frac{E_{d-c}\left(1 + \dfrac{\pi + \omega t_1 - \omega t_2}{2\omega RC}\right)}{\sqrt{2}}$$

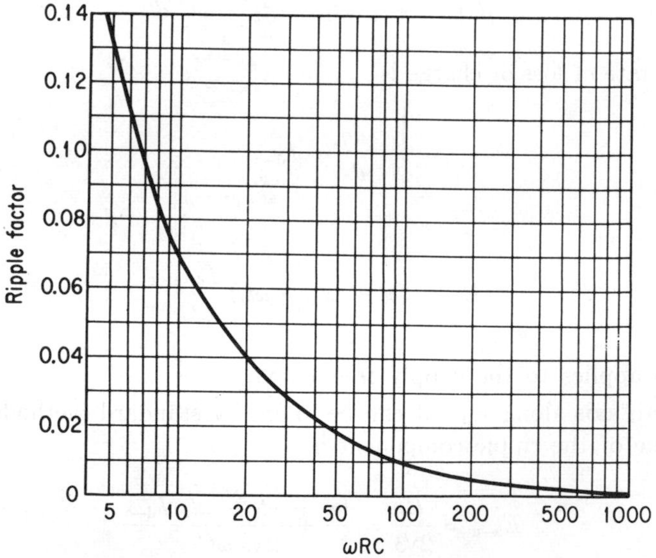

Fig. 5–13. Ripple-wave factor versus ωRC, full-wave, capacitor filter.

For large ωRC the conduction angle may be neglected. The relation may be used to determine the approximate secondary voltage, E_{rms}, of one half of the transformer.

5–6. The series-inductor filter

An inductor may be used in series with the rectifier load as a filter, storing magnetic energy when the current is above the average value and releasing that energy to the circuit when the current tends to fall below the average level. An inductor may also be looked upon as a high impedance to the alternating components in the diode output, reducing the amplitude of all with respect to the d-c component, and thereby lowering the ripple. The circuit of a half-wave rectifier with an inductor L in the load circuit appears in Fig. 5–14(a).

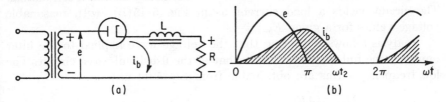

(a)　　　　　　　　　　　　　　　(b)

Fig. 5–14. (a) Series-inductor filter, half-wave circuit; (b) current and voltage waves.

Usual circuit analysis may be used to write the differential equation for the circuit through the conducting diode as

$$\frac{di_b}{dt} + \frac{Ri_b}{L} = \frac{E_m \sin \omega t}{L}$$

Combining the transient and steady-state solutions gives

$$i_b = \frac{E_m}{\sqrt{R^2 + \omega^2 L^2}} \left[\sin (\omega t - \theta) + \epsilon^{-R\omega t/\omega L} \sin \theta \right] \qquad (5\text{--}35)$$

where $\theta = \tan^{-1} \omega L/R$, and after noting that at $\omega t = 0$, then $i_b = 0$. The current pulses of Fig. 5–14(b) are of this form. As the inductance is increased, the exponential term decays more slowly, and current exists for considerable periods after $\omega t = \pi$. A positive emf is maintained on the anode of the diode during this time by reason of the $L\, di/dt$ voltage produced by a decreasing current in L. The half-wave inductive filter circuit produces a low average d-c voltage for a given E_m, and is rarely used.

In full-wave rectifiers with an inductive load, the conduction angle of a diode exceeds $180°$ and overlaps the conduction angle of the other diode,

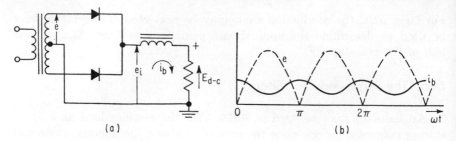

Fig. 5–15. (a) Inductor filter on full-wave rectifier; (b) load current wave form for (a).

giving continuous current in the load. The current commutates between diodes at supply voltage zero (neglecting transformer reactance effects as small), and the diode having the positive anode at any instant is conducting. The circuit yields a load current as in Fig. 5–15(b), with reasonable voltage values for a given E_m.

Analysis follows by noting that the voltage wave applied to the filter input by the full-wave rectifier is that of the usual full-wave circuit. The low frequency terms are obtainable from Eq. 5–14 as

$$e_i = \frac{2E_m}{\pi} - \frac{4E_m}{\pi} \left(\tfrac{1}{3} \cos 2\omega t + \tfrac{1}{15} \cos 4\omega t + \tfrac{1}{35} \cos 6\omega t \cdots \right)$$

It is not possible to have an average voltage across an inductance, and so the d-c voltage $2E_m/\pi$ will appear entirely across the inductor resistance R_c and the load R. The d-c load quantities then are

$$E_{d-c} = \frac{2E_m}{\pi} \left(\frac{1}{1 + R_c/R} \right), \qquad I_{d-c} = \frac{2E_m}{\pi} \left(\frac{1}{R_c + R} \right) \quad (5\text{--}36)$$

Obviously the choke or inductor resistance should be small for good efficiency and high output voltage. Assuming this to be the case, R_c will hereafter be neglected.

The input impedance of the filter and load resistor at the second harmonic of the supply is

$$Z_2 = R\sqrt{1 + 4\omega^2 L^2/R^2} \quad (5\text{--}37)$$

At the frequency of the next higher, or fourth harmonic

$$Z_4 = R\sqrt{1 + 16\omega^2 L^2/R^2} \quad (5\text{--}38)$$

If $\omega^2 L^2/R^2 \gg 1$, as is usual, then

$$\frac{Z_4}{Z_2} \cong 2$$

From the series for the applied voltage it can be seen that $E_2/E_4 = 5$, so that

$$\frac{I_2}{I_4} = \frac{E_2/Z_2}{E_4/Z_4} \cong 10 \qquad (5\text{--}39)$$

This result indicates that the fourth and all higher harmonic amplitudes are small with respect to the second in producing ripple components in the load current, and only small error will be introduced by using the second harmonic alone in computing the ripple for this filter circuit.

Then

$$I_2 = \frac{4E_m}{3\sqrt{2}\pi} \frac{1}{R\sqrt{1 + 4\omega^2 L^2/R^2}}$$

$$I_{\text{d--c}} = \frac{2E_m}{\pi R}$$

and the ripple will be

$$\gamma = \frac{I_2}{I_{\text{d--c}}} = \frac{\sqrt{2}}{3\sqrt{1 + 4\omega^2 L^2/R^2}} \qquad (5\text{--}40)$$

It was previously assumed that $\omega^2 L^2/R^2 \gg 1$, so

$$\gamma \cong \frac{0.236}{\omega L/R} \qquad (5\text{--}41)$$

The result shows that the *ripple will decrease* as R decreases, or *as the load current rises*. This is in contrast to the shunt-capacitor filter in which the ripple increases with increasing load current. The capacitor filter produces a higher d-c output voltage for a given E_m, but with greater peak current demands on the diodes. Neither simple filter is capable of sufficiently low ripple for supplying much electronic equipment without large capacitors or inductors.

5–7. The LC filter

To meet the demand for lower ripple factors than are possible with the circuits already discussed, shunt capacitance and series inductance can be combined as in Fig. 5–16. The previous method of analysis cannot be fully employed in the *LC* circuit because of uncertainty concerning the points of cut-in and cutout for the diodes. However, information gained from the analysis of the capacitor filter explains the action of the circuit at light loads. At heavy loads analysis by the method of the previous section is possible.

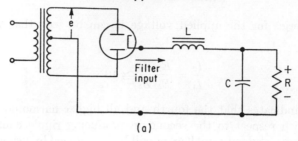

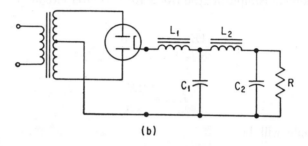

Fig. 5–16. *LC* filters.

For light loads when $R \cong \infty$, the capacitor will charge to the peak of the a-c voltage, and the output d-c voltage will be E_m on open circuit. As a small current is taken by the load, or R is decreased, the diode switches the emf onto the circuit for an instant, and the capacitor charges on the peak of each cycle of applied voltage; the conduction angle of each diode is small, and the d-c voltage is lowered slightly owing to the average capacitor voltage being below the peak of the a-c wave. The current flowing is so low that the small energy stored in the inductor has almost no effect on the circuit except to lengthen the conduction time slightly. The circuit action is almost the same as with the full-wave capacitor-filter circuit. In general, the voltage follows the dashed portion of the load voltage curve of Fig. 5–17(b), decreasing with increasing load current, exactly as if two half-wave diodes were supplying a capacitor filter.

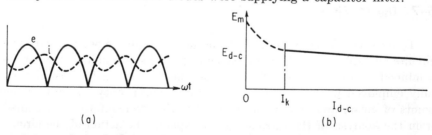

Fig. 5–17. (a) Voltage and current in filters of Fig. 5–16; (b) E_{dc} vs I_{dc} for single section *LC* filter.

For still lower values of R or larger load currents, the conduction angle lengthens owing to both the discharging effect on the capacitor and the presence of the inductor, and the average voltage is further decreased. At some value of current, I_k, the conduction angle of each diode is 180°. Further increases in load current build up the stored energy in the inductance so that the current is maintained and the conduction angle overlaps that of the second diode. The current in the inductor is then never zero.

With the full-wave rectifier and inductor the diodes act simply as synchronous switches to connect to the filter whichever transformer winding happens to be the more positive, and the current transfers smoothly from diode to diode. In effect, the usual full-wave rectifier output of sinusoidal half waves as at Fig. 5–17(a) is applied to the filter input.

Therefore, with load current above I_k, or with continuous current in the load, an alternating emf of known harmonic content is applied to an impedance, and ordinary circuit-analysis methods apply. From Eq. 5–14 the emf of Fig. 5–17(a) is

$$e = \frac{2E_m}{\pi} - \frac{4E_m}{\pi} \left(\tfrac{1}{3} \cos 2\omega t + \tfrac{1}{15} \cos 4\omega t + \tfrac{1}{35} \cos 6\omega t + \cdots \right)$$

The inductance of L will be chosen to have a high reactance at the second harmonic of the supply frequency, and will have double this value of reactance at the fourth harmonic. Upon consideration of the voltage amplitudes, the fourth-harmonic current in the circuit will be only 10 per cent of the second-harmonic current as was previously shown. The reactance of the capacitor C at the fourth harmonic is one half of the second-harmonic value, so that any load voltage produced by flow of fourth-harmonic current will be only 5 per cent of the second-harmonic voltage. Therefore, currents owing to the higher harmonics will be neglected and only the second harmonic will be considered in the following analysis. A design of a filter satisfactory for the lowest-order harmonic will be even more effective for higher harmonics.

Since the capacitor C is intended to by-pass as much as possible of the alternating current around the load, it is desirable to choose C such that

$$\frac{1}{2\omega C} \ll R \tag{5–42}$$

Under this condition, the input impedance of the filter circuit of Fig. 5–16(a) at the second-harmonic frequency 2ω is

$$Z_2 = 2j\omega L - \frac{jR/2\omega C}{R - j/2\omega C}$$

If the inequality of Eq. 5–42 is applied as a condition of circuit design, then

$$| Z_2 | = \frac{4\omega^2 LC - 1}{2\omega C} \qquad (5\text{–}43)$$

Use of the rms value of the second-harmonic emf from the voltage series above allows the alternating current in the inductor L to be written as

$$| I_L | = \frac{8\omega C E_m}{3\pi\sqrt{2}(4\omega^2 LC - 1)} \qquad (5\text{–}44)$$

If I_C and I_R are the alternating currents through the capacitor C and the resistor R, then by inspection

$$| I_R | = \frac{1}{2\omega CR} | I_C | \qquad (5\text{–}45)$$

but $I_C \cong I_L$, by reason of the assumption of Eq. 5–42, so

$$| I_R | = \frac{4E_m}{3\pi\sqrt{2}R(4\omega^2 LC - 1)} \qquad (5\text{–}46)$$

The d-c load voltage is given by the first term of the Fourier series so the d-c load current is $2E_m/\pi R$. The ripple in the output current then is

$$\gamma = \frac{\pi}{2E_m} \frac{4E_m}{3\pi\sqrt{2}(4\omega^2 LC - 1)} = \frac{0.47}{4\omega^2 LC - 1} \qquad (5\text{–}47)$$

Ripple factor is plotted as a function of $\omega^2 LC$ in Fig. 5–18. As long as conduction of current is continuous in the inductance L, and $X_C \ll R$, the ripple factor is independent of the load current flowing. This is a valuable feature, since it permits the design of filters having given ripple factors that will operate over a considerable current range. The ripple factors obtainable may be seen as smaller than are possible with reasonably sized inductors or capacitors in the circuits previously discussed. Obviously, for small ripple the condition of $4\omega^2 LC = 1$ should be avoided.

A second section of filter may be added, as in Fig. 5–16(b), to achieve still further reduction in ripple. The current I_L of Eq. 5–44 flows almost entirely through capacitor C_1, providing a voltage drop of

$$E_{C_1} = \frac{4E_m}{3\pi\sqrt{2}(4\omega^2 L_1 C_1 - 1)}$$

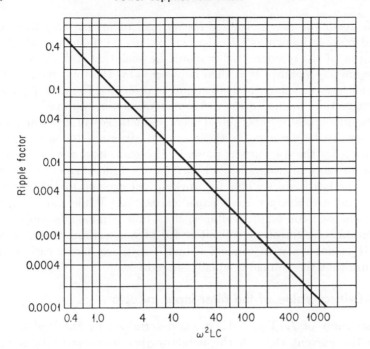

Fig. 5–18. Ripple factor versus $\omega^2 LC$ for inductor-input LC filter with continuous current flow.

Under the assumption that $X_C \ll R$ then I_2, the current in the second inductor L_2, is

$$|I_2| = \frac{8E_m\omega C_2}{3\pi\sqrt{2}\,(4\omega^2 L_1 C_1 - 1)\,(4\omega^2 L_2 C_2 - 1)} \tag{5–48}$$

The currents in C_2 and R will also be related by Eq. 5–45, and the a-c component of load current will be

$$|I_{R_2}| = \frac{4E_m}{3\pi\sqrt{2}\,R\,(4\omega^2 L_1 C_1 - 1)\,(4\omega^2 L_2 C_2 - 1)} \tag{5–49}$$

The ripple can then be calculated as

$$\gamma = \frac{I_{R_2}}{I_{d-c}} = \frac{0.47}{(4\omega^2 L_1 C_1 - 1)\,(4\omega^2 L_2 C_2 - 1)} \tag{5–50}$$

The equation for the ripple could be extended to include the effects of any number of sections, since each section reduces the ripple factor by $1/(4\omega^2 LC - 1)$.

To avoid the rise in voltage for no load or for currents less than I_k, a fixed resistor known as a *bleeder* may be placed in shunt with the load. The value of the bleeder resistor should be such that it draws a current of approximately I_k amp. It is then impossible for the total rectifier load to drop below I_k in value, the load circuit is protected from the high voltage at light rectifier load, and the rectifier regulation is improved.

The inductors or *chokes* used have inductances of the order of 5 to 30 henrys, with air gaps in the magnetic structure to reduce magnetic saturation by the d-c current present. The capacitors are of the order of 2 to 40 or more microfarads, and may be of oil-filled paper or electrolytic types. The latter are suitable for working voltages up to 450, occupy less space, and are cheaper than paper capacitors. While paper capacitors are often used for higher voltages, it is now common to employ series connections of electrolytic capacitors for higher working voltages. In this case, it is necessary to connect a high resistance across each capacitor to insure that the voltage is equally shared.

5–8. Critical value of the filter input inductor

The value of I_k, Fig. 5–17(b), is determined by the load current at which the current through the inductor just becomes continuous. This means that the negative peak of the current wave just touches the zero axis, and the current wave form looks like that of Fig. 5–19 for a full-wave rectifier. With continuous current flow, the analysis of the preceding section is applicable. The current of Fig. 5–19 consists of the d-c value plus a-c harmonics, of which the second is of major importance.

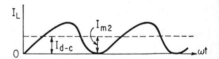

Fig. 5–19. Current wave through inductor filter when $I_{d-c} = I_k$.

With higher harmonics neglected, for the current just to touch the zero axis requires that the peak of the second-harmonic wave just be equal to the I_{d-c} value. By use of values of second-harmonic voltage from Eq. 5–14,

$$E_{d-c} = \frac{2E_m}{\pi} \qquad E_{m_2} = \frac{4E_m}{3\pi}$$

and since the resistance of the circuit to direct current is R and the impedance to second-harmonic alternating current is given in Eq. 5–43, the direct current I_{d-c} and peak second-harmonic current I_{m_2} may be equated to find the conditions that determine I_k as

$$\frac{2E_m}{\pi R} = \frac{4E_m/3\pi}{Z_2}$$

from which

$$R = 1.5\,Z_2 \tag{5–51}$$

This equation states that the current in the input inductor becomes continuous and the output voltage levels off, at a load having a resistance equal to 1.5 times the second-harmonic impedance of the filter circuit.

It is usually true that

$$\omega L \gg \frac{1}{\omega C}$$

and Eq. 5–43 for Z_2 becomes

$$Z_2 = 2\omega L$$

Then Eq. 5–51 may be solved for the critical value of the input inductor as

$$L_k = \frac{R}{3\omega} \cong \frac{R}{1100} \tag{5–52}$$

for a supply at 60 cycles. Using the load specified by Eq. 5–51, the value of I_k may then be written as

$$I_k = \frac{2E_m}{3\pi\omega L} = \frac{0.212 E_m}{\omega L} \tag{5–53}$$

ω still being used as the angular frequency of the supply circuit.

If the critical current I_k is reduced, then the range over which the load current can be varied without having E_{d-c} rise can be increased. Likewise, a larger bleeder resistance can be used to reduce the power wasted in that circuit. The critical value I_k can be reduced by raising the a-c impedance of the filter circuit, since this operation permits R to be increased for the critical current. The capacitor reactance is already small, so that raising the circuit impedance means increasing the input inductance. However, this raises the cost and may require the use of an inductor larger than would be needed to give the required filtering.

This problem can be solved by use of a *swinging choke*. Such an inductor takes advantage of the variation of inductance of an iron-core reactor due to saturation by the d-c current, and is designed to have an inductance at full load just large enough for the filtering required. At lighter current loads, the value of inductance rises, increasing the a-c circuit impedance and reducing the value of current I_k at which discontinuous current flow begins in the inductor and the d-c voltage begins to climb.

The use of a swinging choke improves the dynamic voltage regulation under sudden load current swings. At heavy load currents the inductance is small and load current surges can be supplied directly from the diode and transformer. If L were constant at or above the critical value, its current could not readily change; a surge could be immediately supplied only by the output capacitor and the voltage would fall during the surge.

5–9. The π filter

Frequently a capacitor is placed across the input terminals of the LC filter to form the π filter of Fig. 5–20. Analysis of the circuit performance follows by the methods of Sec. 5–5 although with some difficulty, owing to the lack of knowledge of cut-in and cut-out angles for diode conduction.

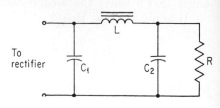

Fig. 5–20. The π filter.

The use of an input capacitor results in a light-load (high R) voltage higher than obtainable from the L-section filter with the same a-c input voltage, since the voltage maintained by capacitor C_1 approaches E_m. At heavy current loads (low R) the average capacitor voltage will fall below E_m; consequently the regulation of a π or capacitor-input circuit may be poor unless a high input capacitance is used.

Capacitor C_1 draws a charging-current pulse twice each cycle and charges to E_m, the peak of the applied voltage, before being disconnected from the source by a diode. The capacitor then discharges through the inductor L and load R until the second diode connects the source on the next half cycle. The discharge current of C_1 is difficult to evaluate, but for an approximate analysis it may be assumed, during the interval in which neither diode is conducting, that the current out of C_1 is constant at value I_{d-c}. Since inductor L will tend to maintain constant current, this is a reasonable assumption, at least for large L and filter designs which will lead to small ripple.

Following the method of Section 5–5, the wave form may be approximated by Fig. 5–21. If the filter is designed for small ripple, then ωRC

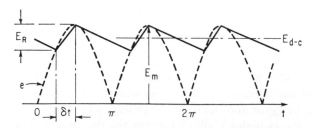

Fig. 5–21. Approximate input wave across C_1, ripple much magnified.

will be large, and δt small. The conduction angle $\delta t = \omega t_2 - \omega t_1$ may be neglected in Eq. 5–32 and therefore the ripple voltage follows as

$$E_R = \frac{\pi I_{\text{d-c}}}{\omega C_1} \tag{5–54}$$

The d-c output voltage will then be given by Eq. 5–31

$$E_{\text{d-c}} = E_m - I_{\text{d-c}}\left(\frac{\pi}{2\omega C_1} + R_c\right) \tag{5–55}$$

where R_c is the choke resistance. It can be seen that the output voltage is thus a function of the first capacitor.

The triangular ripple wave form of Fig. 5–21 has a Fourier series given by

$$e_R = -\frac{E_R}{\pi}\sin 2\omega t + \frac{E_R}{2\pi}\sin 4\omega t - \frac{E_R}{3\pi}\sin 6\omega t \cdots \tag{5–56}$$

where ω still refers to the supply frequency. This ripple voltage is applied across L and C_2 in series in Fig. 5–20, if $1/2\omega C_2 \ll R$ where R is the load and bleeder resistances in parallel. The term of $2f$ frequency is predominant in producing a ripple current through L and C_2. The ripple voltage across C_2, or across R, is

$$E_2 = \frac{E_R}{\pi\sqrt{2}}\left(\frac{1}{4\omega^2 LC_2 - 1}\right)$$

Use of E_R from Eq. 5–54 and $E_{\text{d-c}} = I_{\text{d-c}}R$ allows the ripple to be determined as

$$\gamma = \frac{E_2}{E_{\text{d-c}}} = \frac{1}{\sqrt{2}\omega RC_1(4\omega^2 LC_2 - 1)} \tag{5–57}$$

For the LC filter the ripple was independent of load R, but for the capacitor-input π filter the ripple is inversely proportional to R or increases with load current. The ripple is a function of both C_1 and C_2, and the output voltage is a function of C_1.

The input capacitor provides a means of obtaining a higher voltage from a given transformer than is possible in the LC or L-section filter, and materially reduces the ripple. The penalty is in high peak currents in the diodes, since the conduction time must be very short for small ripple. In vacuum diode service this is undesirable, since the ratio of rated peak to average currents in vacuum diodes is relatively small. When semiconductor diodes are employed this ratio can be considerably larger, and the circuit then becomes economical.

5–10. The resistive filter

Because of cost and space requirements, the inductor of the LC filter is occasionally replaced with a resistor, as in Fig. 5–22. This increases the internal voltage drop and is usually suited to small current drain, as in cathode-ray oscillograph or television power supplies. The methods of the previous sections allow analysis of performance when used with a full-wave rectifier. As has been pointed out, the second-harmonic voltage is the major source of ripple and at the input to the filter has the rms value

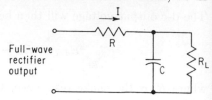

Fig. 5–22. The RC filter.

$$E_2 = \frac{4E_m}{3\sqrt{2}\,\pi}$$

while the d-c value is $E_{\text{d-c}} = 2E_m/\pi$. As is usual, $1/2\omega C \ll R$, and the current

$$I \cong \frac{4E_m}{3\sqrt{2}\,\pi R}$$

produces a ripple voltage across the capacitor of

$$E_c = \frac{\sqrt{2}\,E_m}{3\pi\omega RC} \tag{5–58}$$

so that by definition the ripple is

$$\gamma = \frac{0.236}{\omega RC} \tag{5–59}$$

Large values of C will provide low ripple values.

5–11. The bridge rectifier

The circuit of Fig. 5–23 is called a *bridge rectifier* for obvious reasons. Its use with vacuum diodes called for a multiplicity of cathode heater supplies, and the circuit was not often employed for low voltages. However, the availability of semi-conductor diodes which require no heater power is increasing the importance of the circuit. Its perform-

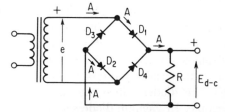

Fig. 5–23. The bridge rectifier.

ance is that of a full-wave rectifier, but without the requirement for a center connection on the a-c supply transformer.

In the half cycle in which the transformer potential e has the polarity indicated, current flows through diodes D_1 and D_2 as indicated by the arrows marked A. Diodes D_3 and D_4 are then reverse-biased and non-conducting. In the next half cycle, D_3 and D_4 carry current in their forward directions, causing another pulse of current in the load in the same direction as the pulse from the first half cycle. Two diodes then conduct simultaneously and in series

The same d-c voltage can be obtained from a transformer in a bridge circuit as from another transformer having twice the secondary turns in a full-wave circuit. Since current flows continuously in the secondary for the bridge circuit, and only half the time in each winding for the center-tapped transformer, the current rating for a transformer when used in a bridge circuit is about two-thirds that for the same transformer in the center-tap connection.

Observation of the bridge circuit will show that the peak inverse voltage across either of the nonconducting diodes is equal to the peak of the transformer voltage. If this circuit is contrasted with the ordinary center-tapped full-wave circuit, it can be seen that approximately twice as large a d-c voltage can be obtained with the bridge rectifier, using a diode of given P.I.V. rating.

5–12. Voltage-multiplying rectifiers

As for the bridge rectifier, the flexibility of semiconductor diodes is making the circuits of Fig. 5–24 attractive. In the voltage-doubler of Fig. 5–24(a), with the upper a-c terminal assumed positive, diode D_1 passes current and charges capacitor C_1 to the peak of the a-c voltage. During the next half cycle the a-c polarity reverses, and diode D_2 conducts and charges capacitor C_2 to the peak of that half cycle. Capacitors C_1 and C_2 are effectively in series for the output circuit and produce an output voltage which, at no load, approximates the sum of the positive and negative peaks of the applied a-c voltage, or twice the peak value of a symmetrical a-c wave form.

The diodes conduct high peak currents for very short time intervals, and capacitors C_1 and C_2 must be of large capacitance in order to supply the output energy during the nonconduction periods of the diodes. For high values of ωRC (large C, or high voltage and large R) the circuit provides both good regulation and low ripple. Conventional filters can follow if the ripple of the rectifier is not sufficiently small.

Other circuits of similar nature are occasionally used for tripling and quadrupling the input voltage, as shown in Fig. 5–24.

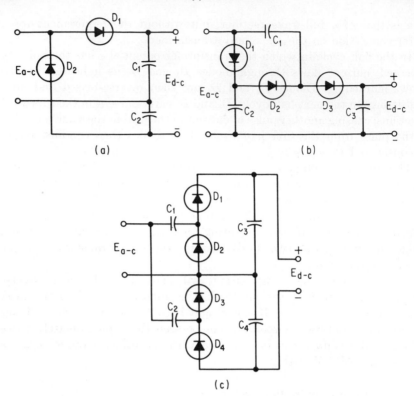

Fig. 5–24. Voltage-multiplying rectifiers: (a) doubler; (b) tripler; (c) quadrupler.

5–13. Diode ratings

Certain limits of diode operation are important in choosing rectifier circuits and the particular diode types to operate in them.

Voltage ratings are usually given in terms of maximum peak inverse voltage for vacuum diodes, or maximum reverse voltage for semiconductor diodes. The vacuum diode rating is fixed by the breakdown limits of the tube insulation. The rating for the semiconductor is fixed by the allowable reverse leakage current.

The maximum or peak current in a forward direction is also an important rating. It is related to the maximum possible emission in the hot-cathode type of rectifier, and in the semiconductor diode it is fixed by the maximum allowable instantaneous heat loss in the semiconductor. The average current output is also a limit, and is determined by the allowable heat loss.

Vacuum diodes are limited in the ratio of peak to average current by the available electron emission. Semiconductor diodes permit very much higher ratios of peak to average current, but will not tolerate excessive voltages because of the limit imposed by avalanche breakdown.

Rectifier circuits employing input filter chokes have been utilized in the past to protect the vacuum diodes from excessive current peaks, with a concurrent reduction in d-c output voltage obtainable from a given transformer. Shunt-capacitor filters have been avoided because of possible rectifier damage or shortened life. Figures 5–10(b) and 5–13 show, however, that excellent voltage regulation, high output voltage, and low ripple may be obtained from shunt-capacitor circuits, or from voltage multipliers, if ωRC values are made larger than 100.

The availability of moderately priced silicon diodes, in which peak to average current ratios as high as fifteen are common, and the utilization of large electrolytic capacitors in series for high voltages, has changed the design concept. The input filter choke, with its cost, weight, space requirements, and effect in lowering the output voltage, can be eliminated and large ωRC values used in shunt-capacitor filters. Without the input choke, and with filter input voltage always approximating E_m, there is no need for bleeder resistors of low value with their accompanying heat loss.

Shunt-capacitor filters have excellent dynamic characteristics for use with varying loads, such as are encountered when supplying certain types of amplifiers, and load swings of ten to one will not adversely affect the voltage regulation, as indicated by (b), Fig. 5–10. As has been pointed out, choke-input filters cannot quickly respond to sudden load demands, and oscillations in load voltage may result.

Silicon diodes may be placed in series to handle larger reverse voltages. When so connected each diode should be shunted with a resistor of 100,000 ohm order, to equalize the diode reverse voltages, which would otherwise divide in proportion to the diode reverse resistance values. These values may differ considerably. Similarly, electrolytic filter capacitors in series should also be individually resistance shunted, since their d-c resistances may vary and cause unequal distribution of the applied d-c voltage. These resistors may then serve to discharge the filter capacitors for safety when the circuit is turned off.

Power dissipation ratings are also important, although if other ratings are followed then the power limit is not likely to be exceeded in rectifier service with sine-wave input, because of the interrelations between the various currents.

Operating temperatures are important for semiconductor diodes, germanium usually being limited to a range of $-50°$ to $+90°$C, silicon to a range of $-75°$ to $+200°$C. The results of operating at excessive

temperature have already been explained in terms of increased i_o
leakage. Since the actual operating
temperature of the junction is the
critical point, high ambient temperatures can require that the electrical load on the diode be reduced
to keep the junction temperature
within limits. A typical derating
curve is shown in Fig. 5–25. Heat
sinks or mechanical cooling may be
required in some applications.

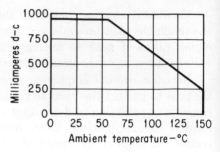

Fig. 5–25. Derating curve for a small silicon diode.

5–14. Circuit design

Rectifier circuits have been analyzed in some detail here, in order to provide an understanding of the functions of diodes as switches in rectifier circuits. Circuits employing semiconductor diodes of germanium or silicon will perform in a manner closely approaching theoretical, and the relations derived are suitable for design purposes.

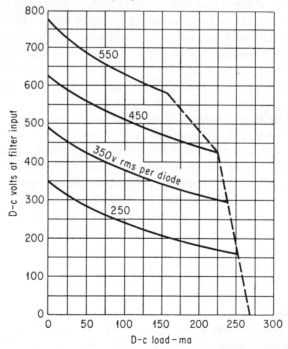

Fig. 5–26. Output of 5U4G tube in full-wave circuit, capacitor input filter, $C_1 = 10 \ \mu\text{f}$.

Actual design of rectifiers utilizing vacuum diodes is frequently carried out by use of *operation characteristics*, as shown in Figs. 5–26 and 5–27, in order to include the effect of the diode resistance. The curves are plots of the performance of particular vacuum diode types, in terms of d-c voltage available from the indicated filter types. The curves of Fig. 5–26 for a capacitor-input filter with $C_1 = 10 \ \mu f$ show the effects previously discussed, namely the rise to E_m at low current and the rather poor voltage

regulation with an input capacitor. Using values selected from the chart it is possible to subtract the voltage drop in the choke and transformer, and arrive at probable values of d-c output voltage. The problem may be reversed to determine the a-c transformer voltage required for a given d-c output.

Figure 5–27 is of similar nature for a choke-input filter. The improved voltage regulation is apparent, as well as the tendency for the circuit to become a capacitor-input type at light currents, where the effect of L disappears.

It should be noted that specific charts should be employed for each diode type employed.

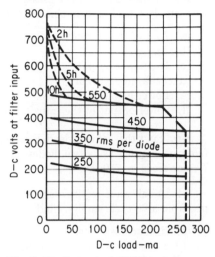

Fig. 5–27. Output of 5U4G in full-wave circuit, inductor input, $C = 16 \ \mu f$.

Problems

5-1. A resistor of 300 ohms has applied to it a voltage having $e = 50 + 1000t$ v for the period $t = 0$ to $t = 0.1$ sec, and $e = -50 - 1000 \ (t - 0.1)$ from $t = 0.1$ to $t = 0.2$ sec, after which the cycle repeats. Find the d-c current through the resistor and the heat loss therein.

5-2. A diode carries a current wave given by $i = 60t$ amp. The wave starts at $t = 0$ and falls abruptly to zero at $t = 1/60$ sec, after which it repeats. Find the d-c voltage across a 50-ohm load, the power loss in the load, and the ripple factor.

5-3. A diode is rated $I_m = 675$ ma, average $I = 350$ ma. Two of these units are used in a full-wave circuit with a transformer supplying 210 v rms on each side of the center tap. Neglect diode resistance.

(a) What value of load resistance must be present to give the greatest d-c power output without exceeding any diode rating?

(b) Specify the d-c load voltage and current for (a).

5-4. A half-wave rectifier uses an applied voltage of 250 rms and 60 cycles, and the load is 1750 ohms. Find:

(a) I_{d-c}.
(b) E_{d-c}.
(c) I_{rms} in load.
(d) Power loss in the diode.

5-5. A full-wave rectifier uses a 5U4G tube with identical diodes. The rectifier is to supply a load of 3000 ohms at 3000 v, direct current. Find:

(a) E_{rms} of the transformer required.
(b) I_{d-c}.
(c) D-c power output.
(d) Peak tube current.
(e) Power lost in 5U4G tube.
(f) Power output of the transformer.

5-6. Find the value of load R required for maximum d-c power output from a full-wave rectifier using two diodes rated at P.I.V. = 400 v, I_m per diode = 5 amp, I_{av} per diode = 750 ma.

5-7. A full-wave rectifier is to supply a resistive load with d-c at 350 v and 100 ma, from a 60-cycle supply. Find:

(a) E_{rms} across the load.
(b) Transformer secondary voltages, assuming semiconductor diodes.

5-8. Starting with Eq. 5-20, develop Eq. 5-23 for the current through a half-wave diode.

5-9. Using the method which led to Eq. 5-34, develop a similar expression for the ripple in the output of a half-wave circuit with shunt-capacitor filter.

5-10. Using a good linear approximation to the volt-ampere curve of the selenium rectifier of Fig. 3-33, determine the a-c transformer voltage required to supply two selenium disks in series as a half-wave rectifier to charge a 6-v battery of resistance 0.1 ohm at an average charging rate of 3 amp.

5-11. A 60-cycle transformer having 400 rms v each side of the center tap supplies a full-wave rectifier. The rectifier load is 1000 ohms, with a shunt capacitor of 60 μf. Find:

(a) The d-c voltage across the load.
(b) The peak current demand on a diode.
(c) The ripple factor.

5-12. Prove that the rms value of the triangle ripple voltage of Fig. 5-12 is given by $E_R/2\sqrt{3}$.

5-13. One diode of Problem 5-11 becomes faulty and open-circuits. Recompute the rectifier performance as above.

5-14. A 5-henry choke and a 10-μf capacitor are available. With a full-wave rectifier supplying a load taking 0.2 amp at 300 v, calculate the per cent ripple to be expected when these elements are used in shunt-capacitor, series inductor, and L-section filters.

5-15. A full-wave rectifier uses two 30-μf capacitors and a 10-henry choke in a π filter. With the load taking 200 ma at 300 v, determine E_{a-c} and the ripple.

5-16. A shunt-capacitor filter supplies a resistance load from a half-wave rectifier. The following readings are taken in the load: $E_{d-c} = 425$ v, $I_{d-c} = 227$ ma, $I_{rms} = 275$ ma. Find the value of ripple and the size of capacitor being used.

5-17. Plot a diode current wave form for the shunt-capacitor circuit and full-wave rectification with $\omega RC = 10$, $E_m = 270$ v, and $I_{d-c} = 300$ ma.

5-18. Design an L-section filter for a 60-cycle full-wave rectifier with a 3000-ohm load, if $E_{d-c} = 300$ v and the ripple is to be 0.005. Use the critical size of inductor for the choke.

5-19. A full-wave rectifier uses a π-section filter with $C_1 = C_2 = 20$ μf, $L = 20$ henrys. The transformer supplies 250 v each side of center at 60 cycles, and the load is 3000 ohms. Find the ripple factor and the d-c output voltage.

5-20. For Problem 5-19 the design is changed to call for 100-μf capacitors. Redetermine the ripple and E_{d-c}.

5-21. A full-wave rectifier uses the 5U4G tube of Figs. 5-26 and 5-27. For a load requiring 300 v and 175 ma, find the a-c transformer secondary voltages for a capacitor input filter with $C_1 = 10$ μf, and for an inductor input filter with output $C = 16$ μf. Choke inductance and resistance is 10 henrys and 250 ohms in each case.

5-22. The silicon diode of Fig. 5-1 is used to charge a 12-v battery from a 36-v rms source in a half-wave circuit. If the average charging rate is to be 50 amp, find the value of series resistance needed, assuming the battery resistance is 0.07 ohm.

5-23. In a full-wave circuit, supplying a resistance load with an L-section filter, the applied rms voltage per side of the transformer is 300, $f = 60$ cycles, $L = 10$ henrys, $C = 4$ μf. Find the value of E_{d-c}, the value of ripple, and the maximum value which R may have without allowing the d-c voltage to rise excessively.

5-24. Utilizing the methods of the shunt-capacitor filter analysis, find an expression for the ripple of the voltage-doubling rectifier of Fig. 5-24 (a), in terms of ωRC, assuming $C_1 = C_2$.

References

1. Dellenbaugh, F. S., Jr., and Quimby, R. S., "The Important First Choke in High-Voltage Rectifier Circuits," *QST*, **16,** 14 (February 1932); **16,** 27 (March 1932); **16,** 33 (April 1932).

2. Henkels, H. W., "Germanium and Silicon Rectifiers," *Proc. I.R.E.*, **46,** 1086 (1958).

3. Schade, O. H., "Analysis of Rectifier Operation," *Proc. I.R.E.*, **31,** 341 (1943).

4. Waidelich, D. L., "Analysis of Full Wave Rectifier and Capacitive Input Filter" *Electronics*, **20,** 120 (September 1947).

5. ———, "The Full-Wave Voltage-Doubling Rectifier Circuit," *Proc. IRE*, **29,** 554 (1941).

6. ———, "Diode Rectifying Circuits with Capacitance Filters," *Trans. A.I.E.E.*, **60,** 1161 (1941).

Four-terminal Active Networks | 6

Most network theory applies to linear, bilateral electrical networks, and it can be shown over limited operating ranges that the transistor and triode vacuum tube may be assumed linear. Since any linear electrical network, whether active or passive, can be represented as a four-terminal (two-port) network, and since four-terminal networks have been extensively studied, it is helpful to borrow such studies, and to apply the results in the study of the transistor and triode wherever applicable.

The student with sufficient network theory behind him need not include this chapter in his studies.

6–1. Four-terminal networks

A general four-terminal network with defined positive currents and voltages appears in Fig. 6–1. Currents are defined as positive inward in both cases so that specification of input or output does not alter an analysis.

It is the terminal quantities v_1, i_1, v_2, i_2 by which the network drives or reacts to external circuits, and specification of these quantities is equivalent to specification of performance of the internal network arrangement. For this reason it is possible to study four-terminal networks as a class, without regard to the exact internal circuitry. It can be reasoned that such a study, dependent on terminal quantities, applies whether a network be active or passive. It is also possible to develop the network relations in a general manner, so as to apply to circuits or devices that do not have linear volt-ampere curves, although near or quasi-linearity will be assumed in the range over which the device is operated. Linearity is illustrated in Fig. 6–2(a), and quasi-linearity or a condition of constant slope over the region from A to B, in Fig. 6–2(b).

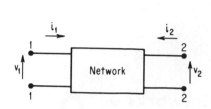

Fig. 6–1. Four-terminal network.

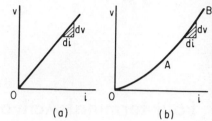

Fig. 6–2. (a) volt-ampere curve for a linear device; (b) same for a non-linear device.

Greatest generality will be given to the analysis if a condition of quasi-linearity be specified, with operation restricted to a portion of the volt-ampere curve which is of constant slope. Thus the linear device is also included by definition.

As has been stated, network behavior is specified by v_i, i_1, v_2 and i_2 as external quantities. Any pair of these may be arbitrarily chosen as independent variables, leading to two equations which may then be solved for the other two dependent variables. Choice of three of the twelve possible independent variable pairs as i_1 and i_2, v_1 and v_2, and v_2 and i_1, leads to three sets of circuit parameter definitions which have been found useful in electronic circuit work.

6–2. Open-circuit impedance parameters

Making the choice of i_1 and i_2 as the independent variables implies the following general functional relations for the network of Fig. 6–1:

$$v_1 = f(i_1, i_2)$$

$$v_2 = f(i_1, i_2)$$

The circuits of interest are to be operated with changing or a-c currents, and the effect of varying voltages or currents is to move along the slope of the volt-ampere curve. These changes may be mathematically specified by taking the total differentials as

$$dv_1 = \frac{\partial v_1}{\partial i_1} di_1 + \frac{\partial v_1}{\partial i_2} di_2 \qquad (6-1)$$

$$dv_2 = \frac{\partial v_2}{\partial i_1} di_1 + \frac{\partial v_2}{\partial i_2} di_2 \qquad (6-2)$$

If a-c voltages are employed, and operation is over only the quasi-linear region of the appropriate volt-ampere characteristics, then *the partial derivatives become constants with dimensions of impedance.* For sufficiently small a-c signals the above equations may be written as

$$V_1 = z_i I_1 + z_r I_2 \tag{6–3}$$

$$V_2 = z_f I_1 + z_o I_2 \tag{6–4}$$

which in matrix form become

$$\begin{bmatrix} V_1 \\ V_2 \end{bmatrix} = \begin{bmatrix} z_i & z_r \\ z_f & z_o \end{bmatrix} \begin{bmatrix} I_1 \\ I_2 \end{bmatrix} \tag{6–3}$$

$$\tag{6–4}$$

An advantage of the use of matrix notation is here demonstrated, in that it separates and identifies the independent variables I_1 and I_2, the circuit function, and the dependent variables V_1 and V_2 on the left side.

The z impedances may also be written

$$z_i = z_{11} \qquad z_f = z_{21}$$

$$z_r = z_{12} \qquad z_o = z_{22}$$

but the letter subscripts seem preferred in electronic work and will be used here.

While the z parameters have been defined only as partial derivatives, or as the slopes of the volt-ampere relations, they may be further correlated with actual measurements made on the network with assigned open-circuit terminations. If the network is open-circuited at the 2,2 terminals, then $I_2 = 0$, and Eq. 6–3 leads to $z_i = V_1/I_1$. By use of the same termination in Eq. 6–4, $z_f = V_2/I_1$. If the network is open-circuited at the 1,1 terminals, then $I_1 = 0$, and the equations yield $z_r = V_1/I_2$, and $z_o = V_2/I_2$. These ratios can be measured on the network, using a-c signals small enough that operation does not pass outside the assumed linear region.

The z impedances have become known as the *open-circuit impedance parameters* for the four-terminal network, and their definitions may be collected as:

$$z_i = z_{11} = \frac{\partial v_1}{\partial i_1} = \frac{V_1}{I_1} = \text{open-circuit input impedance, } I_2 = 0$$

$$z_r = z_{12} = \frac{\partial v_1}{\partial i_2} = \frac{V_1}{I_2} = \text{open-circuit reverse transfer impedance, } I_1 = 0$$

$$z_f = z_{21} = \frac{\partial v_2}{\partial i_1} = \frac{V_2}{I_1} = \text{open-circuit forward transfer impedance, } I_2 = 0$$

$$z_o = z_{22} = \frac{\partial v_2}{\partial i_2} = \frac{V_2}{I_2} = \text{open-circuit output impedance, } I_1 = 0$$

$$\tag{6–5}$$

Measurements of this nature could be made upon any linear, or quasi-linear network, whether active or passive, and these definitions and others like them are extremely fundamental.

6–3. Short-circuit admittance parameters

If a choice of v_1 and v_2 as the independent variables of the four-terminal network be made, then the general functional relations become

$$i_1 = f(v_1, v_2)$$

$$i_2 = f(v_1, v_2)$$

and upon taking the total differentials as before:

$$di_1 = \frac{\partial i_1}{\partial v_1} dv_1 + \frac{\partial i_1}{\partial v_2} dv_2 \tag{6-6}$$

$$di_2 = \frac{\partial i_2}{\partial v_1} dv_1 + \frac{\partial i_2}{\partial v_2} dv_2 \tag{6-7}$$

If a-c currents are employed and operation is over a range in which the slopes of the volt-ampere curves or the partial derivatives are constant, then

$$I_1 = y_i V_1 + y_r V_2 \tag{6-8}$$

$$I_2 = y_f V_1 + y_o V_2 \tag{6-9}$$

or

$$\begin{bmatrix} I_1 \\ I_2 \end{bmatrix} = \begin{bmatrix} y_i & y_r \\ y_f & y_o \end{bmatrix} \begin{bmatrix} V_1 \\ V_2 \end{bmatrix} \qquad \begin{matrix}(6-8)\\ \\(6-9)\end{matrix}$$

The **y** parameters may be defined from measurements on the four-terminal network, or from the above equations, by using short-circuit terminations. If the 2,2 terminals be short-circuited, then $V_2 = 0$, and Eq. 6-8 yields $y_i = I_1/V_1$, while Eq. 6-9 gives $y_f = I_2/V_1$. If the 1,1 terminals be short-circuited, appropriate measurements may be made, or since $V_1 = 0$ then Eqs. 6-8 and 6-9 give $y_r = I_1/V_2$ and $y_o = I_2/V_2$.

These admittances have become known as the *short-circuit admittance parameters* for the four-terminal network, and their definitions can be summarized as:

$$\mathbf{y}_i = \mathbf{y}_{11} = \frac{\partial i_1}{\partial v_1} = \frac{\mathbf{I}_1}{\mathbf{V}_1} = \text{short-circuit input admittance, } \mathbf{V}_2 = 0$$

$$\mathbf{y}_r = \mathbf{y}_{12} = \frac{\partial i_1}{\partial v_2} = \frac{\mathbf{I}_1}{\mathbf{V}_2} = \text{short-circuit reverse transfer admittance,}$$
$$\mathbf{V}_1 = 0$$

$$\mathbf{y}_f = \mathbf{y}_{21} = \frac{\partial i_2}{\partial v_1} = \frac{\mathbf{I}_2}{\mathbf{V}_1} = \text{short-circuit forward transfer admittance,}$$
$$\mathbf{V}_2 = 0$$

$$\mathbf{y}_o = \mathbf{y}_{22} = \frac{\partial i_2}{\partial v_2} = \frac{\mathbf{I}_2}{\mathbf{V}_2} = \text{short-circuit output admittance, } \mathbf{V}_1 = 0$$

$$(6\text{--}10)$$

6–4. Hybrid parameters

It has been found that the third choice of i_1 and v_2 as independent variables leads to a set of network parameters of considerable value in transistor circuit measurements. If this choice of variables is made,

$$v_1 = f(i_1, v_2)$$

$$i_2 = f(i_1, v_2)$$

Taking the total differentials

$$dv_1 = \frac{\partial v_1}{\partial i_1} di_1 + \frac{\partial v_1}{\partial v_2} dv_2 \qquad (6\text{--}11)$$

$$di_2 = \frac{\partial i_2}{\partial i_1} di_1 + \frac{\partial i_2}{\partial v_2} dv_2 \qquad (6\text{--}12)$$

Again, for small a-c signals limited to the quasi-linear region the partial derivatives become constants and

$$\mathbf{V}_1 = \mathbf{h}_i \mathbf{I}_1 + \mathbf{h}_r \mathbf{V}_2 \qquad (6\text{--}13)$$

$$\mathbf{I}_2 = \mathbf{h}_f \mathbf{I}_1 + \mathbf{h}_o \mathbf{V}_2 \qquad (6\text{--}14)$$

or

$$\begin{bmatrix} \mathbf{V}_1 \\ \mathbf{I}_2 \end{bmatrix} = \begin{bmatrix} \mathbf{h}_i & \mathbf{h}_r \\ \mathbf{h}_f & \mathbf{h}_o \end{bmatrix} \begin{bmatrix} \mathbf{I}_1 \\ \mathbf{V}_2 \end{bmatrix} \qquad \begin{matrix} (6\text{--}13) \\ \\ (6\text{--}14) \end{matrix}$$

The **h** coefficients are known as the *hybrid parameters*, since both open- and short-circuit terminations are used in defining them from the general network. By appropriate choice of open-circuit ($I_1 = 0$) and short-circuit ($V_2 = 0$) conditions as applied to Eqs. 6–13 and 6–14, it is possible to arrive at definitions for the small-signal a-c values of the **h** parameters as

$$\mathbf{h}_i = \mathbf{h}_{11} = \frac{\partial v_1}{\partial i_1} = \frac{\mathbf{V}_1}{\mathbf{I}_1} = \text{short-circuit input impedance, } \mathbf{V}_2 = 0$$

$$\mathbf{h}_r = \mathbf{h}_{12} = \frac{\partial v_1}{\partial v_2} = \frac{\mathbf{V}_1}{\mathbf{V}_2} = \text{open-circuit reverse voltage ratio, } \mathbf{I}_1 = 0$$

$$\mathbf{h}_f = \mathbf{h}_{21} = \frac{\partial i_2}{\partial i_1} = \frac{\mathbf{I}_2}{\mathbf{I}_1} = \text{short-circuit forward current ratio, } \mathbf{V}_2 = 0$$

$$\mathbf{h}_o = \mathbf{h}_{22} = \frac{\partial i_2}{\partial v_2} = \frac{\mathbf{I}_2}{\mathbf{V}_2} = \text{open-circuit output admittance, } \mathbf{I}_1 = 0$$

$$(6\text{–}15)$$

While all these defined parameters have meaning as the slope of an appropriate graphical characteristic, their actual magnitudes are most usually obtained by measurement, using small signals in appropriately terminated circuits. A particular advantage of the hybrid parameters is the accuracy with which they can be measured in circuits of the type encountered with electronic devices.

In particular, the input measurements $\mathbf{h}_i$ and $\mathbf{h}_f$ are made with a short circuit on the output. For the usual high-impedance outputs this is very easily provided, and the accuracy is good since the shunting effects of capacitances and leakage might be severe if open-circuit measurements were attempted. Likewise, output measurements $\mathbf{h}_r$ and $\mathbf{h}_o$ are made with an open circuit on the input, and this gives greater accuracy if low-impedance inputs are encountered, since effective a-c short circuits are difficult to obtain at low impedance levels.

Relations which permit the **z** parameters to be calculated from **h** measurements are often needed, and can be obtained by solution of Eqs. 6–3, 6–4, 6–13, and 6–14, leading to

$$\mathbf{h}_i = \mathbf{z}_i - \frac{\mathbf{z}_r \mathbf{z}_f}{\mathbf{z}_o} \qquad \mathbf{h}_f = -\frac{\mathbf{z}_f}{\mathbf{z}_o}$$

$$\mathbf{h}_r = \frac{\mathbf{z}_r}{\mathbf{z}_o} \qquad\qquad \mathbf{h}_o = \frac{1}{\mathbf{z}_o}$$

$$(6\text{–}16)$$

and the inverse relations

$$z_i = h_i - \frac{h_r h_f}{h_o} \qquad z_f = -\frac{h_f}{h_o}$$

$$z_r = \frac{h_r}{h_o} \qquad z_o = \frac{1}{h_o}$$

(6–17)

6–5. Input, output, transfer impedances of the four-terminal network

As a general circuit parameter, the *driving-point* or *input impedance* at the 1, 1 terminals of the loaded four-terminal network of Fig. 6–3 may be found in terms of the **z** parameters as Z_i. From Eq. 6–3

$$Z_i = \frac{V_1}{I_1} = z_i + z_r \frac{I_2}{I_1}$$

(6–18)

using the upper-case **Z** to indicate an external circuit value.

With a load Z_L on the 2, 2 terminals, $V_2/I_2 = -Z_L$, the negative sign appearing because of the defined direction of I_2. Then from Eq. 6–4

$$\frac{I_2}{I_1} = \frac{-z_f}{z_o + Z_L}$$

(6–19)

and this result will be useful later. Using this loaded current ratio in Eq. 6–18, the input impedance becomes

$$Z_i = z_i - \frac{z_r z_f}{z_o + Z_L}$$

(6–20)

By definition z_i is the open-circuit input impedance. Under load its value is modified by the coupled-in effect of the output circuit and load, with $z_r z_f$ as coupling members.

The *output impedance* looking back into the 2, 2 terminals, can be found as

$$Z_o = \frac{V_2}{I_2} = z_f \frac{I_1}{I_2} + z_o$$

(6–21)

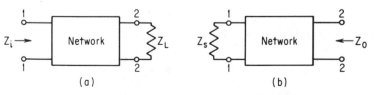

Fig. 6–3. Input and output impedance determination.

With source impedance Z_s across the terminals, $V_1/I_1 = Z_s$. Then from Eq. 6–3,

$$\frac{I_1}{I_2} = \frac{-z_r}{z_i + Z_s} \tag{6–22}$$

Therefore the network output impedance is

$$Z_o = z_o - \frac{z_r z_f}{z_i + Z_s} \tag{6–23}$$

The open-circuit output impedance is z_o by definition. Under conditions of drive by a generator of impedance Z_s, the value of z_o is modified by the coupled-in effect of the input circuit.

The *transfer impedance* Z_T is defined as the ratio of voltage applied in one mesh to the current produced in a second mesh, all other emf's being removed, so that

$$Z_{T12} = \frac{V_1}{I_2} = z_r - \frac{z_i(z_o + Z_L)}{z_f} \tag{6–24}$$

which is also a useful relation.

6–6. Network impedances by matrix manipulation

Use of relations from matrix theory leads to equivalent results for the input and output impedances in a direct manner. For a network with a load Z_L as in Fig. 6–3(a), the circuit matrix is

$$[Z] = \begin{bmatrix} z_i & z_r \\ z_f & z_o + Z_L \end{bmatrix}$$

which has a determinant

$$\Delta = z_i(z_o + Z_L) - z_r z_f$$

The input impedance at the r, r terminals is given by the ratio of Δ to the determinant formed by deleting the rth row and rth column from $[Z]$. Thus

$$Z_{ir} = \frac{\Delta}{\Delta_{r,r}} \tag{6–25}$$

and for the input impedance at the 1, 1 terminals

$$Z_{i1} = \frac{\Delta}{z_o + Z_L} = z_i - \frac{z_r z_f}{z_o + Z_L}$$

as in Eq. 6–20.

For the output impedance the network has a matrix

$$[Z] = \begin{bmatrix} z_i + Z_s & z_r \\ \\ z_f & z_o \end{bmatrix}$$

with a determinant

$$\Delta = z_o(z_i + Z_s) - z_r z_f$$

Using the rule of Eq. 6–25 for the 2, 2 terminals or $r = 2$ gives

$$Z_{o2} = \frac{\Delta}{z_i + Z_s} = z_o - \frac{z_r z_f}{z_i + Z_s}$$

The transfer impedance is

$$Z_{Tmn} = \frac{\Delta}{\Delta_{mn}} (-1)^{m+n} \tag{6–26}$$

where the determinant in the denominator is formed by eliminating the mth row and nth column from the matrix. For Z_{T12} of the circuit of Fig. 6–3(a)

$$Z_{T12} = \frac{\Delta}{\Delta_{12}} = \frac{\Delta(-1)}{z_f} = z_r - \frac{z_i(z_o + Z_L)}{z_f}$$

as in Eq. 6–24.

For the **y** short-circuit parameters the loaded circuit matrix may be written

$$[Y] = \begin{bmatrix} y_i & y_r \\ \\ y_f & y_o + Y_L \end{bmatrix}$$

By the previous rules, the input admittance at the 1, 1 terminals is

$$Y_{i1} = y_i - \frac{y_r y_f}{y_o + Y_L} \tag{6–27}$$

and this will be a useful result.

6–7. Inductively-coupled circuits

An inductively coupled circuit, as at Fig. 6–4(a), is frequently employed as a coupling element between successive amplifier tubes or transistors. The magnetic flux path is assumed predominantly air, or made of magnetic material such as powdered iron with substantially constant permeability.

The mutual inductance present then determines a *coefficient of coupling* k, where

$$k = \frac{M}{\sqrt{L_1 L_2}} \tag{6-28}$$

The leakage flux may be quite large and the value of k small but under control of the designer, who can choose numbers of turns, dimensions, and physical coil location in fixing k.

For convenience in circuit analysis, it is desirable to replace the inductively coupled circuit of Fig. 6–4(a), with a simple T network which is equivalent at the specified frequency or over a specified frequency range. By

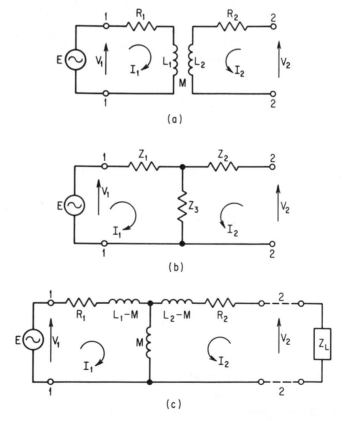

Fig. 6–4. (a) inductive coupling; (b) equivalent T network for (a); (c) constants for (b).

reference to (a) and using the definitions of Section 6–2, it can be found that

$$z_i = R_1 + j\omega L_1$$

$$z_o = R_2 + j\omega L_2$$

$$z_f = z_r = j\omega M$$

Similar application of the z parameter definitions to the T network of Fig. 6–4(b) leads to

$$z_i = z_1 + z_3$$

$$z_o = z_2 + z_3$$

$$z_f = z_r = z_3$$

It should here be noted that the relation $z_f = z_r$ holds in general only for linear, passive networks.

If the T network of Fig. 6–4(b) is to be equivalent to the inductively-coupled circuit of Fig. 6–4(a), then these measured parameters must be equal to force external voltage and current equality. It follows that

$$z_1 = z_i - z_r = R_1 + j\omega(L_1 - M) \tag{6–29}$$

$$z_2 = z_o - z_r = R_2 + j\omega(L_2 - M) \tag{6–30}$$

$$z_3 = z_f = z_r = j\omega M \tag{6–31}$$

These quantities may be used to replace the elements of the T network, resulting in the circuit in Fig. 6–4(c). This circuit is then equivalent to the inductively-coupled circuit of Fig. 6–4(a).

6–8. Equivalent circuits for active networks

A T or π network may be developed as equivalent to any linear, bilateral, passive network. However, it is possible to extend the equivalent circuit method to active circuits, such as those employing transistors or vacuum tubes, in which $z_r \neq z_f$, but where neither z_r or z_f are zero. If either of the reverse or forward transfer parameters is zero, then the network is unilateral. Networks having the transfer parameters equal are composed of passive elements only.

Again choosing I_1 and I_2 as the independent variables, along with the z open-circuit parameters, the general four-terminal relations are

$$\begin{bmatrix} V_1 \\ V_2 \end{bmatrix} = \begin{bmatrix} z_i & z_r \\ z_f & z_o \end{bmatrix} \begin{bmatrix} I_1 \\ I_2 \end{bmatrix} \tag{6–32}$$
$$\tag{6–33}$$

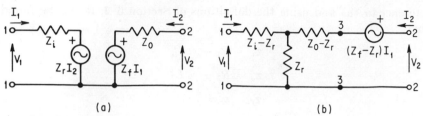

Fig. 6–5. Four-terminal active equivalent network: (a) two-generator form; (b) one-generator form.

This pair of equations is represented by the equivalent circuit of Fig. 6–5(a), as can be shown by comparing the circuit equations with the diagram. The circuit is complicated by the presence of two transfer generators, and a more convenient one-generator form may be obtained by algebraic manipulation of the equations.

Addition and subtraction of $z_r I_1$ to Eq. 6–33 allows the equations to be written as

$$\begin{bmatrix} V_1 \\ V_2 - (z_f - z_r)I_1 \end{bmatrix} = \begin{bmatrix} z_i & z_r \\ z_r & z_o \end{bmatrix} \begin{bmatrix} I_1 \\ I_2 \end{bmatrix} \qquad \begin{matrix} (6\text{–}34) \\ (6\text{–}35) \end{matrix}$$

and these equations, still mathematically equivalent to Eqs. 6–32 and 6–33, can be represented by the circuit of Fig. 6–5(b). It can be noted that the circuit matrix is that of a passive T circuit which appears between the 1, 1 and 3, 3 terminals. The addition of the generator $(z_f - z_r)I_1$ in the output circuit provides the active circuit element. This equivalent will be found useful in transistor circuit analysis.

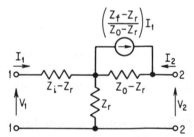

Fig. 6–6. Current-source four terminal network equivalent.

A modified circuit form appears in Fig. 6–6, where the transfer generator has been transformed to a current-source. This source, bridged across $z_o - z_r$, must supply a current of

$$\frac{z_f - z_r}{z_o - z_r} I_1$$

and thus with output open the generator introduces into the circuit a potential of

$$\mathbf{E} = (z_f - z_r)I_1$$

as did the voltage-source generator of Fig. 6–5(b).

Equivalent circuits for the **y** parameters may also be found. Taking the equations

$$\begin{bmatrix} I_1 \\ I_2 \end{bmatrix} = \begin{bmatrix} y_i & y_r \\ y_f & y_o \end{bmatrix} \begin{bmatrix} V_1 \\ V_2 \end{bmatrix}$$

the two-generator circuit of Fig. 6–7(a) can be drawn. By adding and subtracting $y_r V_1$ in the second equation it is possible to write

$$\begin{bmatrix} I_1 \\ I_2 - (y_f - y_r)V_1 \end{bmatrix} = \begin{bmatrix} y_i & y_r \\ y_r & y_o \end{bmatrix} \begin{bmatrix} V_1 \\ V_2 \end{bmatrix} \qquad (6\text{–}36)$$
$$\qquad (6\text{–}37)$$

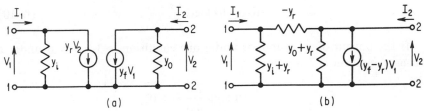

Fig. 6–7. Equivalent circuits using y parameters.

and these equations are represented by the circuit of Fig. 6–7(b). Again a passive network appears represented by a symmetric impedance matrix, to which is added an active element, the transfer generator.

The hybrid Eqs. 6–13 and 6–14 lead to an equivalent circuit as shown in Fig. 6–8.

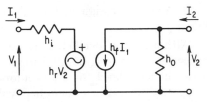

Fig. 6–8. The hybrid parameter equivalent circuit.

6–9. The decibel and VU

The measurement of the output of many active circuits or amplifiers is made by use of a unit of *power ratio* known as the *decibel*. The gain of a cascaded amplifier can be found from the individual stage gains as

$$A = A_1 \times A_2 \times A_3 \times \cdots \qquad (6\text{–}38)$$

However, if the gains were expressed as powers of 10, then

$$A = 10^a \times 10^b \times 10^c \times \cdots$$
$$= 10^{a+b+c+\cdots}$$

or

$$\log_{10} A = a + b + c + \cdots$$

Use of a logarithmic unit allows gains or losses to be directly added or subtracted. The telephone industry proposed a logarithmic unit, named the *bel* for Alexander Graham Bell. The bel is defined as the logarithm of a power ratio, or

$$\text{number of bels} = \log_{10} \frac{P_2}{P_1} \tag{6–39}$$

It has been found that a unit one tenth as large is more convenient, since such a unit approximates the power change required to produce a just detectable change in the intensity of a sound. This smaller unit is called the *decibel*, abbreviated db, defined as

$$\text{db} = 10 \log_{10} \frac{P_2}{P_1} \tag{6–40}$$

If the output of an amplifier under one condition is 3.5 w and under a second condition is 7 w, then

$$\text{db} = 10 \log_{10} \frac{7.0}{3.5} = 3.01$$

A change of power of 2 to 1 has resulted in a change of 3.01 db in power level. A negative sign in the result would indicate that a power loss has taken place.

Although the decibel is a power ratio and not an absolute power measurement, it can be used for absolute measurements if a certain reference, or zero, level for P_1 is adopted beforehand and known or stated. A variety of various reference values have been used; one which has become common is 0.001 w. Consequently, the amplifier above with 7 w output is

$$10 \log_{10} \frac{7}{0.001} = 38.45 \text{ db}$$

above zero level. The amplifier under the 3.5 w output condition would then have an output level of 35.44 db above zero level, and this would be stated as +35.44 db above 0.001 w reference.

Even though the usage is technically improper, it has become conventional to state amplifier gain in decibels. That is

$$\text{db gain} = 10 \log_{10} \frac{|E_2|^2}{|E_1|^2} = 20 \log_{10} \frac{|E_2|}{|E_1|} = 20 \log_{10} \frac{|I_2|}{|I_1|} \tag{6–41}$$

where E_2 and E_1 are output and input voltages, and are not power as is required by the decibel definition.

In the broadcast field when 1 mw is employed as the zero reference, and a special instrument of prescribed dynamic response is used, it is common practice to state absolute power in terms of *volume units*, or VU, where 10 db above 0.001 w equals 10 VU. In other words,

$$VU = 10 \log_{10} \frac{P}{0.001} \tag{6–42}$$

where P is the amount of power measured. The term VU applies only when the monitoring is done with a meter of standardized damping.

Since the output of many amplifiers is ultimately converted to sound and received by the human ear, it is important to have a power unit consistent with properties of the ear, and the decibel is such a unit. Experiment shows that the ear hears sound intensities on a proportional, or logarithmic scale, and not on a linear one. Therefore the use of the decibel unit is justified on a psychological as well as convenience basis.

Problems

6-1. Calculate the **z** parameters for the circuit of (a), Fig. 6–9.

6-2. Determine the **h** parameters for the circuit of (a), Fig. 6–9.

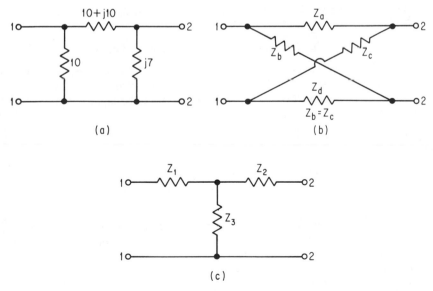

(a)   (b)

(c)

Fig. 6–9.

6-3. Calculate the **y** and **h** parameters for the circuit of (b), Fig. 6–9.

6-4. If the T network of (c), Fig. 6–9, is to be equivalent to the π network of (a), compute the values of the T elements.

6-5. Write the general circuit equations for (b), Fig. 6–9, using V_1 and V_2 as the independent variables.

6-6. If V_2 and I_2 are selected as independent variables for a four-terminal network, write the definitions of the appropriate circuit parameters which may be designated b, with appropriate subscripts.

6-7. Find expressions for z_1, z_2, and z_3 which will make the T network of (c) equivalent to that of (b), Fig. 6–9.

6-8. Derive and draw a one-generator active equivalent circuit for a four-terminal active network, using the **h** parameters.

6-9. Derive and draw a one-generator active equivalent circuit for a four-terminal active network using I_1 and V_2 as independent variables.

6-10. A microphone of 400 ohms impedance has an output at -56 db below a 1-mw reference. The microphone supplies an amplifier which is to have an output level of $+37$ db into a 100-ohm load.
(a) What is the output voltage of the microphone?
(b) Find the amplifier gain in decibels.
(c) Compute the amplifier power output, load current, and voltage.
(d) The output power is to be reduced to 60 per cent of original value. What will be the reduction in db output?

6-11. Determine the input, output, and transfer impedances for the circuit of Fig. 6–9 (a).

6-12. Derive the transfer admittance for the circuit of Fig. 6–9 (b).

6-13. A transistor having $h_i = 28$ ohms, $h_r = 8 \times 10^{-4}$, $h_f = 0.98$, and $h_o = 0.6$ μmhos, is used in a circuit equivalent to Fig. 6–8. If the load across which V_2 is measured is 10,000 ohms, find the output voltage V_2 if the input current is 0.015 amp.

6-14. The loss on a radio-frequency transmission line is 2.3 db per 100 ft. How long can the line be and still have a power efficiency of 85 per cent?

6-15. A generator with power output of 5 mw supplies an amplifier which feeds a 500-ohm load. If the load power level is to be $+16$ VU, what must be the db gain in the amplifier?

6-16. A radio receiver has an input impedance which is 300 ohms resistive. The antenna signal applied to this input is 50 μv. The electrical output to the loudspeaker is to be 1.8 w. Find:
(a) The input db level, 1-mw reference.
(b) Receiver db gain.
(c) Output power level, 1-mw reference.

References

1. Brown, J. S., and Bennett, F. D., "The Application of Matrices to Vacuum-Tube Circuits," *Proc. I.R.E.*, **36,** 844 (1948).

2. Giacoletto, L. J., "Terminology and Equations for Linear Active Four-Terminal Networks Including Transistors," *RCA Rev.*, **14** (1953).

3. Guillemin, E. A., *Communication Networks*, Vol. 2. John Wiley and Sons, Inc., New York, 1935.

4. LeCorbeiller, P., *Matrix Analysis of Electric Networks*, John Wiley and Sons, Inc., New York, 1950.

5. Peterson, L. C., "Equivalent Circuits of Linear Four-Terminal Networks," *Bell Syst. Tech. J.*, **27,** 593 (1948).

6. Ryder, J. D., *Networks, Lines, and Fields*, 2nd ed. Prentice-Hall, Inc., Englewood Cliffs, N. J., 1955.

7. Shekel, J., "Matrix Representation of Transistor Circuits," *Proc. I.R.E.*, **40,** 1493 (1952).

Control Devices: The Transistor 7

In 1948 Bardeen and Brattain discovered that if a second electrode, with reverse bias, is mounted very close to the usual contact on a point-contact germanium diode, then the current through the normal diode contact in forward bias could control the current to the reverse-biased electrode. This discovery, christened the *transistor*, as a contraction of the name transfer resistor, has now led to a whole family of solid-state or semiconductor devices, having control or amplifying properties.

The transistor raised a host of problems in the metallurgy of previously little-known elements, and new methods of purification of the elements, growth of single crystals, and of soldering and welding of contacts, have been developed. Characteristically a low-impedance, current-operated device, the internal and contact resistances have had to be kept small. Capable of operation in extremely small size, and necessarily so if high frequencies are to be reached, the dissipation of internal heat losses is another serious problem. This factor is compounded by the fact that both of the usual transistor materials, germanium and silicon, become intrinsic conductors at relatively low temperatures, so that circuit design and mounting must be developed to keep internal temperature rise low. Many of these problems have been solved, but they are mentioned here to point out that the development and application of transistors is not a simple art.

7–1. The junction transistor

While the original discovery resulted from research with point-contact semiconductor diodes, it was very soon found possible to eliminate the delicate pointed-wire contacts, and to grow a crystal of semiconductor with a thin P region between two N layers, forming two opposed diode junctions, N to P, and P to N. The properties of such individual junctions were studied in Chapter 3. It was also found possible to produce units having an arrangement of PNP layers, and various manufacturing techniques are now employed to produce either type, as will be discussed later.

Because of similarities in function to the early point-contact units, the common layer becomes the *base*, the input element of the first or forward-biased diode is called the *emitter*, and the output element of the reverse-biased diode is the *collector*. These elements, as well as the biasing for an NPN unit, are shown in Fig. 7–1(a). The bias potentials for a PNP unit will be reversed. Also shown in Fig. 7–1(b) are the standard $IEEE$ circuit symbols for NPN and PNP forms of transistors. The arrow on the emitter lead signifies the direction of conventional forward current when the emitter is biased in the forward or low-resistance direction.

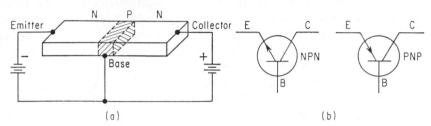

(a)   (b)

Fig. 7–1. (a) Grown junction NPN transistor; (b) circuit symbols for NPN and PNP transistors. Emitter arrow indicates direction of forward current.

Figure 7–2 shows the potential variation through the NPN transistor, Fig. 7–2(a) representing the situation without bias, the barrier potential then being sufficient to just prevent current across the junctions, as was discussed in Chapter 3. In Fig. 7–2(b) is shown the potential relations

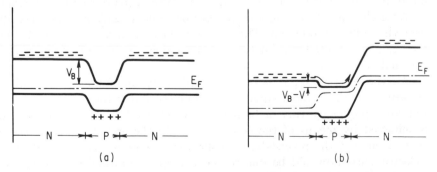

(a)   (b)

Fig. 7–2. (a) Unbiased potential levels in NPN transistor; (b) levels when biased for operation.

with normal potentials applied, upward then being the easy direction of electron movement. The diode equation of Section 3–14 will apply to the forward-biased emitter-base junction. The bias lowers the potential barrier and this increases the emitter-base current, represented largely by electrons in the *NPN* transistor.

The potential in the base is essentially uniform so that diffusion acts to move the charges to the base-collector junction. The charges crossing that junction are then attracted to the collector by the collector potential. The base layer is made very thin, of the order of 0.001 cm or less; there is little opportunity for electrons to recombine with holes in the hole-rich base region of the *NPN* transistor, and the current reaching the collector will be only a few per cent less than the emitter current.

In the *PNP* transistor, the forward bias on the emitter would inject holes, with the return electron component from the base minimized by making the emitter a *P* material of higher conductivity than the base. The main function of the emitter is to inject holes into the base region, and the ratio of hole current to total emitter current, or of majority carriers to total carriers is defined as the *emitter efficiency* γ. In good material design this ratio will be close to unity.

The holes injected into the base region diffuse and most reach the collector region, forming the hole component of collector current, as indicated in Fig. 7–3. The ratio of the holes reaching the collector to the emitted hole current is called the *transport factor*, and this is also near but less than unity. The electrons which contribute to recombination in the base, or to small electron components

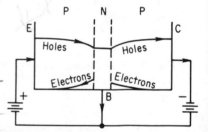

Fig. 7–3. Currents in *PNP* transistor.

diffusing into emitter or collector, constitute a base electron current.

At high collector voltages there may be some avalanche multiplication near the collector junction. The collected current may be increased, and the ratio of collected current to current incident on the collector junction is called the *collector efficiency* δ.

As the emitter input current is varied by an applied potential in accordance with the diode equation, it can be seen that the collector current will correspondingly vary or be modulated. Control of the output current is achieved by means of the *input current* to the emitter, since without emitter current the reverse-biased collector current would be small. This collector current would be due to the reverse saturation current I_o, frequently referred to as I_{C0}. More accurately, the reverse saturation current,

I_{C0}, is defined as the collector current with the collector reverse biased, and with $I_E = 0$.

If the base-emitter potential is varied, the effective height of the emitter-base barrier is changed, and the current predicted by the diode equation will also vary. The base-emitter potential can therefore be considered as controlling the collector current, as well.

The ratio of a change in collector current Δi_C, to a change in emitter current Δi_E, with collector voltage held constant, is defined as the *short-circuit current amplification factor* α. That is, in the limit

$$\alpha = -\left.\frac{\partial i_C}{\partial i_E}\right]_{v_{CB}=\text{constant}} \tag{7-1}$$

This is at times written as α_{FB}. Because the recombination in the base is small, usual values of α are in the range of 0.95 to 0.99. The forward-biased input resistance of the emitter-base junction is low, usually a few hundred ohms. The ouput circuit between collector and base may have an internal resistance in the range from 10,000 ohms to several megohms, because of the reverse bias. The input power level is low because of the low input resistance, while the output power level is much higher, owing to the high output impedance. Power and voltage amplification have taken place because of the substantial difference in impedance levels of input and output circuits.

A second amplification factor, called the *collector-to-base short circuit current amplification factor h_{fe}*, (also written α_{fe} or β) is defined in terms of the ratio of change in collector current Δi_C to the change in base current Δi_B, with collector voltage constant. That is,

$$h_{fe} = \left.\frac{\partial i_C}{\partial i_B}\right]_{v_{CE}=\text{constant}} \tag{7-2}$$

The base current has been mentioned as largely resulting from recombination losses of only a few per cent, so that the above ratio may reach values as high as 200. It is also apparent from the definition of Eq. 7–1 that

$$- \Delta i_C = \alpha \, \Delta i_E$$

and since

$$\Delta i_B = - \Delta i_E - \Delta i_C = - \Delta i_E(1 - \alpha)$$

then

$$h_{fe} = \frac{\alpha}{1 - \alpha} \tag{7-3}$$

The junction transistor is available in many designs, has a large region of linearity of volt-ampere characteristics, and will be the type assumed here for further study.

7–2. Manufacturing methods

Both silicon and germanium have been found suitable for the manufacture of transistors. Germanium, because of its greater ease of purification and lower resistance, has been developed into a large number of types, but it seems inherently limited to the lower ambient temperatures by its temperature limit of about 85°C. Silicon is used in many further types, capable of operating to 200°C.

Several general manufacturing methods are employed, and those used at the present time lead to grown junctions, fused alloy junctions, rate-grown junctions, diffused junctions, and epitaxial junctions. The grown NPN junction is produced during the pulling of a large crystal from a purified semiconductor melt which has been doped with a small amount of N impurity. At an appropriate time in the growth process, impurity material of opposite or P type such as gallium or indium is introduced in an amount sufficient to override the initial doping. After a short interval the material is once more doped with an N impurity such as arsenic, and the growth process is repeated with the melt in this condition. As a result, the crystal has a very thin layer of P material sandwiched between two thick N layers. This successive addition of impurities reduces the resistivity of the melt and thus ends the usefulness of a batch of material without repurification.

A slab is then cut, parallel to the junction and including it, and this is subsequently diced into suitable wafers, possibly 2.5 mm long by 1 mm on a side. After chemical etching and cleaning, contact wires are welded or soldered on the ends and on the central base zone, the latter being located either by microscopic examination of the etched surface or by electrical measurements. The result is indicated in Fig. 7–4(a).

It has been found that the relative solubility of some impurity materials in the solid and liquid depends on the rate at which the crystal is grown. A suitably doped melt, having both P and N impurities present, can be used to produce *rate-grown* transistor junctions. Gallium and indium, as P materials, tend to enter the solid at a rate independent of rate of growth, so that at a slow growth rate a P material is formed. With a rapid rate of growth N–forming antimony impurity tends to enter the solid state at a faster rate than the gallium or indium, so an N material is produced. By cycling the growth rate, alternate N and P layers or junctions are formed. The method leads to a crytal containing a number of PN junctions.

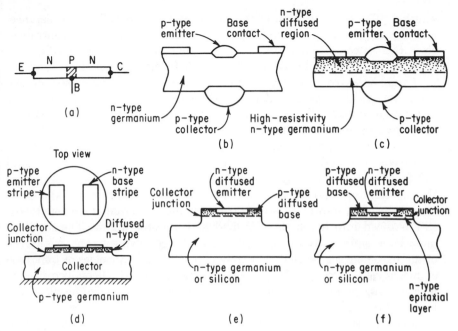

Fig. 7–4. (a) *NPN* grown junction; (b) *PNP* alloy-junction transistor; (c) drift-field alloy transistor; (d) *PNP* mesa transistor; (e) *NPN* double-diffused mesa type; (f) epitaxial *NPN* transistor.

The *PNP* transistor is most usually made by an alloy process, as illustrated in Fig. 7–4(b). A tiny pellet of *P* material, such as indium or gallium, is placed in the center of a small wafer of germanium. The whole is then heated under a controlled atmosphere to a temperature above the melting point of indium but below that of germanium. The indium melts and diffuses slightly into the germanium, forming a *P* germanium layer, the remainder of the indium pellet serving as a contact. The process is repeated with a pellet of indium on the reverse side. The depth of penetration of the indium into the germanium is controlled by time and temperature so that an unaltered *N* zone of about 0.0025 mm is left to form the base region. After etching, the connections are made to these electrodes.

Further progress has been made through use of the process of diffusion between solid materials at elevated temperatures. Junctions are produced by coating the surface of the semiconductor wafer, say an *N* collector material, with a layer of boron to produce a *P* phase, after which heating causes the boron to migrate into the semiconductor. The initial coating of boron (or phosphorus for an *N* result) may be produced by deposition from a vapor in vacuum or by painting on a layer of a weak solution. The concentration of the diffusant varies rapidly with distance, and the depth of the diffused base layer can be accurately controlled, since the process of diffusion may take several hours. As a result, base thicknesses of the order of 0.00004 to 0.0001 cm are possible.

Large areas of thin semiconductor wafers can be processed in one operation, yielding good uniformity of characteristics. A small area may be exposed to an N diffusant by masking on the base layer, and an emitter layer formed on top of the base.

Masks with tiny slits are then used to protect the emitter electrode and a base electrode area, and the material is etched down to the original collector level, leaving tiny base and emitter contact areas standing above the surroundings, like mesas in the desert. Such transistors are known as *mesa* units, shown in Fig. 7–4(d). After etching, the original semiconductor slice is diced into hundreds of individual transistor wafers. The resulting units have sufficiently low collector capacitance, owing to the small area of the base contact, so that they may be useful at frequencies of hundreds of megacycles. The process is particularly suited to silicon because its high melting point allows the diffusion process to be carried on at a high temperature and a fast rate.

Mesa construction requires a relatively thick collector wafer for mechanical support of the other elements of the transistor. This thickness lengthens the collector current path and raises the internal forward saturation resistance. The situation might appear to be correctible by use of collector material of high doping or low resistivity, but it is found that this lowers the breakdown voltage and also raises the collector-base capacitance, reducing the upper frequency limit of operation and the speed of switching for on-off use of the transistor.

As a means of avoiding the design compromise which the above situation forces, *epitaxial* construction has made possible the deposition of a high-resistance thin film collector, 0.1 mm or less thick, on a low-resistance silicon substrate. Epitaxy is defined as oriented intergrowth of the two solid materials, wherein the lattice structure of the wafer provides crystal orientations for the growth of the high-resistance collector material. The growth occurs from a gaseous compound at elevated temperature.

In this construction, the excess material needed for mechanical strength of the substrate can be heavily doped to a low resistivity, and the epitaxial layer independently grown from material with much less doping, giving the desired high-resistance collector characteristics. A base layer may then be diffused through a mask into the epitaxial layer by usual methods, followed by diffusion of the emitter onto the base through a second mask.

The use of the epitaxial layer provides lower collector saturation resistance, higher voltage breakdown and therefore higher possible output voltage, permits reduced emitter and base area with lower capacitances and increased upper frequency limits, and lowers the switching time in on-off operation. The method of epitaxial growth provides the device designer with great freedom in the selection of his material characteristics.

7–3. Transistor circuit notation

Transistor circuits involve many different currents and voltages. The Institute of Electrical and Electronics Engineers has adopted certain standards of notation, many of which are carried over from usual circuit analysis since the transistor is, after all, a circuit element.

Instantaneous values of current and voltage, which vary with time, are represented by lower-case letters. Referring to Fig. 7–5, total instantaneous quantities will have upper-case subscripts, as i_C, whereas the instantaneous value of the varying components will have lower-case subscripts, as i_c.

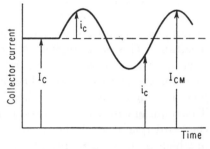

Fig. 7–5. Transistor current notation.

Steady or d-c quantities will be identified by upper-case letters with upper-case subscripts, and a-c rms quantities by upper-case letters with lower-case subscripts. Maximum values will usually be designated by a second subscript m or M.

The subscripts c or C, e or E, b or B will refer to collector, emitter, and base quantities, respectively, with a second letter subscript on voltages to indicate the common or reference electrode, when needed.

Supply voltages will be indicated by repeating the letter subscript as V_{EE}, V_{CC}, V_{BB}.

Internal transistor resistances or impedances will be lower case, r, y, z, h; for external impedances or admittances capital letters will be used. Lower-case subscripts will indicate small-signal values; upper-case subscripts will represent static or d-c parameters.

For measured parameters, both numerical and letter subscripts are used. However, letter subscripts will be preferred, using i, r, f, and o as first subscripts to designate the particular measured quantity. To indicate the type of circuit to which a given measured parameter applies, a second subscript may be added to the above as c, e, or b, indicating the common or reference electrode of the circuit. There result such combinations as z_{ib}, y_{oe}, h_{fe}, and the like.

These symbols will become familiar through use.

7–4. Graphical characteristics of the transistor

Various volt-ampere plots can be employed for study of the transistor. A complete forward and inverse collector characteristic is shown for a *PNP* transistor in Fig. 7–6. The collector current i_C is plotted against collector voltage, with i_B, the base current, as parameter. The usual forward volt-ampere curve of the collector junction of a semiconductor diode appears in the first quadrant. This is a region of no interest for transistor operation, since for the transistor the collector junction must be reverse biased. This requirement places operation in the third quadrant of the diagram, in which is shown a family of i_C, v_C curves for the transistor.

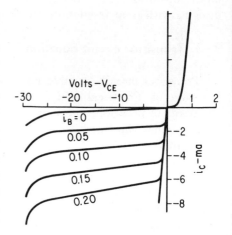

Fig. 7–6. Four quadrant common emitter characteristics, with i_B as parameter.

The transistor can be seen as linear, or has curves of constant slope, down to quite low voltage levels. The curvature at the higher inverse voltages is due to the beginning of avalanche multiplication, as discussed for the Zener diode in Chapter 3, and this increase in current may indicate an undesirable circuit condition.

The *output characteristics* from the reverse-biased quadrant are expanded in Fig. 7–7(c), with i_C as the independent variable and i_B as parameter. The slopes of these curves must represent $1/r_o$, where r_o is the output resistance, and is large as indicated by the low slope of the curves. The operation swing could carry down to a collector-emitter voltage of about 0.2 v in Fig. 7–7(c), with good linearity. This represents the approximate minimum voltage for any current level, and is called the saturation voltage. The *transfer characteristics* of Fig. 7–7(b) are not linear for very small signals, and this property will find application at a later time.

The graphical output circuit relations of Fig. 7–8 may be used to provide greater understanding of the operation of a transistor as an amplifier. The method is general, applying equally well to any nonlinear device. The characteristic curves relating v_{CB} and i_C can be functionally expressed as

$$v_{CB} = f(i_E, i_C) \tag{7–4}$$

for the circuit of Fig. 7–9. The current-voltage relations existing in the collector circuit, using total current notation, can be written as

$$v_{CB} = V_{CC} - R_L i_C \tag{7–5}$$

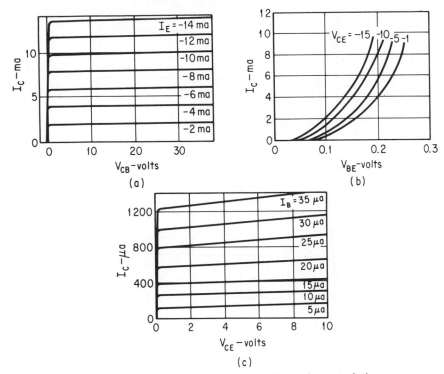

Fig. 7–7. Common-base and common-emitter characteristics.

Since the transistor and load are in series, the current must be the same for both, and simultaneous solution of Eqs. 7–4 and 7–5 would give a value for the transistor voltage. Because of the functional relation expressed by Eq. 7–4, these two equations cannot be simultaneously solved by analytical methods for values of i_C or v_{CB}; however, a simultaneous graphical solution is possible.

Since V_{CC} as a source voltage is constant, then Eq. 7–5 is a linear equation of form

$$y = b + mx$$

with x intercept V_{CC}, slope of $-1/R_L$, and y intercept $i_C = V_{CC}/R_L$. Drawing such a line on the output characteristics of a typical transistor gives the *d-c load line* of Fig. 7–8. This line determines the current and voltage conditions present in the collector circuit of the transistor under the resistive load condition selected. In Fig. 7–8 the line is drawn for $V_{CC} = 40$ v, $R_L = 8000$ ohms, so that the y intercept = 40/8000 = 0.005 amp, and the x intercept = $V_{CC} = 40$ v. A straight line drawn between these intercepts will have a slope of the proper amount and is the *d-c load line* for the particular load, defining all possible combinations of current and voltage which may exist in this series combination of load and transistor.

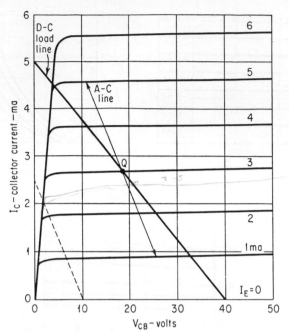

Fig. 7–8. Use of load line.

If alternating components are to appear in the output, and the transistor amplifier is to approach linearity, then a central *operating point*, or *quiescent point*, Q, must be chosen, and operating swings of voltage or current will occur about it as an origin. In this way both positive and negative swings may occur about the operating point and along the load line without exceeding the bounds of the linear region of the characteristics.

If V_{EE} be chosen so that with zero a-c signal the input current $I_E = 3$ ma, then the Q point will be located at the intersection of the $I_E = 3$ ma characteristic and the load line at Q. The transistor voltage will then be $v_{CB} = 18$ v, and $I_C = 2.7$ ma.

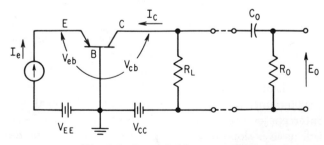

Fig. 7–9. Grounded base amplifier.

The transistor parameters are related to the slopes of the characteristic curves, thus selection of the Q point determines the values to be assigned to the transistor parameters used in circuit analysis. As the slopes of the various curve families change, the transistor parameters will also vary in value.

If a branch composed of C_o and R_o in series is added as an RC coupling network, the circuit becomes representative of a large class of actual circuits wherein the d-c and a-c current paths in the load are not identical. The d-c line still fixes the Q point and the parameters, but an additional *a-c load line* is needed to define the path of operation with an a-c signal input and a-c present in the load.

For zero a-c input, the transistor is at the Q point, or the Q point is on the a-c load line. If $R_o = 8000$ ohms, then a line passed through the Q point with a slope of $-1/R_{a-c}$ or having a slope of $-1/4000$ for the example, will be the a-c load line shown in Fig. 7–8.

A line drawn with x intercept $= 10$ v, and y intercept $= i = 100/R_{a-c}$ will determine the proper slope, as shown by the dashed line in the corner of Fig. 7–8. The a-c load line is drawn parallel and through the Q point. All points on the a-c load line then represent solutions of Eqs. 7–4 and 7–5 for varying inputs. As shown, for an rms input current of 1.4 ma, the collector current will vary between 5 ma and 1 ma, and the output voltage can be calculated as

$$E_o = \frac{25 - 11}{2\sqrt{2}} = 5.0 \text{ v rms}$$

The operating current gain can be written from

$$A_i = \left| \frac{I_c}{I_e} \right| = \frac{4.6 - 0.9}{5 - 1} = 0.925$$

General rules for setting up the load lines may be stated as follows:

1. Draw a d-c load line on the output characteristics with y intercept V_{CC}/R_L and slope equal to the negative reciprocal of the external d-c circuit resistance, or with x intercept equal to V_{CC}.
2. Locate the Q point on this d-c load line.
3. Draw through the Q point an a-c load line with slope equal to the negative reciprocal of the a-c load resistance.
4. Determine the a-c operation on the a-c load line.

To help in drawing the d-c line, it may be noted that the voltage intercept of the d-c line always occurs at a value equal to the output supply voltage. Graphical characteristics will be further discussed in the study of amplifier operation under large-signal conditions. For analysis of small signal transistor amplifiers, the large regions of quasi-linearity make analytic solutions attractive and accurate, and the design of linear transistor amplifiers is largely carried out by use of conventional circuit analysis, combined with active equivalent circuits for the transistor. The latter are based on the four-terminal network theory developed in Chapter 6.

7–5. Basic small-signal linear transistor amplifiers

The basic transistor has three internal electrodes, and if it is to be studied as a four-terminal (two-terminal pair) device, then one of the internal electrodes must be made common to both input and output circuits. Dependent on this choice of common electrode, there are then three possible circuit arrangements, and these are illustrated in Fig. 7–10 as the common-base, common-emitter, and common-collector circuits. The defined currents and voltages for each circuit appear in Fig. 7–10, with positive currents inward at both input and output as is conventional. If equivalent circuits are developed for the transistor, then analysis of operation will be possible for small signals under an assumption of operation within regions of quasi-linearity on the characteristics. By small signals is meant that level of varying input or output which will maintain operation within these limits of quasi-linearity, and the usual output characteristics permit a considerable range of operation.

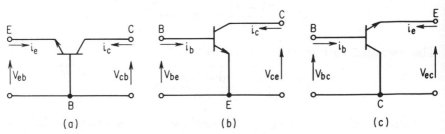

Fig. 7–10. Transistor circuit forms: (a) common base; (b) common emitter; (c) common collector.

Equivalent circuits may be derived, using the small-signal input and output currents of the circuit diagrams, in accordance with the methods of Chapter 6. The first transistors were employed in the common-base circuit; certain internal transistor parameters (r_e, r_b, r_c, r_m) were defined as they appeared in that circuit and are still convenient in analysis, although the common-emitter circuit form is more commonly used. These internal parameters become resistive at low frequency, and are employed in a T circuit which can be physically related to the actual transistor.

These z or r impedance parameters will have the same value for a given transistor and operating point, regardless of the particular circuit form adopted. However, these parameters, while useful in analysis, are not susceptible to easy and accurate measurement from the transistor, and their values must usually be calculated from more easily measured values.

This more easily measured set of parameters is referred to as the h or hybrid parameters, as given in Eqs. 6–13 and 6–14. The equivalent circuits may again be of T form, but differing from those used for the impedance parameters.

The hybrid parameters have values which are different for each of the three basic transistor circuits; they must be measured or specified for the particular circuit in use. However, the gain and performance equations, once derived, remain of the same form and are general, regardless of basic circuit choice. Substitution of common-base h parameters leads to common-base circuit performance, common-emitter h parameters are used for common-emitter circuit performance, and so on.

The z or r parameters will be used here where convenient, and analysis will often be duplicated in the h or hybrid forms, since it is desirable to be familiar with both forms of specification.

7–6. The common-base equivalent circuit

Since the transistor is to be considered as a linear active four-terminal device, it would be possible to directly utilize the z impedance parameters of Eqs. 6–34 and 6–35, and the equivalent circuit of Fig. 6–5(b), and proceed to develop the appropriate parameter values. This procedure will be followed later for the vacuum tube, but here it seems desirable to parallel the previous development in order to insure more complete understanding.

The common-base circuit of Fig. 7–10(a) indicates the input and output variables to be v_{EB}, i_E, v_{CB}, and i_C. To utilize the impedance parameters, the currents i_E and i_C will be chosen as the independent variables, and the two general network equations written as

$$v_{EB} = f(i_E, i_C) \tag{7–6}$$

$$v_{CB} = f(i_E, i_C) \tag{7–7}$$

For a-c signals or small variations from the designated I_E and I_C quiescent values, it is the change in current, rather than the current magnitude, which is of interest. To show the effect of varying currents, the total derivative of the above functional relations may be taken as

$$dv_{EB} = \frac{\partial v_{EB}}{\partial i_E} \, di_E + \frac{\partial v_{EB}}{\partial i_C} \, di_C$$

$$dv_{CB} = \frac{\partial v_{CB}}{\partial i_E} \, di_E + \frac{\partial v_{CB}}{\partial i_C} \, di_C$$

If the changes are small, then the operating range over the volt-ampere characteristics may be assumed linear, and the partial derivatives become constants. If the changes are sinusoids, then the partial derivatives may be recognized as the open-circuit impedance parameters of Chapter 7. The above equations then become

$$\mathbf{V}_{eb} = z_{ib}\mathbf{I}_e + z_{rb}\mathbf{I}_c \qquad (7\text{--}8)$$

$$\mathbf{V}_{cb} = z_{fb}\mathbf{I}_e + z_{ob}\mathbf{I}_c \qquad (7\text{--}9)$$

where the voltages and currents are given by their rms or effective values. If $\mathbf{I}_c = 0$, or the output circuit is open, then

$$z_{ib} = \frac{\mathbf{V}_{eb}}{\mathbf{I}_e} = \text{open-circuit input impedance} \qquad (7\text{--}10)$$

$$z_{fb} = \frac{\mathbf{V}_{cb}}{\mathbf{I}_e} = \text{forward transfer impedance} \qquad (7\text{--}11)$$

Similarly, if $\mathbf{I}_e = 0$, or the input circuit is open, then

$$z_{rb} = \frac{\mathbf{V}_{eb}}{\mathbf{I}_c} = \text{reverse transfer impedance} \qquad (7\text{--}12)$$

$$z_{ob} = \frac{\mathbf{V}_{cb}}{\mathbf{I}_c} = \text{open-circuit output impedance} \qquad (7\text{--}13)$$

all applying to the common-base circuit as indicated by b as the second subscript, and defining the z or *open-circuit impedance parameters* for that circuit. By use of these defining equations the parameters may be measured, or they may be considered as the slopes of the appropriate curve families.

For low-frequency use, the above impedances reduce to resistances and Eqs. 7-8 and 7-9 become

$$\begin{bmatrix} \mathbf{V}_{eb} \\ \mathbf{V}_{cb} \end{bmatrix} = \begin{bmatrix} r_{ib} & r_{rb} \\ r_{fb} & r_{ob} \end{bmatrix} \begin{bmatrix} \mathbf{I}_e \\ \mathbf{I}_c \end{bmatrix} \qquad \begin{matrix}(7\text{--}14) \\ \\ (7\text{--}15)\end{matrix}$$

These equations suggest the two-generator equivalent circuit of Fig. 7-11(b), following Fig. 6-5 in method. As in Eqs. 6-34 and 6-35, suitable terms may be added and subtracted from each equation, leading to

$$\mathbf{V}_{eb} = (r_{ib} - r_{rb})\mathbf{I}_e + r_{rb}(\mathbf{I}_e + \mathbf{I}_c) \qquad (7\text{--}16)$$

$$\mathbf{V}_{cb} = (r_{fb} - r_{rb})\mathbf{I}_e + (r_{ob} - r_{rb})\mathbf{I}_c + r_{rb}(\mathbf{I}_e + \mathbf{I}_c) \qquad (7\text{--}17)$$

These equations permit drawing the equivalent circuit of Fig. 7-11(c).

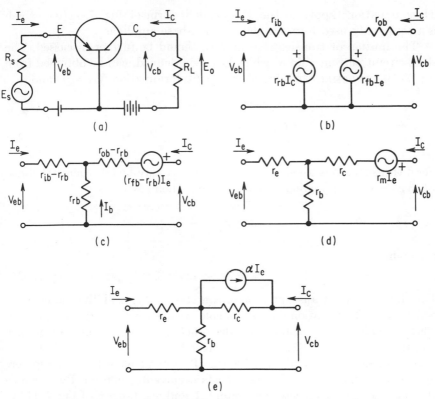

Fig. 7–11. Development of the common-base equivalent circuit.

It seems conceivable that the emitter, base, and collector regions of the transistor should have internal impedance or resistance properties, and a reasonable physical circuit model for the transistor follows by altering the equivalent circuit to that at Fig. 7–11(d), bringing in the low-frequency resistance parameters r_e, r_b, r_c, and r_m. The following definitions may be employed:

$$r_{ib} - r_{rb} = r_e = \text{emitter resistance}$$

$$r_{rb} = r_b = \text{base resistance}$$

$$r_{ob} - r_{rb} = r_c = \text{collector resistance}$$

$$r_{fb} - r_{rb} = r_m = \text{mutual resistance}$$

Equations 7-16 and 7-17 may then be rewritten as

$$\begin{bmatrix} \mathbf{V}_{eb} \\ \mathbf{V}_{cb} \end{bmatrix} = \begin{bmatrix} r_e + r_b & r_b \\ r_b + r_m & r_b + r_c \end{bmatrix} \begin{bmatrix} \mathbf{I}_e \\ \mathbf{I}_c \end{bmatrix} \qquad (7\text{–}18)$$
$$\qquad (7\text{–}19)$$

These equations apply to the T-equivalent form of Fig. 7–11(d), which is a commonly used form for the common-base amplifier.

The mutual or transfer resistance r_m should be further discussed. The short-circuit current gain α, which has been defined, can be obtained from Eq. 7–19 by noting that for short-circuit termination $\mathbf{V}_{cb} = 0$, and

$$(r_b + r_m)\mathbf{I}_e = -(r_c + r_b)\mathbf{I}_c$$

$$\frac{|\mathbf{I}_c|}{|\mathbf{I}_e|} = \alpha = \frac{r_b + r_m}{r_c + r_b} = \frac{r_{fb}}{r_{ob}} \tag{7–20}$$

For a transistor it is usual that $r_b \ll r_c$, since r_b may be less than 100 ohms, whereas r_c may approximate one megohm. Then

$$\alpha \cong a = \frac{r_m}{r_c}$$

from which

$$r_m = ar_c \cong \alpha r_c \tag{7–21}$$

For the junction transistor α approximates unity, and the value of r_m will be large. The relation that $\alpha = a$ holds well except at higher frequencies where r_c may appear shunted by the collector-base junction capacitance and the inequality $z_b \ll z_c$ may no longer hold.

A second very useful form of the T equivalent with r parameters appears at Fig. 7–11(e) utilizing a constant-current generator. By Norton's theorem the series-connected generator $r_m\mathbf{I}_c$ and resistance r_c of Fig. 7–11(d) can be replaced by a current-source generator and shunted resistance r_c, if the generator current is

$$\mathbf{I} = \frac{r_m\mathbf{I}_e}{r_c} \cong \alpha\mathbf{I}_e$$

and it is so shown in Fig. 7–11(e).

The equivalent circuits of Fig. 7–11(d) and (e) indicate a mutual or transfer generator, transferring an emf or current to the second mesh which is proportional to an input current. There will also be a forward transfer of an emf by reason of the coupling provided by r_b; feedback from output to input circuit is provided by the $r_b\mathbf{I}_c$ voltage drop.

The r parameters of Eqs. 7–18 and 7–19, as measured in or calculated for the common-base circuit, are frequently used in transistor circuit analysis. They have physical meaning in that each resistance (or impedance at higher frequencies) is associated with one of the internal transistor elements. *Their values will be independent of the particular circuit configuration employed.*

The base resistance r_b may actually be considered as composed of two portions, in series; that which is due to the material lying between the junctions and which contains somewhere a point of true base potential, and the ohmic resistance of the base material between the contact and this point of true base potential. The ohmic resistance is dependent on design and the distribution of current in the base and is relatively constant; but the resistance between the junctions is some function of collector potential, since as the inverse bias on the collector is varied, the thickness and resistance of the depletion layer vary. This latter component, which is related to signal magnitude, is sometimes referred to as r_b'. Since it is often small, it may be neglected as a first approximation, and will be so considered here.

Equation 6–15 defined the easily-measured hybrid parameters. Applying these definitions to Eqs. 7–18 and 7–19 allows the hybrid parameters to be written *for the common-base circuit*, in terms of the transistor internal impedances. For example

$$h_{ib} = \frac{\mathbf{V}_1}{\mathbf{I}_1}\bigg]_{\mathbf{V}_2=0} = \frac{\mathbf{V}_{eb}}{\mathbf{I}_e}\bigg]_{\mathbf{V}_{cb}=0} \tag{7–22}$$

From Eq. 7–19

$$(r_b + r_m)\mathbf{I}_e = -(r_b + r_c)\mathbf{I}_c$$

so that from Eq. 7–18

$$h_{ib} = r_e + r_b - \frac{r_b(r_b + r_m)}{r_b + r_c} \cong r_e + r_b(1 - a) \tag{7–23}$$

By similar methods

$$h_{ob} = \frac{\mathbf{I}_c}{\mathbf{V}_{cb}}\bigg]_{I_e=0} = \frac{1}{r_b + r_c} \cong \frac{1}{r_c} \tag{7 24}$$

$$h_{rb} = \frac{\mathbf{V}_{eb}}{\mathbf{V}_{cb}}\bigg]_{I_e=0} = \frac{r_b}{r_b + r_c} \cong \frac{r_b}{r_c} \tag{7–25}$$

$$h_{fb} = \frac{\mathbf{I}_c}{\mathbf{I}_e}\bigg]_{\mathbf{V}_{eb}=0} = -\alpha \quad \cong -a \tag{7–26}$$

From the above it can be found that

$$\left. \begin{array}{ll} r_b = \dfrac{h_{rb}}{h_{ob}}, & r_c = \dfrac{1 - h_{rb}}{h_{ob}} \\[4mm] r_e = h_{ib} - \dfrac{h_{rb}(1 + h_{fb})}{h_{ob}}, & \alpha = -h_{fb} \end{array} \right\} \tag{7–27}$$

which are useful relations, since much transistor data is frequently supplied in *h*-parameter form.

7-7. Performance of the common-base amplifier

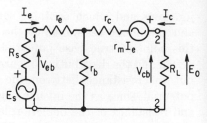

The common-base equivalent-T circuit of Fig. 7-12 may be utilized to determine the voltage and current gain, and other performance data of the amplifier. Measurements of r parameters, taken on a typical NPN transistor, are as follows:

Fig. 7-12. Equivalent-T circuit for the common-base amplifier.

$$r_e = 30 \text{ ohms,} \qquad r_c = 1.1 \times 10^6 \text{ ohms}$$

$$r_b = 150 \text{ ohms,} \qquad r_m = 1.06 \times 10^6 \text{ ohms}$$

$$\alpha = 0.96$$

These values will prove useful in justifying certain approximations to be made in the derivation of performance relations for the common-base transistor amplifier.

The mesh equations for the amplifier of Fig. 7-12 are

$$\begin{bmatrix} \mathbf{E}_s - R_s \mathbf{I}_e \\ -R_L \mathbf{I}_c \end{bmatrix} = \begin{bmatrix} \mathbf{V}_{eb} \\ \mathbf{V}_{cb} \end{bmatrix} = \begin{bmatrix} r_e + r_b & r_b \\ r_b + r_m & r_b + r_c \end{bmatrix} \begin{bmatrix} \mathbf{I}_e \\ \mathbf{I}_c \end{bmatrix} \qquad \begin{matrix} (7\text{-}28) \\[1.2em] (7\text{-}29) \end{matrix}$$

The *input resistance* $R_{ib} = \mathbf{Z}_{ib}$, at terminals 1, 1 can be found by solution of the above pair of equations for $\mathbf{V}_{eb}/\mathbf{I}_e$, or by use of Eq. 6-20

$$R_{ib} = r_i - \frac{r_r r_f}{r_o + R_L} = r_e + r_b - \frac{r_b(r_b + r_m)}{r_b + r_c + R_L}$$

$$= r_e + \frac{r_b[r_c(1 - a) + R_L]}{r_b + r_c + R_L} \qquad (7\text{-}30)$$

Since r_c and r_m will usually be of megohm order, it is probable that R_L will be small with respect to either, to reduce the effects of shunting capacitances and to increase the maximum usable frequency or the bandwidth. It is also usual that $r_b \ll r_c$. Then Eq. 7-30 reduces to

$$R_{ib} = r_e + r_b(1 - a) \qquad (7\text{-}31)$$

The input resistance of the common-base circuit is low and will differ only slightly from r_e, since $r_b(1 - a)$ will be small for usual values of a, or α.

The *output resistance* $R_{ob} = Z_{ob}$, at the 2, 2 terminals, can be obtained under the requirement that $E_s = 0$, and noting that $V_{cb} = -R_L I_c$. By use of Eq. 6–23, and Eqs. 7–28 and 7–29

$$R_{ob} = r_o - \frac{r_r r_f}{r_i + R_s} = r_b + r_c - \frac{r_b(r_b + r_m)}{r_e + r_b + R_s}$$

$$= r_c\left(1 - \frac{ar_b}{r_e + r_b + R_s}\right) \quad (7\text{–}32)$$

after the usual assumption that $r_m \gg (r_e + R_s)$. The output resistance of the common-base circuit is fairly high, and the circuit is suited to step-up impedance transformation, or operation from a low-impedance source to a high-impedance load.

Amplifiers are usually employed to provide current or voltage multiplication or *gain*. *Current gain* is defined as the ratio of the output current to the input current, or

$$\text{Current gain} = \mathbf{A}_i = \frac{I_{\text{out}}}{I_{\text{in}}} \quad (7\text{–}33)$$

In general this result will be complex, or will include a phase angle.

For the common-base amplifier the result of Eq. 6–19 may be used directly as

$$\mathbf{A}_{ib} = \frac{I_c}{I_e} = -\frac{r_f}{r_o + R_L} = -\frac{r_b + r_m}{r_b + r_c + R_L} \quad (7\text{–}34)$$

We may assume that $r_c \gg R_L$, and $r_m \gg r_b$, so that

$$\mathbf{A}_{ib} \cong -a \cong -\alpha \quad (7\text{–}35)$$

The current gain is near but less than unity, and with an inherent phase reversal, as shown by the negative sign.

The *voltage gain* is defined as the ratio of the output-voltage rise to the input-voltage rise, or

$$\text{Voltage gain} = \mathbf{A}_v = \frac{\mathbf{E}_o}{\mathbf{E}_s} \quad (7\text{–}36)$$

The common-base voltage gain is available from Eq. 7–28, by use of Eq. 7–34. Then

$$\mathbf{A}_{vb} = \frac{\mathbf{V}_{cb}}{\mathbf{E}_s} = \frac{R_L(r_b + r_m)}{(r_e + r_b + R_s)(r_b + r_c + R_L) - r_b(r_b + r_m)} \quad (7\text{–}37)$$

Under the usual magnitude assumptions this expression simplifies to

$$\mathbf{A}_{vb} = \frac{aR_L}{r_e + r_b(1 - a) + R_s} \qquad (7\text{--}38)$$

Since $a < 1$ the gain will be positive, or there will be no phase reversal as appeared for the current gain.

Since power must be supplied to the input, the operating power gain is a useful figure. For the resistive load the power gain is $|\,A_{vb}A_{ib}\,|$, so from Eqs. 7–35 and 7–38

$$\text{P.G.} \cong \frac{a^2R_L}{r_e + r_b(1 - a) + R_s} \qquad (7\text{--}39)$$

and the results are usually given in decibels. Power gains up to 35 or 40 db can be realized with proper loads.

Use of the measured NPN transistor data given previously in this section, and the approximate relations, gives the performance of a common-base amplifier with $R_s = 500$ ohms, $R_L = 50,000$ ohms, as

$$R_{ib} = 36 \text{ ohms}, \qquad A_{ib} = -\,0.96$$

$$R_{ob} = 0.867 \text{ megohm}, \qquad A_{vb} = 89.5$$

$$P.G. = 86 = 19.3 \text{ db}$$

7–8. The common-emitter amplifier

The elements of the common-base equivalent circuit can be rearranged into the form of the common-emitter amplifier as in Fig. 7–13(b). A difference between the common-base and the common-emitter circuits is that the input signal polarity is reversed with respect to emitter and base, and this will account for the phase reversal which will be found to occur in the common-emitter voltage gain.

Equations may be written for the network of Fig. 7–13(b), as

$$\mathbf{V}_{be} = (r_b + r_e)\mathbf{I}_b + r_e\mathbf{I}_c \qquad (7\text{--}40)$$

$$\mathbf{V}_{ce} = r_e\mathbf{I}_b + r_m\mathbf{I}_e + (r_e + r_c)\mathbf{I}_c \qquad (7\text{--}41)$$

It would be more convenient and consistent if the transfer generator were a function of the input current $\mathbf{I}_b$, rather than a function of $\mathbf{I}_e$. It is possible to so arrange the circuit by noting that

$$\mathbf{I}_e = -\,(\mathbf{I}_b + \mathbf{I}_c) \qquad (7\text{--}42)$$

so that Eq. 7–41 becomes

$$\mathbf{V}_{ce} = (r_e - r_m)\mathbf{I}_b + (r_c - r_m + r_e)\mathbf{I}_c \qquad (7\text{--}43)$$

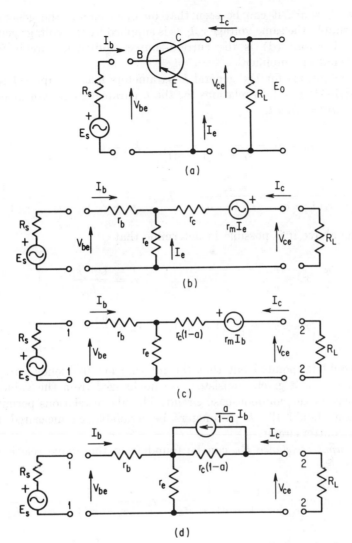

Fig. 7-13. Evolution of the common-emitter equivalent circuit.

The equation pair may then be written as

$$\begin{bmatrix} V_{be} \\ V_{ce} \end{bmatrix} = \begin{bmatrix} r_b + r_e, & r_e \\ r_e - r_m, & r_e + r_c(1-a) \end{bmatrix} \begin{bmatrix} I_b \\ I_c \end{bmatrix} \qquad (7\text{-}44)$$
$$\qquad\qquad\qquad\qquad\qquad\qquad\qquad\qquad\qquad\qquad (7\text{-}45)$$

and these equations are represented by the equivalent circuit at (c). This is the usual form for the common-emitter equivalent circuit.

Since $r_m = ar_c$, it can be seen that on open circuit the generator of (d) will supply the same voltage $r_m I_b$ as is supplied by the voltage generator in (c). Therefore (d) is the current-source equivalent circuit for the common-emitter amplifier.

The definitions for the general h parameters may be applied to Eqs. 7-40 and 7-41 to obtain relations for the h parameters *as measured in the common-emitter circuit*:

$$h_{ie} = r_b + \frac{r_e r_c}{r_e + r_c(1 - a)}, \qquad h_{fe} = \beta = \frac{\alpha}{1 - \alpha}$$

$$h_{re} = \frac{r_e}{r_e + r_c(1 - a)} \cong \frac{r_e}{r_c(1 - a)} \qquad h_{oe} = \frac{1}{r_e + r_c(1 - a)} \cong \frac{1}{r_c(1 - a)}$$

From the above it is possible to determine that

$$\left. \begin{array}{ll} r_e = \dfrac{h_{re}}{h_{oe}}, & r_c = \dfrac{1 + h_{fe}}{h_{oe}} \\[3mm] r_b = h_{ie} - \dfrac{h_{re}}{h_{oe}}(1 + h_{fe}), & r_m = \dfrac{h_{re}}{h_{oe}} + \dfrac{h_{fe}}{h_{oe}} \end{array} \right\} \qquad (7\text{-}46)$$

It should be pointed out that the internal low-frequency parameters r_e, r_b, r_c, r_m, for a given transistor, are unchanged from the values they would have in the common-base circuit. The above relations permit their calculation should the h parameters be available as measured in the common-emitter circuit.

The *input resistance* R_{ie} can be found from the above relations and Eq. 6-20, as

$$R_{ie} = r_b + r_e - \frac{r_e(r_e - r_m)}{r_e + r_c(1 - a) + R_L} = r_b + \frac{r_e(r_c + R_L)}{r_e + r_c(1 - a) + R_L}$$

$$(7\text{-}47)$$

If it be assumed that $r_e \ll r_c(1 - a)$, and $R_L \ll r_c$, then

$$R_{ie} \cong r_b + \frac{r_e}{(1 - a)} \qquad (7\text{-}48)$$

which indicates that the circuit has a moderately high input resistance. The *output resistance* can be similarly obtained from Eq. 6-23 as

$$R_{oe} = r_e + r_c(1 - a) - \frac{r_e(r_e - r_m)}{r_b + r_e + R_s} \qquad (7\text{-}49)$$

and assuming $r_b \ll r_m$ leads to an approximation

$$R_{oe} \cong r_c(1 - a) + \frac{r_e r_m}{r_b + r_e + R_s} \tag{7-50}$$

The *current gain* $\mathbf{A}_{ie}$ can be found by use of Eq. 6-19:

$$\mathbf{A}_{ie} = \frac{\mathbf{I}_c}{\mathbf{I}_b} = -\frac{r_f}{r_o + R_L} = \frac{r_m - r_e}{r_e + r_c(1 - a) + R_L} \tag{7-51}$$

For $r_e \ll R_L \ll r_c(1 - a)$

$$\mathbf{A}_{ie} \cong \frac{a}{1 - a} \cong \frac{\alpha}{1 - \alpha} \tag{7-52}$$

The *voltage gain* can be found from Eq. 7-44, by use of the relations $\mathbf{V}_{be} = \mathbf{E}_s - R_s\mathbf{I}_b$ and $\mathbf{V}_{ce} = -R_L\mathbf{I}_c$. Then

$$\mathbf{A}_{ve} = \frac{\mathbf{V}_{co}}{\mathbf{E}_s} = \frac{-R_L(r_m - r_e)}{(r_b + r_e + R_s)[r_e + r_c(1 - a) + R_L] + r_e(r_m - r_e)} \tag{7-53}$$

$$\cong \frac{-aR_L}{r_e + (r_b + R_s)(1 - a)} \tag{7-54}$$

the negative sign indicating the predicted phase reversal. High gain is possible as a function of R_L, and the circuit is popular for that reason.

As before, the power gain is $|\, A_{ie}A_{ve}\,|$ or

$$\text{P.G.} = \frac{a^2 R_L}{r_e(1 - a) + (r_b + R_s)(1 - a)^2} \cong \frac{a}{1 - a} \frac{aR_L}{r_e} \tag{7-55}$$

Both terms in this expression may be large, so that high power gain is possible.

The circuit is also capable of a large current gain $a/(1 - a)$. The output impedance is lower than that of the common-base circuit by approximately the factor $(1 - a)$, and the input impedance is higher than that of the common-base circuit. The raising of the input impedance and lowering of the output impedance allows such stages to be cascaded without impedance-matching transformers and without a severe loss in gain. This is an economic advantage.

Using the previously described NPN transistor, with $R_s = 500$ ohms and $R_L = 10,000$ ohms, performance in this circuit can be calculated as:

$$R_{ie} = 900 \text{ ohms}, \qquad A_{ie} = 24$$

$$R_{oe} = 90,000 \text{ ohms}, \qquad A_{ve} = -171$$

$$\text{P.G.} = 4100 = 36.1 \text{ db}$$

These data support the statements concerning reduced output and increased input resistances. The high power gain makes this a very frequently applied circuit.

7–9. The common-collector amplifier

It is possible to rearrange the common-emitter equivalent circuit into an equivalent for the common collector circuit, as in Fig. 7–14 (a), (b), and (c). The resulting circuit, also called an *emitter follower*, has a relatively high input impedance, a low output impedance, and a voltage gain near but less than unity.

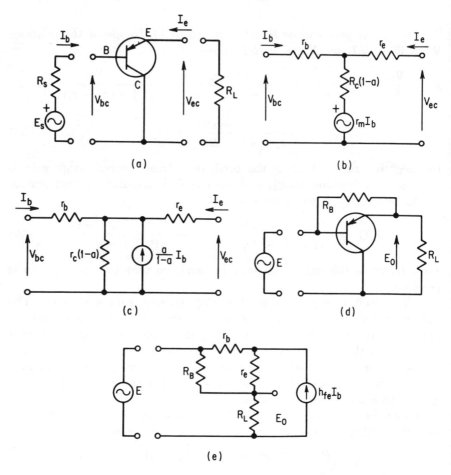

Fig. 7–14. Evolution of the common-collector equivalent circuit.

Since the common-emitter equivalent circuit was a direct descendant of the original common-base circuit, then the circuit for the common-collector amplifier could be derived directly from the common-base form if so desired.

The network equations reduce to

$$\begin{bmatrix} \mathbf{E}_s - R_s \mathbf{I}_b \\[6pt] -R_L \mathbf{I}_e \end{bmatrix} = \begin{bmatrix} \mathbf{V}_{bc} \\[6pt] \mathbf{V}_{ec} \end{bmatrix} = \begin{bmatrix} r_b + r_c & r_c(1-a) \\[6pt] r_c & r_e + r_c(1-a) \end{bmatrix} \begin{bmatrix} \mathbf{I}_b \\[6pt] \mathbf{I}_e \end{bmatrix} \qquad \begin{matrix}(7\text{–}56)\\[12pt](7\text{–}57)\end{matrix}$$

The performance of the common-collector circuit can be calculated as before. Thus for the *input resistance*

$$R_{ic} = r_b + \frac{r_c(r_e + R_L)}{r_e + r_c(1-a) + R_L} \qquad (7\text{–}58)$$

If as is usual, $r_e \ll R_L$ and $r_b \ll r_c$, then

$$R_{ic} \cong \frac{R_L}{1 - a + R_L/r_c} \qquad (7\text{–}59)$$

With a near unity, the input resistance may be high. The *output resistance* is obtainable from Eq. 6–23 as

$$R_{oc} = r_e + \frac{r_c(1-a)(r_b + R_s)}{r_b + r_c + R_s} \cong r_e + (1-a)(r_b + R_s) \qquad (7\text{–}60)$$

after again assuming r_c large; the result is a low resistance, approximating r_e in value.

The *current gain,* from Eq. 6–19, is

$$\mathbf{A}_{ic} = \frac{\mathbf{I}_e}{\mathbf{I}_b} = \frac{-r_f}{r_o + R_L} = \frac{-r_c}{r_e + r_c(1-a) + R_L} \cong \frac{-1}{1-a} \qquad (7\text{–}61)$$

the approximation holding for r_e and R_L small with respect to $r_c(1-a)$.

The *voltage gain* can be obtained as

$$\mathbf{A}_{vc} = \frac{\mathbf{V}_{ec}}{\mathbf{E}_s} = \frac{R_L r_c}{(r_b + R_s)[r_e + r_c(1-a) + R_L] + r_c(r_e + R_L)} \qquad (7\text{–}62)$$

If the usual magnitude assumptions are made, then

$$\mathbf{A}_{vc} \cong \frac{1}{1 + (1-a)(r_b + R_s)/R_L} \qquad (7\text{–}63)$$

which is usually near but less than unity. The expression also shows no phase reversal.

The power gain, using the approximate expressions, is

$$\text{power gain} = \mid A_{vc} A_{ic} \mid = \frac{1}{(1-a) + (1-a)^2 (r_b + R_s)/R_L}$$

$$\cong \frac{1}{1-a} \tag{7-64}$$

which is equal to the current gain in magnitude, and large.

Using the transistor of the previous examples, the performance in the common-collector circuit can be calculated with $R_L = 500$ ohms and $R_s = 10{,}000$ ohms as:

$$R_{ic} = 12{,}500 \text{ ohms}, \qquad A_{ic} = -25$$

$$R_{oc} = 430 \text{ ohms}, \qquad A_{vc} = 0.56$$

$$\text{P.G.} = 14 = 11.4 \text{ db}$$

The circuit finds its chief usefulness as an impedance transformer between high input and low output resistances, including use as a power amplifier to match low-impedance loads.

Since transistor data is frequently supplied in h-parameter form, transformation relations to compute the r parameters are useful as:

$$\left. \begin{aligned} r_e &= \frac{1 - h_{rc}}{h_{oc}}, \qquad\qquad r_c = -\frac{h_{fc}}{h_{oc}} \\[2mm] r_b &= h_{ic} + \frac{h_{fc}(1 - h_{rc})}{h_{oc}} \qquad \alpha = \frac{1 + h_{fc}}{h_{fc}} \end{aligned} \right\} \tag{7-65}$$

The input resistance may be further raised by the addition of resistor R_B in Fig. 7-14(d). A lengthy analysis which uses the equivalent circuit of Fig. 7-14(e), leads to an input expression

$$R_{ic} = R_L(1 + h_{fe}) \tag{7-66}$$

and a gain close to unity. The usual inequality $r_c(1 - a) \gg R_L$ has been assumed. The circuit is useful for high-input resistance measurements.

7–10. Summary of transistor amplifier characteristics

The common-base connection provides low input resistance, high output resistance, and no inherent phase reversal. The current gain is less than unity, but it gives reasonable voltage and power gains.

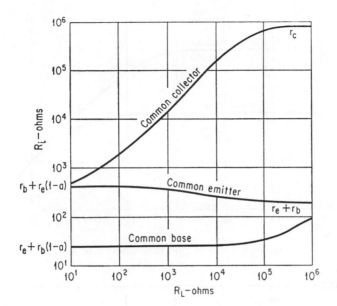

Fig. 7–15. Variation of R_i with load.

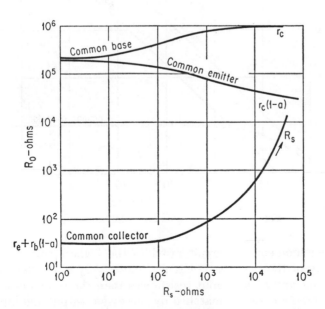

Fig. 7–16. Variation of R_o with input source resistance.

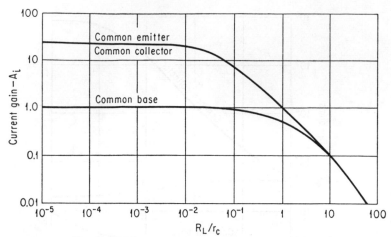

Fig. 7–17. Current gain as a function of R_L/r_c.

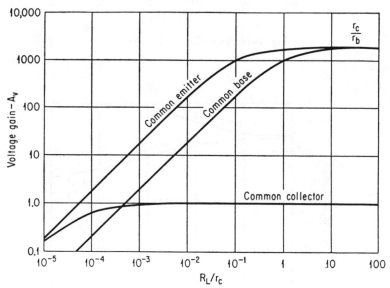

Fig. 7–18. Voltage gain as a function of R_L/r_c.

The common-emitter circuit provides the highest voltage and power gain of any of the three basic circuits and is very generally used. It has lower output and higher input resistances than the common-base circuit, and these are more nearly matched by successive output and input values, so that cascading without impedance-matching transformers becomes possible without major gain loss. Since R_{ie} is a function of $1/(1 - a)$

TABLE 10. APPROXIMATE TRANSISTOR AMPLIFIER RELATIONS*

	Common-base	Common-emitter	Common-collector
R_i	$r_e + r_b(1 - a)$	$r_b + r_e/(1 - a)$	$R_L/(1 - a)$
R_i range	30–1000	200–1500	$10^3 - 5 \times 10^5$
R_0	$r_c - \dfrac{r_b r_m}{r_c + r_b + R_s}$	$r_c(1 - a) + \dfrac{r_e r_m}{r_b + r_e + R_s}$	$r_e + (1 - a)(r_b + R_s)$
R_0 range	$10^5 - 10^6$	5000–100,000	$10^2 - 10^4$
A_v	$\dfrac{a R_L}{r_e + R_s + r_b(1 - a)}$	$\dfrac{-a R_L}{r_e + (1 - a)(r_b + R_s)}$	1
A_i	$-a$	$a/(1 - a)$	$-1/(1 - a)$
Power gain	$\dfrac{a^2 R_L}{r_e + R_s + r_b(1 - a)}$	$\dfrac{a^2 R_L}{(1 - a)r_e}$	$1/(1 - a)$
Power gain, range, db	15–30	30–40	12–16

* Assuming $(r_e + r_b) \ll R_L \ll r_c(1 - a)$.

and R_{oe} a function of $(1 - a)$, then choice of a transistor with a high value of α increases the input resistance and reduces the output resistance, making a match more possible.

The grounded- or common-collector circuit has a voltage gain slightly less than unity, with a low output resistance, and a high input resistance. It has no internal phase reversal. It is used primarily as an impedance-matching or buffer amplifier.

General performance of the three basic transistor amplifiers is summarized in Table 10 and in Figs. 7–15, 7–16, 7–17, and 7–18. Since the transistor has mutual effects in both forward and reverse directions, the output is not isolated from the input, and vice versa. Thus the load affects the input resistance, and the input circuit varies the output resistance.

7–11. The h parameters

A different approach to the derivation of a transistor equivalent circuit comes from the choice of the h parameters to describe the transistor characteristics. Following Eqs. 6–13 and 6–14, the common-base equations with the h parameters are

$$\begin{bmatrix} \mathbf{V}_{eb} \\ \\ \mathbf{I}_c \end{bmatrix} = \begin{bmatrix} h_{ib} & h_{rb} \\ \\ h_{fb} & h_{ob} \end{bmatrix} \begin{bmatrix} \mathbf{I}_e \\ \\ \mathbf{V}_{cb} \end{bmatrix} \qquad (7\text{–}67)$$

$$\qquad (7\text{–}68)$$

The h parameters are obtained by use of open and short circuit terminations, in accord with the following definitions for the common-base form:

$$h_{ib} = \frac{\mathbf{V}_{eb}}{\mathbf{I}_e} = \text{short-circuit input impedance,} \qquad (\mathbf{V}_{cb} = 0)$$

$$h_{rb} = \frac{\mathbf{V}_{eb}}{\mathbf{V}_{cb}} = \text{open-circuit reverse voltage ratio,} \qquad (\mathbf{I}_e = 0)$$

$$\qquad (7\text{–}69)$$

$$h_{fb} = \frac{\mathbf{I}_c}{\mathbf{I}_e} = \text{short-circuit forward current ratio,} \qquad (\mathbf{V}_{cb} = 0)$$

$$h_{ob} = \frac{\mathbf{I}_c}{\mathbf{V}_{cb}} = \text{open-circuit output admittance} \qquad (\mathbf{I}_e = 0)$$

It should be noted in the use of the h parameters that h_i is an impedance, h_o an admittance, and h_r and h_f are dimensionless ratios.

It was pointed out in Chapter 6 that an advantage of the h parameters is their relative ease of accurate measurement. In particular, the input measurements h_{ib} and h_{fb} are made with a short circuit on the output.

For the usual high-impedance output or collector circuits of the transistor a good short circuit is easily made, and the shunting effects of leakage and capacitance are also eliminated. The output measurements h_{rb} and h_{ob} are made with the input circuit open; this gives greater accuracy since effective a-c open circuits are easy to obtain in the usual low-impedance input circuits.

The h parameters lead to an equivalent circuit as drawn in Fig. 7–19(a), following Eqs. 7–67 and 7–68, for the common-base circuit. Since Eq. 7–67 is a voltage or mesh equation, the first mesh includes a voltage source; Eq. 7–68 is of nodal form and includes a current source. This current source represents the forward transfer generator, with current output proportional to the input current I_e; if desired it could be converted to a series-connected voltage source. The output current divides between the conductance h_{ob} and the load R_L. Since the transistor transmits in both directions, a portion of the output voltage is fed back to the input circuit and appears as the reverse transfer generator $h_{rb}\mathbf{V}_{cb}$.

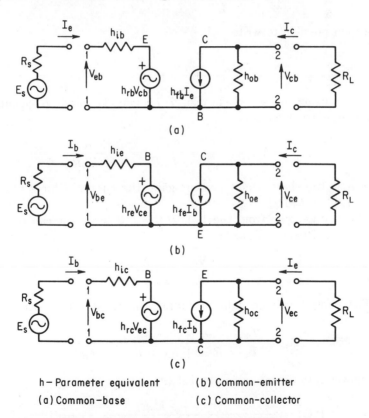

(a)

(b)

(c)

h – Parameter equivalent   (b) Common–emitter

(a) Common–base   (c) Common–collector

Fig. 7–19. h-parameter equivalent circuits.

Using Fig. 7–19(a) the operating equations may be written as

$$\mathbf{E}_s - R_s \mathbf{I}_e = \mathbf{V}_{eb} = h_{ib}\mathbf{I}_e + h_{rb}\mathbf{V}_{cb} \tag{7-70}$$

$$0 = h_{fb}\mathbf{I}_e + \left(h_{ob} + \frac{1}{R_L}\right)\mathbf{V}_{cb} \tag{7-71}$$

Equation 7–71 may be solved for $\mathbf{I}_e$; then

$$R_{ib} = \frac{\mathbf{V}_{eb}}{\mathbf{I}_e} = \frac{R_L\Delta + h_{ib}}{h_{ob}R_L + 1} \tag{7-72}$$

where $\Delta = h_{ib}h_{ob} - h_{rb}h_{fb}$, the determinant of the h matrix.

The output resistance can be found by letting $\mathbf{E}_s = 0$ and noting that $\mathbf{V}_{cb}/R_L = -\mathbf{I}_c$, so that

$$0 = (R_s + h_{ib})\mathbf{I}_e + h_{rb}\mathbf{V}_{cb} \tag{7-73}$$

$$\mathbf{I}_c = h_{fb}\mathbf{I}_e + h_{ob}\mathbf{V}_{cb} \tag{7-74}$$

It is then possible to write

$$R_{ob} = \frac{\mathbf{V}_{cb}}{\mathbf{I}_c} = \frac{R_s + h_{ib}}{R_s h_{ob} + \Delta} \tag{7-75}$$

Again using $\mathbf{V}_{cb} = -R_L\mathbf{I}_c$, Eq. 7–71 may be used to calculate the operating current gain as

$$\mathbf{A}_{ib} = \frac{\mathbf{I}_c}{\mathbf{I}_e} = \frac{h_{fb}}{1 + h_{ob}R_L} = \frac{-\alpha}{1 + h_{ob}R_L} \tag{7-76}$$

Since α is the short-circuit current gain, the circuit reduces this by the factor $1/(1 + h_{ob}R_L)$.

The voltage gain from the 1, 1 to the 2, 2 terminals can be obtained from Eqs. 7–70 and 7–71 as

$$\mathbf{A}_{vb} = \frac{\mathbf{V}_{cb}}{\mathbf{V}_{eb}} = \frac{-h_{fb}R_L}{R_L\Delta + h_{ib}} \tag{7-77}$$

The overall voltage gain, including the resistance of the source, is

$$\mathbf{A}_{vb} = \frac{\mathbf{V}_{cb}}{\mathbf{E}_s} = \frac{-h_{fb}R_L}{R_L\Delta + h_{ib} + R_s(1 + h_{ob}R_L)} \tag{7-78}$$

The power gain is again given by $|\,A_{ib}A_{vb}\,|$, or

$$\text{P.G.} = \frac{h_{fb}^2 R_L}{(1 + h_{ob}R_L)(R_L\Delta + h_{ib}) + R_s(1 + h_{ob}R_L)^2} \tag{7-79}$$

Thus the h parameters may be as easily employed for performance calculations as were the r parameters. The fact that many transistor types are now being supplied with h-parameter data makes these results of importance. The choice of which set to employ is arbitrary.

The common-emitter circuit may be represented by the h-parameter equations

$$\begin{bmatrix} \mathbf{V}_{be} \\ \mathbf{I}_e \end{bmatrix} = \begin{bmatrix} h_{ie} & h_{re} \\ h_{fe} & h_{oe} \end{bmatrix} \begin{bmatrix} \mathbf{I}_b \\ \mathbf{V}_{ce} \end{bmatrix}$$

(7–80)

(7–81)

These equations suggest the equivalent circuit of Fig. 7–19(b), between the terminals 1, 1 and 2, 2. This circuit has exactly the same form as that for the common-base amplifier in Fig. 7–19(a), but with different parameter values. These new parameters for the common-emitter circuit will be as given by Eqs. 7–69, but with the measurements made in the common-emitter circuit, or with e as the second subscript.

Thus Eqs. 7–72, 7–75, 7–76, 7–77, and 7–78, although derived for the common-base circuit, apply equally well to the common-emitter circuit, providing the appropriate h_{-e} parameters are employed.

Since the h parameters are often stated in terms of their common-base counterparts, it will be convenient to relate the h_{-e} parameters to the common-base values and the r-equivalent T parameters. Then

$$\left.\begin{aligned}
h_{ie} &= \frac{h_{ib}}{1 + h_{fb}} = r_b + \frac{r_e}{1 - \alpha} \\[2ex]
h_{re} &= \frac{h_{ib} h_{ob}}{1 + h_{fb}} - h_{rb} = \frac{r_e}{(1 - \alpha) r_c} \\[2ex]
h_{fe} &= \frac{-h_{fb}}{1 + h_{fb}} = \frac{\alpha}{1 - \alpha} \\[2ex]
h_{oe} &= \frac{h_{ob}}{1 + h_{fb}} = \frac{1}{(1 - \alpha) r_c}
\end{aligned}\right\}$$

(7–82)

The parameter h_{fe} is frequently employed instead of β in giving rated values for transistors.

For the common-collector circuit

$$\begin{bmatrix} \mathbf{V}_{bc} \\ \mathbf{I}_e \end{bmatrix} = \begin{bmatrix} h_{ic} & h_{rc} \\ h_{fc} & h_{oc} \end{bmatrix} \begin{bmatrix} \mathbf{I}_b \\ \mathbf{V}_{ec} \end{bmatrix}$$

(7–83)

(7–84)

and these equations suggest Fig. 7–19(c), as an equivalent circuit. This is again a duplicate of those of Figs. 7–19(a) and (b), except for the use of h parameters measured in the common-collector circuit, and designated as h_{-c}.

Calculation of the h_{-c} parameters from the common-base values may often be necessary, so

$$
\left.
\begin{aligned}
h_{ic} &= \frac{h_{ib}}{1 + h_{fb}} = r_b + \frac{r_e}{1 - \alpha} \\[2ex]
h_{rc} &= 1 - \frac{h_{ib}h_{ob}}{1 + h_{fb}} + h_{rb} \cong 1 \cong 1 - \frac{r_e}{r_c(1 - \alpha)} \\[2ex]
h_{fc} &= \frac{-1}{1 + h_{fb}} = \frac{-1}{1 - \alpha} \\[2ex]
h_{oc} &= \frac{h_{ob}}{1 + h_{fb}} = \frac{1}{r_c(1 - \alpha)}
\end{aligned}
\right\} \qquad (7\text{–}85)
$$

It may also be convenient to have the h_{-c} parameters in terms of the h_{-e} values, and these can be derived from Eqs. 7–82 and 7–85 as:

$$
\left.
\begin{aligned}
h_{ic} &= h_{ie} & h_{fc} &= -(1 + h_{fe}) \\[2ex]
h_{rc} &= 1 - h_{re} & h_{oc} &= h_{oe}
\end{aligned}
\right\} \qquad (7\text{–}86)
$$

Thus the equations for transistor performance apply to all three transistor amplifier forms with the h parameters, only the values of the parameters changing with the choice of circuit. This is an advantage of the manner in which the h-parameter equivalent circuits are utilized.

The choice between r and h parameters and their respective equivalent circuits is arbitrary, and use will be made of both as dictated by ease of application in a particular analysis.

7–12. Matching of transistor impedances

Since transistors require input power, the maximum power gain would be achieved if the source resistance R_s and the transistor input resistance R_i were equal or matched, and if the output resistance R_o were also matched to the load R_L. In many cases the source resistance will be the output resistance of a preceding amplifier stage, and the load will be the input resistance of the following amplifier. Since R_o is a function of R_s, and R_i a function of R_L, the optimum conditions for power gain are not easily determined.

In the analysis which follows, generality will be preserved by use of only the first subscript on the h parameters, since all expressions used are the same for all three amplifier connections. This will also demonstrate an advantage of the h parameters.

Under matched conditions, where $R_i = R_s$, the source would supply power to the transistor input in the amount

$$P_{in} = \frac{E_s^2}{4R_s} \qquad (7\text{--}87)$$

Using I_i as the input current of any amplifier type, the input voltage can be written as $E_s = I_i(R_s + R_i)$, and since $R_s = R_i$ for matching, then

$$P_{in} = I_i^2 R_i$$

Output power is $I_o^2 R_L$, where I_o is the output current of any of the three amplifier types. Then for matched conditions the power gain can be written as

$$\text{Available power gain} = \frac{I_o^2 R_L}{I_i^2 R_i} \qquad (7\text{--}88)$$

where $R_L = R_o$ is assumed.

Under the matching assumption it is necessary that

$$R_s = R_i = \frac{R_L \Delta + h_i}{h_0 R_L + 1}$$

from Eq. 7–72. If the output circuit is also matched to obtain the *maximum available power gain*, then

$$R_L = R_0 = \frac{R_s + h_i}{R_s h_0 + \Delta}$$

from Eq. 7–75. Solving simultaneously leads to

$$R_s = \sqrt{\frac{h_i \Delta}{h_0}}, \qquad R_L = \sqrt{\frac{h_i}{h_0 \Delta}} \qquad (7\text{--}89)$$

which relates the source and load to parameters of the transistor chosen, in order to obtain matched input and output conditions. Utilizing these conditions and the current gain from Eq. 7–76, it is possible to write for the maximum available power gain,

$$\text{Max. available power gain} = \frac{h_f^2}{(\sqrt{\Delta} + \sqrt{h_0 h_i})^2} \qquad (7\text{--}90)$$

this being the result with matched conditions at both input and output.

The result appears as a function of the transistor parameters only and is a theoretical limit under matched conditions. The perfection with which amplifiers are matched can be measured by comparing the M.A.P.G. value with the computed actual power gain. In usual amplifiers the M.A.P.G. value can be obtained only with use of impedance-matching transformers between amplifier stages.

Since the equations were derived without specification of the particular form of amplifier circuit, then the results are usable for all three types by substitution of the appropriate h parameters. Whether transformers are used is dependent on the operating frequency range, and questions of space and cost; in many applications it is found that reasonably good gain can be obtained without matching. This is especially true of the common-emitter circuit, or may also apply in cases where common-base or common-collector types may be employed as transformers to modify impedance values.

7–13. Variation of parameters with temperature

Both germanium and silicon are temperature-limited, the former to about 85°C, the latter to between 150° and 200°C. At high temperatures the saturation collector current I_{co} and α increase, the change in saturation

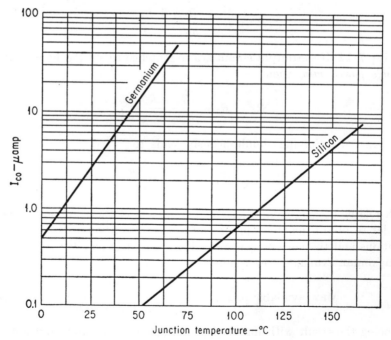

Fig. 7–20. Temperature dependence of I_{co}.

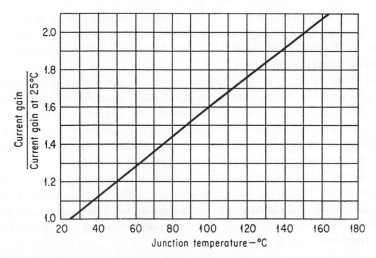

Fig. 7–21. Variation of current gain of silicon transistor in common-emitter circuit as a function of temperature.

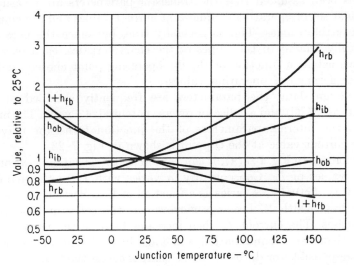

Fig. 7–22. Variation of common-base characteristics with temperature; silicon unit, $V_C = 5$ v, $I_E = 1$ ma.

current then masking the desired control current changes. The collector saturation current is plotted in Fig. 7–20 as a function of temperature for both silicon and germanium units.

For the germanium unit the saturation current I_{C0} doubles for each 11°C rise in operating temperature. The silicon unit shows the current doubling for each 18°C rise, but the silicon saturation current may be found to be only 0.01 or less of the germanium current at 25°C. Thus silicon may be used to much higher temperatures before the saturation current in the collector circuit becomes large enough to seriously affect the control current changes.

The effect of change of temperature on α is important because of the manner in which α (or a) enters the input and output impedance relations as $1 - a$ or $1/(1 - a)$. Figure 7–21 shows the variation in current gain of a grown junction transistor in a common-emitter circuit, as a function of temperature. The relative effects of temperature on the various internal parameters are indicated in Fig. 7–22.

In certain junction transistors the density of minority charges in the collector region increases with temperature, thereby promoting a space-charge situation, and causing α to rise above unity. This may create circuit instability due to negative input or output resistance, in quantities in which the term $1 - \alpha$ appears.

7–14. Variation of parameters with current

It has been assumed that the transistor parameters are measured at a particular set of operating or quiescent current values and are constants over reasonable ranges. This is generally true, but since the parameters are basically related to the slopes of the characteristics, each parameter is to some extent a function of the d-c operating point chosen, and may vary over a range of operating values.

For design data, the parameters are frequently specified at room temperature (25°C) and a collector reverse potential of 5 volts. The manner in which the internal parameters of the junction transistor may vary with the current value at the Q point is shown in Fig. 7–23.

By reference to Fig. 7–7(a), it can be seen that I_C is not quite a constant for fixed values of I_E. Consequently, α varies with I_E in the manner of Fig. 7–23(a). Actually, α varies as a function of V_{CB}. Section 3–16 showed that the base width W becomes narrower as the collector base voltage V_{CB} increases. The current I_C then increases because the narrower base gives less chance for recombination, and it also increases the charge gradient which is responsible for diffusion of the charges across the base.

The emitter junction is forward biased, and its characteristics are predictable from the diode equation, by solving for V_{EB} as

$$V_{EB} = \frac{kT}{e} \ln{(I_E + I_{C0})} - \ln{I_{C0}} \tag{7–91}$$

and taking the derivative, which gives

$$h_{ib} = \frac{\partial V_{EB}}{\partial I_E} = \frac{kT}{e} \frac{1}{I_E + I_{C0}} \cong \frac{kT}{e} \frac{1}{I_E} \cong r_e \tag{7–92}$$

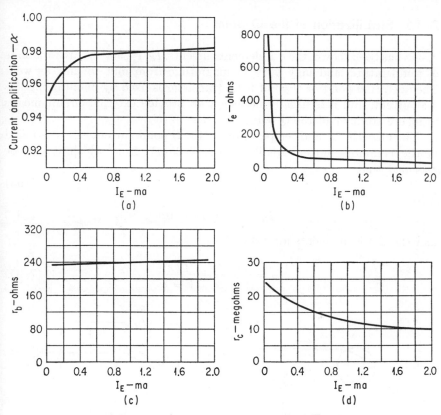

Fig. 7–23. Variation with emitter current at $V_C = 5$ v.

if $I_E \gg I_{C0}$, and $r_e \gg r_b(1 - a)$. This result predicts the hyperbolic relation of Fig. 7–23(b) between the input parameter and the emitter current.

Because of the base narrowing with applied collector potential, the collector resistance is also not a constant, and may take the form of the curve in Fig. 7–23(d). Beyond the Zener breakdown, or at the voltage at which avalanching begins, the collector resistance will decrease rapidly. Surface leakage can also affect the collector resistance, but encapsulating procedures attempt to minimize this.

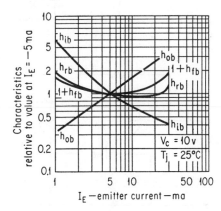

Fig. 7–24. Variation of h parameters with Q point current I_E.

Figure 7–24 illustrates the variation of the h parameters with emitter current.

7–15. Stabilization of the Q point

As has been shown, the d-c element currents, I_E, I_B, and I_C, are functions of temperature, and may vary in magnitude from unit to unit as well. The operating point or Q point for a transistor is fixed by maintaining the d-c current, and it is usually necessary to provide external circuit means to insure stability of the Q point.

The effect of I_{C0} and temperature on the Q point current can be studied in the common-emitter circuit of Fig. 7–25(a), from which it can be reasoned that

$$I_C + \alpha I_E = I_{C0} \tag{7–93}$$

Also

$$I_E + I_B + I_C = 0 \tag{7–94}$$

and the d-c components are related as

$$I_C = \frac{I_{C0}}{1 - \alpha} + \frac{\alpha I_B}{1 - \alpha} \tag{7–95}$$

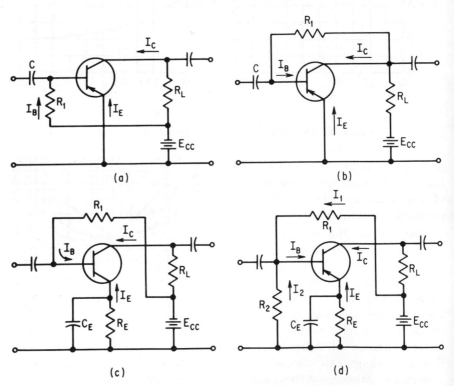

Fig. 7–25. (a) Fixed bias; (b) collector stabilization; (c) emitter bias; (d) combined form.

The effect of a change in I_{C0} on the collector current I_C is seen to be multiplied by a large factor $1/(1 - \alpha)$. Thus if the collector current causes the temperature of the collector-base junction to rise, the intrinsic current I_{C0} will increase. This increase causes an enlarged I_C, further heating the junction, and again increasing I_{C0}. Without some form of stabilization of current values this situation can create a thermal runaway with destruction of the transistor.

In order to compare the relative effectiveness of various circuits in reducing the temperature effect on I_C, a *stability factor* S has been defined as the ratio of a change in collector current to the change in reverse saturation current producing it, or

$$S = \frac{dI_C}{dI_{C0}} \qquad\qquad (7\text{–}96)$$

Ideally, this factor should be unity; that is, any change in I_C should be only equal to the change in the I_{C0} component. It is found, however, that most circuits amplify the effect of I_{C0} changes, and reduction of S to unity is never fully achieved.

For example, the circuit of Fig. 7–25(a) uses a simple fixed current bias provided by E_{CC} and resistor R_1. It may be analyzed for stability by writing a circuit equation as

$$E_{CC} - V_{BE} - R_1 I_B = 0$$

The forward bias on the emitter-base junction indicates that V_{BE} will be only a small fraction of a volt, or negligible with respect to an E_{CC} value of several volts. Then

$$R_1 = \frac{E_{CC}}{I_B} \qquad\qquad (7\text{–}97)$$

may be used to determine an appropriate value for R_1.

Using the above relation and Eq. 7–95 gives

$$I_C = \frac{I_{C0}}{1 - \alpha} + \frac{\alpha}{1 - \alpha} \frac{E_{CC}}{R_1}$$

from which

$$S = \frac{dI_C}{dI_{C0}} = \frac{1}{1 - \alpha} \qquad\qquad (7\text{–}98)$$

This unstabilized form of the common-emitter circuit with fixed current bias appears to have possible S values of 30 to 100 for usual transistors, or the change in I_C will be 30 to 100 times larger than any change in I_{C0}.

The circuit in Fig. 7–25(b) is similar to that in (a), but returns the bias resistor R_1 to the collector rather than to E_{CC}. If I_C increases, the drop across R_L also increases. This lowers the base bias current through R_1, and tends to reduce I_C toward its original value. Writing a voltage equation

$$E_{CC} - V_{EB} + R_1 I_B + (I_B + I_C) R_L = 0 \qquad (7\text{--}99)$$

Again neglecting V_{EB} as small

$$I_B = \frac{E_{CC} - R_L I_C}{R_1 + R_L} \qquad (7\text{--}100)$$

and using this in Eq. 7–95 gives

$$I_C = \frac{I_{C0}}{1 - \alpha} + \frac{\alpha}{1 - \alpha}\left(\frac{E_{CC} - R_L I_C}{R_1 + R_L}\right)$$

$$= \frac{I_{C0}}{1 - \alpha + \dfrac{\alpha R_L}{R_1 + R_L}} + \frac{\alpha E_{CC}}{(1 - \alpha) R_1 + R_L} \qquad (7\text{--}101)$$

from which

$$S = \frac{1}{1 - \alpha + \alpha R_L/(R_L + R_1)} \qquad (7\text{--}102)$$

If R_1 could be reduced, then S might approach unity as the ideal. However, the gain would disappear.

To show the stability improvement of the circuit in Fig. 7–25(b) over the unstabilized circuit in (a), consider a transistor with $\alpha = 0.98$, $E_{CC} = -9$ v, and Q point bias $I_B = 50$ μa. In Fig. 7–25(a), Eq. 7–97 gives R_1 as 180,000 ohms. Using Eq. 7–98 it is found that $S = 50$, and a ΔI_{C0} of 20 μa becomes a ΔI_C variation of 1 ma.

For the stabilized circuit of Fig. 7–25(b), Eq. 7–100 applies to determine R_1. With $I_C = 1$ ma, $R_1 = 75,000$ ohms to provide the desired bias, and the value of S is determined from Eq. 7–102 as $S = 12.3$. For the same $\Delta I_{C0} = 20$ μa, the ΔI_C value is only 243 μa, a considerable improvement in stability of the operating point.

The circuit of Fig. 7–25(c) improves the performance of (a) by the addition of an emitter resistor R_E. The net bias will be the difference between $R_E I_E$ and $R_1 I_B$. To analyze for S a circuit equation may be written as

$$E_{CC} - R_E I_E - V_{EB} + R_1 I_B = 0$$

Use of Eq. 7–94 allows Eq. 7–95 to be written as

$$I_C = \frac{I_{C0}}{1 - \alpha} - \frac{\alpha}{1 - \alpha} \frac{E_{CC} + R_E I_C}{R_E + R_1} \qquad (7\text{--}103)$$

and S may be obtained as

$$S = \frac{1}{1 - \dfrac{\alpha R_1}{R_E + R_1}} \qquad (7\text{--}104)$$

The stability factor has been reduced over the unstabilized form of Eq. 7–98 by the factor multiplying α. An increase of R_E will reduce S (an improvement in stability), but since R_E and R_1 are interrelated to provide the proper bias, no great range is possible for R_E, and usual values are found in the range of 500 to 2000 ohms. The effect of R_E in reducing the a-c gain can be counteracted by using capacitor C_E. This effectively removes R_E from the a-c equivalent circuit provided that its reactance is small with respect to R_E at the lowest operating frequency.

The use of an unbypassed R_E reduces the voltage gain but will increase the input resistance in both the common-base and common-emitter circuits. Improved loading conditions for the preceding stage may often make the use of R_E worthwhile, in addition to its effect on stabilization of the Q point.

Addition of a third resistor as R_2 in Fig. 7–25(d), permits the designer greater freedom in obtaining a desired S value, since the bias voltage and S factor become independent. Use of the previous methods leads to a statement for S as

$$S = \frac{1}{1 - \alpha + \dfrac{\alpha R_E(R_1 + R_2)}{R_E(R_1 + R_2) + R_1 R_2}} \cong \frac{1}{1 - \alpha + \dfrac{\alpha}{R_1 R_2/(R_1 + R_2) R_E}} \qquad (7\text{--}105)$$

where the approximate form holds for usual circuit values. The ratio of R_1 and R_2 determine the bias, whereas their parallel value enters the S relation.

The design of the circuit in Fig. 7–25(d) may be easily determined as an example. Assume a choice of a 2N333 NPN transistor, and that parameters and currents are specified as:

$I_C \cong I_E = 0.003$ amp $E_{CC} = 40$ v $h_{fb} = 53$

$h_{fe} = 30$ $V_{BE} = 0.7$ v $h_{rb} = 2.0 \times 10^{-4}$

$T \cong 25°C$ $S \le 10$ $h_{ob} = 0.2 \ \mu mho$

Custom would dictate that about ten per cent of the applied source voltage might be allowed to appear across R_E, the remainder divided equally between R_L and the transistor at the Q point. The voltage across R_E will be 4 v, and the voltages across R_L and the transistor will each be 18 v. With $I_E = 3$ ma, then $E_{RE}/I_E = 4.0/0.003 = 1333$ ohms, and the nearest standard value of 1200 ohms would be used. Then $R_L = 18/0.003 = 6000$ ohms, and the transistor voltage will be 18.4 volts, instead of the design value of 18 v.

The base must be slightly positive to the emitter, and V_{BE} has been selected as 0.7 v, so that the drop across R_2 must be 4.7 v. Resistor R_2 should be chosen large with respect to r_b of the transistor, which can be obtained from h_{rb}/h_{ob} as 1000 ohms; and R_2 might be selected as 10,000 ohms. With $h_{fe} = 30$, then $I_B = I_C/h_{fe} = 0.0001$ amp. The current through R_2 is $I_2 = 4.7/10,000 = 0.00047$ amp, and the current through R_1 will be 0.00057 amp, not an excessive drain on E_{CC}.

The value of $R_1 = 35.3/0.00057 = 62,000$ ohms, which is a standard value.

The stability can be computed from Eq. 7–105, and $S = 6.7$, after obtaining $\alpha = 0.97$. This is well within the specified range, and the circuit would be found quite stable. If I_{C0} changes by 20 μamp, then I_C will change by only 134 μamp, in a total collector current of approximately 3 ma.

7–16. Temperature-sensitive elements in bias stabilization

Stability may also be obtained by the use of temperature-sensitive resistive elements as in Fig. 7–26. A diode here replaces resistor R_2 of Fig. 7–25(d). This diode should be selected to have a temperature dependence similar to that of the collector junction of the transistor. As the temperature rises, the value of I_C tends to increase. However, at the same time the resistance of the diode decreases, placing a smaller bias voltage on the base and restoring I_C toward its original value. Adjustment of such circuits is usually by experiment.

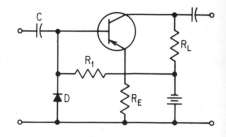

Fig. 7–26. Temperature compensation with a diode.

7–17. Noise in transistors

Noise in transistors is due to the inherent particle nature of conduction, and to the randomness of path of individual charges. Transistor noise differs from thermal and shot noise, however, in that the transistor noise power per unit of band width varies inversely with frequency, thus being at its highest value for low frequencies. In such variation, each frequency octave contains the same noise power.

As for any active electrical device, the noise is described in terms of the *noise figure*, in db. The noise figure is defined as the ratio of the noise output from the transistor to the noise output from thermal agitation in the input source resistance, R_s, measured over the same frequency band in each case. Thus, if G is the stage power gain

$$F = \frac{N_{\text{out}}}{kT(\Delta f)G} \qquad (7\text{--}106)$$

Noise figures at present are as low as 3 db for especially quiet units. The variation of noise with frequency for a typical *NPN* transistor in the common-emitter circuit is shown in Fig. 7–27.

The value of F depends on the choice of operating point, and the noise is usually reduced by a low value of collector voltage. It is generally not an important function of collector current. The common-collector circuit develops more noise than the other two circuits, whose noise figures usually are approximately equal.

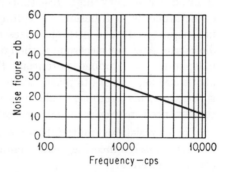

Fig. 7–27. Noise figure for *PNP* unit in common-emitter circuit.

The noise figure of a two-stage amplifier will be given by

$$F = F_1 + \frac{F_2 - 1}{G_1} \qquad (7\text{--}107)$$

where G_1 is the power gain of the first stage. The noise figure can usually be minimized by matching of the source resistance and the transistor input resistance.

In addition to noise it is also necessary to recognize that in certain circuits the randomness of charge path may mean variation in time of arrival of the charges, and pulses may develop "tails." Other random effects owing to storage or delay of charges in remote sections of the semiconductor become apparent in pulse reproduction, but these effects are being reduced by improvements in device design.

7–18. Integrated circuits

The techniques of purification of materials, crystal growth, alloying, diffusion of material, and epitaxial growth have been applied to complete circuits, including resistors and capacitors as well as the active elements. The substrates may be wafers of germanium, silicon, glass, or ceramic, as dictated by the particular application.

Silicon, germanium, nichrome, or other alloys, deposited by diffusion or sputtering in vacuum, can be used in thin layers as resistors. The deposition occurs through masks, and can be controlled to yield films of only 100 to 1000 Å thickness, equivalent to 30 to 300 atomic layers of material.

In the reverse-biased direction a PN junction represents a capacitance shunted by a very high resistance. Unfortunately for many uses, this capacitance is a function of voltage applied. However, thin tantalum films sputtered onto ceramic bases can be oxidized to form a very thin dielectric. Another electrode is then deposited above, to produce a capacity independent of applied potential. Tantalum capacitor losses rise above about 500 kc, and in its place, silicon monoxide can be formed on a silicon substrate. This produces dielectrics useful to megacycle frequencies, with capacitances in excess of $0.01 \ \mu f/cm^2$.

Lower resistance materials, such as gold or aluminum can be deposited to form interconnecting leads, eliminating many solder connections in complete circuits.

Transistors and diodes can be directly deposited in place in the circuit, in accordance with practices previously discussed. Since most integrated circuits are produced by techniques of diffusion in large areas or large quantities, then circuits employing large numbers of deposited diodes or transistors may have greater uniformity of characteristics than is often possible with assembly of individually produced units.

Integration of a considerable number of circuit functions and components onto one wafer is a result of these methods. Small size is often an

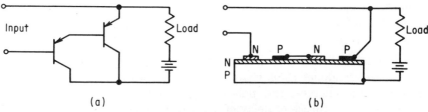

Fig. 7–28. (a) Amplifier circuit; (b) equivalent in integrated circuit form.

objective and is possible, since mask slits for deposition as small as a few thousandths of a centimeter are possible, and few internal connections need be made by human operators. Circuit reliability is improved by the elimination of soldered interconnections. The general method is under active research, and further developments are to be expected.

A two-stage transistor amplifier produced as an integrated circuit is diagrammed in Fig. 7–28, as typical of simple integrated units.

Problems

7-1. Determine the a-c output voltage and current gain for the transistor of Fig. 7–8 in the circuit of Fig. 7–9, if $R_s = 1000$ ohms, $R_L = 2500$ ohms, $R_o = 10,000$ ohms, and the reactance of $C =$ negligible. The Q point is to be at $I_E = 2.5$ ma, and the a-c input current is sinusoidal of 2.5 ma peak.

7-2. Determine the y parameters for the circuit of, Fig. 7-11(d), using the basic definitions of Eq. 6-10.

7-3. Using the exact relations, determine the input and output resistances, current and voltage gains, and power gain for a common-base circuit with a junction transistor having $r_b = 30$ ohms, $r_e = 400$ ohms, $r_c = 750,000$ ohms, $\alpha = 0.95$, and with $R_L = 1000$ ohms, $R_s = 400$ ohms.

7-4. Repeat Problem 7-3 for the common-emitter circuit.

7-5. Repeat Problem 7-3 for the common-collector circuit.

7-6. The constants of a junction transistor are $\alpha = 0.96$, $r_c = 10^6$ ohms, $r_e = 400$ ohms, $r_b = 37$ ohms. Determine the current gain to be expected if two of these transistors are connected in cascade, with a second-stage load of 1000 ohms. Neglect the effect of any interstage network, and assume d-c coupling. The common-base circuit is used.

7-7. Using the transistor of Problem 7-6, determine and plot the variation of r_i, as a function of R_L; also the variation of R_o as a function of R_s. Use the exact relations.

7-8. A transistor, having $r_e = 25$ ohms, $r_b = 400$ ohms, $r_c = 10^6$ ohms, $r_m = 0.95 \times 10^6$ ohms, delivers an output of 6 v across a 1500-ohm resistive load, in the common-emitter circuit. What is the a-c input current?

7-9. The transistor of Fig. 7-29 is used in a common-emitter circuit with a Q point at $I_B = 200$ μamp and collector supply of 30 v. Determine the voltage gain, current gain, and the power gain, if the input is 0.21 v rms across R_i of 3000 ohms. Use $R_L = 5000$ ohms.

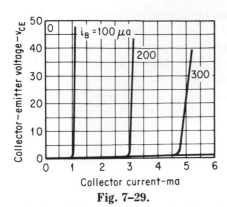

Fig. 7–29.

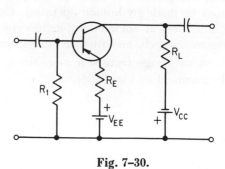

Fig. 7–30.

7-10. The h constants of an NPN transistor are given as: $h_{ib} = 35$ ohms, $h_{rb} = 1.3 \times 10^{-4}$, $h_{fb} = -0.94$, $h_{ob} = 1.2$ μmho. Find the power gain possible when this transistor is used in a common-emitter circuit with $R_L = 20{,}000$ ohms, $R_s = 250$ ohms.

7-11. Design a circuit to employ the transistor of Problem 7-10, to give the maximum available power gain.

7-12. An NPN transistor has the following constants: $r_b = 130$ ohms, $r_e = 27$ ohms, $r_c = 2.1$ megohms, $\alpha = 0.96$. Design a circuit to utilize this transistor and obtain the maximum available power gain. State the gain in db.

7-13. Determine the value of maximum available power gain possible with the transistor of Problem 7-10 in each of the three basic amplifier types.

7-14. For the amplifier of Fig. 7-30, determine the expression for S, the stabilization factor.

7-15. Prove Eq. 7-105 for S.

7-16. For the 2N64 transistor (characteristics in Appendix) in the circuit of Fig. 7-25(b), and with $R_L = 2000$ ohms, I_B at Q point $= 90$ μa, and $E_{CC} = 20$ v, find the needed value of R_1, determine the Q point collector current, and find S.

7-17. Using a 2N160 silicon transistor (characteristics in Appendix) in the circuit of Fig. 7-25(c), and $V_{EB} = 0.5$ v, $E_{CC} = 30$ v, quiescent collector current $= 3$ ma, $R_L = 6000$ ohms, $R_E = 500$ ohms, calculate R_1 and S. Redetermine the values of S and R_1 if R_E is changed to 1000 ohms.

7-18. (a) A 2N160 transistor is used in the circuit of Fig. 7-25(a), with the Q point parameters given in the Appendix. If R_1 is large compared to R_{ie}, calculate the value of R_L for maximum power gain, assuming the circuit is supplied by a source of 500 ohms internal resistance.

(b) If the input circuit is matched to the generator by an input transformer, compute the maximum possible power gain.

References

1. Bardeen, J., and Brattain, W. H., "The Transistor, a Semiconductor Triode," *Phys. Rev.*, **74**, 230 (1948).

2. ———, ———, "Physical Principles Involved in Transistor Action," *Phys. Rev.*, **75**, 1208 (1949).

3. Bevitt, W. D., *Transistors Handbook*. Prentice-Hall, Inc., Englewood Cliffs, N. J., 1956.

4. Early, J. M., "Design Theory of Junction Transistors," *Bell. Syst. Tech. Jour.*, **32**, 1271 (1953).

5. Giacoletto, L. J., "Junction Transistor Equivalent Circuits and Vacuum-Tube Analogy," *Proc. I.R.E.*, **40**, 1490 (1952).

6. Hunter, L. P., *Handbook of Semiconductor Electronics*. McGraw-Hill Book Co., Inc., New York, 1956.

7. *I.R.E. Standards on Letter Symbols for Semiconductor Devices*, 56 I.R.E. 28 S1, *Proc. I.R.E.*, **44**, 934 (1956).

8. Keonjian, E., and Schaffner, J. S., "An Experimental Investigation of Transistor Noise," *Proc. I.R.E.*, **40**, 1456 (1952).

9. *Proceedings of the I.R.E.*, **40**, 1289 *et seq.* (1952), a number of selected papers.

10. *Proceedings of the I.R.E.*, **46**, 947 *et seq.* (1958).

11. Ryder, R. M., and Kirchner, R. J., "Some Circuit Aspects of the Transistor," *Bell Syst. Tech. Jour.*, **28**, 367 (1949).

12. Shea, R. F., *Principles of Transistor Circuits*. John Wiley and Sons, Inc., New York, 1953.

13. Shockley, W., *Electrons and Holes in Semiconductors*. D. Van Nostrand Co., Inc., New York, 1950.

14. Shockley, W., Sparks, M., and Teal, G. K., "The *P-N* Junction Transistors," *Phys. Rev.*, **83**, 151 (1951).

15. Wallace, R. L., Jr., and Pietenpol, W. J., "Some Circuit Properties and Applications of *n–p–n* Transistors," *Proc. I.R.E.*, **39**, 753 (1951).

16. Wallace, R. L., Schimph, L. G., and Dickten, E., "A Junction Transistor Tetrode for High-Frequency Use," *Proc. I.R.E.*, **40**, 1395 (1952).

Control Devices: The Vacuum Tube | 8

The addition of a grid to the vacuum diode by deForest in 1906 to form the triode is regarded as the most important invention of vacuum-tube electronics. His discovery made possible the control of power by an electric field at almost zero energy level. Later Hull and others introduced additional grids leading to the *tetrode, pentode,* and *hexode* as further members of the family.

The transistor was not developed until 1947, and is historically second to the vacuum tube. The order of treatment has here been reversed over that of history, because of the present wide application of the transistor, and of the transistor's even broader implications for general advancement in solid-state devices in the future.

The general method of treatment of the tube will follow that previously developed for the transistor, and it will be assumed that certain fundamental ideas and methods are familiar from their use in the preceding chapter.

8–1. Function of the grid

The cathode of the vacuum diode emits electrons having a wide distribution of energies, as shown for a cathode at 2600°K in Fig. 8–1. This curve shows that a certain fraction of the emitted electrons have sufficient

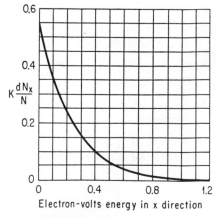

Fig. 8–1. Maxwellian energy distribution among electrons emitted from a source at 2600°K, with x-directed velocities.

energy to move away from the cathode and reach a point of -0.4 v potential, this fraction being represented by the ratio of the area under the curve to the right of 0.4 to the whole area under the curve. A larger fraction of the total would have sufficient energy to move away and reach the same point if the potential there were reduced to -0.3 v. It follows that by varying a retarding potential on a plane set up in front of the cathode, the number of electrons leaving the cathode can be controlled and varied.

In Chapter 4 it was found that a potential minimum was established by the space charge in front of the diode cathode and that this potential minimum, acting as a velocity filter for the emitted electrons, was able to control the current flowing. It can be seen that this control was possible because of the manner in which the energies of the emitted electrons vary.

From the reasoning above, it can be seen that variation in potential on the anode will cause the space charge potential barrier to rise or fall, changing the current reaching the anode. If the anode potential were kept constant, but the potential minimum near the cathode raised or lowered at will, as indicated in Fig. 8–2, the space-charge retarding field at the cathode surface would be varied in just the same manner as by change in anode potential. If a grid of wire mesh is placed in the region near the cathode, as in Fig. 8–3, a retarding field can be made to appear in front of the emitted electrons. The grid wires establish a potential in the space which is determined by the voltage between grid and cathode. Since the

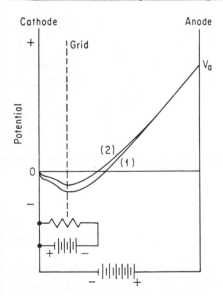

Fig. 8–2. Potential variations between triode electrodes with space charge.

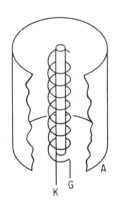

Fig. 8–3. Typical triode structure.

grid is not a solid metal sheet but has spaces between the wires, it does not establish an equipotential surface, but the average potential in the grid plane can be influenced over a considerable range. This results in a variation of the field at the cathode surface and permits control of the electron current to the anode.

If the anode potential above cathode is called e_b, it can be seen that the field strength at the cathode and the current would be a function of e_b, as in the diode. If the grid potential is e_c, the field strength at the cathode and the current are also a function of e_c. Thus it may be reasoned in general fashion that

$$i_b = f(e_c, e_b). \tag{8-1}$$

The grid is closer to the cathode than is the anode, and one volt on the grid produces a larger electric field at the cathode surface than does one volt on the anode. The ratio of effectiveness of a potential change at the grid to the same potential change at the anode is known as the *amplification factor* of the triode, and is represented by the symbol μ. Since the anode current is effectively controlled by the field near the cathode surface, the field produced by a one-volt change on the grid is μ times as effective on the current as a one-volt change on the anode.

The above functional relationship must apply between anode current and grid voltage if the relative effect of the grid-cathode voltage is written as μe_c to allow for the greater effectiveness of potentials on the grid. It is then possible to revise Eq. 8-1 as

$$i_b = f(\mu e_c + e_b). \tag{8-2}$$

Both these relationships will be of use in the study of the triode.

Since the grid has an appreciable physical area in the electron stream, a few electrons will be so directed and will have sufficient energy to overcome the usually negative grid field and reach the grid. For tubes with grids negative at all times, this current is small and may be neglected. Some tubes are designed for operation with grids at a positive potential, and, with these tubes, special methods of analysis are available to account for the grid current.

8-2. Vacuum-tube circuit notation

As for the transistor, the Institute of Electrical and Electronics Engineers has adopted certain standard symbols for use in circuit analysis involving vacuum tubes, and these symbols will be used in this text.

Much electron tube analysis was carried out before the standardization of network theory and matrix notation, and so the following notation reflects historical usage and does not usually profit from the precise notation possible with the transistor. For instance, in the early days of radio broadcasting, batteries supplying filament, plate, and grid circuits were referred to as A, B, and C, respectively, and these letters have carried over as subscripts. Frequent use is also made of the letters g, k, and p, as subscripts on quantities related to the grid, cathode, and plate circuits.

As for the transistor, small or lower-case letters designate instantaneous or varying currents or voltages, while upper-case letters denote rms or d-c values. Some of the more common symbols are:

e_c = instantaneous total grid-cathode voltage
e_g = instantaneous value of a-c component of grid-cathode voltage
E_c = average or quiescent value of grid-cathode voltage
E_g = effective or rms value of a-c component of grid-cathode voltage
i_b = instantaneous total anode current
i_p = instantaneous value of a-c component of anode current
I_b = average or quiescent value of anode current
I_p = effective or rms value of a-c component of anode current
e_b = instantaneous total anode voltage
e_p = instantaneous value of a-c component of anode voltage
E_b = average or quiescent value of anode voltage
E_p = effective or rms value of a-c component of anode voltage
E_{bb} = anode-circuit supply voltage
E_{cc} = grid-circuit supply voltage
e_s = instantaneous value of a-c input voltage to the grid circuit
E_s = effective or rms value of a-c grid-circuit input voltage

Certain types of tubes may have more than one grid, and for these a system of numerical subscripts is used, as e_{c1}, e_{c2}, with the grid nearest the cathode being counted as grid 1. If no numerical subscript is given, then only one grid is implied, or the grid used for control of anode current by the input signal is meant.

A typical triode circuit diagram is shown in Fig. 8–4. It may be assumed, for purposes of analysis, that the grid input signal e_s is sinusoidal and has an rms value E_s. The potential e_c actually appearing between grid and cathode is then the sum of the d-c bias voltage, E_{cc}, and an instantaneous alternating value e_g, which in Fig. 8–4 is equal to e_s, although this is not always the case. The total instantaneous grid-cathode voltage e_c is then

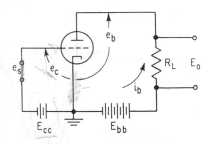

Fig. 8–4. Triode amplifier circuit.

$$e_c = E_{cc} + e_g \qquad (8\text{–}3)$$

The variation of e_c with time is plotted for a sinusoidal case in Fig. 8–5(a). The grid-bias voltage E_{cc} is usually negative to the grid, and if so, a negative sign should be introduced in the equation.

If $e_g = 0$, the anode current is steady or constant, and the tube is said to be in a *quiescent* condition, with anode current of I_b. Variation of the grid-cathode voltage will cause the anode current to vary with an instantaneous total value i_b. This is defined as

$$i_b = I_b + i_p \tag{8–4}$$

where i_p is the instantaneous value of the varying or a-c component.

When the grid voltage swings positive (becomes less negative), the plate current increases and is also in its positive half cycle, as demonstrated by Fig. 8–5 (a) and (b). With steady anode current I_b the anode-cathode voltage is E_b, obtained by subtraction of the $I_b R_L$ load voltage drop, or

$$E_b = E_{bb} - I_b R_L \tag{8–5}$$

The a-c component of anode current produces a drop in the load, and the instantaneous total tube voltage is

$$e_b = E_{bb} - (I_b + i_p) R_L = E_b - i_p R_L \tag{8–6}$$

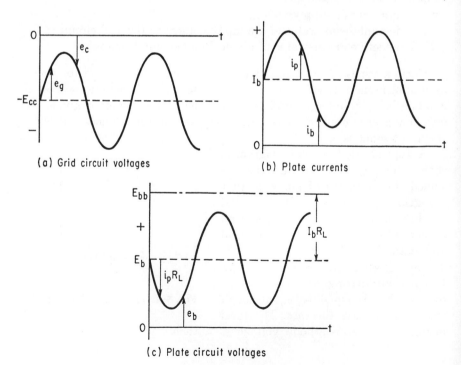

(a) Grid circuit voltages

(b) Plate currents

(c) Plate circuit voltages

Fig. 8–5. Currents and voltages of the triode.

from which the load-voltage *rise* from cathode is

$$e_o = -i_p R_L = e_b - E_b \qquad (8\text{--}7)$$

and this relation is plotted in Fig. 8–5 (c). The anode current increases with positive swing of grid voltage, and so the load voltage also increases. The tube voltage then decreases, since the sum of tube and load voltages is constant and equal to E_{bb}. Therefore the tube voltage is 180° out of phase with the grid voltage.

8–3. Graphical characteristics

Since the vacuum tube is, in general, a nonlinear circuit device, a usual means for expressing its operating characteristics is in the form of volt-ampere curves. The operation of the tube has been predicted by a functional relation of i_b, e_c, and e_b, and thus three sets of two-variable curves can be drawn, holding one variable constant in each case.

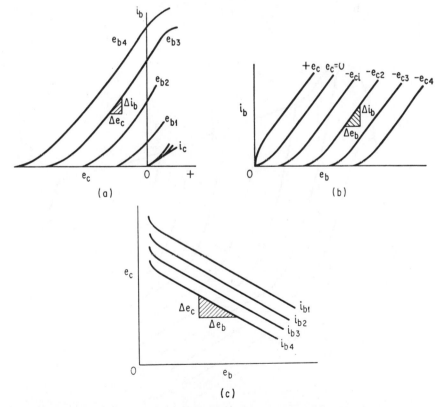

Fig. 8–6. (a) Grid voltage-plate current triode family; (b) grid voltage-plate voltage family; (c) constant-current family.

For the tube greater reliance is placed on the employment of graphical characteristics than is done for the transistor, since with $i_c = 0$ the triode represents a situation of considerably greater simplicity.

Figure 8–6(a) is one set of curves, relating i_b and e_c for fixed e_b values. The curves are for progressively higher e_b values; also indicated is a current i_c to the grid for positive values of e_c. This curve family is the *transfer characteristic*, since it relates voltage in the grid-circuit to current in the anode circuit.

With fixed grid voltage and varying anode voltage, the anode current changes in a manner shown by the curve in Fig. 8–6(b), the subscripts on e_c increasing with more negative grid voltage. These are the *plate characteristics*. For a given plate voltage, the anode current may be brought to zero by making the grid voltage more negative. The value of grid voltage that just reduces the anode current to zero, for a given anode voltage, is called the *cutoff voltage* or the *cutoff bias*. By the definition of μ it can be reasoned that for cutoff:

$$e_c = -\frac{e_b}{\mu}$$

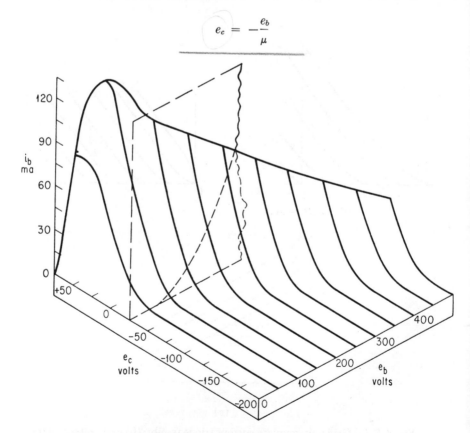

Fig. 8–7. The triode characteristic surface.

The third type of characteristic may be obtained if the anode current is held constant by simultaneous variation of e_b and e_c. The results appear in Fig. 8–6(c), and are called the *constant-current family*. These curves will be found useful for analysis of certain types of tube operation.

Because the triode performance is a function of three variables, it can only be completely represented on a surface in three-dimensional space, as in Fig. 8–7. By passing planes parallel to the various axes, the several curve families can be obtained. For instance, the intersections of planes parallel to the i_b, e_b axes yield the curves called the plate family, and one such plane, for -25 grid volts, is indicated by the dashed lines in Fig. 8–7.

8–4. Vacuum-tube parameters

The vacuum triode is in the general class of nonlinear or quasi-linear devices, where the slope de/di of the volt-ampere curves is not constant. There will, however, be large regions in which a reasonable assumption of linearity can be made, and this assumption will be applied frequently in analyses of performance which follow, as it was for the transistor.

As in the case of the transistor, the vacuum tube is employed largely in circuits in which it is the *change* in current produced by a *change* in voltage, or vice versa, that is of interest. The change takes place around a particular operating or Q point on the curve, so that for a particular change of i the corresponding change in e will be found along the curve. It is thus the slope of the curve that is important.

Referring to the triode family at Fig. 8–6(a), the slope may be written as

$$\text{slope} = \left.\frac{\partial i_b}{\partial e_c}\right]_{e_b=k} = g_m \tag{8–8}$$

Here the partial derivative is used to indicate that the third variable, e_b, is held constant or the change is made *along* the transfer curve.

The dimensions of the derivative may be noted as current over voltage, but the current is measured in the anode circuit and the voltage in the grid circuit, so that a transfer conductance is implied. The derivative in Eq. 8–8 is given the symbol g_m, and is called the *grid-plate transconductance*, or the *mutual conductance*. In tubes having several grids, the transconductance between the control grid and the anode is meant unless denoted otherwise. The transconductance is an important figure of merit and gives an indication of the magnitude of current change possible per volt of grid-potential change. For convenience in avoiding decimals, it is customary to state the values of g_m in micromhos, or 10^{-6} mho. Vacuum triodes are manufactured with values of g_m ranging from a few hundred to above 50,000 micromhos.

The curves of Fig. 8–6(b) indicate the variation of anode current to be expected with changes in anode potential. For a fixed e_c value, changes of anode current occur along the curve. The reciprocal of the slope is dimensionally a resistance defined as

$$\frac{1}{\text{slope}} = \frac{\partial e_b}{\partial i_b}\bigg]_{e_c=k} = r_p \tag{8–9}$$

and given the name *plate resistance*.

The quantity $g_m = \partial i_b/\partial e_c$ measures the effectiveness of the grid voltage in controlling the plate current. Likewise, $1/r_p = \partial i_b/\partial e_b$ measures the effectiveness of the plate voltage in changing the current. A factor μ was defined in Section 8–1 as the ratio of the effect of the grid voltage to the effect of the plate voltage on the electric field near the cathode surface, or on the current flowing. Therefore, from Eqs. 8–8 and 8–9, it can be seen that by definition

$$\mu = \frac{g_m}{g_p} = \frac{\partial i_b/\partial e_c}{\partial i_b/\partial e_b} = -\frac{\partial e_b}{\partial e_c} \tag{8–10}$$

The partial derivative requires that i_b must be held constant. The negative sign indicates that to hold i_b constant the changes of e_b and e_c must be made in opposite directions.

The term μ is the *amplification factor*, and since the derivative has dimensions of voltage over voltage, μ is dimensionless.

Equation 8–10 is more frequently written as

$$\mu = g_m r_p \tag{8–11}$$

which relates the three tube coefficients at the point of operation and shows that they are interdependent. This imposes limitations in the design of vacuum tubes.

The three coefficients are in general variables over a range of operating conditions, although they may be considered constants over considerable regions. The amount and type of variation is shown for a small triode, type 12AU7, in Fig. 8–8. The coefficient g_m is most affected by the size of cathode, whereas μ and r_p are largely controlled by location and spacing of the grid wires. Therefore, for a given cathode design, μ and r_p may be expected to increase or decrease together as the grid design is changed. Grids are ordinarily made as wire-wound helices; and a closely wound grid, or a grid close to the cathode, will have greater effect on the cathode field and a higher μ than open-wound grids or grids relatively far from the cathode. Means of calculating these effects are available for design purposes but are so involved that design work is usually carried out by experiment.

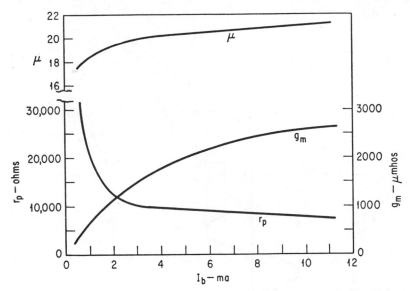

Fig. 8–8. Variation of μ, g_m, and r_p for one-half of a 12AU7 double triode.

8–5. The dynamic curve; the Q point

The curves of Fig. 8–6(a) are taken without load impedance in the external anode circuit, and consequently are called *static* characteristics. These curves differ from actual performance because the anode supply voltage is usually held constant and the anode-cathode voltage varies. To predict the performance in a circuit it is necessary to draw a *dynamic* curve by plotting the variation of i_b with e_c, for a load R_L and a fixed E_{bb}. The slope of the dynamic curve is always less than the static curve, and the dynamic curve is also more linear.

Use of the dynamic transfer curve allows graphical determination of the wave form of anode current for a given form of e_c, as is demonstrated in Fig. 8–9. This wave form may or may not be similar to the grid-voltage wave form, depending on whether the dynamic curve is linear or not. The dynamic curve will frequently be used as a starting point in mathematical analyses of tube operation, but it is rarely used for solution of practical design problems because other analytic methods are readily available.

The point Q on the dynamic curve is the *operating point*, since swings of voltage or current occur about it as an origin. Choice of the fixed supply voltages E_{bb}, E_{cc}, or the current I_b fixes the operating or Q point. For linear amplifier use, this point is usually placed in the center of the negative linear region of the dynamic characteristic.

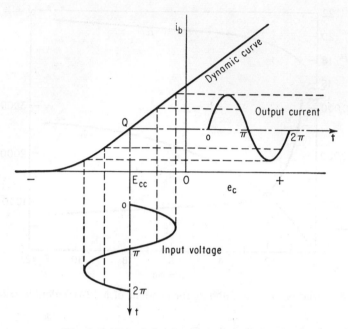

Fig. 8–9. Use of the dynamic transfer curve.

8–6. Graphical analysis of triode performance

When a large input signal is applied in a circuit of the form of Fig. 8–10, operational swings will occur over a major portion of the dynamic curve, and its nonlinearity must be given consideration for accuracy of performance analysis. A graphical method is available for such use, paralleling that of Section 7–4 for the transistor.

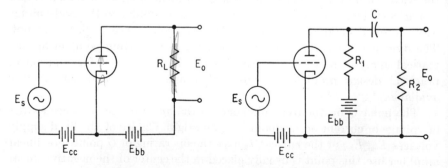

Fig. 8–10. (a) d-c circuit; (b) a-c load circuit added.

In Eq. 8–1 it was reasoned that the performance of a triode could be stated by a functional relation between the variables i_b, e_c, and e_b, as

$$i_b = f(e_c, e_b) \tag{8–12}$$

the grid current i_c being assumed zero. The relations existing in the series load circuit in Fig. 8–10(a), can be derived as

$$i_b = \frac{E_{bb}}{R_L} - \frac{e_b}{R_L} \tag{8–13}$$

A solution for the current may be obtained by simultaneous solution of Eq. 8–13 and Eq. 8–12, the latter being represented by the graphical plate characteristics.

Equation 8–13 is that of a straight line, with y intercept E_{bb}/R_L, slope of $-1/R_L$, and x intercept E_{bb}. Drawing such a line on the plate characteristics of a typical triode gives the *d-c load line* of Fig. 8–11. The line of the figure is drawn for $E_{bb} = 300$ v, $R_L = 4000$ ohms, so that the y intercept $= 300/4000 = 0.075$ amp, and the x intercept $= E_{bb} = 300$ v. If the E_{cc} bias is chosen as -20 v, the Q point for zero input signal will fall at the intersection fixed by the load line and the characteristic curve for $e_c = -20$ v. This intersection indicates a Q point plate current $I_b = 37$

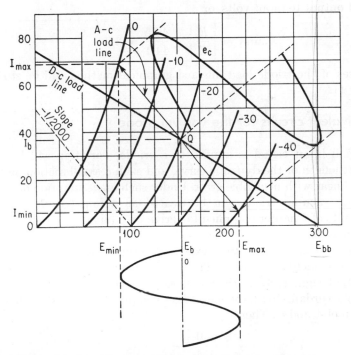

Fig. 8–11. General method of drawing d-c and a-c load lines.

ma, and a plate-cathode voltage $E_b = 152$ v, the load voltage then being $300-152 = 148$ v.

The circuit of Fig. 8–10(b), adds an a-c load, composed of C and R_2 in series, with the reactance of C considered negligible. If R_2 is made 4000 ohms, then $R_{a-c} = 2000$ ohms for the amplifier under consideration. A line drawn with x intercept $= 100$ v, and y intercept $= i = 100/2000$ is shown in the corner of the figure as a construction line of proper load slope. The *a-c load line* may then be drawn through the Q point parallel to the construction line.

In the circuit of Fig. 8–10(a) it may be considered that the d-c and a-c load lines coincide. In some circuits the resistor R_1 will be replaced with an inductor of low d-c resistance. The d-c load line will be determined by the inductor resistance and may be nearly vertical.

For the indicated input of $E_s = 14.1$ rms v, or 20 v peak, the output voltage may be read from the a-c load line and the rms value calculated as a first-order approximation, as

$$E_o = \frac{215 - 89}{2\sqrt{2}} = 45.4 \text{ v rms}$$

The magnitude of the *voltage gain* of the amplifier is obtainable from the ratio of output to input volts, or

$$|\text{ Gain }| = \left| \frac{E_o}{E_s} \right| = \frac{45.5}{14.1} = 3.2$$

Further uses of the triode load line and graphical method will be studied in Chapter 11.

8–7. Equivalent circuits for the vacuum triode

If a small input signal is applied to a triode, variation will be over only a short length of the dynamic curve, and such a small section may be considered linear with negligible error. Under such an assumption of quasi-linearity the vacuum triode can be treated as a four-terminal device, and the results of Chapter 6 applied to derive an equivalent circuit for use in circuit analysis.

The operation of a triode can be expressed through use of three variables as in Eq. 8–1, namely i_b, e_c, and e_b. The fourth variable i_c is usually assumed zero for small signals. It is then necessary to choose two independent variables in accordance with the methods of Chapter 6, and custom dictates the selection of e_c and e_b. Then

$$i_c = 0$$

$$i_b = f(e_c, e_b) \tag{8–14}$$

To show the effects of variation of voltage or current the total derivative of the functional relation may be taken as

$$di_b = \frac{\partial i_b}{\partial e_c} de_c + \frac{\partial i_b}{\partial e_b} de_b \qquad (8\text{–}15)$$

If the operation is limited to a linear region of the characteristics, then the partial derivatives, as slopes, become constants, with conductance dimensions. In fact they may be recognized as

$$\frac{\partial i_b}{\partial e_c} = g_m, \qquad \frac{\partial i_b}{\partial e_b} = g_p = \frac{1}{r_p}$$

Currents and voltages of the triode were defined in Section 8–2 as

$$i_b = I_b + i_p, \qquad e_c = E_{cc} + e_g, \qquad e_b = E_b + e_o$$

where e_o is the instantaneous load voltage rise from cathode, as reference. The d-c components determine the point of operation and the g_m and g_p values, but are eliminated in the operation producing Eq. 8–15. The changes di_b, de_c, and de_b are equivalent to varying components i_p, e_g, and e_o, and for a-c or sinusoidal signals have effective values I_p, $\mathbf{E}_g$, and $\mathbf{E}_o$.

It can be seen that the partial derivatives correspond to y_f and y_o of Eqs. 6–10, and that the network relations for the vacuum triode could also be written

$$\begin{bmatrix} \mathbf{I}_g \\ \mathbf{I}_p \end{bmatrix} = \begin{bmatrix} 0 & 0 \\ y_f & y_o \end{bmatrix} \begin{bmatrix} \mathbf{E}_g \\ \mathbf{E}_0 \end{bmatrix} \qquad (8\text{–}16)$$

This immediately suggests the use of the y-parameter equivalent circuits of Fig. 6–7, and the two generator form is redrawn in Fig. 8–12(a). It is apparent that

$$y_i = 0, \qquad y_f = g_m$$

$$y_r = 0, \qquad y_o = 1/r_p$$

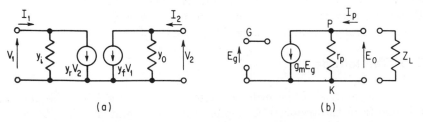

(a)   (b)

Fig. 8–12. (a) Two generator equivalent circuit with y parameters; (b) current source equivalent for the triode.

and so the equivalent circuit of Fig. 8–12(b) follows as that of the vacuum triode. This circuit is extremely important in the study of the triode.

In the equivalent form a current generator $g_m\mathbf{E}_g$ supplies current to the internal tube plate resistance r_p and a current $\mathbf{I}_p$ to the load. The voltage $\mathbf{E}_g$ is measured as a rise from cathode to grid of the tube. Since all d-c quantities were eliminated in taking the derivative, then *the equivalent circuit applies only for variable or alternating quantities.*

The above paragraph may be further supported by writing Eq. 8–15 with rms quantities as

$$\mathbf{I}_p = g_m\mathbf{E}_g + \frac{\mathbf{E}_o}{r_p} \qquad (8\text{–}17)$$

where $\mathbf{E}_o$ is the load voltage rise from cathode. It can be reasoned that this equation applies to the equivalent circuit of Fig. 8–12(b), as a current summation at P.

Equation 8–17 may be rewritten as

$$-\mu\mathbf{E}_g + \mathbf{I}_p r_p = \mathbf{E}_o \qquad (8\text{–}18)$$

and it can be seen that this can apply to a circuit of the form of Fig. 8–13. The alternating current $\mathbf{I}_p$ exists in a series circuit in which a voltage generator $\mu\mathbf{E}_g$ acts on an internal resistance r_p and an external load $\mathbf{Z}_L$. This circuit is known as the *voltage-source equivalent* and implies the use of the same assumptions as were employed in the development of the current-source circuit.

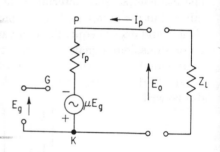

Fig. 8–13. Voltage-source equivalent for the triode.

It is desirable to standardize the procedures in setting up the equivalent circuit. Assuming the signal voltage positive to the grid, the transfer generator $g_m\mathbf{E}_g$ or $\mu\mathbf{E}_g$ should be made positive to the cathode, to account for the reversal of phase with respect to the grid-cathode voltage. The current $\mathbf{I}_p$ should be set up consistent with the polarity of the generator. Equations may then be written in the usual manner for solution of the triode equivalent as an ordinary circuit device.

8–8. The tetrode

At frequencies of the order of a megacycle per second, the gain obtainable from the triode tube begins to decrease, and the circuits tend to become unstable, often going into self-oscillation. The trouble is caused by feedback of energy from the anode to the grid circuit through the ca-

pacitance between plate and grid. The anode, being at a higher a-c potential, tends to drive a current back through C_{gp} to the grid circuit, as in
Fig. 8–14(a). If C_{gp} is broken into two capacitances at Fig. 8–14(b), and
the junction connected to cathode, flow of capacitive current from anode
to grid in the tube is impossible. A wire-mesh grid is one means of breaking
C_{gp} into two capacitances, or of establishing a plane of zero or cathode
a-c potential in the space, while still permitting the passage of electrons.
This second grid is called a *screen grid* because it acts as an electrostatic
screen between anode and grid. The capacitance between grid and anode
can be reduced from a value of 3 to 5 pf for a triode to about 0.01 pf or less
for a tetrode.

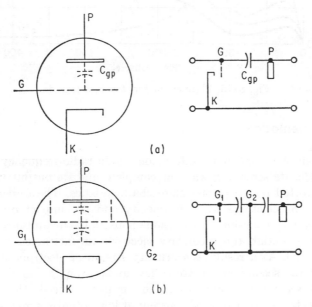

Fig. 8–14. Grid-plate capacitances in (a) triode; (b) tetrode.

Introduction of the cathode-potential screen results in almost zero
accelerating field due to the anode voltage. To permit a plate current to
flow, a positive potential is applied to the screen; however, the screen is
maintained at cathode a-c potential for shielding by a capacitor of low
reactance between screen and cathode. A reactance of a few hundred
ohms at operating frequency may usually be tolerated.

Plate characteristics for a tetrode are shown in Fig. 8–15. The flatness
of the curves indicates a large r_p, and typical values are 400,000 ohms to
one megohm. For anode voltages below screen potential the output current
curves are irregular and nonlinear.

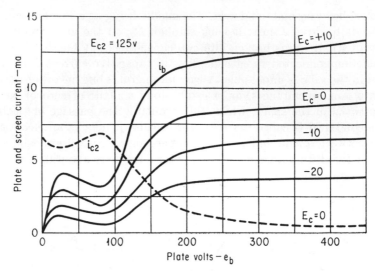

Fig. 8–15. Plate characteristics of a tetrode.

8–9. The pentode

Although the original tetrode made stable radio-frequency amplification possible, its screening was not complete and its output was limited by the distorted region of the plate characteristics. The screen potential accelerates the electrons to high velocity and the impact on the anode causes secondary emission. If the anode potential is instantaneously below the screen potential, the secondary electrons are attracted to the more positive screen. As a result, the primary stream of electrons flows to the anode, but the secondary electrons flow away from the anode. Since the number of secondaries may approach, or even exceed, the number of primary electrons, the net anode current at low potentials may be reduced, and may even reverse direction. Secondary electron emission, therefore, accounts for the nonlinearity of the tetrode characteristics at low anode voltages.

The cure for the difficulty lay in the elimination of the effect of secondary emission. This led in 1930 to the development of the *pentode*, which has very largely superseded the tetrode in its original form.

The pentode employs an additional grid, called a *suppressor*, placed between screen and anode and normally connected directly to cathode. The primary electron stream from the cathode has sufficient energy to override the retarding field introduced by the suppressor, and to reach the anode. The secondary electrons, always emitted with low energy, are faced by the repelling field owing to the suppressor. They are then forced to return to the anode with no resultant effect on the anode current. The distribution of potential in the space region of a tetrode and a pentode is demonstrated in Fig. 8–16.

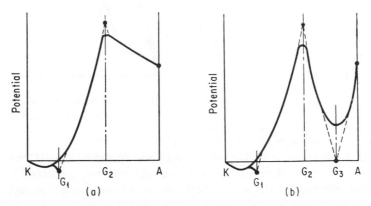

Fig. 8–16. (a) Potential distribution in a tetrode with anode below screen potential; (b) same in pentode, suppressor at cathode potential.

The characteristics of an amplifier pentode are shown in Fig. 8–17 and the improvement in linearity is well shown in Fig. 8–18, where the characteristics of the same tube, successively connected as a tetrode and as a pentode, are compared.

Owing to the additional grid-anode screening made possible by the suppressor, the value of C_{gp} for a pentode is further reduced to

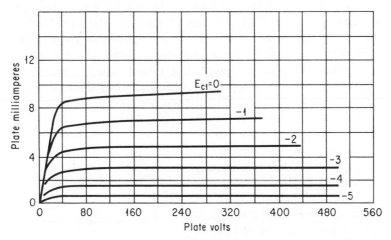

Fig. 8–17. Plate characteristics of a pentode; $E_{c_2} = 100$ v.

values approximating 0.004 pf. The
low slope of the plate curves of Fig.
8–17 indicates a very high plate
resistance, with r_p for typical amplifier pentodes usually above 1 megohm. At the same time the value of
μ is high, reaching 2000 in some
tubes. For special functions, voltages
may be applied to the suppressor for
control of the current.

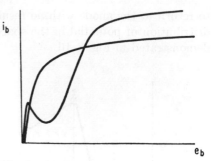

Fig. 8–18. Plate characteristic for a 6SJ7 as a pentode and as a tetrode.

The anode and screen are compe-
ting for the electrons in the space
current, and the division of current will be determined by the ratio of screen
area to anode area, and the screen and anode potentials. If the anode
potential is removed the space current will be little affected, but will
then flow entirely to the screen. The screen cannot readily dissipate the
energy conveyed to it, and may be overheated. For this reason, the anode
potential should never be removed from a tetrode or pentode without also
removing the screen potential.

8–10. The equivalent circuit of a pentode

In the characteristics of Fig. 8–17, a large linear region may be seen.
In this region, μ, g_m, and r_p may be assumed as constants with small error,
and under this assumption an equivalent circuit of the type derived for
the triode is justified.

If a resistance load that is large with respect to r_p is used, an excessive
value of E_{bb} will be required to overcome the load voltage drop, since the
load must have a value of several megohms, so that the plate loads usually
employed are of the order of 100,000 to 250,000 ohms. Thus, a tube with
r_p greater than 1 megohm may be considered as operating as a constant-
current source, the current being determined almost entirely by the
generator resistance and being nearly independent of the load impedance.
The current-source equivalent circuit then becomes the most convenient.

In the current-source form of
equivalent circuit r_p and $\mathbf{Z}_L$ are directly in parallel. If, then, $r_p \gg \mathbf{Z}_L$,
as is usually the case, the current may
be assumed as flowing entirely
through the $\mathbf{Z}_L$ branch, with r_p
dropped from the circuit. This situation leads to a simple form of equivalent circuit for the pentode, as drawn
in Fig. 8–19.

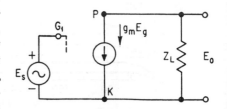

Fig. 8–19. Current-source equivalent for pentode and load.

8–11. The beam tube

Although the pentode is excellent for small signal use, it develops several minor difficulties in the amplification of very large signals. The screen, being highly positive and located directly in the electron stream, intercepts considerable numbers of electrons with resultant loss of power in the screen. Also, the rounded shoulders of the i_b-e_b curves at low anode voltages result in nonlinear response for large voltage outputs. Some secondary emission from the anode is still taking place, and the rounded portions of the curves are the remnants of the twisted tetrode curves in this region. The suppressor grid has holes to permit the primary electron stream to pass to the anode, and hence it cannot be a perfect equipotential plane.

In a modified form of tube the screen-grid wires are wound with the same pitch as the control grid, and in assembly they are accurately aligned behind the control-grid wires or in their shadow. The number of electrons captured by the screen is reduced in this way. The electron stream is concentrated into thin slices, or beams, in passing between the wires of the two grids, and the stream is further concentrated by cathode-connected beam-forming plates, as shown in Fig. 8–20. The high electron density achieved between the screen and anode depresses the potential in this space such that a potential plane similar to that of the suppressor in the pentode is produced. Suppressor action is nearly perfect, since the negative-potential plane set up by the space charge need have no holes. Because of the formation of the electrons into beams, such a tube is called a *beam*

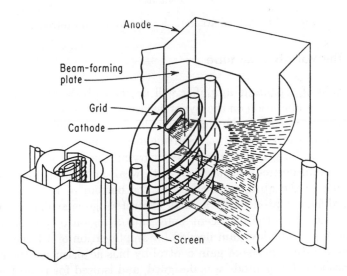

Fig. 8–20. Internal structure of a beam tube.

tube. Although the construction of the tube makes it a tetrode, its characteristics are more like those of a pentode.

Figure 8–21 shows the plate characteristics of a 6L6 beam tube. The beam tube has advantages over the pentode when large power outputs are desired, since a lower input voltage is required for a given power output. This implies an increased value of g_m; in fact, the g_m of a beam tube may be appreciably larger than that of a comparable pentode.

The current-source equivalent circuit is most suitable as an equivalent for analysis of performance. The plate resistance of the beam tube is usually low enough and the load high enough that r_p cannot be neglected with respect to Z_L, however.

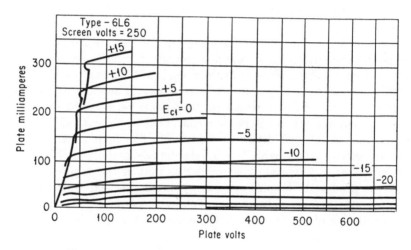

Fig. 8–21. Plate characteristics of a 6L6 beam tetrode.

8–12. The variable-mu tube

The gain of a pentode amplifier will be shown to be given by $-g_m Z_L$. As the point of operation on the dynamic grid characteristic is moved down the curve toward cutoff, the slope, or value of g_m, becomes less, reaching zero at cutoff as in Fig. 8–22(a). Shifting of the quiescent point by change of bias voltage E_{cc} provides a means of varying the gain of an amplifier in order to obtain desired output from both weak and strong signals. However, owing to the abrupt curvature at the bottom of the characteristic for the ordinary pentode, only a small control range is available when the bias is set to bring the quiescent point into a region of low slope, as it would be to give the low gain needed for amplification of a large signal.

To improve this means of gain control by bias adjustment, the *variable-mu*, or *remote-cutoff* pentode was designed, and is used for radio-frequency

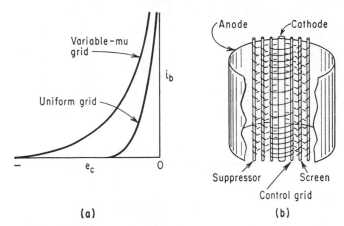

Fig. 8–22. (a) Transfer curve for variable-μ and uniform grid pentodes; (b) grid structure of a variable-μ pentode.

amplifiers where large signals may be encountered. The special design creates a dynamic grid characteristic with a smoother variation of slope and g_m, resulting in improved control for signals of several volts amplitude. The tube provides a region of considerable linearity at low slope (g_m) and can handle larger signals at low gain per stage than is possible with variable bias on a fixed-μ pentode.

The result is obtained by use of a specially wound grid as shown at Fig. 8–22(b). The control-grid wires are wound with coarse spacing at the middle and with close spacing at the ends. When low negative grid bias is applied to the tube, the value of g_m, or of μ, is high, obtained as an average of the effects of the coarsely and finely spaced portions of the grid. As the bias is increased negatively, the closely spaced portions of the grid cut off the plate current, and the g_m or μ takes a lower value, as an average of the effects of the remaining coarser-spaced portions of the grid. The gain can be smoothly varied by adjustment of the bias, either manually or by automatic volume control (AVC) circuits.

The transconductance of a 6BA6 remote-cutoff pentode may be 4000 μmho at -3 v E_{cc}, giving a gain of 400 with a load of 0.1 megohm. At a grid bias of -20 v, the g_m is reduced to 40 μmho and the gain to four.

8–13. Basic vacuum-tube amplifier circuits

A vacuum tube has three active internal elements: *cathode, control grid,* and *anode* or *plate*. Multi-element tubes can be described in terms of the same three elements, and they operate in the same basic circuits. Con-

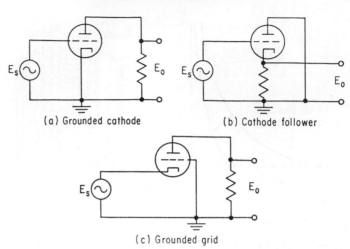

Fig. 8–23. Basic amplifier circuits.

sidering a tube as a four-terminal device makes it apparent that it should have two terminal pairs. Since there are four terminals and only three active internal elements, then one element must be common to both input and output.

Three circuit types have had major usage, representing the three possible selections of the common internal element. The *grounded-* or *common-cathode circuit* in Fig. 8–23(a), was the earliest form of circuit and remains the most important form. The *cathode-follower* in Fig. 8–23(b) is of use as a current amplifier and for step-down impedance transformation. The *grounded-grid circuit* in Fig. 8–23(c) has applications in high-frequency amplification and as an impedance transformer of step-up characteristics.

It is customary to consider the common terminal as a reference point, and it is usually placed at ground potential. The reasons for grounding involve a desire for electric-field shielding between input and output circuits, and convenience of connection.

8–14. Cascaded amplifiers

In electronic practice, a small signal voltage is built up to a large voltage by cascading of successive tubes, each with its own associated circuit. The first tubes in the chain handle small voltage signals; the last tube will be supplied a signal of large voltage amplitude and may be required to furnish considerable power in its output circuit.

In a cascaded amplifier the output voltage of the first tube becomes the input voltage of the second tube, and so on. Means must be provided to introduce the a-c voltage drop across the load into the grid-cathode circuit of the following tube, and at the same time to block the d-c voltage from reaching the second tube grid and altering its bias voltage. Coupling circuits may consist of resistors to provide the load voltage drop and capacitors to block out the d-c voltages, as in resistance-capacitance coupled stages, inductors and capacitors as in impedance or choke-coupled amplifiers, and transformers.

Observation of the typical coupling circuits of Fig. 8–24 shows that in addition to the coupling resistor or inductance, a resistor called the *grid leak* is connected between grid and cathode of the second tube. If this resistor were not present no path would exist through which an operating bias voltage could be supplied to the grid. Also, a few electrons strike the grid even though it is negative, and these would build up a negative potential on the grid if they could not *leak off*. The resistance of the grid leak should be high enough that it does not seriously reduce the value of R_L as the load impedance, and low enough that a charge cannot be built up on the grid. The value of R_g is usually chosen between 250,000 and 1,000,000 ohms.

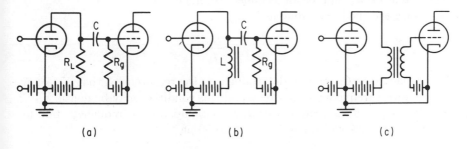

(a)   (b)   (c)

Fig. 8–24. Amplifier coupling circuits.

Although batteries may be shown as sources of d-c power for reasons of simplicity, it should be understood that they will be replaced with rectifiers and filters when operation from a-c power lines is desired.

Because of the cascade connections in amplifiers, it is possible to study them initially on a per-stage basis, and this greatly simplifies electronic circuit analysis. The three basic forms of the preceding section will be here studied in this way, in a form suited to low-frequency operation.

8–15. The grid-bias RC circuit

A separate voltage source for the Q-point grid-bias voltage can be eliminated by placing a resistor in the cathode lead. The polarity of the voltage across this resistor makes the grid negative to the cathode, as usually desired. However, if a resistor R_k is inserted in the common-cathode lead of an amplifier, it will be found that the gain is reduced because the a-c voltage across the resistor will subtract from the input signal. This is a form of negative feedback, discussed further in Chapter 10.

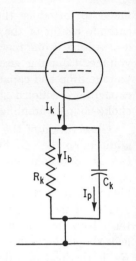

Fig. 8–25. The RC circuit for cathode bias.

The reduction of gain can be prevented if R_k is paralleled by a capacitor of small reactance with respect to R_k. If this reactance is also small with respect to other circuit impedances, then the a-c voltage developed across the capacitor will be negligible, and the C_k, R_k combination eliminated from the a-c equivalent circuit.

This condition being met, the d-c and a-c components may be assumed to divide as in Fig. 8–25, with the alternating current passing through C_k. The value of R_k can be determined from Ohm's law, for a specified E_{cc} value, as

$$R_k = \frac{E_{cc}}{I_b} \tag{8–19}$$

The capacitance C_k may be determined by the requirement that $X_{ck} \ll R_k$ at the lowest frequency of interest, and this condition may be met if $X_{ck} \lesseqgtr R_k/10$. Required capacitor sizes vary with operating frequency, but for audio frequencies will range from 0.1 to 50 μf.

8–16. Grounded-cathode amplifier; voltage gain

The grounded-cathode basic circuit is commonly employed because it yields the highest voltage gain for a given tube. Usual circuit connections for triode and pentode are shown in Fig. 8–26, and equivalent circuits are drawn in Fig. 8–27. In both cases the cathode resistors are assumed ideally by-passed and dropped from the a-c equivalent circuit.

For the pentode of Fig. 8–26(b), the value of the screen dropping resistor R_s may be computed through use of the difference of E_{bb} and the desired screen potential, and the rated screen current. Capacitor C_s must offer a reactance low with respect to the screen-cathode path within the tube, and this may call for a reactance not exceeding a few hundred ohms at the lowest operating frequency.

The load impedance $\mathbf{Z}_L$ is defined as that due to all circuit elements external to the tube output, through which a-c flows, and $\mathbf{Z}_L$ is indicated by the dashed box in the equivalent circuit. The reactance of C is assumed

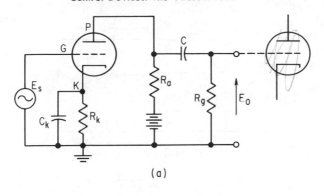

(a)

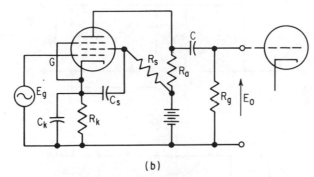

(b)

Fig. 8–26. (a) Triode in grounded-cathode circuit; (b) same for pentode.

negligible with respect to R_g for our present purposes. Then, since $\mathbf{E}_o = -\mathbf{Z}_L\mathbf{I}_p$, the output voltage can be written from Fig. 8–27 as

$$\mathbf{E}_o = \frac{-\mu\mathbf{Z}_L\mathbf{E}_g}{r_p + \mathbf{Z}_L} \qquad (8\text{–}20)$$

Since the input current i_c is assumed zero, the current gain of a triode amplifier has no meaning. However, voltage gain is defined as for the transistor; that is, as the ratio of the output-voltage rise to the input-voltage rise. Then

$$\text{Voltage gain} = \mathbf{A} = \frac{\mathbf{E}_o}{\mathbf{E}_s} \qquad (8\text{–}21)$$

where the result will be complex, in general. The angle associated with the gain is called the *phase shift*.

Using Eq. 8–21, the voltage gain for the grounded-cathode circuit can be written as

$$\mathbf{A} = \frac{\mathbf{E}_o}{\mathbf{E}_s} = \frac{\mathbf{E}_o}{\mathbf{E}_g} = \frac{-\mu\mathbf{Z}_L}{r_p + \mathbf{Z}_L} = \frac{-g_m\mathbf{Z}_L}{1 + \mathbf{Z}_L/r_p} \qquad (8\text{–}22)$$

The phase reversal indicated by the negative sign is inherent in this circuit.

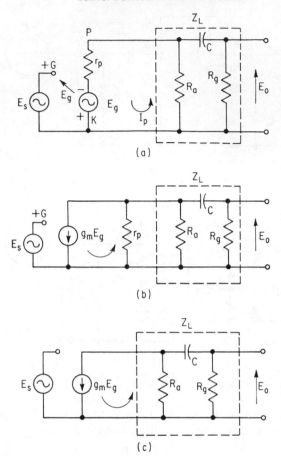

Fig. 8–27. Equivalent circuits for grounded-cathode amplifier: (a), (b) triode; (c) pentode.

If $\mathbf{Z}_L$ is made large, the gain may approach but not exceed μ. Figure 8–28 shows the variation of gain for a typical triode as a function of load. For this tube with μ of 20, a gain of 16 is about the maximum to be expected. Since the load is usually resistive, the d-c voltage drop becomes large for high resistances, lowering E_b and raising r_p, and the gain does not continue to rise for large resistances.

Use of the current-source circuit allows the pentode gain to be written from

$$\mathbf{E}_o = -g_m \mathbf{Z}_L \mathbf{E}_g,$$

$$\mathbf{A} = \frac{\mathbf{E}_o}{\mathbf{E}_s} = \frac{\mathbf{E}_o}{\mathbf{E}_g} = -g_m \mathbf{Z}_L \tag{8–23}$$

again neglecting the reactance of C as small.

The gain is shown proportional to g_m for both triode and pentode, and this is an important tube criterion. Since pentodes usually have larger g_m values, they are preferred for most applications.

Thevenin's theorem can be used to show that the output impedance of the tube is equal to r_p, at frequencies at which the internal tube capacities can be neglected. However, other considerations such as distortion make the use of matching loads undesirable in most applications.

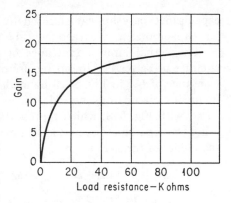

Fig. 8–28. Variation of gain with load; $\mu = 20$, $r_p = 6500$ ohms.

8–17. Input admittance of the grounded-cathode amplifier

The input or grid-cathode circuit of the grounded-cathode amplifier with negative grid has an admittance dependent on the internal tube capacitances, and the tube load. The capacities are C_{gk}, the grid-cathode capacitance; C_{gp}, the grid-plate capacitance; and C_{pk}, the plate-cathode capacitance. They are represented in Fig. 8–29(a), and for triodes are of the order of a few picofarads each.

Under negative grid conditions it might appear that the admittance into which the input generator operates would be wholly due to these capacitances; however, the active circuit alters the situation, and the

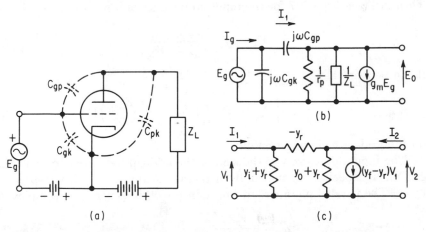

Fig. 8–29. (a) Triode showing internal capacities; (b) equivalent circuit; (c) four-terminal equivalent for (b).

capacitance may appear shunted by a resistance. The fact that the input capacitance may exceed the tube capacitance is called the *Miller effect*.

The actual input admittance of the triode in the grounded-cathode circuit can be readily found by use of the methods of Section 6–8. If the reactance of C_{pk} in Fig. 8–29 be made part of $\mathbf{Z}_L$, then the complete high-frequency circuit may be redrawn in the form of Fig. 8–29(b), and compared with Fig. 6–8, which represents the four-terminal equivalent circuit using the y parameters, and is redrawn in Fig. 8–29(c). Using direct correspondence of terms

$$y_i + y_r = j\omega C_{gk}, \qquad (y_f - y_r)\mathbf{V}_1 = g_m \mathbf{E}_g$$

$$y_r = -j\omega C_{gp}, \qquad y_o + y_r = (r_p + \mathbf{Z}_L)/r_p \mathbf{Z}_L$$

It can be seen that $\mathbf{V}_1$ must be $\mathbf{E}_g$, and that

$$y_i = j\omega(C_{gk} + C_{gp}), \qquad y_f = g_m - j\omega C_{gp}$$

$$y_r = -j\omega C_{gp}, \qquad y_o = j\omega C_{gp} + (r_p + \mathbf{Z}_L)/r_p \mathbf{Z}_L$$

An admittance matrix for the triode is then

$$[Y_g] = \begin{bmatrix} j\omega(C_{gk} + C_{gp}) & -j\omega C_{gp} \\ g_m - j\omega C_{gp} & j\omega C_{gp} + (r_p + \mathbf{Z}_L)/r_p \mathbf{Z}_L \end{bmatrix} \qquad (8\text{--}24)$$

and this is useful for high frequencies. Note that the matrix is unsymmetrical as might be expected for an active circuit.

The term $j\omega C_{gp}$ may be neglected as small in the expressions for y_f and y_o; this is equivalent to saying that the current I_1 is negligible in its effect in the load compared to the current circulating there due to $g_m \mathbf{E}_g$. Then utilizing Eq. 6–27 for the input admittance of a network,

$$Y_i = y_i - \frac{y_r y_f}{y_o + Y_L} \qquad (8\text{--}25)$$

it can be seen that

$$Y_g = j\omega \left[C_{gk} + C_{gp} \left(1 + g_m \frac{r_p \mathbf{Z}_L}{r_p + \mathbf{Z}_L} \right) \right] \qquad (8\text{--}26)$$

for the grid-cathode input circuit.

The input admittance is the sum of the grid-cathode capacity, and the grid-plate capacity multiplied by a factor usually large with respect to unity. The parallel plate circuit impedance will, in general, be complex as

$$\mathbf{Z}' = \frac{r_p \mathbf{Z}_L}{r_p + \mathbf{Z}_L} = R' + jX' \qquad (8\text{--}27)$$

Substituting in Eq. 8–26 results

$$\mathbf{Y}_g = -g_m\omega C_{gp}(\pm X') + j\omega[C_{gk} + C_{gp}(1 + g_mR')] \qquad (8\text{–}28)$$

In Fig. 8–30 the input admittance can be written as

$$\mathbf{Y} = \frac{1}{R_{\text{in}}} + j\omega C_{\text{in}}$$

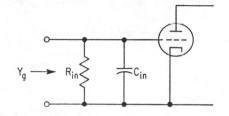

and by comparing with Eq. 8–28, it can be seen that

$$R_{\text{in}} = -\frac{1}{g_m\omega C_{gp}(\pm X')} \qquad (8\text{–}29)$$

Fig. 8–30. Equivalent input circuit of a triode.

$$C_{\text{in}} = C_{gk} + C_{gp}(1 + g_mR') \qquad (8\text{–}30)$$

Three possible cases arise from the signs in Eq. 8–29:

1. The load reactance may be inductive; X' then has a plus sign, and R_{in} becomes a negative resistance.
2. The load reactance may be zero (load resistive), and R_{in} is infinite, or represents an open circuit.
3. The load reactance may be capacitive; X' has a minus sign, and R_{in} becomes a positive resistance.

The input capacity C_{in} is the same for all three cases.

Presence of a negative resistance in the grid circuit indicates that power is being supplied to the circuit, rather than dissipated as in a positive resistance. Actually, when R_{in} is negative, or the load is inductive, the current $\mathbf{I}_{yp}$ has a phase relation with respect to $\mathbf{E}_y$ such that power is being received in the grid circuit from the plate circuit through C_{gp}. Whenever the power fed back per cycle is greater than the input-circuit losses per cycle, the net circuit resistance is zero or negative, and the tube becomes an oscillator. Because of this possibility of instability in triodes, such tubes are limited to amplification at only the lower radio frequencies. It is also found that C_{in} becomes prohibitively large for triodes. However, the pentode has a very small C_{gp} by design, and is capable of satisfactory amplification at frequencies of several hundred megacycles in the grounded-cathode circuit.

When the load is resistive the input circuit is a capacitance with a value considerably larger than C_{gk}. For capacitive loads, the input resistance is positive and the grid circuit absorbs power from the source. Since ω appears in the denominator of R_{in}, the magnitude of R_{in} is a function of frequency.

A more rigorous analysis, in which C_{pk} is considered separately and in which no assumption is made regarding the relative magnitude of the reactance of C_{gp} and the parallel impedance of r_p and $\mathbf{Z}_L$, leads to a modified result for Case 1. The input resistance R_{in} is found to be

$$R_{in} = \frac{(R_L^2 + \omega^2 L_L^2)\left[\left(\dfrac{1}{r_p} + \dfrac{R_L}{R_L^2 + \omega^2 L_L^2}\right)^2 + \omega^2\left(C_{gp} + C_{pk} - \dfrac{L_L}{R_L^2 + \omega^2 L_L^2}\right)^2\right]}{\omega^2\{R_L C_{gp}^2 + g_m C_{gp}[A(R_L^2 + \omega^2 L_L^2) - L_L]\}}$$

(8–31)

where

$$A = C_{gp}[(\mu + 1)/\mu] + C_{pk}$$

It can be seen from the denominator that R_{in} is not negative for all values of inductive load, as implied in Case 1 above. Equating the denominator of Eq. 8–31 to zero leads to a quadratic from which

$$L_L = \frac{1 \pm \sqrt{1 - \dfrac{4\omega^2 A R_L}{g_m}(C_{gp} + A g_m R_L)}}{2\omega^2 A}$$

(8–32)

This determines two limiting values of L_L, between which R_{in} takes on negative values. If R_L is very large, the solution for the limiting values of L_L may be imaginary, and there is no value of load inductance that will give a negative input resistance.

8–18. The grounded-grid amplifier

The amplifier with input between cathode and grid and output between plate and grid is called a *grounded-grid amplifier*, although the grounding of the grid is not a necessity but is done to obtain electrostatic shielding between the input and output circuits. At very high frequencies this shielding reduces the transfer of energy between output and input, prevents oscillation, and permits the use of some triodes.

For small input signals at nominal frequencies the equivalent circuit may be drawn as in Fig. 8–31(b), by rearranging the elements of the equivalent circuit for the triode. The internal capacitances shown in Fig. 8–31(a) are neglected. The plate current flows through the signal source, and the internal impedance of the source must be included as R_1. This impedance is frequently that of a resonant circuit, and therefore it is permissible to consider it as resistive.

Writing equations for the two current meshes gives

$$\mu \mathbf{E}_g + \mathbf{E}_s = \mathbf{I}_p(r_p + R_1 + \mathbf{Z}_L) \tag{8–33}$$

$$\mathbf{E}_g - \mathbf{E}_s = -\mathbf{I}_p R_1 \tag{8–34}$$

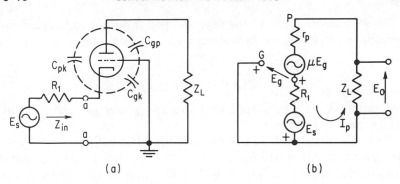

Fig. 8–31. Grounded-grid amplifier at (a); (b) equivalent, neglecting capacities.

and the plate current then is

$$I_p = \frac{(\mu + 1)\mathbf{E}_s}{r_p + (\mu + 1)R_1 + \mathbf{Z}_L}$$

The load voltage rise from grid to plate is $\mathbf{E}_o = -\mathbf{I}_p\mathbf{Z}_L$, and since $\mathbf{E}_s$ represents a negative rise above the common terminal, the gain for the circuit is

$$\mathbf{A} = \frac{\mathbf{E}_o}{\mathbf{E}_s} = \frac{(\mu + 1)\mathbf{Z}_L}{r_p + (\mu + 1)R_1 + \mathbf{Z}_L} \tag{8–35}$$

The output of the amplifier is in phase with the input signal.

Since $\mathbf{E}_s$ is directly in series with the equivalent transfer generator $\mu\mathbf{E}_g$, the input voltage adds to that of the equivalent generator, giving an apparent increase in amplification factor of the tube to $(\mu + 1)$. Equation 8–35 also shows that the effective output impedance of the tube in the grounded-grid circuit is

$$r_p' = r_p + (\mu + 1)R_1$$

At frequencies at which the tube capacitive reactances can be considered large with respect to the shunting circuit impedances, the input impedance of the tube at terminals a, a is

$$\mathbf{Z}_{\text{in}} = \frac{\mathbf{E}_g}{\mathbf{I}_p} = \frac{r_p + \mathbf{Z}_L}{\mu + 1} \tag{8–36}$$

The input impedance appears as the total plate circuit impedance divided by $(\mu + 1)$. The tube capacitance C_{gk} will appear in parallel with this impedance, but because $\mathbf{Z}_{\text{in}}$ is usually small, the effect of C_{gk} is not noted until quite high frequencies are reached. For a tube of $\mu = 20$, $r_p = 7700$ ohms, and a load of 50,000 ohms, the value of $\mathbf{Z}_{\text{in}}$ is 2750 ohms.

There is power input to the tube and power output to the load, so the circuit may be considered as a power amplifier with a power gain given by

$$\frac{P_{\text{out}}}{P_{\text{in}}} = \frac{\mathbf{E}_o^2/R_L}{\mathbf{E}_s^2(\mu + 1)/(r_p + R_L)} = |A| \tag{8-37}$$

from terminals a, a to output load R_L. The power gain is equal to the voltage gain magnitude.

Since the input and output currents are identical, the circuit appears analogous to a pump which raises water from a low-pressure system to a high-pressure pipe line. The circuit is of value in transforming from a source of low impedance, such as an antenna, to a load of high impedance. Another advantage is the reduction of coupling between input and output circuits by reason of the shielding introduced by the grid. Instead of C_{gp} being the capacitance which couples input and output as in grid input-plate output circuits, that function is now taken over by C_{pk}, which can be reduced to a very low value by reason of the shielding introduced by the grid.

8–19. The cathode follower

An amplifier with input between grid and plate and output between cathode and plate, or with the plate common, is usually called a *cathode follower*. This name is applied because the cathode a-c potential or output is practically equal to the grid-signal voltage. The circuit and its equivalent in voltage-source form is drawn in Fig. 8–32.

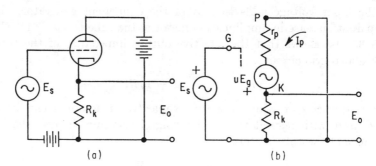

Fig. 8–32. Cathode follower amplifier and voltage-source equivalent.

By neglecting the tube capacitances, the voltage equations can be written as

$$\mathbf{E}_g = \mathbf{E}_s - \mathbf{I}_p R_k$$

$$\mu \mathbf{E}_g = \mathbf{I}_p(r_p + R_k)$$

Solving for I_p gives

$$I_p = \frac{g_m E_s}{1 + g_m R_k + R_k/r_p} \qquad (8\text{–}38)$$

The voltage amplification is then

$$A = \frac{g_m R_k}{1 + g_m R_k + R_k/r_p} = \frac{\mu R_k}{r_p + (\mu + 1) R_k} = \frac{1}{1 + \dfrac{1}{g_m R_k} + \dfrac{1}{\mu}} \qquad (8\text{–}39)$$

Since the quantities in the denominator are all positive, it can be seen that the gain is always less than unity, but approaches unity as $g_m R_k$ increases. For the pentode, where $r_p \gg R_k$ and $\mu \gg 1$, the expressions simplify. When a pentode is used in this circuit, the screen-bypass capacitor should connect to cathode and not to ground, since the screen must be held at zero a-c potential *with respect to cathode* for proper screening action.

The impedance which the cathode follower presents to its load circuit may be obtained from Fig. 8–32(b). Assume a current I_1 into the upper E_o terminal. The impedance looking into the E_o terminals is then the ratio of E_o to I_1, with the internal source E_s shorted. The mesh equations are

$$E_o = R_k I_1 + R_k I_p = -E_g \qquad (8\text{–}40)$$

$$\mu E_g = R_k I_1 + (r_p + R_k) I_p \qquad (8\text{–}41)$$

Solving for I_p gives

$$I_p = \frac{-(\mu + 1) R_k I_1}{r_p + (\mu + 1) R_k}$$

Inserting this result in Eq. 8–40 and dividing by I_1 yields

$$Z_o = \frac{E_o}{I_1} = \frac{R_k}{1 + g_m R_k + R_k/r_p} = \frac{r_p R_k/(\mu + 1)}{R_k + r_p/(\mu + 1)} \qquad (8\text{–}42)$$

as the output impedance. From the first expression it is apparent that $Z_o = A/g_m$. The latter relation is that of two resistors in parallel, namely, R_k and the effective tube resistance $r_p/(\mu + 1) \cong 1/g_m$.

The cathode follower has a reduced input admittance over the grounded-cathode circuit. From Fig. 8–33, with the current-source equivalent used for convenience, and with C_{pk} neglected, it is possible to write

$$I_g = I_{gp} + I_{gk} = j\omega C_{gp} E_s + j\omega C_{gk}(E_s - E_o) \qquad (8\text{–}43)$$

Division by E_s gives

$$Y_g = \frac{I_g}{E_s} = j\omega [C_{gp} + C_{gk}(1 - A)] \qquad (8\text{–}44)$$

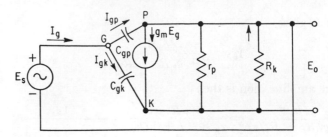

Fig. 8-33. Equivalent circuit for the cathode follower, including capacitances.

since $\mathbf{E}_o/\mathbf{E}_s = \mathbf{A}$. With the load consisting of R_k, the gain $\mathbf{A}$ is real and positive, so that the input admittance is wholly due to a capacitance

$$C_{\text{in}} = C_{gp} + C_{gk}(1 - A) \tag{8-45}$$

The gain A will be less than unity but ordinarily near it, and so the capacitance is almost entirely due to C_{gp}.

The circuit is often used as an impedance transformer to couple a high-impedance source to a low-impedance load. It also provides an output with one side at ground, and without a phase reversal. In general the circuit may be viewed as a current amplifier, analogous to the emitter-follower form of transistor circuit.

8-20. Modified cathode follower

Frequently the desired value for R_k as a load for a cathode follower leads to excessive bias, and the circuit of Fig. 8-34 may then be useful. It has the added value of a very high input resistance, a property of value in vacuum-tube voltmeters and other measuring equipment.

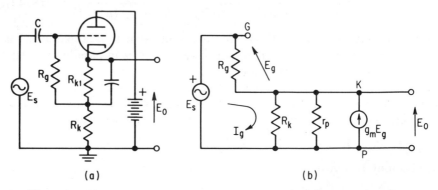

Fig. 8-34. Circuit of high input impedance cathode follower and emitter follower.

The resistor R_{k1} may be selected to provide the desired bias, while eliminated from the a-c output by the bypass capacitor. The a-c load for the circuit is then furnished by R_k. The circuit relations may be written

$$\mathbf{E}_g = \mathbf{E}_s - \mathbf{E}_o = R_g \mathbf{I}_g$$

$$\mathbf{E}_o = (\mathbf{I}_g + g_m \mathbf{E}_g)(R_k r_p / (R_k + r_p)$$

Solution for the gain $\mathbf{A} = \mathbf{E}_o/\mathbf{E}_s$, gives

$$\mathbf{A} = \cfrac{1}{1 + \cfrac{(r_p + R_k) R_g}{R_k r_p (1 + g_m R_g)}} \tag{8–46}$$

It is usually easy to make $g_m R_g \gg 1$, and then the gain approaches unity if μR_k is large.

Neglecting the tube capacitances, it can be found that the input resistance is greater than R_g, because of the active form of the circuit. Using the circuit equations

$$R_{\text{in}} = \frac{\mathbf{E}_s}{\mathbf{I}_g} = R_g \left(1 + \frac{\mathbf{E}_o}{\mathbf{E}_s - \mathbf{E}_o}\right) = R_g \left(\frac{1}{1 - \mathbf{A}}\right) \tag{8–47}$$

Since $|\mathbf{A}|$ will be less than but near unity, the input resistance can be considerably greater than R_g alone, and this is of value in circuits which operate across sources of very high resistance. The circuit is then comparable to the emitter follower of Section 7–9.

8–21. Cathode-coupled circuits

The output impedance of a cathode follower is low. The input resistance of a grounded-grid amplifier is also low. It is obvious that someone would think of the possibilities inherent in using a cathode follower to excite a grounded-grid stage, since the impedances may be easily made an approximate match. Such a two-tube circuit is said to be *cathode-coupled*; a circuit is shown in Fig. 8–35.

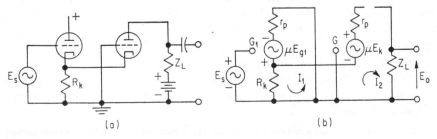

(a)   (b)

Fig. 8–35. A cathode-coupled amplifier.

Ordinarily the two tubes are identical, and frequently a double triode is used. Starting with

$$\mathbf{E}_s - \mathbf{E}_{g1} = R_k \mathbf{I}_1 - R_k \mathbf{I}_2$$

$$\mu \mathbf{E}_{g1} = (r_p + R_k)\mathbf{I}_1 - R_k \mathbf{I}_2$$

$$-\mu \mathbf{E}_k = \mu \mathbf{E}_{g2} = R_k \mathbf{I}_1 - (r_p + R_k + \mathbf{Z}_L)\mathbf{I}_2$$

it is possible to obtain

$$\mathbf{A} = \frac{\mathbf{E}_o}{\mathbf{E}_s} = \frac{\mu \mathbf{Z}_L}{r_p \left[2 + \dfrac{r_p + \mathbf{Z}_L}{(\mu + 1)R_k}\right] + \mathbf{Z}_L} \qquad (8\text{--}48)$$

This expression indicates that the cathode-coupled amplifier behaves like an ordinary grounded-cathode stage having a tube of amplification factor μ and a plate resistance greater than twice r_p of one of the triodes. There is also no inherent phase shift.

Although maximum gain is theoretically obtained with R_k large, its effect in Eq. 8–48 is small and the value giving correct bias is usually chosen and found satisfactory.

8–22. Noise in amplifiers

Amplifiers are limited in their useful sensitivity by electrical "noise" or erratic currents generated in the circuits of the amplifier, or by noise introduced into the input with the signal.

The noise generated within the amplifier is caused by random motions of electric charges in circuit elements and tubes or transistors. For very weak signals the number of charges moved per second is quite small, and the inherent particle nature of electric current becomes apparent. The introduction of a weak signal into an amplifier becomes analogous to the pouring of a varying number of marbles through a pipe, rather than to the varying flow of a stream of water as in the usual hydraulic-analogy concept. In addition, the marbles have random velocities in all directions, which usually exceed the directed components of velocity due to the input signal.

Ordinarily, noise generated in the circuits is a limiting factor only in the first stage of an amplifier, since after some amplification the output from the first stage is usually sufficient to override any noise generated in a second stage.

Noise which is generated externally and arrives with the signal cannot be greatly reduced by receiver design. In the usual reception of signals with frequencies below about 20 megacycles, it is the external noise which limits receiver sensitivity. For frequencies above 20 megacycles it is usually internal noise which provides the sensitivity limit. In any case, the limit is that ratio of signal to noise which just permits satisfactory reception of the transmitted information.

8–23. Noise sources

The noise in an input circuit is usually due to the random motions of the free charges present, and is called *thermal noise*. The noise energy is uniformly distributed over the whole of the frequency spectrum now in use, and is believed to be due to impacts of electrons with molecules. Each impact produces a very short pulse, which if analyzed can be found to consist of a continuous distribution of frequencies. The noise energy is proportional to absolute temperature, since the impacts appear due to thermal vibrations. The thermal noise voltage developed in a resistor R is found to be

$$E_{\text{noise}} = \sqrt{4kTR\,\Delta f}$$

where

k = Boltzmann's constant = 1.38×10^{-23} joule/°K

T = temperature, °K

R = resistance, ohms

Δf = frequency band measured, cycles per second.

The noise source is often considered as equivalent to a generator of voltage E_{noise}, in series with a noiseless resistor R. It is apparent that the maximum power which such a thermal-noise source could supply to the external load would be obtained when the load is matched to R, the source resistance; then

$$W_{\text{max}} = \frac{E_{\text{noise}}^2}{4R} = kT\,\Delta f \qquad (8\text{–}49)$$

the noise power then depends on the frequency band accepted by the amplifier; wide-band amplifiers are inherently more noisy than narrow-band circuits.

For a band width of 4 megacycles, and room temperature of 300°K, the thermal noise present in a circuit, and independent of the resistance as indicated by Eq. 8–49, is 1.6×10^{-14} w. This power would be that due to a signal of 1.26 μv across a 100 ohm circuit.

For the above, the definition of band width to be employed is indicated in Fig. 8–36.

The noise power is a temperature function, and the lowering of the temperature of the input circuit of a device offers an attractive means of reducing the thermal noise; this method is applied in some forms of very sensitive amplifiers. The temperature reduction is accomplished by the use of liquid gases as cooling media. Other methods of noise reduction in reception of radio signals will be discussed later.

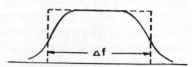

Fig. 8–36. Designation of band width for use in calculation of noise power, where the solid curve is the square of the usual voltage gain-frequency curve.

For use in appraising the performance of circuits with respect to noise, a comparative *noise figure*, F, has been defined as the *ratio of the noise power output, N, from a network with a thermal noise source, to the power input directly from the thermal noise source times the power gain G of the network.*

Thus
$$F = \frac{N_{\text{out}}}{N_{\text{in}}G} = \frac{N_{\text{out}}}{kT\,\Delta f G} \tag{8–50}$$

The noise figure as a ratio is always greater than unity, and is usually expressed in decibel units.

Sources of noise particularly attributed to the presence of vacuum tubes in a circuit comprise the following:

Shot noise results from the random emission of electrons from a cathode. When tubes are operated under space-charge-limited conditions this noise is reduced because of the smoothing effect of the reservoir of electrons in the virtual cathode. This noise is uniformly distributed over the useful frequency region.

Cathode-flicker effect is observed with oxide-coated cathodes and is associated with variations in emission efficiency of the emitting surface. The effect is reduced by space-charge operation of the tube, and is not of importance at high frequencies.

Gas noise is due to ionization of gas molecules still remaining in the tube, the positive ions causing random current disturbances as they penetrate the space charge. The noise is not usually appreciable above 10 megacycles.

Induced grid noise is due to random fluctuations in the space charge which induce voltages in the grid circuit. This noise is appreciable above 30 megacycles.

Partition noise is caused by the irregular division of current between two or more positive electrodes. That is, it is an arbitrary matter whether a particular electron goes to the screen or to the anode, although the time average may be constant. Partition noise makes pentodes or tetrodes more noisy than triodes.

For the comparison of tubes on a noise basis, it is convenient to express the noise output in terms of the value of R_{eq}, an equivalent resistor which if inserted in series with the control grid of a noise-free tube, would generate the same noise current in the output circuit, as is created by the actual tube. An approximate expression for this resistance for *triodes* has been developed as

$$R_{\text{eq}} \cong \frac{2.5}{g_m} \text{ ohms}$$

where the noise is predominantly due to the shot effect. For pentodes the partition noise also enters and the equivalent resistance is equal to the sum of resistors representing the effects of the two types of noise, or

$$R_{\text{eq}} \cong \frac{2.5}{g_m} + \frac{20I_s}{g_m I_k}$$

where I_s and I_k are screen and cathode currents, respectively.

It should be emphasized that the noise figure is a variable between different tubes of the same type, possibly because of residual gas and of accidents of alignment in manufacture. A set of typical noise resistances appear in Table 11.

TABLE 11. EQUIVALENT NOISE RESISTANCE OF TUBES

Type	g_m	R_{eq}, ohms
Triodes		
6AK5	6,670	385
6C4	2,200	1,140
6J4	12,000	210
6J6	5,300	470
9002	2,200	1,140
6CW4	12,500	200
Pentodes		
6AG5	5,000	1,640
6AK5	5,000	1,880
9001	1,400	6,600

Many circuit and tube combinations have been investigated in an effort to reduce the noise generated in amplifier inputs. It has been found that combinations of the basic circuits with certain tube types can appreciably reduce the noise figure. Considerable variability between tubes of the same type is always to be expected; a tube which conducts an appreciably large cathode current for a given set of applied voltages will usually be noisy. The presence of residual gas may contribute to this situation. A set of average values of noise figure is given in Table 12 for a few basic circuit combinations.

TABLE 12. NOISE FIGURES OF AMPLIFIERS

Circuits	Tube Type	Frequency mc	Band Width, Δf	Average Noise Figure, db
Pentodes				
Two-stage, grounded-cathode circuits	6AK5, 6AK5	30	6	3.3
Triodes				
Two-stage, grounded-grid circuits	6J4, 6J4	180	2.5	7.0
Two-stage, grounded plate, grounded grid	6J4, 6J4	30	3.4	2.5
Two-stage, grounded cathode, grounded grid	6AK5, 6J4	30	6	1.35

Data from Valley, G. E., Jr., and Wallman, H., *Vacuum Tube Amplifiers*, McGraw-Hill Book Co., Inc., New York, 1948.

Problems

8-1. (a) Using the plate characteristics for the 12AU7 tube in the Appendix, plot the static transfer characteristic for $E_b = 200$ v.

(b) In the same way, plot the dynamic characteristic for $E_{bb} = 200$ v, the load resistor being 25,000 ohms.

8-2. From the following data taken on a triode find μ, g_m, and r_p, independently:

i_b, ma	e_c, v	e_b, v
8.2	0	165
6.0	0	130
6.0	−1	165
4.1	−1	130
4.1	−2	165

8-3. If the function of Eq. 8-2 is expanded, it yields

$$i_b = k_0 + k_1(\mu e_c + e_b) + k_2(\mu e_c + e_b)^2 + \cdots.$$

Using the first three terms of the series, find values for k_0, k_1, and k_2 which will produce an equation fitting the $e_c = -2$ curve for the 12AT7 tube. Plot your curve at large scale with the actual curve for comparison.

8-4. For a certain triode, the function of Eq. 8-2 may be expanded as

$$i_b,\ \text{amp} = 87 \times 10^{-6}(\mu e_c + e_b) + 1.5 \times 10^{-7}(\mu e_c + e_b)^2.$$

If $\mu = 15$ and the operating point is at $e_c = -7$ v and $e_b = 210$ v, find i_b, r_p, and g_m.

8-5. A triode has $g_m = 3300\ \mu\text{mho}$, $r_p = 5100$ ohms.
(a) Find the plate-current change produced by variation of the grid voltage from -2 to -6 v, at $E_b = 140$ v.
(b) What change in plate voltage will bring the plate current back to its original value, with e_c remaining at -6 v?

8-6. For a particular triode the plate current can be found from

$$i_b,\ \text{ma} = 0.0042(4.2e_c + e_b)^2.$$

If $e_b = E_b = 200$ v, $E_{cc} = -10$ v, and $e_g = 3$ v peak sine wave, find the average, maximum, and minimum values of plate current.

8-7. Two tubes having the following parameters are connected in parallel:

$$\mu = 4.2 \qquad\qquad \mu = 17$$

$$g_m = 4500\ \mu\text{mho} \qquad g_m = 1250\ \mu\text{mho}$$

Find the μ, g_m, and r_p of a single tube which would be equivalent in operation.

8-8. (a) If the dynamic grid transfer characteristic can be expressed by an equation of the form

$$i_b = a_0 + a_1 e_g + a_2 e_g^2,$$

show that a small input voltage $e_g = E \sin \omega t$ will produce an output current

$$i_b = a_0 + \frac{a_2 E^2}{2} + a_1 E \sin \omega t - \frac{a_2 E^2}{2} \cos 2\omega t.$$

(b) Find the expression for the output current if $e_g = E_1 \sin \omega t + E_3 \sin 3.5\ \omega t$.

8-9. (a) Draw the voltage-source equivalent circuits for circuits (a) to (f) of Fig. 8-37.
(b) Indicate assumed loop currents produced by varying signal components.

8-10. Draw current-source equivalent circuits of the circuits (g) to (h) of Fig. 8-37.

8-11. By use of equivalent circuits find the gain or ratio E_0/E of the circuit of (f), Fig. 8-37.

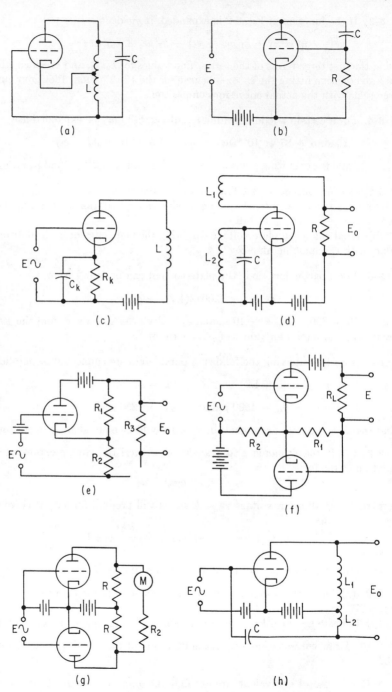

Fig. 8–37.

8-12. By use of the current-source equivalent circuit for (g), Fig. 8-37, if $R = 10,000$ ohms, $\mu = 10$, $r_p = 7000$ ohms, find the a-c current through meter M of resistance $R_2 = 100$ ohms, if $E = 1.0$ v. Assume identical tubes.

8-13. In (e), Fig. 8-37, let $R_1 = 10,000$, $R_2 = 3000$, $R_3 = 5000$, $r_p = 10,000$ ohms, $g_m = 2500$ μmho. Find the voltage E_0, and the current through the tube, if $E = 2.0$ v.

8-14. For loads of 5000, 10,000, 25,000, and 50,000 ohms, determine graphically from the curves in the Appendix the values of E_b and I_b for a 12AT7 triode with $E_{bb} = 300$ v and $E_{cc} = -3$ v. What load resistance will be required to place the Q point at $I_b = 6$ ma, $E_{cc} = -2$ v, with $E_{bb} = 320$ v?

8-15. A 2A3 tube (characteristics in the Appendix) is operated in the circuit of Fig. 8-10, (b), with $R_1 = 3000$ ohms, $R_2 = 1500$ ohms, and C very large. The grid is supplied with a sine wave input of 30 v peak, 1000 cycles, and $E_{cc} = -40$ v, $E_{bb} = 350$ v.

(a) Find the a-c output voltage and the d-c power lost in the tube.

(b) What are the peak and rms plate current values?

8-16. (a) What load resistance will place the Q point at $I_b = 10$ ma, $E_{cc} = -2$ v, for a plate supply voltage $E_{bb} = 325$ v, with a 12AT7 tube?

(b) Calculate the gain of the tube operated as in (a).

8-17. If E is short-circuited, the meter M of (g), Fig. 8-37, reads zero, with identical tubes of $\mu = 22$, $g_m = 1600$, $R_1 = 15,000$ ohms, $R_2 = 2000$ ohms. Find the reading of meter M if $E = 1.0$ v rms, 60 cycles.

8-18. The characteristic of a triode is given by

$$i_p, \text{ ma} = 0.00037(8e_c + e_b)^{1.6}.$$

Find the small-signal gain of an amplifier using this tube at 100 cycles per second if the plate load is a 15.9-henry inductor of zero resistance, with $E_{cc} = -10$ v, $e_{bb} = 200$ v. Assume the equivalent circuit is usable over the small-signal region.

8-.19 A 6BA6 pentode has the following characteristics:

$$g_m = 4400 \ \mu\text{mho} \qquad\qquad E_{c2} = 100 \text{ v}$$

$$r_p = 1.5 \text{ megohms} \qquad\qquad I_{c2} = 4.2 \text{ ma}$$

$$I_b = 5.5 \text{ ma} \qquad\qquad C_{gk} = 5.5 \text{ pf}$$

$$E_{bb} = 250 \text{ v} \qquad\qquad C_{gp} = 0.0035 \text{ pf}$$

$$E_{c1} = -3 \text{ v} \qquad\qquad C_{pk} = 5.0 \text{ pf}$$

and is used in the circuit of Fig. 8-26 (b).

(a) Calculate desirable values for R_k, C_k, R_s, C_s which will be satisfactory over the frequency range 500 to 1500 kc.

(b) With a resonant load at 1.25×10^6 cycles, of resistive impedance of 125,000 ohms, find the gain.

8-.20 A 6BA6 is to provide an output voltage of 35 v with $I_p = 0.24$ ma.

(a) Find the required rms signal voltage.

(b) What per cent error is introduced in (a) by use of the approximate equivalent circuit with r_p infinite?

8-.21 A type 6BA6 pentode is operated as an amplifier with a resistive load of 25,000 ohms, other values as in Problem 8-19. Calculate the input capacity of this amplifier at a frequency of 140 megacycles.

8-22. (a) A 12AT7 tube (see Appendix) has a plate-circuit load consisting of a 100-microhenry inductance at a frequency of 10^6 cycles. Compute the value of R_{in} and C_{in}.

(b) Repeat at a frequency of 10^8 cycles. Would this tube input constitute a suitable load for a radio-receiver antenna circuit having 5000 ohms impedance at this frequency?

8-23. In Fig. 8-38, with $\mu = 35$ and $r_p = 27,000$ ohms, what input voltage will be required to give an output of 1.0 v rms at 300 cycles?

8-24. A 6AT6 triode has the following characteristics at a normal Q point:

$$\mu = 70 \qquad E_{bb} = 250 \text{ v} \qquad C_{gk} = 2.3 \text{ pf}$$

$$g_m = 1200 \text{ } \mu\text{mho} \qquad E_{cc} = -3 \text{ v} \qquad C_{gp} = 2.1 \text{ pf}$$

$$I_b = 1.0 \text{ ma} \qquad\qquad\qquad C_{pk} = 1.1 \text{ pf}$$

With a plate load of $3000 + j3000$ ohms, plot curves of input resistance and reactance over a range of 1 to 100 megacycles, using a logarithmic frequency scale.

8-25. In Fig. 8-34(a), $R_g = 10$ megohms, $R_{k1} = 2000$ ohms, $R_k = 25,000$ ohms. The tube is one half of a 12AU7.

(a) Find the input impedance seen by the generator E_s. Neglect the reactance of C.

(b) If $E_s = 2$ v rms, find the output voltage and power.

(c) Find the decibel power gain in the amplifier.

8-26. The grounded-grid amplifier of Fig. 8-31 uses a tube having $\mu = 70$, $R_p = 40,000$ ohms. With $R_1 = 300$ ohms, $Z_L = 25,000$ ohms resistance, find the decibel power gain and the impedance seen by the signal source.

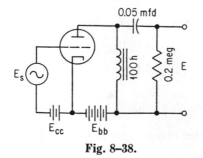

Fig. 8–38.

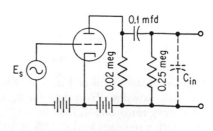

Fig. 8–39.

8-27. A generator has a resistance of 500 ohms and generated voltage of 0.05 v. With a grounded-grid amplifier having $\mu = 20$, $_p = 7000$ ohms, design a circuit having an input resistance matching the generator and determine the output voltage to be expected.

8-28. The circuit of Fig. 8-39 is to be used with one half of a 12AU7 tube. If $E_{bb} = 250$ v and $I_b = 4.5$ ma, determine a value for R_k which will replace the battery for $E_{cc} = -6$ v. Designate a value for C_k if the lowest frequency is to be 30 cycles, and calculate the gain at 30 cycles with R_k and C_k connected.

8-29. A 6AT6 is to have $E_{cc} = -3$ v, $I_b = 1$ ma, with $\mu = 70$ and $r_p = 44{,}000$ ohms. The value of R_k must ensure a gain of 0.90 in a cathode follower. Draw a circuit which will permit the proper value of bias to be obtained, as well as the value of R_k for the desired gain.

8-30. In Fig. 8-35, $\mathbf{Z}_L = 50{,}000$ ohms, $R_k = 1000$ ohms, and the tube is a 12AU7, containing two triodes. If $E_s = 1$ v rms, find the output voltage across $\mathbf{Z}_L$.

References

1. *American Standards for Graphical Symbols for Electronic Devices.* American Standard Z32.10—1944, American Standards Association, New York.

2. Ballantine, S., and Snow, H. A., "Reduction of Distortion and Cross-Talk in Radio Receivers by Means of Variable-Mu Tetrodes," *Proc. I.R.E.*, **18**, 2102 (1930).

3. Butler, F., "Analysis of the Bootstrap Follower," *Wireless World*, 69, 21, 1963.

4. *Coordination of Electrical Graphical Symbols.* American Standard Z32.11—1944, American Standards Association, New York.

5. Jones, M. C., "Grounded-Grid Radio-Frequency Voltage Amplifiers," *Proc. I.R.E.*, **32**, 423 (1944).

6. Miller, J. M., "Dependence of Input Impedance of a Three-Electrode Vacuum Tube upon the Load in the Plate Circuit," *Sci. Paper* 351, National Bureau of Standards, Washington, D. C.

7. Richter, W., "Cathode-Follower Circuits," *Electronics*, **16**, 112 (November 1943).

8. Schade, O. H., "Beam Power Tubes," *Proc. I.R.E.*, **26**, 137 (1938).

9. Seely, S., *Electron-Tube Circuits.* McGraw-Hill Book Co., New York, 1950.

10. *Standards on Abbreviations, Graphical Symbols, Letter Symbols, and Mathematical Signs.* Institute of Electrical and Electronics Engineers, New York, 1948.

Linear Small-Signal Amplifiers | 9

Linear amplifier applications of tube and transistor now cover a wide field. Certain circuits are fundamental, however, and will be utilized here to illustrate the methods employed in the determination of the response of amplifiers to signals of varying frequency.

The restriction of such analysis to small input signals will insure that the region of operation be limited to linear portions of the device characteristics, providing constant tube or transistor parameter values. This permits the use of the equivalent circuit; analysis under large-signal conditions follows in Chapter 11.

Primary considerations in amplifier analysis and design may include gain, frequency response over narrow or wide frequency bands, phase shift or delay, noise generation, desirable values of input and output impedance, and others. The methods illustrated are in general applicable to either transistor or tube, and will be demonstrated with either without implying any lack of generality. Where differences arise, they will be discussed.

Amplifiers may be utilized with input signals which have component frequencies covering wide frequency ranges, and thus the circuit reactances can have important effects in altering loads and impedances. One common class of amplifier handles *audio frequencies* for reproduction of speech and music, with the frequency band covering the range from 100 to 12,000 cycles per second as a minimum to a range of 20 to 100,000 cycles per second as a maximum in well-designed equipment. The so-called *video amplifier* of the television system must handle the broad range of frequencies from 30 cycles to 4.5 megacycles. Amplifiers such as these, in which the frequency response starts near zero frequency and extends to a higher frequency of some hundreds or thousands of kilocycles, are studied in the next few sections of this chapter. Amplifiers which are centered on, or *tuned* to a given range of frequencies remote from zero frequency, are covered at a later point in the chapter.

9–1. Wave-form distortion

Linear operation of an amplifier implies that the output wave form be an accurate reproduction of the wave form applied to the input circuit. This includes the common application of speech or music amplifiers, in which the ideal is to hear the recreated sound as if it were heard in the original.

If at any point in the system an alteration of the wave form occurs, the output information is altered, or the sound is not heard as it was introduced to the input microphone. Phenomena in a circuit or network which cause a difference between input and output wave forms are said to produce *distortion*.

Three possible causes of distortion are recognized and classified according to the cause, as:

1. Frequency distortion.
2. Nonlinear (amplitude) distortion.
3. Phase or delay distortion.

Frequency distortion is produced by unequal amplification of the component frequencies introduced by the input signal. At Fig. 9–1 (a), a certain input wave form is analyzed into a fundamental and a second-harmonic component. If this input wave is applied to an amplifier with gain of n

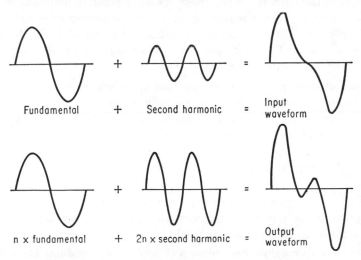

Fundamental   +   Second harmonic   =   Input waveform

n x fundamental   +   2n x second harmonic   =   Output waveform

Fig. 9–1. Frequency distortion: (a) above, (b) below.

times for the fundamental frequency, and $2n$ times for the second-harmonic, the two components will have output amplitudes as shown in Fig. 9–1(b), and their sum will constitute the output wave form. This output wave is different from the input wave form, and frequency distortion has taken place.

The presence of frequency distortion is usually indicated by plotting a curve of amplifier output in volts or db against frequency, for a constant-amplitude sinusoidal input. The ideal amplifier should have equal gain at all frequencies, and frequency distortion is present if the plot is not a horizontal line, as shown in Fig. 9–2. The curve of gain against frequency is normally

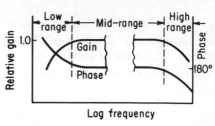

Fig. 9–2. Typical gain and phase shift curves.

plotted on semilogarithmic paper with frequency on the log scale, to encompass large frequency ranges. The ordinate may also be logarithmic, if the gain is plotted in db.

Frequency distortion is largely a result of the circuits associated with the active device. It can be reduced by adequate sizing of the reactive components, in order to minimize their effects in the circuit. The reactive elements in the tube or transistor remain as a final limit to the success of this method.

Nonlinear, or amplitude distortion is produced if the input-output amplitude curve of the amplifier is not linear. This is a result of nonlinear dynamic characteristics for the vacuum tube, or of nonlinear base-collector or emitter-collector relations for the transistor. The effect is illustrated for the tube in Fig. 9–3. The output current contains harmonics which were generated by the nonlinear action.

A special form of nonlinear distortion is known as *intermodulation*. If two or more frequencies are simultaneously present in the input, then besides the harmonics, additional frequencies which are the sums and differences of integral multiples of all the frequencies present will also appear in the output. These sum and difference frequencies bear no harmonic relation to the original frequencies and in audio amplifier outputs are heard as noise.

The effects of nonlinear distortion can be minimized by operation over linear portions of the characteristics and by use of circuits which will reduce some of the distortion produced.

The above discussion is based on a steady-state situation. The response of circuits to transients may be different from their response to steady-state conditions, and will also represent distortion.

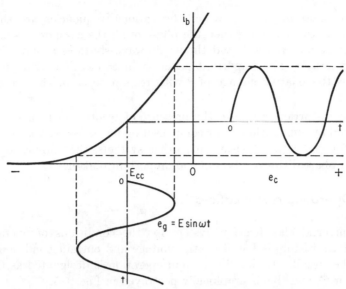

Fig. .9–3. Distortion due to nonlinear dynamic characteristic.

Phase or delay distortion occurs if the phase relation between the various frequency components making up the wave is not the same in the output as in the input. This means that the time of transmission through the circuit is different for various frequencies. If, in Fig. 9–4(a), an input wave form of fundamental and second harmonic is again chosen, and the time of transmission of the second harmonic is different from the time of the fundamental, then the output wave form may be appreciably altered, as in Fig. 9–4(b), and this alteration constitutes phase distortion.

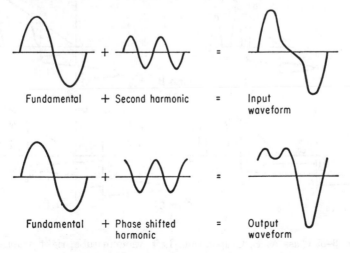

Fig. 9–4. Phase distortion (a) above, (b) below.

If the phase angle θ by which the various frequencies are shifted is proportional to frequency, then the phase of all the components is shifted by the same *time interval*, and the whole wave shifts as a unit, giving no phase distortion. The important criterion in connection with phase distortion is the relative change of θ with respect to ω, or that $d\theta/d\omega$ be a constant.

Phase distortion is due to the presence of reactive elements, and may be reduced by elimination of, or compensation for, these reactances. In amplifiers for use with television and other systems, the elimination of the effects of phase distortion becomes an important matter.

9–2. Operating classifications

A universal classification system for the conditions of operation of tubes or transistors is based on the voltage and current conditions existing in the circuits. Under this system operation is designated as Class A, AB, B, or C, and this is graphically portrayed in Fig. 9–5.

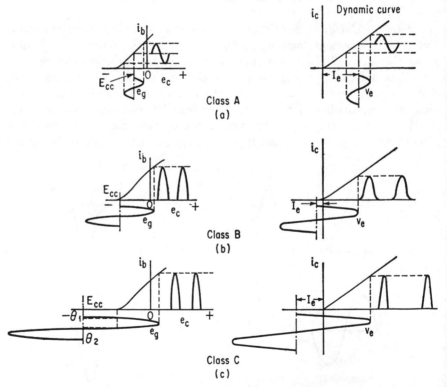

Fig. 9–5. Class A, B, C operation. Left, vacuum tube; right, transistor.

Under Class A operating conditions the bias at the Q point is so set that *plate or collector current flows at all times*, and the output wave form is similar to the input wave form, or the distortion is low. The voltage amplification is high, but the efficiency of conversion of d-c power to a-c power is poor, having a maximum theoretical value of 50 per cent. In practice this may reach 48 or 49 per cent for transistors but only 2 to 25 per cent for tubes.

Class A amplifiers are used where linearity or freedom from distortion is the design criterion, and this constitutes a large percentage of all amplifier services.

For Class B operation the Q point is set at approximate cutoff. The *plate current or collector current then flows for 180° of the input cycle,* and the pulses of output current approach closely the wave form of the positive or forward half cycles of the input. Since the negative or reverse half cycles are absent, the distortion is high. The signal input may be large and higher power output is obtainable than with Class A conditions. For the vacuum tube the grid may be driven positive at times. The maximum theoretical conversion efficiency is 78 per cent. Special circuits have been devised to remove much of the distortion.

Class AB operation is intermediate between Classes A and B, the Q point being set between Class A and Class B, and the *plate current or collector current flows for more than 180° but less than 360° of the input cycle.* Hence performance is intermediate to the two bounding classes, resulting in more power output than in Class A, and less distortion than in Class B. For the vacuum tube, grid current may be permitted to flow at times, such a condition being noted as AB_2. Without grid current the condition is designated as AB_1.

Class C operation requires that the Q point be set at a bias greater than cutoff, usually two or more times cutoff. The *plate or collector current then flows through an angle less than 180° of the input cycle.* The pulses of output current may flow over angles as small as 50° or less of the cycle, and they may bear only slight wave-form resemblance to the input wave and distortion is very high. Large inputs may be used, and large power outputs are obtainable; the maximum theoretical conversion efficiency is 100 per cent.

Since the distortion is so high, Class C operation is used for high power output at frequencies where the distortion products can be removed by simple filter circuits.

9–3. Transistor performance at higher frequencies

In the measurement of transistor characteristics, it is found that every transistor type has some elevated frequency range in which the short-circuit current gain $-h_{fb} = \alpha$ falls off in magnitude. At such frequencies it is found that

$$\alpha = \frac{\alpha_o}{1 + j\omega/\omega_\alpha} = \frac{-h_{fbo}}{1 + j\omega/\omega_\alpha} \tag{9-1}$$

The term $-h_{fbo} = \alpha_o$ is the magnitude of h_{fb} at a low frequency for which diffusion time is not important. The frequency $f_\alpha = \omega_\alpha/2\pi$ is the so-called *alpha cutoff frequency*, at which the value of $|\alpha| = |h_{fb}| = h_{fbo}/\sqrt{2}$, or where the current gain is 3 db below its low-frequency value.

The complex nature of h_{fb} is explainable by the delay introduced by the diffusion process in the base. This charge diffusion time is so important in limiting the upper frequency performance that the so-called *drift* transistors are designed to develop a small potential across the base layer, thus providing an electric field drift component in addition to the base diffusion current, and reducing the base transit time.

If the frequency of transistor operation is to approach an appreciable fraction of f_α, then Eq. 9-1 may be used to give reasonable prediction of amplifier performance. This is particularly true for the much-used common-emitter circuit, since the gain of that circuit is a function of $1/(1 + h_{fb})$, or is multiplied by a large factor dependent on h_{fb} or α.

That is, using the equations of Section 7-11, the current gain of the common-emitter amplifier is

$$\mathbf{A}_{ie} = \frac{h_{fe}}{1 + h_{oe}R_L} \cong h_{fe} = \frac{-h_{fb}}{1 + h_{fb}}$$

By use of Eq. 9-1, the gain in the frequency range near f_α may be written as $\mathbf{A}_{ieH}$, or

$$\mathbf{A}_{ieH} = \left(\frac{-h_{fbo}}{1 + h_{fbo}}\right)\left(\frac{1}{1 + \dfrac{j\omega}{\omega_\alpha(1 + h_{fbo})}}\right) \tag{9-2}$$

The first term is the approximate current gain of the amplifier in the frequency range where $h_{fb} = h_{fbo}$. The second term shows the modification of gain incident to operation at frequencies near f_α of the transistor. It is then convenient to define

$$\omega_{ae} = \omega_\alpha(1 + h_{fbo}) \cong \frac{\omega_\alpha}{h_{fe}} \tag{9-3}$$

and this leads to a simplification of Eq. 9-2 as

$$\mathbf{A}_{ieH} = \left(\frac{-h_{fbo}}{1 + h_{fbo}}\right)\left(\frac{1}{1 + j\omega/\omega_{ae}}\right) \tag{9-4}$$

Equation 9-3 demonstrates the considerable reduction in cutoff frequency imposed on the transistor by operation in the common-emitter circuit. For the 2N139 *PNP* transistor, with f_α given as 4.5 mc by the manufacturer, and with $h_{fbo} = -0.98$, the value of $\omega_{\alpha e}$ becomes only 90,000 cycles. Thus transistors of high f_α values may be required for amplifiers to be used at only audio frequencies.

In the common-base circuit the requirements are not quite so stringent. That is, the approximate current gain is $\mathbf{A}_{ib} \cong -\alpha = h_{fb}$, so that use of Eq. 9-1 gives

$$\mathbf{A}_{ibH} \cong -h_{fbo} \left(\frac{1}{1 + j\omega/\omega_\alpha} \right) \tag{9-5}$$

which is just the variation of h_{fb} with frequency.

The resultant equations are compared in the plot of Fig. 9-6, showing that the common-base circuit makes the most effective use of the frequency range of a transistor, although the gain may not be as high as in the common-emitter form.

The internal capacitances of the transistor may also be effective in limiting the upper-frequency performance of a given transistor amplifier, even though the frequency of operation may be below the f_α of the chosen transistor. In such cases it is necessary to elaborate on the previously-used equivalent circuits. As discussed in Section 3-18, the emitter capacitance may reach values of 100 pf, but it will be in shunt with the low value of r_e in the r-parameter circuit, or with the low value of h_i in the h-parameter equivalent, and its effect can then usually be ignored. The collector-

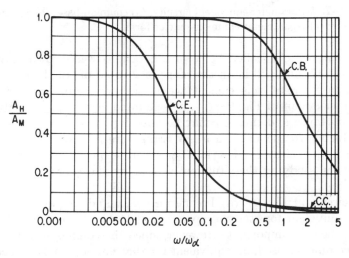

Fig. 9-6. High-frequency performance as limited by $\omega_\alpha (\alpha = 0.98)$.

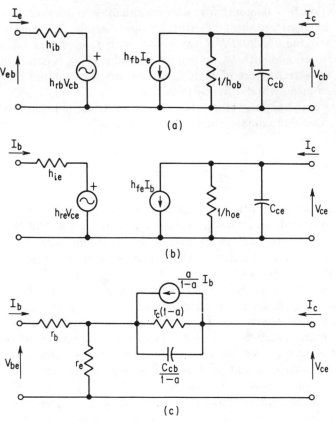

Fig. 9–7. h-Parameter equivalent circuits; (a) common-base; (b) common-emitter; (c) r-parameter common-emitter form.

base capacitance C_{cb} (called C_o in some notation) was studied in Sections 3–16 and 3–17, and will lie in the range of 2 to 50 pf. In the r-parameter common-base circuit this capacitance is shunted across r_c, and in the h-parameter circuit of Fig. 9–7 (a), it is shunted across h_{ob}. The latter is a small admittance and thus C_{cb} may be effective in reducing the load and gain at higher frequencies. In a few transistors its effect may be noted down to frequencies of a few kilocycles per second. This illustrates the necessity for studying the situation created by the capacities as well as that due to f_α.

The circuit in Fig. 9–7 (a) becomes a useful and simple common-base form of equivalent for study of operation at higher frequencies where the capacities become important. However, since the common-emitter circuit is more commonly used, an equivalent for that circuit is also needed. The input circuit transfers readily to that in Fig. 9–7 (b). The output circuit follows if it be noted that the admittance of the output circuit of Fig. 9–7(a) can be given by

$$h'_{ob} = h_{ob} + j\omega C_{cb}$$

By Equation 7–82, the output admittance of the common-emitter circuit is defined as the output admittance of the common-base form divided by $(1 + h_{fb})$. Therefore

$$h'_{oe} = \frac{h_{ob}}{1 + h_{fb}} + \frac{j\omega C_{cb}}{1 + h_{fb}}$$

The first term is identifiable as h_{oe}, a conductance, and since the second term is a susceptance, the capacitance may be given the symbol C_{ce}, called the collector-emitter capacitance, defined as

$$C_{ce} = \frac{C_{cb}}{1 + h_{fb}} \cong h_{fe}C_{cb} \tag{9-6}$$

This is obviously a much larger capacitance than C_{cb}. The common-emitter equivalent circuit with the h parameters then can be drawn as at Fig. 9–7(b).

At Fig. 9–7(c) is shown the r-parameter form of the same circuit. Here again, we will utilize whichever form of parameter, and whichever equivalent circuit that happens to lead to the simplest form of solution of a given problem. In Fig. 9–8 there is given for reference the hybrid-π circuit which is also useful for some high-frequency study.

For complete consideration of both the internal capacities and the effect of f_α, it is useful to have a set of h-parameter definitions which reflect both effects, as

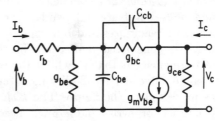

Fig. 9–8. The hybrid-π equivalent circuit.

$$h_{ie} = \frac{h_{ib}}{(1 + h_{fb})(1 + j\omega/\omega_{ae})}$$

$$h_{re} = \frac{h_{ib}(h_{ob} + j\omega C_{cb})}{(1 + h_{fb})(1 + j\omega/\omega_{ae})} - h_{rb}$$

$$h_{fe} = \frac{-h_{fb}}{(1 + h_{fb})(1 + j\omega/\omega_{ae})}$$

$$\tag{9-7}$$

$$h_{oe} = \frac{h_{ob}}{(1 + h_{fb})(1 + j\omega/\omega_{ae})}$$

Also summarizing, we have:

$$C_{ce} = \frac{C_{cb}}{1 + h_{fb}} \cong h_{fe}C_{cb}$$

$$\omega_{ae} = \omega_\alpha(1 + h_{fb}) \cong \frac{\omega_\alpha}{h_{fe}}$$

9–4. The RC-coupled common-emitter amplifier

As was pointed out in Section 8–14, coupling networks are necessary to transfer the a-c signal from the output of one amplifier stage to the input of the next, and to block d-c potentials. Reactances are used to perform these functions, and the internal capacities of the tube or transistor are also present. These associated reactances introduce frequency and delay distortion, and much amplifier design is involved with an effort to predict and design around these deficiencies.

Analysis of audio or video amplifier performance is usually carried out by division of the operating frequency band into three ranges, indicated by Fig. 9–2, in order to simplify the equivalent circuits employed. The so-called *mid-range* of frequencies is identified as that range in which the gain and phase shift are independent of frequency, or the magnitudes of the coupling reactances and inherent internal capacitances are such that they may be considered ineffective in the equivalent circuit. The *low range* of frequencies is that in which the series capacitance or shunt inductance become effective in modifying circuit impedances, and the gain drops as indicated in the figure. The *high range* is that in which the shunt capacitance or series inductance become controlling factors in reducing gain, or producing frequency distortion, as shown by the high-range curve of Fig. 9–2.

The use of RC coupling between two common-emitter transistor amplifiers is illustrated in Fig. 9–9(a). Resistors R_1 and R_2 are present to supply the bias for the base; they will ordinarily be large with respect to the input resistance R_{ie} and may be dropped from the equivalent circuit as at Fig. 9–9(b). Capacitor C_s, while necessary to maintain bias, will usually be small in reactance and neglected, or may be considered by usual methods. The remainder of the equivalent circuit follows from Fig. 9–7.

When used without impedance matching means, the common emitter circuit will have a low load value because of the low input resistance of the following transistor. This input resistance is given by Eq. 7–72 as

$$R_{ie} = \frac{R_L\Delta + h_{ie}}{1 + h_{oe}R_L} \cong h_{ie} \tag{9–8}$$

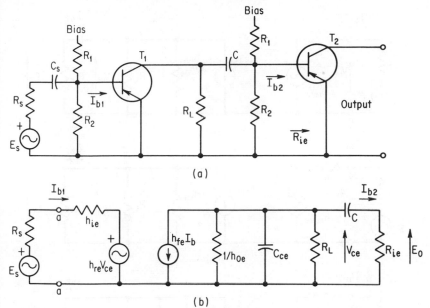

Fig. 9–9. (a) *RC*-coupled common-emitter amplifier; (b) equivalent circuit, neglecting C_s.

the simplified form holding for most transistors. Due to the effect of C_{ce}, this value of input may drop at elevated frequencies. Figure 9–8 furnishes a form of circuit for more exact analysis if such is required.

To determine the current response in the low-frequency range, a current summation may be written for Fig. 9–10(a), as

$$h_{fe}\mathbf{I}_{b1} = -V_{ce}\left[h_{oe} + \frac{1}{R_L} + \frac{1}{R_{ie} - j/\omega C}\right] \tag{9–9}$$

Internal admittance h_{oe} and $1/R_L$ are in parallel, and may be represented as an admittance $1/R_p$. Also

$$\mathbf{V}_{ce} = (R_{ie} - j/\omega C)\,\mathbf{I}_{b2}$$

after noting the assigned direction of I_{b2}. The *low-frequency current gain* is then

$$\mathbf{A}_{iL} = \frac{\mathbf{I}_{b2}}{\mathbf{I}_{b1}} = -h_{fe}\left(\frac{R_p}{R_p + R_{ie}}\right)\left[\frac{1}{1 - j/\omega C(R_p + R_{ie})}\right] \tag{9–10}$$

The expression represents the ideal current gain h_{fe} of a common-emitter amplifier, reduced by the division of current between R_p and the branch containing C and R_{ie}. Often R_{ie} will be small with respect to R_p and the expression will simplify further.

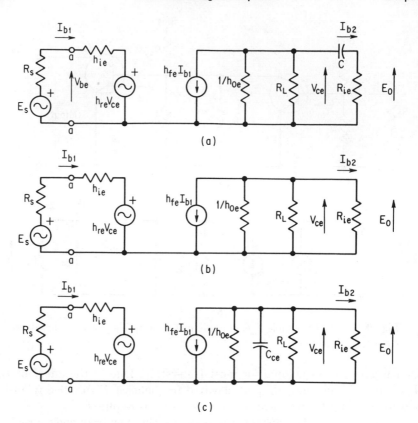

Fig. 9–10. (a) Low-frequency equivalent for common-emitter amplifier; (b) Mid-range equivalent; (c) High-range equivalent.

By definition the mid-frequency region is that band of frequencies in which reactances are negligible in effect. The equivalent circuit is at Fig. 9–10(b), and the *mid-range current gain* follows from Eq. 9–10 by dropping the reactance of C, or

$$\mathbf{A}_{iM} = -h_{fe}\left(\frac{R_p}{R_p + R_{ie}}\right) \qquad (9\text{–}11)$$

The smaller the value of R_{ie}, the more nearly the current gain approaches the h_{fe} value of the transistor; that is, the transistor operates more nearly under short-circuit. While the current gain then rises, the power output and voltage gain drop.

For transistors of large f_α the high-frequency response may be limited by the internal capacitance C_{ce}. The high-frequency equivalent circuit, derived from Fig. 9–9, appears as in Fig. 9–10(c). A current summation yields

$$h_{fe}\mathbf{I}_{b1} = -\mathbf{V}_{ce}\left[\frac{1}{R_p} + \frac{1}{R_{ie}} + j\omega C_{ce}\right] \qquad (9\text{–}12)$$

$$\mathbf{V}_{ce} = R_{ie}\mathbf{I}_{b2}$$

The *high-frequency current gain* then follows as

$$\mathbf{A}_{iH} = \frac{\mathbf{I}_{b2}}{\mathbf{I}_{b1}} = -h_{fe}\left(\frac{R_p}{R_p + R_{ie}}\right)\left(\frac{1}{1 + j\omega C_{ce}\left(\dfrac{R_{ie}R_p}{R_{ie} + R_p}\right)}\right) \qquad (9\text{–}13)$$

which shows the high-frequency current gain dependent on C_{ce} and the parallel value of R_p and R_{ie}.

When used with low values of load resistance, it will usually be found that the effect of C_{ce} is less pronounced in reducing the high-frequency rolloff of gain than is the variation of α with frequency, discussed in Section 9–3. Judgement will have to be exercised in determining whether to use the analysis above, or that of the preceding section, and will be based primarily on the relation of f_α to the upper frequency limit to be amplified.

Assuming that f_α is not limiting, then it may be found possible to define the several frequency bands of a particular amplifier in terms of the relative magnitudes of the reactances and resistances. That is, frequencies at which the reactances become one-tenth the series resistance or ten times the shunting resistances may be considered as approximate limits for the midband region.

Voltage gain relations may also be obtained, by starting with the general statement of Eq. 7–77, written as

$$\mathbf{A}_{ve} = \frac{\mathbf{V}_{ce}}{\mathbf{V}_{be}} = \frac{-h_{fe}R_L}{R_L\Delta + h_{ie}} \cong \frac{-h_{fe}R_L}{h_{ie}} = -g_m R_L \qquad (9\text{–}14)$$

where, for the transistor, $g_m = h_{fe}/h_{ie} = \mathbf{I}_c/\mathbf{V}_{be}$, by use of the basic h-parameter definitions. It may also be found that

$$\mathbf{V}_{be} = \frac{R'_{ie}\mathbf{E}_s}{R_s + R'_{ie}}$$

$$\mathbf{E}_o = \frac{R_{ie}\mathbf{V}_{ce}}{R_{ie} - j/\omega C}$$

$$R_L = \frac{R_p(R_{ie} - j/\omega C)}{R_p + R_{ie} - j/\omega C}$$

from the equivalent circuit in Fig. 9–10(a). The input resistance R'_{ie} is that measured at a, a for the first transistor; resistance R_{ie} is as shown, part of the load circuit of the transistor under study. Utilizing the above expressions the *low-frequency voltage gain* can be found as

$$\mathbf{A}_{veL} = \frac{\mathbf{E}_o}{\mathbf{E}_s} = -g_m \left(\frac{R'_{ie}}{R_s + R'_{ie}} \right) \left(\frac{R_p R_{ie}}{R_p + R_{ie}} \right) \left(\frac{1}{1 - j/\omega C(R_p + R_{ie})} \right)$$

$$(9-15)$$

This result is closely related to the low-frequency current gain of Eq. 9–10. The maximum voltage gain will be obtained with a source resistance R_s of zero value.

The *mid-frequency voltage gain* follows by dropping the reactive term, or

$$\mathbf{A}_{veM} = -g_m \left(\frac{R'_{ie}}{R_s + R'_{ie}} \right) \left(\frac{R_p R_{ie}}{R_p + R_{ie}} \right) \qquad (9-16)$$

The *high-frequency voltage gain* can be written by reference to Fig. 9–10(c), as

$$\mathbf{A}_{veH} = -g_m \left(\frac{R'_{ie}}{R_s + R'_{ie}} \right) \left(\frac{R_p R_{ie}}{R_p + R_{ie}} \right) \left[\frac{1}{1 + j\omega C_{ce} \left(\frac{R_p R_{ie}}{R_p + R_{ie}} \right)} \right] \qquad (9-17)$$

which is closely related to the high-frequency range current gain. The high-frequency response is then a function of C_{ce} and its shunting resistances, especially R_{ie}, since it is usually smaller then R_p.

9–5. Normalized gain and phase curves

Since the amplitude and phase angle of the mid-range gain are independent of frequency, it is useful to normalize the gain and phase relations at other frequencies in terms of the mid-range value as a standard. The performance and design information is then expressed in terms of ratios $\mathbf{A}_{iL}/\mathbf{A}_{iM}$, $\mathbf{A}_{iH}/\mathbf{A}_{iM}$, and the like. These ratios are general for the RC amplifier, and permit specification of amplifier performance as a simple function of circuit parameters.

Taking the ratio of Eqs. 9–10 and 9–11

$$\frac{\mathbf{A}_{iL}}{\mathbf{A}_{iM}} = \frac{1}{1 - j/\omega C(R_p + R_{ie})} \cong \frac{1}{1 - j/\omega C R_p} \qquad (9-18)$$

At large ω the second term in the denominator becomes negligible with respect to unity, and the gain becomes that at mid-range. At some smaller

ω_1 the reactive term equals the resistance term or unity, and we then define ω_1 as

$$\omega_1 = \frac{1}{C(R_p + R_{ie})} \cong \frac{1}{CR_p} \qquad (9\text{–}19)$$

The gain ratio may then be written in general form as

$$\frac{\mathbf{A}_{iL}}{\mathbf{A}_{iM}} = \frac{1}{1 - j(\omega_1/\omega)} = \frac{j(\omega/\omega_1)}{j(\omega/\omega_1) + 1} \qquad (9\text{–}20)$$

The latter form is especially useful since the ratio ω/ω_1 increases with frequency.

The phase angle of the $\mathbf{A}_{iM}$ gain is $180°$ as indicated by the minus sign in Eq. 9–11, and the additional phase shift introduced at low frequencies is given by

$$\varphi_L - \varphi_M = \tan^{-1}(\omega_1/\omega) = \tan^{-1} 1/(\omega/\omega_1) \qquad (9\text{–}21)$$

The frequency defined as ω_1 is uniquely related to the design parameters of the amplifier. At $\omega = \omega_1$ the gain $\mathbf{A}_{iL}$ is $1/\sqrt{2}$ of the mid-range gain, or is 3 db down from that reference, with a phase angle $+45°$ over that of the mid-range. The angular frequency ω_1 is sometimes called the *low-frequency cutoff* of the amplifier.

The ratio $\mathbf{A}_{iH}/\mathbf{A}_{iM}$ may be obtained from Eqs. 9–11 and 9–13 as

$$\frac{\mathbf{A}_{iH}}{\mathbf{A}_{iM}} = \frac{1}{1 + j\omega C_{ce}\left(\dfrac{R_{ie}R_p}{R_{ie} + R_p}\right)} \cong \frac{1}{1 + j\omega C_{ce}R_{ie}} \qquad (9\text{–}22)$$

Defining ω_2 as the angular frequency at which the reactive term equals the resistive, or becomes unity, then

$$\omega_2 = \frac{R_{ie} + R_p}{C_{ce}R_{ie}R_p} \cong \frac{1}{C_{ce}R_{ie}} \qquad (9\text{–}23)$$

and

$$\frac{\mathbf{A}_{iH}}{\mathbf{A}_{iM}} = \frac{1}{1 + j(\omega/\omega_2)} \qquad (9\text{–}24)$$

The additional phase shift in the high band is

$$\varphi_H - \varphi_M = -\tan^{-1}(\omega/\omega_2) \qquad (9\text{–}25)$$

and is $-45°$ at ω_2, where the gain is again 3 db below midband reference.

Equations 9–20 and 9–24 are general and apply to the usual forms of RC amplifier, since the performance is determined by the designer's choice of several circuit parameters. Similar relations can be obtained for the voltage gain expressions, so that the same parameters control both gain functions.

It appears that the low-frequency performance is fixed by the selection of the coupling capacitor C, whereas the high-frequency response is a function of shunt capacitance. Thus the low-frequency band limit is a function of circuit parameters, but the high-frequency band limit is more nearly a function of the active device itself, either by reason of the value of C_{ce}, or through the limiting effect of f_α.

Normalized curves for the gain ratios and phase angles are drawn in Fig. 9–11, which are usable as general response curves for RC amplifiers, since the curves are in terms of arbitrary parameters, ω_1 and ω_2.

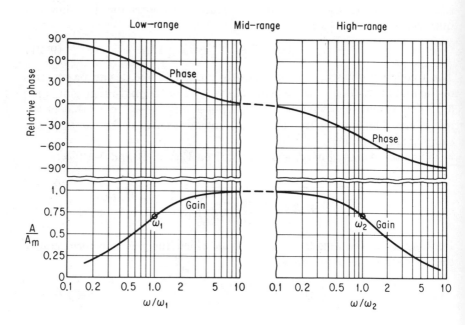

Fig. 9–11. Generalized gain and phase shift curves for RC amplifiers.

A practical two-stage common-emitter amplifier is shown in Fig. 9–12. The circuit values support the several assumptions made above. The use of emitter bias resistors is also shown, but these do not invalidate the above analysis, since they are assumed to be adequately bypassed, and thereby eliminated from the equivalent circuit. The determination of the necessary capacitances for this function and for the coupling capacitor will be the subject of a later section.

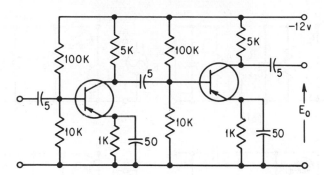

Fig. 9–12. Practical audio-frequency common-emitter amplifier.

9–6. The *RC*-coupled amplifier using triode and pentode

The circuit of Fig. 9–13 may be employed as an example of the resistance-capacitance (*RC*) coupled vacuum-tube amplifier. The input capacitance of the second stage has been found as

$$C_{\text{in}} = C_{gk} + C_{gp}(1 + g_m R')$$

which may be considerably larger than C_{gk} alone. The output circuit of the amplifier is redrawn in equivalent form at Fig. 9–14(a), including C_{pk} and C_{in}. Stray wiring capacity and socket capacity is ordinarily included in C_{in}.

Capacitances C_{pk} and C_{in}, being of picofarad order, have such high reactances in the low-frequency range that they may be dropped from the circuit, leading to the low-frequency form at Fig. 9–14(b). If we define

$$R'_L = \frac{r_p R_L}{r_p + R_L} \tag{9–26}$$

then the current $\mathbf{I}_o$ through R_g is a result of the source $g_m E_g$, multiplied by the current division factor, as

$$\mathbf{I}_o = g_m \mathbf{E}_g \frac{R'_L}{R'_L + R_g - j/\omega C}$$

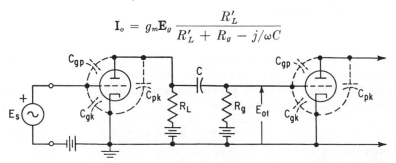

Fig. 9–13. Two-stage *RC* amplifier, including tube capacitances.

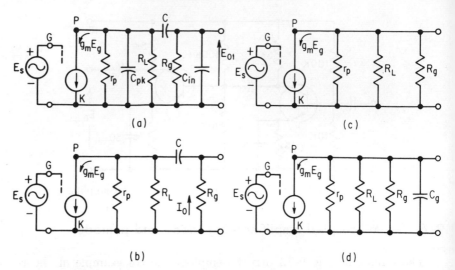

Fig. 9–14. (a) Exact equivalent; (b) Low-range equivalent; (c) Mid-range equivalent; (d) High-range equivalent.

The voltage gain, as a function of $j\omega$, becomes

$$\mathbf{A}_L = \frac{\mathbf{E}_o}{\mathbf{E}_s} = \frac{-g_m R'_L R_g}{R'_L + R_g - j/\omega C} \tag{9–27}$$

This expression for the *low-frequency gain* illustrates the effect of the series coupling capacitor C in reducing the voltage gain at low values of ω. Its parallelism with Eq. 9–10 for the transistor is apparent.

For pentodes $r_p \gg R_L$, and R'_L becomes R_L; also $R_g \gg R_L$, so that the *low-frequency pentode gain* is

$$\mathbf{A}_L = \frac{-g_m R_L}{1 - j/\omega C R_g} \tag{9–28}$$

where the phase angle is

$$\varphi_L = 180° + \tan^{-1} 1/\omega C R_g \tag{9–29}$$

If the frequency is raised, the second denominator term becomes small, or the reactance of C becomes negligible with respect to R_g. The circuit is then that at Fig. 9–14(c), in which the reactances are all neglected, and the *mid-frequency gain for triodes* is

$$\mathbf{A}_M = -g_m R'_L \tag{9–30}$$

and for *pentodes*

$$\mathbf{A}_M = -g_m R_L \tag{9–31}$$

The phase angle is 180°, and both gain and phase angle are independent of frequency in the mid-region. Again the similarity to the result for the transistor is apparent.

If the frequency is raised still further, the capacitances C_{pk} and C_{in} become comparable reactances to the resistance of R'_L and R_g in parallel. These shunt capacities may be grouped as C_g, and the equivalent circuit is shown at Fig. 9-14(d). The *high-range voltage gain* is

$$\mathbf{A}_H = \frac{-g_m R'_L R_g}{R'_L + R_g + j\omega C_g R'_L R_g} \tag{9-32}$$

and under the usual assumptions, this may be specialized to the *pentode* relation

$$\mathbf{A}_H = \frac{-g_m R_L}{1 + j\omega C_g R_L} \tag{9-33}$$

As an approximate bound, the mid-frequency gain expressions of Eqs. 9-30 and 9-31 may be found to apply at frequencies above that at which $X_C \cong R_g/10$, and below that at which $X_{C_g} \cong 10 R'_L R_g/(R'_L + R_g) \cong 10 R'_L$.

The similarity between these expressions for the pentode and those for the common-emitter transistor amplifier should not be a surprise. In both cases the equivalent circuit contains a transfer current generator shunted by a large internal resistance and the load circuit. This parallelism will be useful in several applications to follow, but should not be relied on implicitly if operation of the transistor is to approach the frequency f_α.

9-7. Normalized pentode gain and phase expressions

Pentode tubes are very commonly employed in RC grounded-cathode amplifiers because of the low input capacitance, and normalization of the gain and phase expressions against the mid-range values will be useful.

Following the transistor methods, and using the pentode forms of gain equations:

$$\frac{\mathbf{A}_L}{\mathbf{A}_M} = \frac{1}{1 - j/\omega C R_g} \tag{9-34}$$

By definition the cutoff frequency ω_1 is then

$$\omega_1 = \frac{1}{C R_g} \tag{9-35}$$

so that the gain ratio becomes

$$\frac{\mathbf{A}_L}{\mathbf{A}_M} = \frac{j(\omega/\omega_1)}{j(\omega/\omega_1) + 1} \tag{9-36}$$

The additional phase shift over that at mid-range is

$$\varphi_L - \varphi_M = \tan^{-1} 1/(\omega/\omega_1) \tag{9-37}$$

At ω_1 the gain is 3 db down and the phase angle $+45°$ with respect to the mid-range values. These relations are identical to Eqs. 9–20 and 9–22 for the transistor, and are plotted as a function of ω/ω_1 in Fig. 9–11.

The low-frequency performance of the pentode amplifier is dependent on the values of C and R_g. Large values of C may be required in some applications, but cost is a factor and it must be able to withstand full anode voltage with small leakage current, if the bias of the following stage is not to be upset.

By a similar process for the pentode equations:

$$\frac{\mathbf{A}_H}{\mathbf{A}_M} = \frac{1}{1 + j\omega C_g R_L} \tag{9-38}$$

Defining ω_2 as

$$\omega_2 = \frac{1}{C_g R_L} \tag{9-39}$$

then

$$\frac{\mathbf{A}_H}{\mathbf{A}_M} = \frac{1}{1 + j(\omega/\omega_2)} \tag{9-40}$$

The load R_L may be reduced to increase ω_2, but this will also reduce the gain.

The additional phase shift in the high band is

$$\varphi_H - \varphi_M = -\tan^{-1}(\omega/\omega_2) \tag{9-41}$$

and is $-45°$ at ω_2, where the gain is also 3 db down from its mid-band value.

The normalized curve for the high-frequency response of a transistor amplifier, as plotted in Fig. 9–11, applies equally well to the RC pentode amplifier, since the curves are plotted in terms of ω_2, a design parameter which is arbitrary.

As for the transistor, the low-frequency performance is a function of the series capacitance, whereas the high-frequency response is determined by the shunt capacitance. Thus the transistor and pentode have low-frequency band limits which are functions of circuit parameters, but the high-frequency band limits are largely a function of the active device itself.

9–8. Asymptotic plots of the gain curves

A major advantage which can be attributed to the calculation of the foregoing amplifier gains in decibels is that the overall gain of a multi-stage amplifier is then simply the sum of the individual db gains, and phase shifts.

The magnitudes of the normalized response ratios can be stated for the RC amplifier as

$$\left| \frac{A_L}{A_M} \right| = \left[\frac{1}{1 + (\omega_1/\omega)^2} \right]^{1/2}, \quad \left| \frac{A_H}{A_M} \right| = \left[\frac{1}{1 + (\omega/\omega_2)^2} \right]^{1/2}$$

In the mid-range these ratios become unity or 0 db, and the mid-band gain can then be taken as the reference or zero level for decibel gain use.

The $\left| A_L/A_M \right|$ ratio can be put into decibels as

$$\left| \frac{A_L}{A_M} \right|_{db} = 20 \log \left[\frac{1}{1 + (\omega_1/\omega)^2} \right]^{1/2} = -10 \log \left[1 + (\omega_1/\omega)^2 \right] \qquad (9\text{--}42)$$

At $\omega_1/\omega = 1$ the equation becomes

$$\left| \frac{A_L}{A_M} \right| = -10 \log 2 = -3.01 \text{ db}$$

or at $\omega_1/\omega = 1$ the gain is 3 db below the mid-range value. This was, of course, the definition for ω_1.

Other values of ω_1/ω can be entered in Eq. 9–42 and the values of Table 13 obtained.

At large values of ω_1/ω (small ω/ω_1), the equation becomes

$$\left| \frac{A_L}{A_M} \right|_{db} = -10 \log (\omega_1/\omega)^2 = 20 \log \omega/\omega_1 \qquad (9\text{--}43)$$

TABLE 13. GAIN-FREQUENCY DATA IN DECIBELS

ω/ω_1	Db gain	ω/ω_2	Db gain
0.1	−20	0.1	−0.04
0.3	−10.7	0.3	−0.38
0.5	−7.0	0.5	−0.96
0.7	−4.8	0.7	−1.7
1.0	−3.0	1.0	−3.0
1.5	−1.6	1.5	−5.1
3.0	−0.42	3.0	−10.0
5.0	−0.18	5.0	−14
10.0	−0.04	10.0	−20

This equation represents a straight line on a db vs log-frequency graph, passing through the point 0 db, $\omega/\omega_1 = 1$, and having a slope of $+20$ db per frequency decade. It can also be reasoned that this is equivalent to a slope of 6 db per octave. Such a line is dashed in Fig. 9–15, and is the asymptote which the actual gain curve approaches. The point at 0 db, $\omega/\omega_1 = 1$ is called the *corner frequency*, since the asymptote and the reference level form a corner there. It is easy to plot gain curves using this method, since the asymptote can be readily drawn, the -3 db point located, and the curve sketched in using the data from the table.

The high-frequency relation can be written in db as

$$\left|\frac{A_H}{A_M}\right|_{db} = -10 \log \left[1 + (\omega/\omega_2)^2\right] \tag{9-44}$$

and at high values of ω/ω_2 the asymptote falls with a slope of -20 db per decade. The result appears in Fig. 9–15.

The gain being additive, the two-stage amplifier gain will fall at -40 db per decade at the high-frequencies, (-12 db per octave), the three stage high-frequency gain at -60 db per decade, and so on. The gains at the corner frequencies will be -6 db, and -9 db, for these multistage amplifiers.

In the regions where the gain approaches the asymptotic slope, the single stage excess phase angle will approach $-90°$ for the high-frequency region, and $+90°$ for the low-frequency band. For multi-stage amplifiers these limiting angles become $180°$, $270°$, and the like, not including the inherent $180°$ per stage, if such exists.

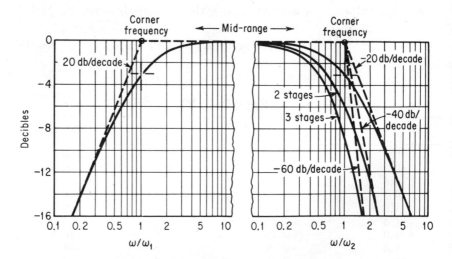

Fig. 9–15. Generalized gain curves in decibels.

9–9. Band width of cascaded amplifiers

The term *band width*, when applied to amplifiers, usually means the width in cycles between the upper and lower cutoff limits on the gain-frequency curve; that is, between ω_2 and ω_1. This is also the band width between -3 db points, as shown in Fig. 9–15. As shown there, the band width of multi-stage amplifiers decreases as the number of stages increases. If an overall band width is specified, that of each stage must be designed as considerably greater, and this creates many design problems.

Using the methods of the preceding section, the ratio of overall high-frequency gain to the mid-range gain for an n-stage amplifier may be written in db as

$$\left| \frac{A_{ov}}{A_M} \right|_{db} = 20n \log \left[\frac{1}{1 + (\omega/\omega_2)^2} \right]^{1/2} = -10n \log \left[1 + (\omega/\omega_2)^2 \right] \quad (9\text{–}45)$$

where the design of the separate stages is identical, or ω_2 is the same for all.

The frequency ω_o is then defined as the cutoff frequency for the overall amplifier. At $\omega = \omega_o$, the gain ratio will be -3 db, by definition, and accordingly Eq. 9–45 may be written as

$$-3.0 = -10n \log \left[1 + (\omega_o/\omega_2)^2 \right]$$

from which ω_2, the upper band limit for a single stage can be obtained as

$$\omega_2 = \frac{\omega_o}{\sqrt{10^{0.3/n} - 1}} = \frac{\omega_o}{\sqrt{2^{1/n} - 1}} \quad (9\text{–}46)$$

The equations for the low-frequency band limit can be obtained by substitution of ω_1/ω_o for the frequency ratio in the above equations.

Table 14 demonstrates the enlarged band width requirements on the individual stages as successive numbers of identical stages are cascaded.

TABLE 14. RELATIVE CUTOFF FREQUENCIES FOR CASCADED AMPLIFIERS

	ω_o = specified cutoff for overall amplifier		
	ω_2 = cutoff for one stage		
n	ω_2/ω_o	n	ω_2/ω_o
1	1.00	5	2.60
2	1.56	6	2.86
3	1.96	7	3.10
4	2.30	8	3.25

9–10. Gain-band width limitations

Both high gain and large band width are usually desired in broad band or video amplifiers, operating to a few megacycles as the upper limit. However, large band width requires reduced R_L values which reduce the gain. This seemingly means that more stages of amplification will be needed, but in turn this raises the ω_2 requirement on each stage, forcing use of lower R_L values and reduced gain per stage. Thus for a given band width there seems to be some upper limit on gain, and this can be shown to be true.

The mid-range gain may be used as a measure of performance, and the greatest voltage gain will be obtained from a common-emitter amplifier if $R_s = 0$, so that Eq. 9–16 gives

$$\mathbf{A}_{ve} = -g_m \frac{R_p R_{ie}}{R_p + R_{ie}} \tag{9–47}$$

The low-frequency cutoff of an amplifier is a function of the circuit elements selected, and ω_1 can usually be made as low as desired. The band width is then a function of the upper cutoff angular frequency ω_2, which is

$$\omega_2 = \frac{R_{ie} + R_p}{C_{ce} R_{ie} R_p} \tag{9–48}$$

for the common-emitter amplifier.

Multiplication of A_{ve} and ω_2 gives the *gain-band width product* as

$$GBW = A \times f_2 = \frac{g_m}{2\pi C_{ce}} = \frac{g_m}{2\pi h_{fe} C_{cb}} \tag{9–49}$$

for the *RC* amplifier, and this is observed as being independent of the effective amplifier load. That is, the band width may be increased by reducing R_p or R_{ie}, but at the same time the gain will fall proportionately (h_{fe} and g_m are functions of the currents flowing, and so this statement is only approximately true).

Thus there is a fundamental limit on the product of gain times band width for a given amplifier. Since both g_m and C_{ce} are transistor parameters, the *GBW* product is a constant for a given transistor type. High *GBW* transistors will have high $g_m = I_c/V_{be}$, low collector capacitance, and a large value of ω_{ae}. High g_m implies large h_{fe} and low h_{ie} values for the parameters. The band width will be greatest with low source and load resistances.

A similar relation can be readily determined for the pentode common-cathode amplifier. Using Eqs. 9–31 and 9–39

$$\text{Pentode } GBW = A \times f_2 = \frac{g_m}{2\pi C_g} = \frac{g_m}{2\pi(C_{in} + C_{pk})} \cong \frac{g_m}{2\pi(C_{gk} + C_{pk})}$$

$$(9\text{–}50)$$

for the RC amplifier. The product is a constant for a given pentode type, and it is not possible to increase band width without comparable decrease in gain. The best pentode types are those of high g_m and low internal capacitance.

If the 6AK5 pentode is taken as an example, with $g_m = 5100$ μmhos, $C_{gk} = 4.0$ pf, $C_{pk} = 2.8$ pf, the GBW product is 120. This indicates that this tube will give a theroetical gain of 30 over a band 4 megacycles wide, a gain of 12 over a 10 megacycle band, or any other combination giving a GBW product of 120.

9–11. Bypass and coupling capacitors

The selection of coupling capacitor C and emitter bypass capacitor C_E in the RC amplifier requires further study, since both low-frequency performance and costs will be affected. Coordination of values is a possibility, since a large capacitor at one point may be somewhat nullified by a too-small capacitor at the other location.

It is usually assumed that C_E is sufficiently large as to have negligible reactance at the lowest frequency of interest, and this will eliminate the effect of R_E from the a-c equivalent circuit, while retaining the benefits of R_E in providing d-c stabilization of the Q-point currents of the transistor. If, however, C_E is insufficient in capacitance to reduce the a-c voltage across R_E to a negligible value, it will be found that this a-c voltage is of such phase as to subtract from the input base-emitter voltage, and the effective gain of the amplifier will be reduced. Thus a large capacitance may be required for C_E at low frequencies in the audio range, and cost and space may become limiting factors. Capacitor C is also effective in reducing low-frequency gain, and cost is also important here.

The two capacitors may be considered as related by a factor m, as $C_E = mC$, where the multiplier m is to be determined. The equivalent circuit of Fig. 9–16(b) uses the h-parameter equivalent for the output circuit of T_1, but greater ease of analysis is possible by use of the r-parameter circuit for the input of transistor T_2. Admittances h_{oe} and $1/R_L$ may again be considered in parallel as admittance $1/R_p$, and the circuit simplified to that at Fig. 9–16(c).

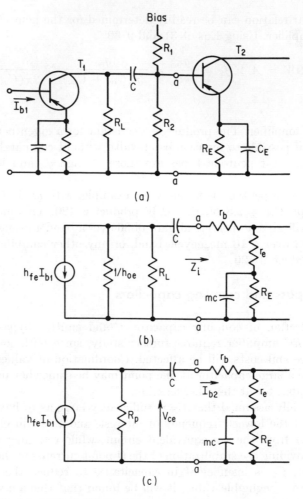

Fig. 9–16. (a) RC amplifier; (b) Low-frequency equivalent, to study effect of C and C_E; (c) reduced equivalent.

In the critical frequency range in which C_E is just becoming effective as a bypass, its reactance will be small with respect to R_E. Resistor R_E may then be dropped from the circuit, leaving C_E as the effective element in the frequency region under study. The input resistance of a common-emitter amplifier, for small loads and using the r-parameter expressions, is

$$R_{ie} \cong r_b + \frac{r_e}{1-a}$$

and for the circuit of Fig. 9–16(c), with the input impedance measured at a, a, we have

$$\mathbf{Z}_i = r_b + \frac{1}{1-a}\left(r_e - \frac{j}{\omega m C}\right) = R_{ie} - \frac{j}{\omega m C(1-a)} \qquad (9\text{--}51)$$

A current summation may be written for Fig. 9–16(c) as

$$h_{fe}\mathbf{I}_{b1} = -\mathbf{V}_{ce}\left\{ \frac{1}{R_p} + \frac{1}{R_{ie} - \dfrac{j}{\omega C}\left[1 + \dfrac{1}{m(1-a)}\right]} \right\} \qquad (9\text{--}52)$$

Noting that

$$\mathbf{V}_{ce} = \mathbf{I}_{b2}\left\{ R_{ie} - \frac{j}{\omega C}\left[1 + \frac{1}{m(1-a)}\right] \right\}$$

then the low-frequency gain is

$$\mathbf{A}_{iL} = -h_{fe}\frac{R_p}{R_p + R_{ie} - \dfrac{j}{\omega C}\left[1 + \dfrac{1}{m(1-a)}\right]} \qquad (9\text{--}53)$$

Forming the ratio $\mathbf{A}_{iL}/\mathbf{A}_{i0}$ by use of Eq. 9–11 gives

$$\frac{\mathbf{A}_{iL}}{\mathbf{A}_{i0}} = \frac{1}{1 - \dfrac{j}{\omega C(R_p + R_{ie})}\left[1 + \dfrac{1}{m(1-a)}\right]} \qquad (9\text{--}54)$$

The lower cutoff frequency for the amplifier can then be seen as

$$\omega_1 - \frac{1}{C(R_p + R_{ie})} + \frac{1}{m(1-a)[C(R_p + R_{ie})]} \qquad (9\text{--}55)$$

This expression directly shows the contribution of each capacitor to the low-frequency cutoff of the amplifier. It again illustrates the property of the common-emitter circuit in multiplying various effects by $1/(1-a)$.

For the lowest possible ω_1, the value of m should be infinite, or the capacitance of C_E should be very large. The equation shows that if $m = 1/(1-a)$, then both capacitances will start reducing the low-frequency gain at the same frequency, or will have equivalent effect. However, this means that C_E will have a capacitance 50 to 100 times that of C. Since C must be of microfarad order for audio frequencies if ω_1 is to be sufficiently low, the value required for C_E may be so large and expensive that it may be more economic to omit C_E, and accept the reduced gain caused thereby. Design considerations for this step are covered in the chapter on Feedback.

9–12. Low-frequency compensation of amplifiers

Extension of the operating frequency range of amplifiers is usually solved by independent consideration of the factors affecting the low frequencies and the high frequencies, since in one case it is the coupling capacitor, and in the other the shunt capacitance which controls the performance. Extension of the low-frequency range is considered in this section, treatment of the high-frequency range being given in the next section.

If a sufficiently large value of C can be allowed, then it is usually not difficult to extend the ω_1 angular frequency to quite low values for the usual RC amplifier. The value of C is, however, often limited by cost or space, and recourse can be had to the circuit of Fig. 9–17 for a compensating method to lower ω_1. If C_x and the resistors be properly chosen, the load impedance can be made to rise with decrease in frequency, the gain also rising to compensate for the increasing voltage drop through C.

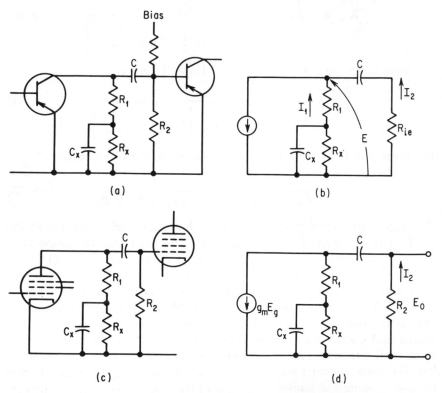

Fig. 9–17. Low-frequency compensating networks.

The parallelism between transistor and vacuum tube circuits at low frequencies is well demonstrated by the equivalent circuits of Fig. 9–17(b) and (d). In both cases it is assumed that the internal resistance, $1/h_{oe}$ or r_p, is large with respect to $R_1 + R_x$, and therefore the internal resistance is dropped from the circuit. In the transistor case current I_2 is to be independent of frequency, while for the vacuum tube the voltage E_o is to be maintained constant.

In Fig. 9–17, (b) and (d) are identical except for the value of the driving current, and the analysis will not differ between transistor and vacuum tube. Writing a current summation for the transistor case:

$$h_{fe}I_{b1} = -E\left[\frac{1}{R_1 + \dfrac{R_x(-j/\omega C_x)}{R_x - j/\omega C_x}} + \frac{1}{R_{ie} - j/\omega C}\right] \qquad (9\text{–}56)$$

and

$$\mathbf{E} - (R_{ie} - j/\omega C)\,\mathbf{I_2}$$

The result is complex, but it is reasonable to assume that $R_x \gg 1/\omega C_x$ at all frequencies of interest, and this reduces Eq. 9–56 to

$$h_{fe}I_{b1} = \mathbf{I_2}\left[\frac{\omega^2 C C_x(R_{ie} + R_1) - j\omega(C + C_x)}{\omega^2 C C_x R_1 - j\omega C}\right]$$

It is desired that $\mathbf{I_2}$ not be a frequency function. Solving the above for $\mathbf{I_2}$, taking $dI_2/d\omega$ and setting equal to zero leads to a circuit condition which will fulfill the requirement. This is

$$C(R_{ie} + R_1) = R_1(C + C_x)$$

$$(9\text{–}57)$$

$$R_{ie}C = R_1C_x$$

This result states that the time constant of the coupling circuit should equal that of the compensating circuit.

The compensation provided by this circuit is not as perfect as it appears, since at extremely low frequencies the assumption that $R_x \gg 1/\omega C_x$ begins to fail. However, the method does provide a means of appreciably extending ω_1 to lower values than are possible with the uncompensated circuit and reasonable values of C.

It can also be shown that equality of the time constants will produce zero phase shift in the coupling circuit, and this is desirable in many applications.

9–13. High-frequency compensation of amplifiers

For wide band service low C_{ce} transistors are most often used in the common-emitter circuit because of the high gain; the pentode vacuum tube is also employed because of its high μ and low input capacitance. The band width is given by

$$BW = (\omega_2 - \omega_1)/2\pi$$

and as has been pointed out, there is usually no serious problem in obtaining a desired ω_1. The limiting factor is ω_2 in both devices; that is, the internal capacitance causes the load impedance and the gain to drop at some elevated frequency. Various circuits have been devised which employ inductive elements to counter the impedance drop, and to extend the ω_2 value.

One such circuit places an inductor in shunt with the bothersome capacitances, as in Fig. 9–18; this form is known as *shunt compensated*. An additional circuit element is thereby available to the designer, and circuit performance can be made to more closely approach the ideal.

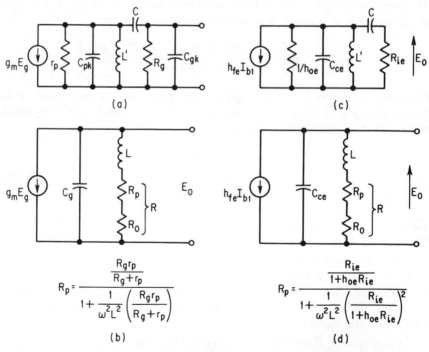

Fig. 9–18. (a), (b) Shunt-compensation for a pentode; (c), (d) same for a transistor.

In both pentode and transistor forms, the internal generator resistance is in parallel with R_g or R_{ie}, since the reactance of C is negligible in the high range. The parallel combination may then be considered as introducing an effective resistance R_p in series with the inductor L. That is, resistance R_p is electrically present due to the presence of h_{oe} and R_{ie} in Fig. 9–18(d), and resistor R_o is added by the designer in addition, giving an overall resistance R.

Since the circuits of Fig. 9–18(b) and (d) are identical in form, the analysis which follows is general for pentode and transistor. Using the transistor form, the equivalent generator operates into a load given by

$$Z_L = \cfrac{1}{\cfrac{1}{R + j\omega L} + j\omega C_{ce}} \tag{9–58}$$

from which

$$|Z_L| = R \sqrt{\frac{1 + \omega^2 L^2/R^2}{1 + \omega^2(C_{ce}^2 R^2 - 2LC_{ce}) + \omega^4 L^2 C_{ce}^2}} \tag{9–59}$$

Without the compensating inductor L, the circuit as a simple RC amplifier would have an upper cutoff frequency

$$\omega_2 = \frac{1}{C_{ce}R}$$

It will also be convenient to define a second parameter as

$$m = \frac{L}{C_{ce}R^2} \tag{9–60}$$

Use of these relations reduces Eq. 9–59 to

$$|Z_L| = R \sqrt{\frac{1 + m^2(\omega/\omega_2)^2}{1 + (1 - 2m)(\omega/\omega_2)^2 + m^2(\omega/\omega_2)^4}} \tag{9–61}$$

The voltage gain is dependent on this load impedance magnitude.

The impedance magnitude of such configurations can be written in general as

$$|Z_L| = R \sqrt{\frac{1 + a_1(\omega/\omega_2)^2 + a_2(\omega/\omega_2)^4 + \cdots}{1 + b_1(\omega/\omega_2)^2 + b_2(\omega/\omega_2)^4 + b_3(\omega/\omega_2)^6 + \cdots}} \tag{9–62}$$

If the amplifier gain is to be independent of frequency, then this impedance magnitude should be made independent of frequency. The roots of the numerator polynomial will supply a set of zeros, and the roots of the denominator will create a set of poles at various frequencies. Gain variation would be minimized if each zero was placed at the frequency of a pole, thus nullifying each other. There would, of course, be one higher frequency pole still effective to produce loss of gain at some more remote frequency.

Solution of the polynomials is not necessary, since equating of corresponding coefficients as $a_1 = b_1$, $a_2 = b_2$, $\cdots$, will produce maximal flatness of the response curve. Reverting to Eq. 9–61, then equating the coefficients of the $(\omega/\omega_2)^2$ terms gives

$$m^2 = 1 - 2m$$

from which

$$m = -1 \pm \sqrt{2} \qquad (9\text{–}63)$$

Since the negative sign provides no physical meaning to the result, the positive sign is chosen. Then for maximal flatness of gain, or minimal variation of the load impedance:

$$m = 0.414$$

Specification of all parameters is then possible. The maximum value of gain will occur at mid-range where

$$\mathbf{A}_{vM} = \frac{-h_{fe}R}{R\Delta + h_{ie}} \cong -g_m R \qquad (9\text{–}64)$$

If ω_2 is specified, then

$$R = \frac{1}{\omega_2 C_{ce}} \qquad (9\text{–}65)$$

$$L = \frac{0.414R}{\omega_2} \qquad (9\text{–}66)$$

and this completes the design. Note that throughout the discussion, ω_2 is that of the uncompensated amplifier, and it has been assumed that operation is much below f_α of the transistor.

The result of Eq. 9–63 is confirmed by the series of magnitude curves for the impedance Z_L, in terms of the parameter m, plotted in Fig. 9–19. The curve for $m = 0$ is for the uncompensated amplifier with load equal to R. The possible improvement in response by the use of L is apparent, the new cutoff approximating $1.8\omega_2$. The value of $m = 0.41$ provides the maximum cutoff frequency with a uniformly falling high-frequency response; larger m values will produce a peak or hump at the high-frequency end, as indicated for $m = 0.50$ in the figure.

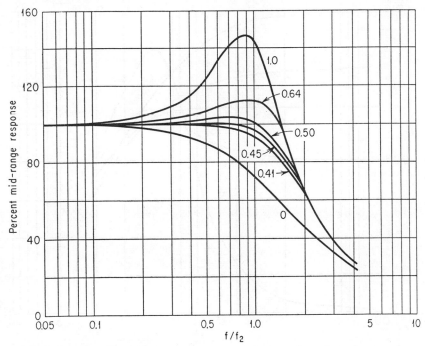

Fig. 9–19. Generalized high-frequency response for the shunt-compensated amplifier.

The phase angle for the shunt-compensated circuit is

$$\varphi - -\tan^{-1}\left[\omega C_{ce}R\left(1 + \frac{\omega^2 L^2}{R^2} - \frac{L}{R^2 C_{ce}}\right)\right]$$

Using the definitions of ω_2 and m

$$\varphi = -\tan^{-1}\frac{\omega}{\omega_2}\left[1 - m + m^2(\omega/\omega_2)^2\right] \qquad (9\text{–}67)$$

By taking the derivative of φ with respect to ω and equating the coefficients, it is found that $m = 0.32$ will provide constant time delay. The time delay in seconds can be found from the phase angle as

$$D = \frac{\varphi}{360f}$$

and the ratio of the delay at ω to the delay at ω_2 is plotted in Fig. 9–20, for various values of m. Since $m = 0.32$ for minimum phase shift, a compromise is necessary between flat gain and minimum phase shift; a value of 0.37 is considered suitable. Later study of the response to pulses will indicate that $m = 0.25$ is optimum when time of rise is important.

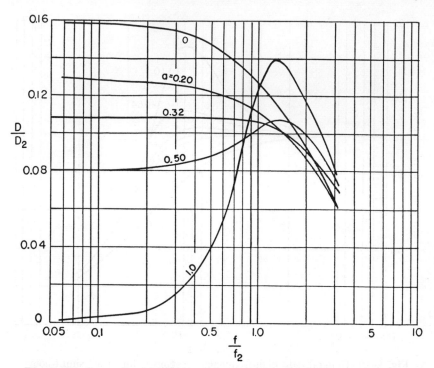

Fig. 9–20. Generalized high-frequency time delay curves for the shunt-compensated amplifier.

More sophisticated circuits are available to the designer, and with their additional circuit elements he is able to further widen the frequency band. However, circuits with additional L and C elements become higher-order systems, subject to oscillatory transients or overshoot in response to a pulse or transient. This tendency is increased if the amplifier has a peak in its high-frequency response, or if the gain drops too rapidly beyond the high-frequency limit. The shunt-peaking circuit, with its fairly smooth drop off of high-frequency gain, appears to give a satisfactory compromise, and is rather generally used in television or video-frequency service.

9–14. Band width requirements for pulse amplification

Since the preceding amplifiers were assumed as having low values of ω_1, they might well be classed as low-pass amplifiers. It is rare that these amplifiers are actually called upon to amplify sinusoidal signals, but they have been so studied because of the value of frequency-domain analysis. The more usual wave forms are transients as in speech, or repeated pulse trains as in data transmission. Time-domain methods provide information

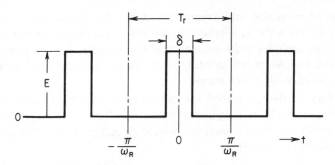

Fig. 9–21. Recurrent rectangular pulses.

on transient performance, and pulses or step-voltages are usual inputs in such study. Design for a desired transient performance may impose more severe restrictions on amplifiers than does design for sinusoidal response, and it is therefore desirable to study amplifier response to pulses or transients.

A general wave is a repetitive chain of pulses or voltage steps, with terminology as in Fig. 9–21. The period of the wave is $2\pi/\omega_R$, or $f_R = 1/T_R$, where f_R is called the *repetition frequency*. Such a chain of pulses may be interpreted on a frequency basis by use of a Fourier series. Such analysis will provide a magnitude for each harmonic term, and needed amplifier band width can be specified to provide gain for all harmonics of importance.

Fourier series representation of a function is given as

$$f(t) = A_o + a_1 \cos \omega_R t + a_2 \cos 2\omega_R t + \cdots$$

$$+ b_1 \sin \omega_R t + b_2 \sin 2\omega_R t + \cdots \quad (9\text{--}68)$$

which can be more concisely stated as

$$f(t) = A_o + \sum_{k=1}^{\infty} a_k \cos k\omega_R t + \sum_{k=1}^{\infty} b_k \sin k\omega_R t \quad (9\text{--}69)$$

By the usual Fourier methods the constant or average term is

$$A_o = \frac{\omega_R}{2\pi} \int_{-\pi/\omega_R}^{\pi/\omega_R} f(t) \, dt \quad (9\text{--}70)$$

and the coefficients are

$$a_k = \frac{\omega_R}{2\pi} \int_{-\pi/\omega_R}^{\pi/\omega_R} f(t) \, \cos k\omega_R t \, dt \quad (9\text{--}71)$$

$$b_k = \frac{\omega_R}{2\pi} \int_{-\pi/\omega_R}^{\pi/\omega_R} f(t) \, \sin k\omega_R t \, dt \quad (9\text{--}72)$$

By reason of even and odd symmetry, it can be shown that if $f(t)$ is an odd function, then the a_k coefficients are zero, and the Fourier series for an odd function includes only sine terms. Conversely, if $f(t)$ is even, then $b_k = 0$, and the series will contain only cosine terms. The constant term may be present with either result.

This may be demonstrated for the wave of Fig. 9–21, with the origin so located as to yield even symmetry, namely $f(x) = f(-x)$. Noting that $f(t) = E$ inside the pulse duration interval given by $t = \pm \delta/2$, and $f(t) = 0$ elsewhere in the period, then

$$A_o = \frac{\omega_R}{\pi} \int_{-\delta/2}^{\delta/2} E \, dt = \frac{\delta}{T_R} E = f_R \, \delta E \qquad (9\text{–}73)$$

where δ is the pulse duration. The a_k coefficients are

$$a_k = 2f_R \int_{-\delta/2}^{\delta/2} E \cos 2\pi f_R k t \, dt$$

$$= 2Ef_R \delta \, \frac{\sin \, (k\pi f_R \delta)}{k\pi f_R \delta} \qquad (9\text{–}74)$$

Thus we have determined the amplitude of the kth harmonic for a series of pulses of duration δ and repetition frequency f_R.

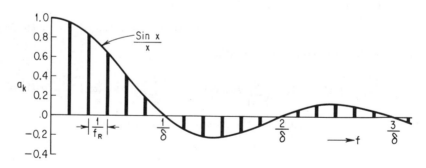

Fig. 9–22. Distribution of harmonic amplitudes in pulse chain.

It can be seen that the amplitude is a function of $(\sin x)/x$ where $x = k\pi f_R \delta$. This relation is further demonstrated in Fig. 9–22, where the envelope of the harmonic amplitudes is a curve of $(\sin x)/x$. This curve allows estimates to be made of the relative importance of high order harmonics to adequate pulse reproduction.

The cross-over frequencies can be found as

$$0 = \frac{\sin\ (k\pi f_R \delta)}{k\pi f_R \delta}$$

$$k f_R = \frac{n}{\delta} \tag{9-75}$$

where $n = 1, 2, 3, \ldots$. The expression indicates that each loop is $1/\delta$ cycles wide, and therefore increases as the pulse duration decreases.

For a pulse of 1 μsec duration, the first zero is at 1 mc, the second at 2 mc, etc. If the repetition frequency is 1000 per second, there will be 1000 harmonics in each loop of the envelope.

The number of harmonics appearing in each loop is inversely proportional to the repetition rate f_R. As this pulse rate is reduced, more harmonics appear in each loop of the enclosing envelope, and in the limit where a pulse occurs only once, or $f_R = 0$, a continuous spectrum of frequencies appears. This spectrum is obtained through use of the Fourier integral, and for the even pulse under discussion, is

$$S(\omega) = \frac{E\delta}{2\pi} \frac{\sin\ (\omega\delta/2)}{(\omega\delta/2)} \tag{9-76}$$

and this is again of the form $(\sin x)/x$. Therefore the continuous spectrum of harmonic amplitudes given by the single pulse is bounded by the envelope curve of Fig. 9–22.

The fidelity of pulse reproduction will depend on the number of harmonics within the amplifier pass band; for short pulses the required band width may be quite large. Experimentally, it is found that if the pass band includes the fourth zero, the pulse reproduction may be considered excellent. Where cost or other factors do not permit such design, reasonably accurate reproduction of the pulse can be obtained with a pass band including only the first zero at a frequency of $1/\delta$.

9–15. Rise time-band width relations

When amplifier band widths are sufficiently narrow that some of the essential pulse harmonics are not transmitted, the received pulses will undergo distortion of the sort indicated in Fig. 9–23(b) or (c). Time $t = 0$ is that at which the input pulse jumps from zero to E or 100 per cent magnitude. The output pulse, however, does not follow until time T_d, due to the time delay between application of the stimulating pulse and the resultant response. Measurement of this time delay is difficult because it involves subjective determination of the time at which the amplitude departs from the base or zero line on an oscilloscope trace.

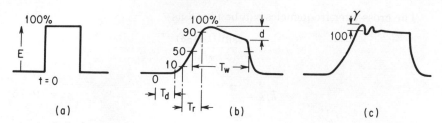

Fig. 9–23. Definitions for received pulse characteristics: (a) transmitted pulse; (b) non-oscillatory form; (c) overshoot present.

As shown in Fig. 9–23(b), the *rise time* of practical amplifiers is always finite, and improvement of this is a matter of considerable design effort. The rise time T_r is defined as the time of rise of output between 10 per cent and 90 per cent amplitude, to reduce error in estimation of the break point from the base line.

In Fig. 9–23(b) a long pulse has been applied, and *tilt*, *sag*, or *droop* of the top of the pulse is indicated as d. This is usually specified as a percentage of the pulse amplitude. In Fig. 9–23(c) an oscillatory condition is indicated, with an *overshoot* above the 100 per cent value. The magnitude of this overshoot is of concern, and is designated as γ. It is a result of a second order circuit equation, usually due to inclusion of inductive elements. The value of d may also be negative, because of an undershoot. While the width or duration of the input pulse of Fig. 9–23(a) is easily measured and definite, the width T_w of the output pulse is not easily determined. The measurement of T_w between the 50 per cent points is indicated, but this is not always the width referred to in the literature.

The study of the transient performance of amplifiers may conveniently begin with the RC-coupled common-emitter amplifier; the equations of Sections 9–5 and 9–7 are so similar in form that the results may easily be extended to the pentode amplifier if desired.

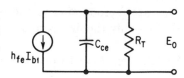

Fig. 9–24. Circuit effective in controlling rise time of RC common-emitter amplifier.

The high-frequency voltage gain expression of Eq. 9–17 may be simplified by dropping the term due to the input circuit; the transient performance will then be that of the interstage network and C_{ce}. Then

$$\mathbf{A}_{veH} = -g_m \left(\frac{R_p R_{ie}}{R_p + R_{ie}} \right) \left(\frac{1}{1 + j\omega \dfrac{C_{ce} R_p R_{ie}}{R_p + R_{ie}}} \right) \qquad (9\text{–}77)$$

Resistance R_p represents the parallel effect of $1/h_{oe}$ and R_L. The circuit and equation both show that R_{ie} is also in parallel with the combination; the combined effect as a load on the transistor may be labelled R_T, where

$$\frac{1}{R_T} = h_{oe} + \frac{1}{R_L} + \frac{1}{R_{ie}}$$

For a study of transient performance Eq. 9–77 may then be written by use of the Laplace transform as

$$\mathbf{A}_{ve}(p) = \frac{-g_m}{C_{ce}} \left(\frac{1}{p + \dfrac{1}{R_T C_{ce}}} \right) \tag{9–78}$$

A unit step input voltage may then be applied, using $E_s(p) = 1/p$, and the output will then be expressible as

$$E_o(p) = \frac{-g_m}{p C_{ce}} \left(\frac{1}{p + \dfrac{1}{R_T C_{ce}}} \right) \tag{9–79}$$

In the time domain the result will be

$$e_o(t) = -g_m R_T (1 - \epsilon^{-t/R_T C_{ce}}) \tag{9–80}$$

which indicates an exponential rise of voltage with time, as shown for the leading edge of the received pulse in Fig. 9–23(b).

The ultimate output or 100 per cent level can be seen to be $E_o = -g_m R_T$, or the mid-range gain. The equation can be solved to show that $e_o(t)$ will reach the 10 per cent level at $t_{10} = 0.106 R_T C_{ce}$, and the 90 per cent level at $t_{90} = 2.303 R_T C_{ce}$. Therefore the defined rise time of the amplifier is

$$T_r = 2.2 R_T C_{ce} \tag{9–81}$$

Both gain and rise time are proportional to R_T, or the transistor resistive load; to design an amplifier for high gain requires large R_T, but this also lengthens the rise time. This dependence is shown by taking the ratio of gain and rise time as

$$\frac{\text{Gain}}{\text{Rise time}} = \frac{A}{T_r} = \frac{g_m}{2.2 C_{ce}} \tag{9–82}$$

and this expression is a constant for a given transistor (or a pentode) involving as it does both g_m and the internal capacitances. It is sometimes referred to as a figure of merit of particular transistor or tube types.

Considering the RC amplifier as a low-pass device, then the band width may be taken as from essentially zero to a frequency given by ω_2. Since from Eq. 9–23

$$\omega_2 = \frac{1}{R_T C_{ce}}$$

then the band width-rise time product is a constant, as

$$BWT_r = \frac{2.2 R_T C_{ce}}{2\pi R_T C_{ce}} = 0.35 \tag{9-83}$$

While thus defined for RC amplifiers, it has been found that this ratio is approximately correct for many types, including the compensated forms. In general BWT_r will lie between 0.35 and 0.45, with the value of 0.35 being best for amplifiers in which the overshoot is small, and 0.45 corresponding to overshoots of five per cent or more. It is also assumed that the amplifier cutoff versus frequency curve is smooth and gradual, and that the time delay is constant through the pass band.

Thus if the band width is known on a sinusoidal basis, it is possible to estimate the rise time to be expected from the amplifier. For cascaded amplifiers of little overshoot, the overall rise time for n stages can be found from

$$T_{rn} = \sqrt{T_{r1}^2 + T_{r2}^2 + T_{r3}^2 + \cdots} \tag{9-84}$$

If the overshoot is of the order of five per cent, the total rise time will be somewhat less than predicted by this equation.

9–16. Rise-time considerations for the shunt-compensated amplifier

It has been previously shown that the shunt-compensated circuit may be used to increase amplifier band width. Consideration must also be given, however, to the effect of such compensation on the rise time for transient input, since with an inductor in circuit the load impedance function becomes of second order and overshoot is possible. Writing Eq. 9–58 for the load impedance of the shunt-compensated amplifier in operational form

$$Z_L(p) = \frac{1}{\dfrac{1}{pL + R} + pC_{ce}} = \frac{1}{C_{ce}} \frac{p + R/L}{p^2 + p(R/L) + 1/(LC_{ce})} \tag{9-85}$$

The voltage gain of an RC-coupled common-emitter amplifier, using this load impedance, is then

$$A_{ve}(p) = \frac{-g_m}{C_{ce}} \frac{p + R/L}{p^2 + p(R/L) + 1/(LC_{ce})} \tag{9-86}$$

For a unit step input $E_s(p) = 1/p$, and the output voltage then is

$$E_o(p) = \frac{-g_m}{C_{ce}} \frac{p + R/L}{p\left[p + \frac{R}{2L} + \sqrt{\frac{R^2}{4L^2} - \frac{1}{LC_{ce}}}\right]\left[p + \frac{R}{2L} - \sqrt{\frac{R^2}{4L^2} - \frac{1}{LC_{ce}}}\right]}$$

(9–87)

In the previous discussion of the shunt-compensated amplifier the parameter m was defined as

$$m = \frac{L}{C_{ce}R^2}$$

(9–88)

and it is now convenient to define a second parameter as

$$\beta = \frac{R}{2L}$$

(9–89)

so that

$$E_o(p) = \frac{-g_m}{C_{ce}} \frac{p + 2\beta}{p[p + \beta(1 + \sqrt{1 - 4m})][p + \beta(1 - \sqrt{1 - 4m})]}$$

(9–90)

This function has poles at $p_0 = 0$, and $p_1 = -\beta(1 + \sqrt{1 - 4m})$, $p_2 = -\beta(1 - \sqrt{1 - 4m})$, located as in Fig. 9–25. The conjugate pair of complex poles present in Fig. 9–25(b) indicates the presence of sine and cosine terms in the output in the time domain, and this will lead to conditions of overshoot for $m > 0.25$.

Writing

$$x = \sqrt{1 - 4m}$$

$$\tau = RC_{ce}$$

then reference to a table of transform pairs gives a solution in the time domain as

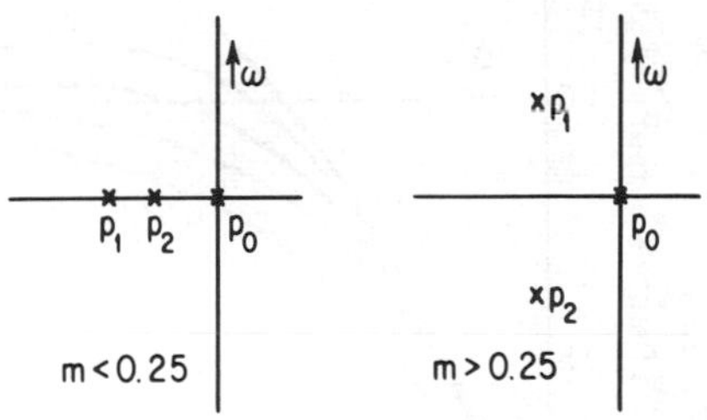

(a)   (b)

Fig. 9–25. Pole-zero plot of Eq. 9–90.

$$e_o(t) = -g_m R \left\{1 - \epsilon^{-t/2m\tau}\left[\frac{1 - 2m}{\sqrt{1 - 4m}}\left(\frac{\epsilon^{\beta xt} - \epsilon^{-\beta xt}}{2}\right) + \left(\frac{\epsilon^{\beta xt} + \epsilon^{-\beta xt}}{2}\right)\right]\right\}$$

(9–91)

For the case in which $m < 0.25$, the above becomes

$$e_o(t) = -g_mR\left\{1 - \epsilon^{-t/2m\tau}\left[\frac{1 - 2m}{\sqrt{1 - 4m}}\sinh\frac{\sqrt{1 - 4m}}{2m}\frac{t}{\tau}\right.\right.$$

$$\left.\left. + \cosh\frac{\sqrt{1 - 4m}}{2m}\frac{t}{\tau}\right]\right\} \quad (9\text{--}92)$$

and if $m > 0.25$

$$e_o(t) = -g_mR\left\{1 - \epsilon^{-t/2m\tau}\left[\frac{1 - 2m}{\sqrt{4m - 1}}\sin\frac{\sqrt{4m - 1}}{2m}\frac{t}{\tau}\right.\right.$$

$$\left.\left. + \cos\frac{\sqrt{4m - 1}}{2m}\frac{t}{\tau}\right]\right\} \quad (9\text{--}93)$$

This result confirms the damped oscillatory prediction made for $m > 0.25$. The pulse output height will be given by g_mR as the final value.

In Fig. 9–26, the relative output $e_o(t)/g_mR$ is plotted as a function of $t/\tau = t/RC_{ce}$, for various values of m. The case of $m = 0$ is that of the uncompensated amplifier, and the improvement in rise time of the compensated circuit is noticeable. Overshoot appears for $m > 0.25$, and it is usually not beneficial to increase m beyond a value of 0.5, since the overshoot increases without a commensurate decrease in rise time.

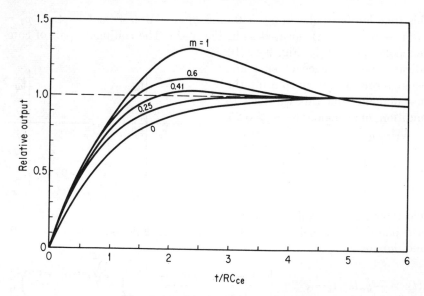

Fig. 9–26. Effect of m on rise time.

Improvement in rise time is shown more clearly in the plot of Fig. 9–27, where the speed is presented as a ratio to $2.2RC_{ce}$, which was the speed of rise of the uncompensated RC circuit. It can be seen that at $m = 0.25$ the rise time is reduced to 0.7 of that of the uncompensated circuit.

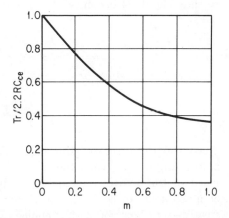

Fig. 9–27. Reduction in rise time over that of the uncompensated amplifier versus m.

It should be remembered that on a sinusoidal basis a value of $m = 0.41$ was proposed as providing a gain-frequency curve having no rise at the high-frequency end. From the transient point of view it is seen that this criterion may not be sufficiently limiting, since $m = 0.41$ will create an overshoot of about five per cent. A value of $m = 0.35$ is often considered a good compromise, keeping ω_2 high and limiting the overshoot on pulses to about two per cent.

Attention should also be called to the fact that in multi-stage amplifiers a small overshoot in each stage will produce a significantly larger overall overshoot. This is particularly true if the individual overshoot exceeds ten per cent.

More complex circuits are available, and with these it is possible to reduce the rise time further.

9–17. Optimum number of stages

For an amplifier of n identical stages, Eq. 9–84 can be written as

$$\text{Overall } T_r = T_{r1}\sqrt{n} = 2.2RC\sqrt{n} \qquad (9\text{–}94)$$

To make the results of this section general, we may consider $C = C_{ce}$ for transistors, and $C = C_g$ for pentodes, with R being the load resistance in each case. Defining G as the overall amplifier gain, then

$$G = (g_m R)^n$$

and

$$R = \frac{G^{1/n}}{g_m}$$

so that Eq. 9–94 becomes

$$T_r = 2.2 \frac{CG^{1/n}\sqrt{n}}{g_m} \tag{9-95}$$

For a single stage $n = 1$, and

$$\frac{G_1}{T_{r1}} = \frac{g_m}{2.2C} \tag{9-96}$$

Since the right side of this expression contains only parameters of the amplifying device, then the ratio of stage gain to rise time is a figure of merit of the device. It is apparent that this result is related to the figure of merit introduced in Eq. 9–49 for the gain-band width product on a steady-state basis, and thus choice of a transistor or pentode for desirable gain-band width product will also yield a device giving the best gain-rise time ratio as well.

Since the rise time is a nonlinear function of the number of stages, it is desirable to determine the optimum number of stages to provide a specified overall gain G, with a minimum overall rise time. Taking dT_r/dn in Eq. 9–95, and setting to zero gives

$$\frac{dT_r}{dn} = 0 = \frac{2.2CG^{1/n}}{g_m\sqrt{n}} \left(\frac{1}{2} - \frac{1}{n} \ln G \right) \tag{9-97}$$

which leads to

$$\text{Optimum } n = 2 \ln G \tag{9-98}$$

From this result $G = \epsilon^{n/2}$ and since the gain per stage is $G^{1/n}$, the optimum gain per stage must be

$$\text{Optimum gain/stage} = \sqrt{\epsilon} = 1.65 \tag{9-99}$$

The minimum overall rise time, using these results, follows as

$$\text{Minimum } T_r = \frac{2.2C\sqrt{\epsilon}\sqrt{2 \ln G}}{g_m} = \frac{5.1C\sqrt{\ln G}}{g_m} \tag{9-100}$$

Therefore, an amplifier to have a gain of 500 and using the 6AH6 pentode with $C_g \cong 12$ pf (neglecting stray capacitance) and $g_m = 9000$ μmhos, should be built with 13 stages, and would have an overall rise time approximating 0.017 μsec. It could be found that the load resistance should then be 183 ohms, and the band width, as measured by ω_2, would be 72 mcs. The number of stages is not critical, and economics may often dictate a reduction.

9–18. Sag or droop of the top of the pulse

The effect of amplifier design on rise time of the amplified pulse has been studied, but so far no consideration has been given to the reproduction of the remainder of the pulse. If the duration δ of the pulse is assumed long with respect to the rise time, it is possible to separate the analysis into two parts as has been done. This is so because the rise time is under control of the shunt capacities of the transistor or tube, or is related to ω_2, whereas the droop or sag of the pulse top is dependent on the series capacities and their capability in maintaining a charge during time δ, and this is related to the low-frequency characteristics of the amplifier.

Consider the pulse of Fig. 9–28(a), applied to the RC amplifier output circuit derived from Fig. 9–10(a) and redrawn in Fig. 9–29. For constant output $e_o = -R_{ie}i_{b2}$ during the time $0 < t < \delta$, the current i_{b2} should be constant, and this requires that C be large. Obviously, there will be some fall in the value of E_o, and this fall will be exponential with time, as shown in Fig. 9–28(b).

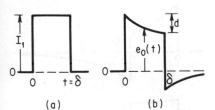

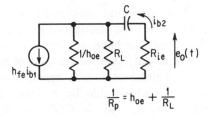

(a)   (b)

Fig. 9–28. Pulse form.   **Fig. 9–29.** Transistor output circuit for study of droop.

We will neglect the rise time as short with respect to the pulse duration δ. Then by use of Eq. 9–10 for the current gain of the RC common-emitter amplifier, the output voltage $E_0 = -I_{b2}R_{ie}$ can be written as the product of gain and input current as

$$E_o = h_{fe}\left(\frac{R_pR_{ie}}{R_p + R_{ie}}\right)\left[\frac{I_{b1}}{1 + \dfrac{1}{j\omega C(R_p + R_{ie})}}\right] \qquad (9\text{–}101)$$

The expression for the pentode RC amplifier would be similar in form, and could be used equally well for this analysis.

Defining

$$\tau' = C(R_p + R_{ie}),$$

$$R = R_pR_{ie}/(R_p + R_{ie}) = \text{mid-frequency load}$$

the output for a transient step input current $I_{b1} = I_1/p$ can be found by writing the Laplace transform of the gain times the input current as

$$e_o(p) = h_{fe}R\frac{I_1}{p}\left(\frac{p}{p + 1/\tau'}\right) \tag{9-102}$$

Then

$$e_o(t) = \mathcal{L}^{-1}e_o(p) = h_{fe}RI_1\epsilon^{-t/\tau'} \qquad 0 < t < \delta \tag{9-103}$$

where I_1 is the amplitude of the input pulse. This equation defines the exponential droop of the amplified pulse in Fig. 9-28(b). It has been assumed that the initial charge on C was zero.

At the instant $t = \delta-$, the amplitude has fallen to the value

$$e_o(\delta-) = h_{fe}RI_1\epsilon^{-\delta/\tau'} \tag{9-104}$$

The input then undergoes a jump of $-I_1$ amplitude at $t = \delta$, so that the output is expressible as

$$e_o(t) = h_{fe}RI_1(\epsilon^{-\delta/\tau'} - 1)\epsilon^{-t/\tau'} \qquad t > \delta \tag{9-105}$$

For minimum distortion of the pulse wave form the output should be flat-topped or have negligible droop, and zero output after the end of the applied pulse at $t = \delta$. Small droop or sag is obtainable by making the time constant $\tau' = C(R_p + R_{ie})$ large with respect to δ; the same condition will make the parentheses of Eq. 9-105 small, resulting in minimum output for $t > \delta$, as is desired. Pulses for several ratios of τ'/δ appear in Fig. 9-30; it appears that this ratio should approximate 50 to 100 for small droop and good pulse reproduction.

The magnitude of the droop d may be readily computed if Eq. 9-104 be written with the exponential term replaced by its series as

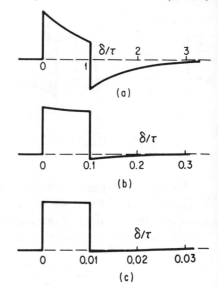

Fig. 9-30. Effect of δ/τ ratio on pulse reproduction: (a) $\delta/\tau = 1$; (b) $\delta/\tau = 0.1$; (c) $\delta/\tau = 0.01$.

$$e_o(\delta) = h_{fe}RI_1\left[1 - \frac{\delta}{\tau'} + \frac{1}{2}\left(\frac{\delta}{\tau'}\right)^2 - \cdots\right] \tag{9-106}$$

For small values of δ/τ' only the first two terms are needed to give a reasonable approximation. The first term expresses the output without droop, the second is therefore the magnitude of the droop. The ratio of these terms then is

$$\text{Per cent droop} = \frac{\delta}{\tau'} \times 100\% = \frac{\delta}{C(R_p + R_{ie})} \times 100\% \quad (9\text{–}107)$$

By previous definition $\omega_1 = 1/C(R_p + R_{ie})$ and so the pulse response of the amplifier may be related to the steady-state frequency response as

$$\text{Per cent droop} = \delta\omega_1 \times 100\% \quad (9\text{–}108)$$

As an example, if $\omega_1 = 20$ cps for an amplifier and if the droop is to be held to two per cent, then the longest pulse which can be amplified is

$$\delta = \frac{0.02}{2\pi \times 20} = 1590 \ \mu\text{secs}$$

For overall droop of a multi-stage amplifier, it is found that the droops of successive stages become additive, and so the droop requirements on each stage become severe. Previously, the relation between coupling capacitor C and the emitter resistance bypass or cathode resistance bypass has been studied. As was suggested for the emitter bypass, transient requirements usually are most easily met by elimination of the bypass, and compensating for the resultant gain reduction. The use of a very small bypass capacitor may improve the rise time, however.

The methods of Section 9–12 are also useful in decreasing the per cent droop.

9–19. The parallel-resonant circuit

Another great class of amplifiers are those handling sinusoidal signals, with the additional requirement that there be some discrimination of frequency bands amplified. For such frequency selectivity the parallel-resonant circuit of Fig. 9–31 is frequently employed as a load, or as an element of a more complex system, to provide appropriate band width.

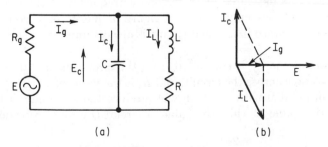

(a)   (b)

Fig. 9–31. Currents in the parallel-resonant circuit.

The resistance R may be that of the inductor, or may be intentionally introduced to absorb power. The capacitor ordinarily has negligible losses. The admittance of this circuit is

$$\mathbf{Y}_T = \frac{R}{R^2 + \omega^2 L^2} - j \left(\frac{\omega L}{R^2 + \omega^2 L^2} - \omega C \right) \tag{9-109}$$

For the condition of parallel resonance, or *antiresonance*, the circuit is defined as having a resistive impedance. Therefore, setting the j term to zero

$$\frac{\omega L}{R^2 + \omega^2 L^2} = \omega C \tag{9-110}$$

from which

$$f_r = \frac{1}{2\pi} \sqrt{\frac{1}{LC} - \frac{R^2}{L^2}} \tag{9-111}$$

as the frequency at which parallel resonance occurs. It should be noted that such antiresonance is impossible for values of R which make $R^2/L^2 > 1/LC$.

Such a circuit stores electric or magnetic energy, and the efficiency with which it performs this function is of interest. A *figure of merit*, Q, has been defined as the relative storage efficiency at resonance, or

$$Q = \frac{2\pi \times \text{maximum energy stored per cycle}}{\text{energy dissipated per cycle}} \tag{9-112}$$

If I_m is the maximum current through the inductive branch, then

$$Q = \frac{2\pi L I_m^2}{I_m^2 R/f_r} = \frac{2\pi f_r L}{R} = \frac{\omega_r L}{R} \tag{9-113}$$

thus defining Q as measured at the resonant frequency of the circuit. The factor Q is sometimes employed as a figure of merit for a coil, but the frequency of resonance in a tuned circuit is always implied in such a statement.

If the stored energy is computed from the circuit capacitance and the maximum voltage across the circuit, and R_e is the value of circuit resistance connected in parallel with C which will produce the same circuit losses as does the series value R, then the value of circuit Q may also be defined as

$$Q = \frac{2\pi C E_m^2}{E_m^2/f_r R_e} = 2\pi f_r C R_e = \omega_r C R_e \tag{9-114}$$

Using the definition of Eq. 9–113, Eq. 9–111 becomes

$$f_r = \frac{1}{2\pi} \sqrt{\frac{1}{LC}} \sqrt{\frac{Q^2}{1 + Q^2}} \tag{9-115}$$

For $Q > 10$, the second radical can be neglected with negligible error.

From Eq. 9–115 it is possible to write

$$\omega_r L = \frac{1}{\omega_r C} \left(\frac{Q^2}{1 + Q^2}\right) \tag{9-116}$$

and the reactances of the inductive and capacitive branches are shown not quite equal at the antiresonant frequency.

At antiresonance, the resistive impedance presented at the terminals of the parallel circuit is given by Eq. 9–109 as

$$\mathbf{Z}_r = R_r = \frac{R^2 + \omega_r^2 L^2}{R} = R + \omega_r L Q \cong \omega_r L Q \tag{9-117}$$

$$= R + \frac{L}{CR} \left(\frac{Q^2}{1 + Q^2}\right) \cong \frac{L}{CR} \tag{9-118}$$

The latter relation indicates that the resonant resistance of the parallel circuit is a function of the L/C ratio chosen by the circuit designer, and that R_r can be quite large if inductors of low resistance are employed.

The several currents in the circuit can be written, at antiresonance, as

$$I_L = \frac{E_C}{\sqrt{R^2 + \omega_r^2 L^2}} = \frac{E_C}{R\sqrt{1 + Q^2}}$$

$$I_C = E_C \omega_r C = \frac{E_C}{\omega_r L} \left(\frac{Q^2}{1 + Q^2}\right)$$

$$I_g = \frac{E_C}{R_r} = \frac{E_C}{R + \omega_r L Q} = \frac{E_C}{R(1 + Q^2)}$$

By rearrangement of the above, it is possible to show that

$$\frac{I_C}{I_L} = \sqrt{\frac{Q^2}{1 + Q^2}} \tag{9-119}$$

indicating that for parallel resonance the currents in the two branches are not equal if the resistance is appreciable. This discrepancy is indicated by the phasor diagram of Fig. 9–31(b).

Also

$$I_C = Q I_g \tag{9-120}$$

and this expression shows that the current circulating at resonance in the L and C branches may be many times larger than the current supplied by the external generator. This high internal current implies a high value of energy storage in the electric and magnetic fields present in the capacitor and inductor. Because of this storage, or because the circuit frequently is used as an energy reservoir, it is quite common to speak of this circuit as a *tank circuit*.

9–20. Impedance variation of the parallel circuit near resonance

Use of Eq. 9–109 to calculate the parallel circuit impedance near but not at resonance calls for the computation of the difference of two large and nearly equal numbers in the reactance term, and accurate calculations require many significant figures. Certain changes in form of the equation are possible, starting with

$$\mathbf{Y}_T = \frac{1}{(R^2 + \omega^2 L^2)/R} - \frac{j}{\omega L}\left(\frac{1}{R^2/\omega^2 L^2 + 1} - \omega^2 LC\right) \quad (9\text{–}121)$$

It is convenient to define a parameter δ as a frequency variation from resonance such that

$$\delta = \frac{f - f_r}{f_r} = \frac{\omega}{\omega_r} - 1, \quad (9\text{–}122)$$

$$\frac{\omega}{\omega_r} = 1 + \delta \quad (9\text{–}123)$$

The definition for Q may then be written as

$$\frac{\omega L}{R} = \frac{\omega}{\omega_r}\frac{\omega_r L}{R} = (1 + \delta)Q \quad (9\text{–}124)$$

so as to permit Q, defined at the resonant frequency, to be written for $\omega L/R$ whenever it appears. Also

$$\omega^2 LC = \omega_r^2 LC(1 + \delta)^2 = \left(\frac{Q^2}{1 + Q^2}\right)(1 + \delta)^2 \quad (9\text{–}125)$$

by use of Eq. 9–116. In practice, Q^2 will usually be large with respect to unity, at least if $Q > 10$. Then Eq. 9–121 becomes

$$\mathbf{Y}_T = \frac{1}{R[1 + Q^2(1 + \delta)^2]} - \frac{j}{RQ(1 + \delta)}\left[\frac{Q^2(1 + \delta)^2}{1 + (1 + \delta)^2 Q^2} - (1 + \delta)^2\right]$$

$$\cong \frac{1 + j2Q\delta(1 + \delta)^2}{RQ^2(1 + \delta)^2} \quad (9\text{–}126)$$

after again neglecting unity with respect to Q^2. The impedance of the circuit then is

$$\mathbf{Z}_T \cong \frac{RQ^2(1 + \delta)^2}{1 + j2Q\delta(1 + \delta)^2} \qquad (9\text{–}127)$$

which is in a form much better suited to computation than is Eq. 9–109. No assumptions other than $Q^2 \gg 1$ have been made, and the expression is usable for any value of δ.

At antiresonance $\delta = 0$, and the impedance reduces to

$$\mathbf{Z}_r = RQ^2 \qquad (9\text{–}128)$$

which confirms Eq. 9–117, derived by other methods. The ratio of the impedance at any frequency to that at antiresonance is then

$$\frac{\mathbf{Z}}{\mathbf{Z}_r} \cong \frac{(1 + \delta)^2}{1 + j2Q\delta(1 + \delta)^2} \qquad (9\text{–}129)$$

Near the resonant frequency where $\delta \ll 1$ this reduces to

$$\frac{\mathbf{Z}}{\mathbf{Z}_r} \cong \frac{1}{1 + j2Q\delta} = A \underline{/\theta^\circ} \qquad (9\text{–}130)$$

The circuit is resistive at resonance, but the phase angle changes rapidly for frequencies off resonance, and the circuit appears inductive for frequencies below resonance $(-\delta)$ and capacitive for frequencies above resonance $(+\delta)$. These phase angle shifts are frequently important when the circuit is employed as a plate load for a tube or transistor.

9–21. Band width of the parallel-resonant circuit

When parallel resonant circuits are employed to sift out or select a narrow band of sinusoidal frequencies from a broad spectrum of signals, it is desirable to have a measure of the *selectivity* of the circuit. This measure or criterion is called band width, in conformity with previous usage of the term.

Band width or the relative frequency selectivity, is defined as the width in cycles of the resonant response curve, measured between the points or frequencies at which the power in the circuit is one-half the power at resonance. Thus the definition is consistent with the definition of band width of low-frequency amplifiers, as the frequency difference between f_2 and f_1.

When a value of frequency deviation δ' is chosen so that $2Q\delta' = 1$, then the impedance given by Eq. 9–130 is equal to $Z_r/(1 + j1)$ or is 0.707 of the impedance at resonance and the phase angle is 45°. Assuming a generator of constant current, as a pentode, the power supplied to the circuit at $\delta = \delta'$ will be one-half the power at resonance. At resonance

$$P_r = I_g^2 RQ^2$$

and at $\delta = \delta'$

$$P' = \frac{I_g^2 RQ^2 \cos 45°}{\sqrt{2}} = \frac{P_r}{2}$$

There is a point δ' on each side of resonance, thus the total band width is $2\delta'$. The band limits are those at which $2Q\delta' = 1$, therefore $2\delta' = 1/Q$. Then

$$BW = \Delta f = 2\delta' f_r = \frac{f_r}{Q} \qquad (9\text{--}131)$$

for the parallel circuit, supplied by a *constant-current* generator, transistor or pentode.

This is the condition assumed for the resonant curve of Fig. 9–32, wherein for $Q = 100$, the band width at the 0.707 Z_r points, or the half-power points, is seen to be 0.01 f_r, as required. The shape of the curve is typical of the frequency selectivity to be expected from a parallel-resonant circuit.

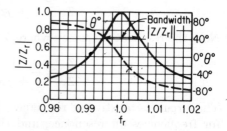

Fig. 9–32. Impedance and phase angle of the parallel-resonant circuit ($Q = 100$).

For the case in which the circuit is *supplied by a constant-voltage generator* of resistance R_g, as by a triode, it can be shown that the band width is

$$\Delta f = \left(\frac{1}{Q} + \frac{1}{Q}\frac{R_r}{R_g}\right)f_r \cong \left(\frac{1}{Q} + \frac{1}{Q}\frac{L}{CRR_g}\right)f_r \qquad (9\text{--}132)$$

showing how the band width is related to the choice of the L/C ratio by the designer. For great selectivity the inductance should be reduced and capacitance increased, although this lowers the value of R_r and may be undesirable from this standpoint. Resonant circuit design is thus a compromise between impedance and selectivity.

9–22. Singly-tuned amplifiers

The circuit of Fig. 9–33(a) is occasionally employed as a coupling means between cascaded amplifiers, particularly in radio-receiver circuits where some frequency selectivity is desired. In such applications E_2

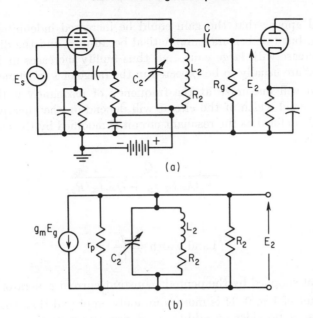

Fig. 9–33. (a) Plate-tuned amplifier; (b) equivalent circuit for (a).

becomes the input signal for the second-stage amplifier and it is usually desired that E_2 have a maximum value.

In vacuum-tube amplifiers it is customary to use pentodes and the equivalent circuit of Fig. 9–33(b) then applies. Usually r_p and R_g will be large with respect to the associated impedances. The equivalent circuit neglects stray magnetic and electric field couplings, and shielding of input and output circuits must be used to obtain stable and predictable results.

The resistance R_2 is that of L_2 plus other resistance due to losses added by eddy currents in metals in the magnetic flux path, or dielectric losses in the coil form. At very high frequencies the admittance of the input circuit of the second stage should also be considered in shunt with the circuit, but will be neglected here.

By use of the approximation of Eq. 9–117 the gain at resonance may be written as

$$A = \frac{E_o}{E_g} = -g_m \frac{1}{1/Q\omega_r L_2 + 1/r_p + 1/R_g} \tag{9–133}$$

If r_p and R_g are large as is usual, then

$$A \cong -g_m Q\omega_r L_2 = -g_m L_2/C_2 R_2 \tag{9–134}$$

where Q is that of the resonant circuit. This result indicates that the gain magnitude is a function of the L/C ratio chosen for the tuned circuit.

It would appear that the gain could be increased indefinitely by increase of L_2, but this becomes impractical because R_2 and the distributed capacity increase with large coils, and thus nullify increases in L_2. Gains of 100 to 300 are usually to be expected in the range of 1 to 10 megacycles.

The gain will maximize at the frequency of resonance of the tuned circuit. The band width of the circuit will depend on the effective circuit parameter Q_e, defined as the resonant circuit Q modified by the presence of r_p and R_g; then

$$Q_e = \frac{Q}{1 + Q\omega_r L_2/r_p + Q\omega_r L_2/R_g} \tag{9-135}$$

and

$$\text{band width} = \frac{f_r}{Q_e}$$

for the circuit supplied by the pentode constant-current generator.

The circuit of Fig. 9–34 is more commonly employed than that of Fig. 9–33, because it provides an additional design parameter, and eliminates the need for C and R_g. If a pentode is used r_p may be neglected in the equivalent circuit. Then

$$\mathbf{I_1} = g_m \mathbf{E}_g$$

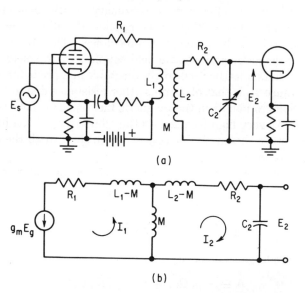

(a)

(b)

Fig. 9–34. Inductively-coupled grid-tuned amplifier and the equivalent.

and by use of Eq. 6–19, and Fig. 6–3,

$$I_2 = \frac{-z_f I_1}{z_o + Z_L} = \frac{-j g_m \omega M \mathbf{E}_g}{R_2 + j(\omega L_2 - 1/\omega C_2)}$$

since the reactance of C_2 may be considered as the load $\mathbf{Z}_L$ of the coupled circuit. The secondary voltage $\mathbf{E}_2$ is

$$\mathbf{E}_2 = \frac{-j \mathbf{I}_2}{\omega C_2} = \frac{-g_m \mathbf{E}_g (M/C_2)}{R_2 + j(\omega L_2 - 1/\omega C_2)} \tag{9–136}$$

This voltage will be maximum at secondary resonance when

$$\omega_r L_2 = 1/\omega_r C_2$$

if the Q is reasonable. The gain of the amplifier is then

$$\mathbf{A} = \frac{\mathbf{E}_2}{\mathbf{E}_g} = \frac{\mathbf{E}_2}{\mathbf{E}_s} = \frac{-g_m M}{R_2 C_2} = -g_m \omega_r M \frac{\omega_r L_2}{R_2} = -g_m Q_2 \omega_r M \tag{9–137}$$

The gain is thus a function of g_m, the secondary Q, and the mutual inductance. The ratio of gain between the plate-tuned circuit and the transformer-coupled circuit as shown by comparison of Eqs. 9–134 and 9–137 is seen to be L_2/M. The latter circuit is more susceptible to design variation, since the gain can be adjusted without change of L_2, or of Q and the band width.

The coupled-in effect of r_p in producing an effective Q_e can be computed as

$$Q_e = \frac{Q}{1 + Q\omega L_2/r_p} \tag{9–138}$$

and the band width is again given by $\Delta f = f_r/Q_e$.

9–23. Transistor singly-tuned amplifiers

The methods and circuits of the preceding section are also employed with transistors. Output impedances in the common-base and common-emitter circuits may not be too different from those encountered with pentode vacuum tubes, but input impedances will be much lower. This requires that the preceding circuits be slightly modified, in order to more nearly match the input impedance, and several such modification methods are shown in Fig. 9–35, where either common-base or common-emitter connections might be used.

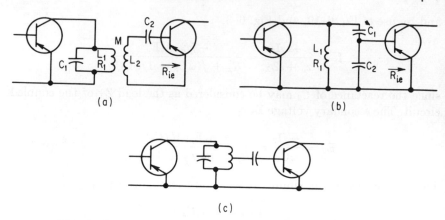

(a)   (b)

(c)

Fig. 9–35. Impedance matching for tuned transistor amplifiers.

In Fig. 9–35(a), the primary impedance is stepped down to the low inductance secondary which is loaded by R_{ie}, the input resistance of the succeeding transistor. If the resistance of the secondary coil be neglected, then the circuit may be drawn in equivalent form in Fig. 9–36, using the equivalent T for a coupled circuit. For the circuit to the right of terminals a, a

$$\begin{bmatrix} E \\ 0 \end{bmatrix} = \begin{bmatrix} j\omega L_1, & j\omega M \\ j\omega M, & R_{ie} + j(\omega L_2 - 1/\omega C_2) \end{bmatrix} \begin{bmatrix} I_1 \\ I_2 \end{bmatrix} \qquad (9\text{–}139)$$

The input impedance at a, a can be obtained by the methods of Chapter 7 as

$$Z_{a,a} = z_i - \frac{z_r z_f}{z_o + Z_L} = j\omega L_1 + \frac{\omega^2 M^2}{R_{ie} + j(\omega L_2 - 1/\omega C_2)} \qquad (9\text{–}140)$$

The impedance reflected into the primary winding and appearing in series there is represented by the second term on the right, and the circuit reduces to Fig. 9–36(b).

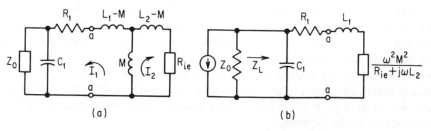

(a)   (b)

Fig. 9–36. Equivalent circuits.

The load impedance Z_L on the first transistor, at secondary resonance at ω_r, or $\omega_r L_2 = 1/\omega_r C_2$, is

$$Z_L = \frac{(R_1 + j\omega L_1 + \omega^2 M^2/R_{ie})\,(-j/\omega C_1)}{R_1 + \omega^2 M^2/R_{ie} + j(\omega L_1 - 1/\omega C_1)} \tag{9-141}$$

With this as a load, the input impedance of the first transistor can be accurately found. The methods used in handling Eq. 9–136 for the vacuum tube are then available for further analysis.

The circuit at Fig. 9–35(b), provides a convenient means of impedance step down to R_{ie} of the second stage. This impedance is reflected across the full resonant circuit as

$$R'_{ie} = \frac{R_{ie} - j/\omega(C_1 + C_2)}{[C_1/(C_1 + C_2)]^2} \tag{9-142}$$

and the load impedance seen by the first stage then is

$$Z_L = \frac{(R_1 + j\omega L_1)\,(-j/\omega C)\,R'_{ie}}{(R_1 + j\omega L_1)\,(-j/\omega C) + R'_{ie}[R_1 + j(\omega L_1 - 1/\omega C)]} \tag{9-143}$$

where

$$C = \frac{C_1 C_2}{C_1 + C_2}$$

Tuning to resonance will make this impedance large. Equation 9–133 may then be modified to employ this result for $Q\omega_r L_2$, replacing r_p with $1/h_{oe}$ for the common-emitter amplifier.

9–24. Doubly-tuned amplifiers

Ideal selectivity would be obtained in an amplifier if a band of frequencies were equally amplified, and all other frequencies completely rejected. A plot of such a response against frequency would be a rectangle with a flat top and vertical sides. The resonant response curve of Fig. 9–32 is obviously a poor approximation of such performance. It can be shown, however, that if the load impedance function has a number of mathematical poles suitably placed in the p plane, a good approximation to the ideal response can be obtained. In the frequency domain, these poles might be represented by parallel resonant circuits, with their high resonant impedances, as approximate physical counterparts of the mathematical poles. Thus the use of a number of parallel resonant circuits, with varying resonant frequencies, is common in the design of wide-band amplifiers. Considerable theoretical work has been done to determine the desirable stagger of the resonant frequencies of the circuits, but much of this is beyond the scope of this text.

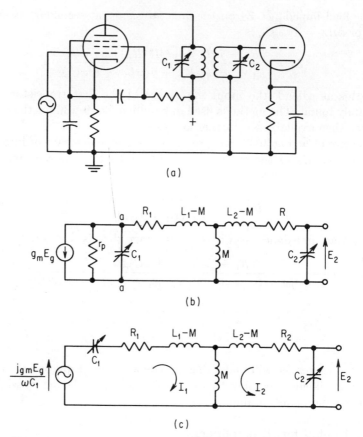

Fig. 9–37. (a) Double-tuned amplifier; (b), (c) equivalent circuits.

The analysis will here be extended only to the effects achievable by the use of two coupled resonant circuits, both the primary and secondary windings of the interstage transformer being tuned with capacitance. Such a circuit, shown in Fig. 9–37, is commonly used in intermediate-frequency amplifiers of radio receivers, where fixed-frequency operation is employed. This avoids the difficulties which would otherwise arise from the necessity for simultaneous tuning of two coupled parallel-resonant circuits.

The gain of the amplifier as a function of frequency is particularly of interest. Pentodes may be used, and with the circuit of Fig. 9–37, the equivalent circuit may be reduced to that in Fig. 9–37(c), by use of Thevenin's theorem, and with r_p large. Then

$$\mathbf{I}_2 = \frac{jg_m\mathbf{E}_g}{\omega C_1 \mathbf{Z}_{T12}} = \frac{jg_m\mathbf{E}_g}{\omega C_1[\mathbf{z}_r - \mathbf{z}_i(\mathbf{z}_o - \mathbf{Z}_L)/\mathbf{z}_r]} \tag{9-144}$$

The transfer impedance may be assembled term by term, starting with

$$\mathbf{z}_i = R_1 + j\left(\omega L_1 - \frac{1}{\omega C_1}\right) = R_1 + j\left(\frac{\omega^2 L_1 C_1 - 1}{\omega C_1}\right) \quad (9\text{--}145)$$

If the parameter δ, discussed in Section 9–20, is introduced, then $\omega = \omega_r(1 + \delta)$, where ω_r is the frequency at which the following approximations hold

$$\omega_r^2 L_1 C_1 \cong 1, \qquad \omega_r^2 L_2 C_2 \cong 1,$$

$$Q_1 = \omega_r L_1/R_1, \qquad Q_2 = \omega_r L_2/R_2$$

Then

$$\mathbf{z}_i \cong \frac{\omega_r L_1}{Q_1} + j\omega_r L_1\left[\frac{(1 + \delta)^2 - 1}{1 + \delta}\right] \quad (9\text{--}146)$$

since $1/(1 + \delta) \cong 1 - \delta$, then the first mesh input impedance is

$$\mathbf{z}_i \cong \frac{\omega_r L_1}{Q_1}(1 + j2Q_1\delta) \quad (9\text{--}147)$$

The second mesh impedance may be written by inspection as

$$\mathbf{z}_o + \mathbf{Z}_L \cong \frac{\omega_r L_2}{Q_2}(1 + j2Q_2\delta) \quad (9\text{--}148)$$

The mutual impedance is

$$\mathbf{z}_r = j\omega M = j\omega k\sqrt{L_1 L_2} = j\omega_r(1 + \delta)k\sqrt{L_1 L_2} \quad (9\text{--}149)$$

by reason of the definition of k as the coefficient of coupling.

Again assuming δ as small, the transfer impedance may be assembled from its components as

$$\mathbf{Z}_T \cong \frac{j\omega_r\sqrt{L_1 L_2}}{k}\left[k^2 + \left(\frac{1}{Q_1} + j2\delta\right)\left(\frac{1}{Q_2} + j2\delta\right)\right] \quad (9\text{--}150)$$

The secondary voltage is then

$$\mathbf{E}_2 = \frac{j\mathbf{I}_2}{\omega C_2} = \frac{j\omega_r L_2}{(1 + \delta)}\left[\frac{jg_m\omega_r L_1 \mathbf{E}_g}{(1 + \delta)\mathbf{Z}_T}\right] = \frac{-g_m\omega_r^2 L_1 L_2 \mathbf{E}_g}{(1 + \delta)^2 \mathbf{Z}_T}$$

after use of the resonance relations. Equation 9–150 may then be used to write the gain as

$$\mathbf{A} = \frac{\mathbf{E}_2}{\mathbf{E}_g} = \frac{-g_m k\omega_r\sqrt{L_1 L_2}}{j\left[k^2 + \left(\frac{1}{Q_1} + j2\delta\right)\left(\frac{1}{Q_2} + j2\delta\right)\right]} \quad (9\text{--}151)$$

These circuits are frequently designed with $Q_1 = Q_2$. For this case

$$\mathbf{A} = \frac{g_m k \omega_r \sqrt{L_1 L_2}}{\dfrac{4\delta}{Q} - j\left(k^2 + \dfrac{1}{Q^2} - 4\delta^2\right)} \tag{9-152}$$

In order to study the circuit response further, it is necessary to find the values of δ which provide maximum gain. Taking the derivative of the absolute gain value, and setting to zero, yields

$$\delta\left(4\delta^2 - k^2 + \frac{1}{Q^2}\right) = 0$$

Obviously, a maximum or minimum occurs at $\delta = 0$. Solution gives

$$\delta = \pm\frac{1}{2}\sqrt{k^2 - \frac{1}{Q^2}} \tag{9-153}$$

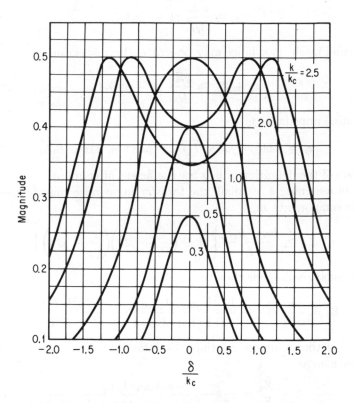

Fig. 9-38. Universal response curves for the circuit of Fig. 9-37, or the magnitude of the bracketed term of Eq. 9-155.

This equation indicates two values of δ at which the gain is a maximum or a minimum. It may be discovered that the above values produce maxima, and δ = 0 gives a minimum.

For the special case in which

$$k = k_c = \frac{1}{Q} \tag{9-154}$$

only one value of δ will produce maximum gain. This value, k_c, of the coefficient of coupling, is called *critical coupling*. For values of $k < k_c$ there will be only one point of maximum response, but the peak value of gain will not be as great in magnitude as that obtained for $k \geq k_c$. The condition of $k < k$ is called *insufficient coupling*.

The gain, written in terms of the ratio k/k_c is

$$|A| = g_m Q \omega_r \sqrt{L_1 L_2} \left[\frac{k/k_c}{\sqrt{(1 + k^2/k_c^2 - 4\delta^2/k_c^2)^2 + 16\delta^2/k_c^2}} \right] \tag{9-155}$$

The magnitude of the term in brackets is plotted as a function of δ/k_c in Fig. 9–38, for various values of the parameter k/k_c. These curves illustrate the double-humped gain characteristic for $k > k_c$.

The response and gain are largely a function of the choices of Q, L_1 and L_2, with the choice of k fixing the selectivity characteristic.

9–25. The overcoupled circuit

For values of $k > k_c$ the circuit is said to be *overcoupled*. Using $k_c = 1/Q$, the frequencies of the peaks of response indicated in Fig. 9–39 are

$$f_a = f_r \left(1 - \frac{k_c}{2} \sqrt{\frac{k^2}{k_c^2} - 1} \right) \tag{9-156}$$

$$f_b = f_r \left(1 + \frac{k_c}{2} \sqrt{\frac{k^2}{k_c^2} - 1} \right) \tag{9-157}$$

The gain magnitude at either maximum may be found by use of $\delta = \delta_a$ or δ_b in Eq. 9–155 so that

$$|A_{\max}| = \frac{g_m Q \omega_r \sqrt{L_1 L_2}}{2} \tag{9-158}$$

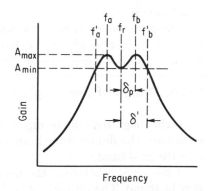

Fig. 9–39. Reference frequencies for the overcoupled transformer.

The gain at the dip or resonant frequency f_r can be found by substitution of $\delta = 0$ in Eq. 9–155, so that

$$| A_{\min} | = g_m Q \omega_r \sqrt{L_1 L_2} \left(\frac{k/k_c}{1 + k^2/k_c^2} \right) \qquad (9\text{--}159)$$

Two additional points on the response curve can also be found. These are the frequencies f_a' and f_b' down each shoulder of the curve, at which the gain has fallen to a level equal to $A_{\min}$. This results in a knowledge of the band width over which the gain does not vary more than $A_{\max} - A_{\min}$. Equating the general gain relation of Eq. 9–155 to $A_{\min}$ leads to

$$\frac{k/k_c}{k^2/k_c^2 + 1} = \frac{k/k_c}{\sqrt{(1 + k^2/k_c^2 - 4\delta'^2/k_c^2)^2 + 16\delta'^2/k_c^2}}$$

where $\pm \delta'$ is the frequency deviation at f_a' or f_b'. Solving for δ' gives

$$\delta' = \pm \frac{k_c}{2} \sqrt{\frac{k^2}{k_c^2} - 1} \qquad (9\text{--}160)$$

It has already been shown that f_a and f_b are separated by

$$2\delta_p = k_c \sqrt{\frac{k^2}{k_c^2} - 1} \qquad (9\text{--}161)$$

so that it is apparent that

$$2\delta' = 2\sqrt{2}\,\delta_p = \sqrt{2}\,(f_b - f_a) \qquad (9\text{--}162)$$

If the difference $A_{\max} - A_{\min}$ is made 3 db, the normal 3 db band width is expressed by Eq. 9–161; it is then apparently $\sqrt{2}$ times the peak separation. For a circuit with critical coupling, and only one peak response, the double-tuned circuit will have a band width $\sqrt{2}$ times as great as the singly-tuned circuit.

The overcoupled circuit is of value in intermediate-frequency amplifiers of radio receivers, where the band width which must be passed with essentially uniform gain is wider than is possible with a single tuned circuit.

9–26. Design of overcoupled circuits

If the magnitude of the dip in the response curve be held to a desirable minimum, the doubly-tuned circuit might give a reasonably flat response over the pass band.

A means of controlling the magnitude of the dip in the response curve may be found. The ratio of $| A_{\max} |$ to $| A_{\min} |$ appears as

$$\left| \frac{A_{\max}}{A_{\min}} \right| = \frac{1 + k^2/k_c^2}{2k/k_c} \qquad (9\text{--}163)$$

Calling the ratio λ, and solving for the value of k/k_c which will insure the desired ratio λ

$$\frac{k}{k_c} = \lambda + \sqrt{\lambda^2 - 1} \qquad (9\text{–}164)$$

choosing the positive sign, since for overcoupled circuits k/k_c is always greater than unity. This relation permits selection of the necessary value of k/k_c to maintain any desired ratio of gain at peaks and dip.

The frequency band Δf_λ in which the voltage deviation remains less than λ is given by

$$\Delta f_\lambda = \sqrt{2} f_r k_c \sqrt{\frac{k^2}{k_c^2} - 1} \qquad (9\text{–}165)$$

The normally defined band width at the half-power points will have $\lambda = 1.41$. It will then be found that k/k_c should be 2.032, and

$$\text{band width, } \Delta f = 2.5 f_r \frac{1}{Q} \qquad (9\text{–}166)$$

Thus by choosing the Q value, and setting the coupling, any desired value of band width and ratio A_{max}/A_{min} may be obtained. It should be noted that if the top of the curve is to be held flat, or if λ is small and Δf is to be large, then the gain will be reduced.

9–27. Butterworth and Chebyshev responses

A great amount of study has been given to the problem of producing, with combinations of simple resonant circuits, an ideal amplifier frequency response as in Fig. 9–40(a). By cascading of amplifiers with resonant loads, and with the loads tuned to predetermined frequencies or *stagger-tuned* across the desired band, a considerable band width can be obtained. The subject is complex, and we will here discuss only the general avenue of approach.

Reference to Eq. 9–130 for the single parallel-tuned circuit gives

$$\mathbf{Z} = \mathbf{Z}_r \frac{1}{1 + j2Q\delta}$$

and the gain of a pentode, using such a load circuit, is

$$\mathbf{A}(\delta) = -g_m \mathbf{Z}_r \frac{1}{1 + j2Q\delta} \qquad (9\text{–}167)$$

By definition the pass band limits are given by $2Q\delta = \pm 1$. For simplicity write $x = 2Q\delta$, with the band limits then being at $x = \pm 1$. The gain of n

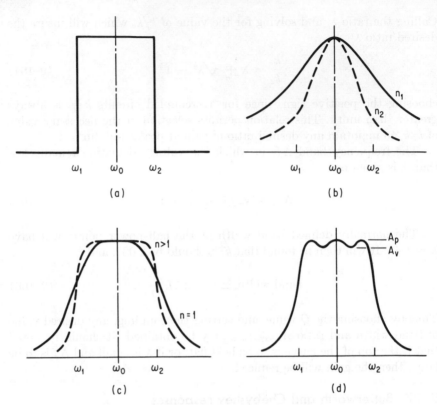

Fig. 9–40. (a) Ideal response; (b) single-tuned circuit; (c) Butterworth response; (d) Chebyshev response.

stages using such circuits, all tuned to the same resonant frequency, is

$$|A(x)| = (g_m Z_r)^n \frac{1}{(1 + x^2)^{n/2}} \qquad (9\text{--}168)$$

The single-stage response is indicated in Fig. 9–40(b) as curve n_1. For multi-stage identical amplifiers the overall band width has already been derived and is $(\sqrt{2^{1/n} - 1})^{-1}$ times the width of the single stage, or is less than the single-stage band width. This result is indicated in curve n_2 in Fig. 9–40(b). Obviously, the result obtained by multiple superimposed resonances does not lead in the desired direction.

However, it has been shown that if the form of Eq. 9–168 be modified to

$$|A(x)| = (g_m Z_r)^n \frac{1}{(1 + x^{2n})^{1/2}} \qquad (9\text{--}169)$$

a *maximally flat* or *Butterworth* response will be obtained as in Fig. 9–40(c).

As n increases, the shape of the response becomes closer to the ideal rectangle, and the band width remains constant, since the cutoff will still occur at $x = \pm 1$, where $|A(x)| = 1/\sqrt{2}$, as defined.

It has also been found that if the gain function be given the form

$$|A(x)| = (g_m Z_r)^n \frac{1}{[1 + \epsilon C_n^2(x)]^{1/2}} \qquad (9\text{–}170)$$

where $C_n(x)$ is a Chebyshev polynomial, then the response will be that of Fig. 9–40(d), called a *Chebyshev* or *equal-ripple* response. These polynomials, which for the first few orders are

$$C_1(x) = x, \qquad\qquad C_3(x) = 4x^3 - 3x,$$

$$C_2(x) = 2x^2 - 1, \qquad C_4(x) = 8x^4 - 8x^2 + 1$$

give values of $C_n^2(x)$ which oscillate between 0 and 1 for the band $-1 \leq x \leq 1$. Equation 9–170 then shows that the magnitude of $A(x)$ oscillates between 1 and $1/\sqrt{1+\epsilon}$, and therefore ϵ is the ripple parameter, defined as

$$\epsilon = \left[\left(\frac{A_p}{A_v} \right)^2 - 1 \right]^{1/2} \qquad (9\text{–}171)$$

This value of ripple can be selected by the designer, as was λ for the over-coupled circuit of Section 9–26. Outside the pass band $C_n^2(x)$ varies as x^{2n}, and therefore outside the pass band the gain falls off as it does for the Butterworth response. The Chebyshev response provides somewhat more gain for the same band width, and a closer approach to constant gain over the band than is possible with the maximally-flat approximation.

Expansion of any of these gain functions with $j\omega = p$, will yield an expression of the form

$$A(p) = \frac{H}{p^n + a_{n-1}p^{n-1} + \cdots + a_2 p^2 + a_1 p + a_o} \qquad (9\text{–}172)$$

$$= \frac{H}{(p - p_1)(p - p_2)(p - p_3) \cdots} \qquad (9\text{–}173)$$

The form of the denominator which results for various n values, and either the maximally-flat or equal-ripple basic equations, is given in tables, of which the first few orders are reproduced in Table 15.

Equations of the form of 9–173 will, in turn, locate the poles or resonances for the tuned circuits. It is found that in the $p = \sigma + j\omega$ plane, the Butterworth response is obtained by poles uniformly spaced on a circle locus and symmetrical about the real axis; the equal-ripple response

TABLE 15
BUTTERWORTH RESPONSE

n	
1	$p + 1$
2	$p^2 + \sqrt{2}p + 1$
3	$(p + 1)(p^2 + 1.000p + 1)$
4	$(p^2 + 0.765p + 1)(p^2 + 1.848p + 1)$

CHEBYSHEV RESPONSE
(½ db ripple; $\epsilon = 0.349$)

n	
1	$p + 2.863$
2	$p^2 + 1.426p + 1.516$
3	$(p + 0.626)(p^2 + 0.626p + 1.142)$
4	$(p^2 + 0.351p + 1.064)(p^2 + 0.845p + 0.356)$

TABLE 16. DESIGN DATA FOR n STAGGER-TUNED CIRCUITS
OVERALL BAND WIDTH = BW_o

n	No. of stages tuned	Tuned to	Stage band width
2	2	$f_o \pm 0.35\, BW_o$	$0.70\, BW_o$
3	1	f_o	BW_o
	2	$f_o \pm 0.43\, BW_o$	$0.50\, BW_o$
4	2	$f_o \pm 0.46\, BW_o$	$0.50\, BW_o$
	2	$f_o \pm 0.19\, BW_o$	$0.92\, BW_o$

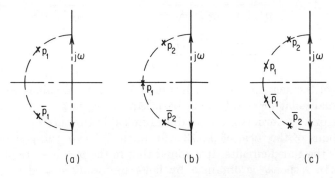

Fig. 9–41. Pole locations for Table 16.

is a result of pole locations spaced along an ellipse. Poles in the right half-plane have no physical meaning in this problem. In each case the diameter or major axis will equal the band width on the $j\omega$ axis, and this is constant for varying n.

In general it is possible by these methods to develop stagger-tuned amplifiers of multiple stages, with overall band widths as high as 30 per cent of the center frequency. Design data is given in Table 16 for the maximally-flat approximation, and for relatively narrow band widths, up to possibly 5 per cent of f_o. Pole locations are shown in Fig. 9–41.

The development of the principles underlying these theories is complex and beyond the scope undertaken by this text. Further information may be found in the references.

Problems

9-1. For the circuit of Fig. 9-42, plot two gain-frequency curves for (a) $C = 0.001$ μf; (b) $C = 0.1$ μf. Circuit values are: $\mu = 25$, $g_m - 1500$ μmhos, $R_1 = 100,000$ ohms, $R_2 = 50,000$ ohms. Cover the frequency range of 20 to 2000 cycles.

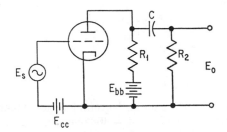

Fig. 9–42.

9-2. In Fig. 9-43, the tubes are halves of a 12AU7 double triode. Including the effects of internal tube capacitances, plot a gain vs. frequency curve from 100 to 100,000 cycles on a semi-logarithmic scale.

9-3. For the first-stage circuit of Fig. 9-43, if $g_m = 2500$ μmhos, $r_p = 12,000$ ohms, $C_{in} = 70$ pf, $C_{pk} = 10$ pf, find the band width $f_2 - f_1$, in cycles.

9-4. Specify the f_1 and f_2 frequencies for each stage of a four identical stage amplifier, if the overall band width is to extend from 100 cycles to 450,000 cycles.

9-5. The tube in Fig. 9-42 has $\mu = 35$, $r_p = 25,000$ ohms, $R_1 = 50,000$ ohms, and $R_2 = 100,000$ ohms. Compute the value of coupling capacitance C required if the gain at 20 cycles is to be 80 per cent of the mid-range gain. Plot the gain vs. frequency curve over the frequency range in which C is effective in altering the gain.

9-6. A given amplifier has an f_2 value of 30 kc. At what frequency is the amplifier gain down only one per cent of its mid-range value?

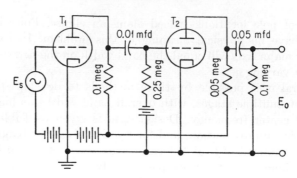

Fig. 9–43.

9-7. An instrument amplifier must have a gain accurate to 0.5 per cent up to 10,000 cycles. What must be the f_2 value of the amplifier? If it is composed of three stages, what will the individual stage f_2 value be?

9-8. Plot the high-frequency gain $\mathbf{A}_{ov}/\mathbf{A}_{mid}$ for a six-stage amplifier with $f_\alpha = 1.0$ mc for each stage.

9-9. Three non-identical amplifier stages are cascaded. The band width limits for the amplifiers are

	f_1 (cycles)	f_2 (cycles)
A	100	252,000
B	82	347,000
C	47	545,000

Determine the overall band width limits.

9-10. Compute the current gain in the common-base circuit, at 100,000 cycles, for a transistor having $r_e = 50$ ohms, $r_b = 400$ ohms, $r_c = 0.75$ megohms, $\alpha = 0.90$, $C_c = 150$ pf, and $R_L = 5000$ ohms, $R_s = 2000$ ohms.

9-11. Repeat Problem 9-10 using the common-emitter circuit. Explain the difference in performance.

9-12. In the circuit of (a), Fig. 9-9, the two transistors are identical, with $\alpha = 0.96$, $r_c = 2$ megohms, $r_b = 500$ ohms, $r_e = 40$ ohms, $R_L = 7000$ ohms, $R_2 = 100,000$ ohms, $C = 1.0$ μf. Find the frequency f_1 and the current gain I_{b2}/I_{b1} at that frequency. The second stage has an output load of 5000 ohms, the input source is 1.0 v, 5000 ohms, and $R_1 = 100,000$ ohms.

9-13. Compute the value of C needed in Problem 9-12 if the response is to be down 1.5 db below mid-range value at 50 cycles.

9-14. A transistor has a mid-range α value of 0.97 and $f_\alpha = 0.45$ mc. Find the magnitude of α at 0.25 mc.

9-15. Calculate the overall current gain of the circuit of Fig. 9-12 at 100 cycles, if the identical transistors have the characteristics of those in Problem 9-12. Neglect effect of bias circuits and assume the input source is 4000 ohms resistive, the output load is 10,000 ohms resistive.

9-16. Redesign the circuit of Fig. 9-12 to provide emitter bypass and coupling capacitances to give $f_1 = 20$ cycles, if the transistors are those of Problem 9-12.

9-17. Using the methods of Section 9-5, derive an expression for the ratio $\mathbf{A}_{iL}/\mathbf{A}_{iM}$ for the common-base first stage circuit of Fig. 9-44.

9-18. Repeat Problem 9-17 for $\mathbf{A}_{iH}/\mathbf{A}_{iM}$.

9-19. (a) If $C_g = 50$ pf, find the value of L needed to shunt-compensate the circuit of Fig. 9-18(a) to as high a frequency as possible, with negligible gain rise. Assume that the tube is a pentode of $g_m = 5000$, with high r_p; $R_g = 1$ megohm; gain $= 15$.
(b) What will the value of R be?
(c) Plot a gain vs. frequency curve.

9-20. Using the coefficient equating method of Section 9-13, determine an expression for R in Fig. 9-45, which will give the flattest low-frequency response curve, and lower f_1. The expression is to be in terms of the tube coefficients and R, L, and C.

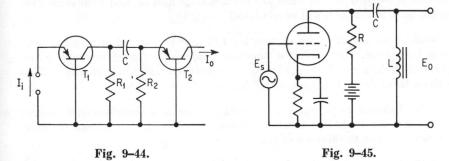

Fig. 9-44.　　　　　　　　Fig. 9-45.

9-21. (a) The circuit of Fig. 9-33(a) is used with a pentode tube of $g_m = 3000$ μmhos, and r_p above a megohm. If $L_2 = 200$ μh with a Q of 200 and $R_g = 2$ meg-ohms, the reactance of C being negligible, find the output voltage E_2 for an input signal $E_s = 0.01$ v, at resonance at 450 kc.
(b) Find the output voltage for a simultaneous equal signal input at 500 kc.

9-22. The circuit of Fig. 9-34 is used with a pentode tube of $g_m = 5000$ μmhos, and r_p over 1 megohm. The air-core transformer has $L_1 = 30$ μh, $L_2 = 200$ μh, $M = 10$ μh, $R_1 = 5$ ohms, $R_2 = 20$ ohms. The input is 0.1 v, 10^6 cycles, and the secondary circuit is resonant at that frequency. Find E_2.

9-23. The air-core transformer of Fig. 9-37(a) has $L_1 = L_2 = 100$ μh, $Q_1 = Q_2 = 100$, with coupling at 150 per cent of critical. The tube is a pentode of high plate resistance and with g_m of 4500 μmho.
(a) Find the values for C_1 and C_2 needed for resonance at 10^6 cycles.
(b) Find the maximum gain available.
(c) Plot a gain vs. frequency curve for the circuit over the range from $0.8f_r$ to $1.2f_r$.

9-24. The amplifier of Fig. 9-46 has a voltage gain $E_O/E_s = 50$, with a transistor having $h_{ie} = 5000$ ohms, $h_{re} = 2.5 \times 10^{-3}$, $h_{fe} = 100$, $h_{oe} = 50$ μmhos, $C = 10$ μf. The operating point is to be at $V_{CE} = +5$ volts, $I_B = -0.5$ ma, $V_{BE} \cong 0$, $I_{CO} = 2$ μa.

(a) Determine the values of R_L, R_E, R_1, and R_2, with stability factor of 5.

(b) How low can f_1 be made by increasing C_E?

9-25. In the circuit of Fig. 9-46, $R_L = 5000$ ohms, $R_1 = R_2 = R_E = 10,000$ ohms, and the transistor is that of Problem 9-24. Determine the values for C and C_E, if they are to each cutoff at the same frequency, and overall $f_1 = 50$ cps.

9-26. The circuit of Fig. 9-44 is used with two transistors of the type specified in Problem 9-24. The load of the second stage is 5000 ohms, and $R_2 = R_1 = 10,000$ ohms; only 10 μf capacitors are available. Design the load circuit so that f_1 is as low as possible.

9-27. Each stage of a three-stage amplifier has $\mathbf{A}_{ov} = 30$ and an f_2 value of 400 kc. The complete amplifier is to be modified to make $f_2 = 600$ kc, by reducing the loads. If $g_m = 2500$ μmhos, what will the new stage load be, and what stage gain, overall gain, and stage f_2 will be available?

9-28. A rectangular pulse of duration 1.57 μsec is repeated at a rate of 3000 times per second. Determine the amplifier band width if good reproduction requires the inclusion of the second zero of the harmonic amplitude envelope. What is the order of the highest transmitted harmonic?

9-29. Tabulate the harmonic amplitudes of all harmonics resulting from a square wave, out to the ninth. Plot these on a frequency plot, with the enclosing spectrum envelope. Explain the absence of even harmonics.

9-30. A rectangular pulse of the form of Fig. 9-47 is applied to an RC-coupled pentode amplifier with $g_m = 4500$ μmhos, r_p and R_g large, $C_g = 22$ pf.

(a) Find the value of R_L for a rise time of 0.25 μsec.

(b) Determine the value of coupling capacitor C to permit only a 10 per cent droop, if $R_g = 0.5$ megohm.

(c) Find the output peak voltage.

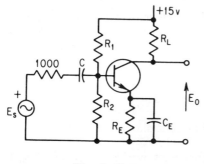

Fig. 9-46.

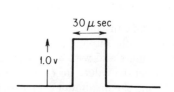

Fig. 9-47.

References

1. Baum, R. F., "Design of Broad-Band I.F. Amplifiers," *Jour. Appl. Phys.*, **17**, 519 (1946).

2. Bedford, A. V., and Fredendall, G. L., "Transient Response of Multi-Stage Video-Frequency Amplifiers," *Proc. I.R.E.*, **27**, 277 (1939).

3. Butterworth, S., "On the Theory of Filter Amplifiers," *Wireless Eng.*, **7**, 536 (1930).

4. Darlington, S., "The Potential Analog Method of Network Synthesis," *Bell System Tech. Jour.*, **30**, 315 (1951).

5. Giacoletto, L. J., "Study of *PNP* Alloy Junction Transistor from D-C through Medium Frequencies," *RCA Rev.*, **15**, 506 (1954).

6. Landon, V. D., "Cascade Amplifiers with Maximal Flatness," *RCA Rev.*, **5**, 347, 481 (1941).

7. Pettit, J. M., and McWhorter, M. M., *"Electronic Amplifier Circuits."* McGraw-Hill Book Co., Inc., New York, 1961.

8. Ryder, R. M., and Kircher, R. J., "Some Circuit Aspects of the Transistor," *Bell Syst. Tech. Jour.*, **28**, 367 (1949).

9. Shea, R. F., *et al.*, *Principles of Transistor Circuits*. John Wiley and Sons, Inc., New York, 1953.

10. Terman, F. E., "Universal Amplification Charts," *Electronics*, **10**, 34 (June 1937).

11. Thomas, D. E., "Transistor Amplifier Cut-Off Frequency," *Proc. I.R.E.*, **40**, 1481 (1952).

12. Valley, G. E., Jr., and Wallman, H., *Vacuum Tube Amplifiers*. McGraw-Hill Book Co., Inc., New York, 1948.

13. Wheeler, H. A., "Wideband Amplifiers for Television," *Proc. I.R.E.*, **27**, 429 (1939).

Feedback;
Direct-Coupled Amplifiers

10

Negative or inverse feedback in amplifiers implies sending back a portion of the output to the input, and a comparison of the two in such a way as to improve their correspondence, on an instantaneous basis. The principle had been previously employed in other fields, but the work of H. S. Black in formalizing the mathematics of the subject in 1934 gave a major impetus to an understanding of the principle, and to its application in electronics. The feedback principle is of broad application to any amplifying system, be it vacuum-tube, transistor, or of other form.

10-1. Feedback in amplifiers

For an amplifier, as in Fig. 10–1, of one or more stages, the gain has been defined as

$$A = \frac{E_o}{E_s}$$

An amplifier with feedback is shown diagrammatically in Fig. 10–1(b), wherein a fraction of the output voltage is introduced or fed back into the input circuit. If intentionally produced, the feedback is achieved by circuit arrangement; if unintentionally, it happens owing to magnetic- or electric-field coupling, or by reason of voltage drops across impedances common to both input and output circuits. The gain with feedback, A', is defined as before

$$A' = \frac{E_o'}{E_s}$$

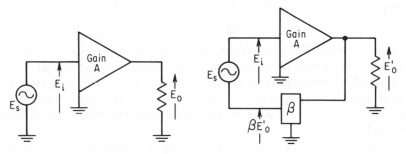

Fig. 10–1. Feedback in an amplifier.

The input voltage $\mathbf{E}'_i$ is given by

$$\mathbf{E}'_i = \mathbf{E}_s + \beta\mathbf{E}'_o \tag{10–1}$$

so that the output voltage $\mathbf{E}'_o$ is

$$\mathbf{E}'_o = (\mathbf{E}_s + \beta\mathbf{E}'_o)\mathbf{A} \tag{10–2}$$

where $\beta\mathbf{E}'_o$ is the portion of the output voltage fed back, altered in magnitude and phase by the complex term β, where

$$\beta = \frac{\text{voltage fed back }\underline{/\theta_1}}{\text{output voltage }\underline{/\theta_2}} \tag{10–3}$$

Then

$$\mathbf{A}' = \frac{\mathbf{E}'_o}{\mathbf{E}_s} = \frac{\mathbf{A}}{1 - \mathbf{A}\beta} \tag{10–4}$$

The overall effective gain with feedback $\mathbf{A}'$ is a function of the internal gain $\mathbf{A}$ and the proportion of output fed back, β, as well as their phase angles.

 If

$$|1 - \mathbf{A}\beta| < 1$$

then gain $\mathbf{A}'$ is greater than $\mathbf{A}$ before feedback was applied. The feedback is then said to be *positive* and the circuit is *regenerative*. In general, positive feedback gives increased gain, decreased stability, and higher distortion. It is avoided for most applications.

 If

$$|1 - \mathbf{A}\beta| > 1$$

the gain $\mathbf{A}'$ is less than $\mathbf{A}$ before feedback was applied. The feedback is then said to be *negative* or *inverse* and the circuit is *degenerative*. Negative feedback increases stability, lowers gain, and reduces noise and distortion generated in an amplifier.

When

$$A\beta = 1 + j0$$

the gain becomes infinite, or the amplifier becomes an oscillator, having an output voltage which is independent of any external input voltage.

While the *feedback factor* $A\beta$* is in general complex, its phase angle may vary widely with frequency. An attempt is usually made to bring its phase angle to $0°$ or $180°$ over the frequency range in which a given amplifier is to be operated.

Negative feedback makes possible an engineering design of an amplifier which will perform as predicted. Calibrated instruments may be designed which will retain their accuracy indefinitely.

10–2. Input conditions

Obviously, as the gain is reduced by negative feedback, the input signal $\mathbf{E}_s$ must be increased to maintain the same output. Rewriting Eq. 10–4 gives

$$\frac{\mathbf{A'}}{\mathbf{A}} = \frac{1}{1 - \mathbf{A}\beta}$$

and for equal output

$$\mathbf{E}_o = \mathbf{E}'_o$$

From the definition for gain, this expression can be converted to

$$\mathbf{A}\mathbf{E}_s = \mathbf{A'}\mathbf{E}'_s$$

so that for equal output voltages

$$\mathbf{E}'_s = (1 - \mathbf{A}\beta)\mathbf{E}_s \tag{10–5}$$

For negative feedback the signal input must be increased to maintain the same output.

10–3. Effects on distortion; feedback in decibels

Equation 10–1 may be written as

$$\mathbf{E}'_i = \mathbf{E}_s - (-\beta\mathbf{E}'_o) \tag{10–6}$$

If distortion of the wave form is to be small, then the output wave $\mathbf{E}'_o$ must not differ in form from the input wave $\mathbf{E}_s$, on a point-by-point or instantaneous basis. The above equation states that if the input and a

---

* In some of the literature the feedback factor $A\beta$ is referred to as $\mu\beta$, with μ being the overall amplifier gain. To avoid confusion with the amplification factor, the term $A\beta$ is used here.

portion β of the output are not to differ, or there is to be no distortion, then $\mathbf{E}'_i$ must be very small. Since $\mathbf{E}'_o = \mathbf{A}\mathbf{E}'_i$ from Fig. 10–1, then

$$\mathbf{E}'_i = \frac{\mathbf{E}_s}{1 - \mathbf{A}\beta} \tag{10–7}$$

If $\mathbf{E}'_i$ is to be small, then $|\,1 - \mathbf{A}\beta\,|$ must be large, and this in turn indicates that $|\,\mathbf{A}\beta\,| \gg 1$ should be a requirement for fidelity of output wave form to input wave form.

The result may be further demonstrated with reference to nonlinear harmonic distortion. Without feedback an input $\mathbf{E}_i$ is applied to an amplifier and the output is

$$\mathbf{E}_o = \mathbf{A}\mathbf{E}_i + \mathbf{E}_h \tag{10–8}$$

where $\mathbf{E}_h$ is the harmonic distortion component. It is assumed that $\mathbf{E}_h$ is a function of output, or increases as the amplifier is driven over a wider range on the dynamic curve.

To add feedback, and keep the same output $\mathbf{E}_o$ requires a new input given as $\mathbf{E}'_i$ and

$$\mathbf{E}_o = \mathbf{A}(\mathbf{E}'_i + \beta\mathbf{E}_o) + \mathbf{E}_h \tag{10–9}$$

But the new input is given in Eq. 10–5 as

$$\mathbf{E}'_i = (1 - \mathbf{A}\beta)\mathbf{E}_i$$

Substitution and solution of Eq. 10–9 for $\mathbf{E}_o$ gives

$$\mathbf{E}_o = \mathbf{A}\mathbf{E}_i + \frac{\mathbf{E}_h}{1 - \mathbf{A}\beta} \tag{10–10}$$

Comparison of this result with Eq. 10–8 shows that for the same output as before the addition of feedback, the harmonic distortion $\mathbf{E}_h$ is reduced in the ratio $1/(1 - \mathbf{A}\beta)$, by the inclusion of negative feedback in the circuit.

Furthermore, if $|\,\mathbf{A}\beta\,| \gg 1$, then Eq. 10–4 approximates

$$\mathbf{A}' \cong -\frac{1}{\beta} \tag{10–11}$$

showing that the gain can be made essentially independent of variations due to components and supply voltages. Since β is usually fixed by a set of resistors, of long-time stability, the gain of an amplifier can be made predictable.

If the amplification depends on β as above, and if β is not a frequency function, then any frequency distortion which may have been present in the amplifier will be reduced by negative feedback. Such a result is often an incidental effect of the usage of inverse feedback to reduce harmonic distortion.

If β is a function of frequency, the amplification will be an inverse function of frequency. If the circuit determining β is designed to reject some particular frequency range, the amplifier will amplify that particular range.

A comparison of Eqs. 10–4 and 10–10 shows that the distortion is reduced in the same ratio as the gain. This would seem to indicate little utility for negative feedback, but such is not the case. Amplitude distortion is usually a result of the application of large signal swings to the dynamic characteristic. Such swings occur in the final amplifier stage, and nearly all amplitude or nonlinear distortion originates there. If the distortion there can be reduced by feedback, the lost gain may often be recovered in small signal stages ahead of the last stage, and an overall reduction in distortion obtained.

Example: A certain amplifier has a gain **A** of 70 at an angle of $0°$, distortion of 10 per cent, and normal input of 1.0 v rms. Find the effects of inverse feedback with a value of $\beta = -0.1$. The feedback factor is then -7.0.

The gain is reduced to

$$A' = \frac{A}{1 - A\beta} = \frac{70}{1 + 7} = 8.75$$

Reduction in distortion to

$$D' = \frac{D}{1 - A\beta} = \frac{0.10}{1 + 7} = 0.0125 = 1.25\%$$

New input voltage is

$$E'_s = E_s(1 - A\beta) = 1.0(1 + 7) = 8.0 \text{ v}$$

Output voltage without feedback is

$$E_o = AE_s = 70 \times 1.0 = 70.0 \text{ v}$$

Output voltage with feedback, using E'_s then

$$E'_o = A'E'_s = 8.75 \times 8.0 = 70.0 \text{ v}$$

The actual input voltage is

$$E'_g = E'_s + \beta E'_o = 8.0 - 0.10 \times 70.0 = 1.0 \text{ v}$$

The preceding example shows input-signal requirements are radically changed with feedback, but the amplifier inside the feedback loop is operating under conditions identical with those existing before the feedback was added—that is, 1.0 v E_g was required to drive the amplifier to 70.0 v output without feedback. With feedback, E_g' is still 1.0 v for the same output; and although the input E_s' supplied is 8.0 v, 7.0 v is returned out of phase through the feedback loop to reduce E_g' to the original 1.0 v.

Feedback applied to an amplifier is occasionally measured in decibels as the ratio of power output with constant input, with and without feedback, or

$$\text{db feedback} = 20 \log \frac{E_o'}{E_o} \qquad (10\text{–}12)$$

In the example above, without feedback the output was 70 v = E_o. With feedback and the same 1.0-v input the output would have been 1.0 × 8.75 = 8.75 v. The reduction in output power, expressed in decibels, would then have been

$$20 \log \frac{70}{8.75} = 20 \times 0.903 = 18.06 \text{ db}$$

The feedback has reduced the amplifier output by 18 db, or it is said that there has been 18 db of feedback applied to the amplifier.

10–4. Gain stability with feedback

In many measurement devices the maintenance of a given gain value is important for retention of a calibration; this is particularly important in electronic voltmeters. While Eq. 10–11 states that the gain can be as stable as the circuit components which fix β, it is not always possible to make $A\beta$ extremely large, so that it is desirable to demonstrate the gain stability given by lesser amounts of feedback. For an incremental change dA in the internal gain, Eq. 10–4 leads to

$$dA' = \frac{(1 - A\beta) \, dA + A\beta \, dA}{(1 - A\beta)^2}$$

$$= \left(\frac{A}{1 - A\beta}\right) \frac{dA}{A} + \left(\frac{A}{1 - A\beta}\right)\left(\frac{\beta}{1 - A\beta}\right) dA$$

$$\frac{dA'}{A'} = \left(\frac{1}{1 - A\beta}\right) \frac{dA}{A} \qquad (10\text{–}13)$$

and thus the percentage change dA'/A' in the negative feedback amplifier is $1/(1 - A\beta)$ as large as the internal percentage change in gain dA/A.

10–5. Effect of feedback on input impedance

Any network which will introduce a fraction of the output voltage into the input circuit, in proper phase, can be used as the β network. Generally, the circuits will produce either *current feedback* or *voltage feedback*.

If the voltage fed back to the input is proportional to the output *current*, the result is *current* feedback. If the voltage fed back is proportional to the output or load *voltage*, the result is labelled *voltage* feedback. The two forms of feedback achieve somewhat different results.

Referring to the amplifier of Fig. 10–2, without feedback the input voltage is $\mathbf{E}_s$, and the input impedance is

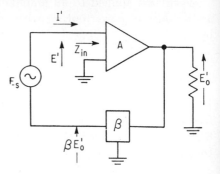

Fig. 10–2. Effect on input impedance.

$$Z_{in} = \frac{\mathbf{E}_s}{I} \tag{10–14}$$

With the feedback circuit introduced

$$\mathbf{E}' = \mathbf{E}_s + \beta \mathbf{E}'_o$$

Also $\mathbf{E}'_o = \mathbf{A}\mathbf{E}'$, and so

$$\mathbf{E}' = \frac{\mathbf{E}_s}{1 - \mathbf{A}\beta} \tag{10–15}$$

The input current with feedback would be

$$I' = \frac{\mathbf{E}'}{Z_{in}} = \frac{\mathbf{E}_s}{(1 - \mathbf{A}\beta)\,Z_{in}}$$

from which

$$Z'_{in} = \frac{\mathbf{E}_s}{I'} = (1 - \mathbf{A}\beta)\,Z_{in} \tag{10–16}$$

so that the input impedance is increased by the factor $1 - A\beta$ over that of the circuit without negative voltage feedback.

Previous discussion of the cathode follower or the emitter follower confirms this result, since they will be shown to be feedback amplifiers. Equation 7–48 for the input resistance of a common-emitter amplifier also shows the effect of the addition of an external resistance to the emitter circuit as a form of feedback.

10–6. Effect of feedback on output impedance

In current feedback the amplifier tends to maintain constant output current. This is the situation which occurs in the current-source equivalent circuit of Fig. 10–3, if r_p is made large and thereby draws a negligible portion of the current. It is therefore apparent that *current feedback raises the internal resistance* of an amplifier.

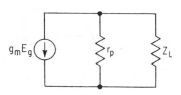

Fig. 10–3. Effect of feedback on apparent internal resistance of an amplifier.

For voltage feedback, the amplifier tends to maintain constant output voltage. Again with reference to Fig. 10–3, this would be the situation if r_p were made small and practically the entire current, $g_m E_g$, passed through it, giving a constant voltage across the load of value $g_m E_g r_p$. Thus it can be seen that *voltage feedback lowers the internal resistance* of an amplifier.

It can be found that with current feedback the output impedance $\mathbf{Z}_o'$ is

$$\mathbf{Z}_o' = (1 - \mathbf{A}\beta)\,\mathbf{Z}_o \tag{10–17}$$

where $\mathbf{Z}_o$ is the output impedance without feedback. For voltage feedback a similar analysis leads to

$$\mathbf{Z}_o' = \frac{\mathbf{Z}_o}{1 - \mathbf{A}\beta} \tag{10–18}$$

10–7. Inverse feedback circuits

Current feedback may be obtained in any circuit in which the drop across an impedance through which load current passes (other than the load itself) is fed back to the input circuit in proper phase.

Current feedback results in the common-emitter circuit of Fig. 10–4(c), by addition of R_E in the common-emitter circuit. The approximate voltage gain expression of Eq. 7–54 becomes

$$\mathbf{A}_{ve} \cong \frac{-aR_L}{r_e + R_E + (r_b + R_s)(1 - a)} \tag{10–19}$$

since R_E may be added directly to r_e wherever it appears in the performance equations. The second denominator term is usually small so that

$$\mathbf{A}_{ve} \cong \frac{-aR_L}{r_e + R_E} \cong -\frac{1}{\beta} \tag{10–20}$$

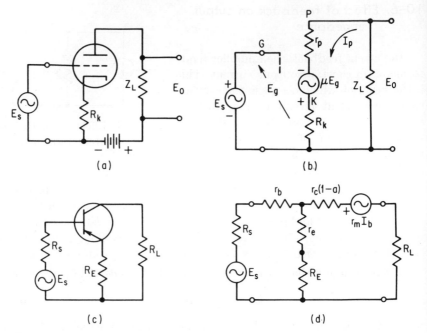

Fig. 10–4. (a), (c) Basic current feedback circuits; (b), (d) their equivalent circuits.

The last approximation is obtained by noting that the definition for β gives

$$\beta = \frac{(\mathbf{I}_c + \mathbf{I}_b)(r_e + R_L)}{\mathbf{I}_c R_L} = \frac{r_e + R_E}{a R_L} \qquad (10\text{--}21)$$

by reason of the definition of $a \cong \alpha$.

The presence of R_E has therefore been shown to reduce the effect of the transistor parameters on the gain. Reference to Eqs. 7–48 and 7–49 shows the addition of R_E will raise the input and output impedances as predicted.

In the vacuum-tube form of Fig. 10–4(a), the feedback is produced by the voltage drop across R_k, introduced in series with the grid-cathode input. The gain may be written as

$$\mathbf{A}' = \frac{\mathbf{E}_o}{\mathbf{E}_s} = \frac{-\mu Z_L}{r_p(1 + g_m R_k) + R_k + \mathbf{Z}_L} \qquad (10\text{--}22)$$

With current feedback, the tube appears to have an internal resistance which is greater than r_p by the factor $(1 + g_m R_k)$. Since without feedback

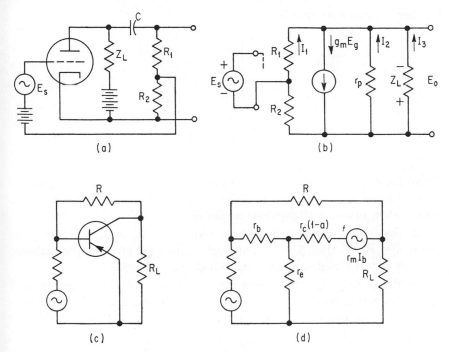

Fig. 10–5. (a), (c) Voltage feedback; (b), (d) equivalent circuits.

$\mathbf{A} = -g_m\mathbf{Z}_L$, and with feedback $\beta = R_k/\mathbf{Z}_L$, then

$$\mathbf{Z}_o' = r_p(1 + g_mR_k) = r_p(1 - \mathbf{A}\beta) \qquad (10\text{–}23)$$

as predicted in the previous section.

A circuit of the voltage-feedback type is shown in Fig. 10–5(a) or (c). In each case the voltage fed back is proportional to the output voltage $\mathbf{E}_o$. Analyzing the vacuum-tube case shows that

$$\beta = \frac{R_2}{R_1 + R_2}$$

and after neglecting the reactance of C, the gain equation is

$$\mathbf{A}' = \frac{\mathbf{E}_o}{\mathbf{E}_s} = \frac{-\mu\mathbf{Z}_L}{r_p + \mathbf{Z}_L\left(1 + \dfrac{r_p}{R_1 + R_2} + \mu\beta\right)} \qquad (10\text{–}24)$$

Further manipulation yields

$$A' = \frac{E_o}{E_s} = \frac{-\left(\dfrac{\mu}{1 + \dfrac{r_p + \mu R_2}{R_1 + R_2}}\right) Z_L}{\left(\dfrac{r_p}{1 + \dfrac{r_p + \mu R_2}{R_1 + R_2}}\right) + Z_L}$$

If the factors in parentheses are considered as equivalent μ and r_p of the tube with voltage feedback, it can be seen that both are reduced by the same factor, in line with previous prediction.

In the cathode follower the voltage fed back is $E_o = I_p R_k$ and the output is also E_o, so that $\beta = 1$. This high value of β gives to the cathode-follower circuit a high stability, and a high input impedance.

Feedback may be applied over more than one amplifier stage. In such applications it is necessary to remember that for circuits of the grounded-cathode or common-emitter type, there is an inherent 180° phase shift, or

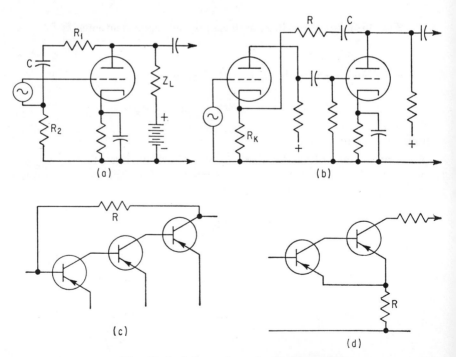

Fig. 10–6. Other voltage feedback circuits.

A is negative for one stage. To maintain $| 1 - \mathbf{A\beta} | > 1$ requires that the feedback voltage be introduced into the circuit properly. For voltage feedback, this β voltage is of such phase in single- or odd-stage amplifiers that it may be introduced into the base or grid circuit, but for amplifiers having an even number of stages the feedback voltage is most conveniently introduced into the emitter or cathode circuit. These principles are illustrated in Fig. 10-6. Some current feedback is also introduced into the first stage by (b) and (d).

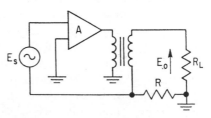

Feedback from the secondary of an output transformer may also be employed as in Fig. 10-7, the polarity of the windings being such as to insure the proper sign of $\mathbf{A\beta}$. This circuit has the advantage that frequency distortion introduced by the transformer may be reduced.

Fig. 10-7. Another example of current feedback.

10-8. Stability of inverse feedback circuits

Since **A** and β are complex quantities and also frequency functions, it is impractical to predict that because $| 1 - \mathbf{A\beta} | > 1$ at some mid-range frequency, it will hold the same relation at all other frequencies. Although an amplifier may be stable over a certain range of frequencies, for some other frequency range $| 1 - \mathbf{A\beta} |$ may be less than unity, or $\mathbf{A\beta}$ may even be equal to $1 + j0$. It is apparent that for the first case the feedback will be positive and the amplifier regenerative, and the amplifier will oscillate under the second condition. Regeneration and oscillation are not desired and lead to instability, a condition which must be investigated.

Consider a plot of $\mathbf{A\beta}\underline{/\theta^\circ} = a + jb$ (θ is the total phase angle) in the complex plane for all frequencies, both positive and negative, from 0 to ∞. Nyquist has shown that such a plot is a closed curve. A critical condition exists where

$$| 1 - \mathbf{A\beta} | = 1$$

or

$$(1 - a)^2 + b^2 = 1 \qquad (10\text{-}25)$$

This equation can be recognized as defining a circle of unit radius, with center at the point $1, j0$. If the $\mathbf{A\beta}$ vector terminates inside this circle, then obviously

$$| 1 - \mathbf{A\beta} | < 1$$

and the amplifier is regenerative, or the feedback is positive. If the $\mathbf{A\beta}$

vector terminates outside this circle

$$| 1 - A\beta | > 1$$

and the amplifier is degenerative.

If the $A\beta$ vector terminates at 1, $j0$, it is apparent from previous discussion that the amplifier will oscillate. Nyquist has shown that, in fact, *if the $A\beta$ curve encloses the 1, $j0$ point, the amplifier will oscillate.* It is therefore obvious that one way to maintain stability and prevent oscillation is to ensure that $| A\beta |$ is less than unity when the angle θ equals zero, or when the feedback voltage appears in phase with the input voltage.

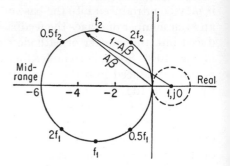

Fig. 10–8. Graphical presentation of the Nyquist criterion for an RC amplifier, one stage.

An $A\beta$ plot for a resistance-coupled grounded-cathode or common-emitter amplifier may be constructed from Fig. 9–11, with an assumption of mid-range gain of -60 and $\beta = 0.1$. The accompanying table results and is plotted in Fig. 10–8.

Frequency	$A\beta$	Frequency	$A\beta$
$0.1f_1$	$0.72 \underline{/264°}$	$0.5f_2$	$5.40 \underline{/154°}$
$0.5f_1$	$2.70 \underline{/243°}$	f_2	$4.20 \underline{/135°}$
f_1	$4.20 \underline{/225°}$	$2f_2$	$2.70 \underline{/117°}$
$2f_1$	$5.40 \underline{/207°}$	$8f_2$	$0.72 \underline{/96°}$
Mid-range	$6.00 \underline{/180°}$		

The polar plot for such an amplifier is a circle, with frequency progressing clockwise from the origin. The entire mid-range appears at the 180° point, where the gain is constant at 6.0. The circle is the locus of $A\beta$ for all frequencies.

A phasor for 1 $\underline{/0°}$ is drawn to the point 1, $j0$ so that the term $1 - A\beta$ may be determined graphically. The regenerative unit circle with center at 1, $j0$ is also shown. It can be seen that the only way for the $1 - A\beta$ phasor to have a magnitude less than unity is for the polar $A\beta$ locus to pass inside the unit circle. This specifies a condition for stability without regeneration as requiring that the $A\beta$ locus not pass through the unit circle around the 1, $j0$ point. A one-stage feedback RC amplifier is obviously nonregenerative, and this is generally true of most one-stage amplifiers, with their inherent $\pm 90°$ phase shift limits. Amplifiers of two stages, which can have total phase angles approaching $180°$, may be unstable, and those having additional stages require care and compensation at extreme frequencies.

Figure 10–9 is that from a transformer-coupled amplifier in which the feedback voltage is taken from the secondary of the transformer. It can be seen that although the 1, $j0$ point is not encircled, the $A\beta$ vector terminates inside the unit circle at high frequencies, indicating some regeneration. Further reduction in gain at those frequencies, by circuit modification, would probably be advisable to ensure stable performance.

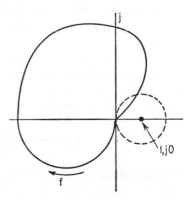

Fig. 10–9. The Nyquist criterion for a transformer-output stage.

In general, oscillation will not occur if the phase angle of the voltage fed back never differs as much as $180°$ from its mid-range value, or if the absolute value of $A\beta$ becomes less than unity when the phase angle of $A\beta$ approaches zero degrees. It is usually possible to design an amplifier so that at least the latter condition may be met.

It is not always necessary to make a Nyquist plot, since stability may be determined by a study of the gain function. Consider once again the operator p as a complex frequency or $p = \sigma + j\omega$. If we look at the exponential

$$\epsilon^{pt} = \epsilon^{\sigma t} + \epsilon^{j\omega t} \tag{10–26}$$

the first term on the right appears as a growing or decaying exponential, and the second term as a sinusoid. Overall, the term ϵ^{pt} represents a growing or decaying sinusoid. The exponent σ controls the rate of change, and ω represents the real frequency. If a circuit develops a growing sinusoid, it is obviously unstable. A growing sinusoid results from a positive σ, and a positive σ in the value for p locates the pole in the right half-plane. A decaying sinusoid requires a negative σ, and the pole will be located in the negative half-plane of the p plot.

We may apply this reasoning to the problem of stability in the feedback amplifier. The gain is

$$G(p) = \frac{A(p)}{1 - A(p)\beta} \tag{10–27}$$

Since $A(p)$ may be expressed in polynomial form, the gain function will have poles and zeros due to numerator and denominator roots. Critical appraisal of the expression shows that the gain $G(p)$ may grow without limit, or the amplifier will be unstable, if any pole contributed by a denominator zero has a positive σ, or if such a pole lies in the right half-plane of the p plot. Thus *for stability there should be no zeros of the denominator* $[1 - A(p)\beta]$ *in the right half-plane.* This is a form of the Nyquist criterion for stability.

This result may be illustrated by consideration of a resistance-capacitance coupled amplifier of two stages, with overall feedback of magnitude β and zero phase shift in the feedback circuit. The high-frequency gain of one stage from Eq. 9–33 is

$$A(p) = \frac{-g_m R}{1 + pRC} = -\frac{g_m}{C}\left(\frac{1}{p + 1/RC}\right) \tag{10-28}$$

The denominator has a zero, or the function has a pole, at $p = -1/RC$, and the amplifier of one stage is evidently stable. The term $-g_m/C$ is the scale factor or mid-frequency gain.

Cascading two identical stages gives

$$A(p) = \left(\frac{g_m}{C}\right)^2 \frac{1}{(p + 1/RC)^2}$$

Using this result in Eq. 10–27 to find the effect of feedback around this amplifier gives

$$G(p) = \frac{\left(\dfrac{g_m/C}{p + 1/RC}\right)^2}{1 - \left(\dfrac{g_m/C}{p + 1/RC}\right)^2 \beta}$$

$$= \left(\frac{g_m}{C}\right)^2 \frac{1}{p^2 + 2p/RC + (1/RC)^2 - (g_m/C)^2\beta} \tag{10-29}$$

The stability of the amplifier can then be determined from a study of the zeros of the denominator, since they will create the poles of the gain function. These zeros are

$$p_1 = -1/RC + \frac{g_m}{C}\sqrt{\beta}$$

$$p_2 = -1/RC - \frac{g_m}{C}\sqrt{\beta}$$

The zero due to p_1 will lie in the right half-plane if

$$g_m R > \frac{1}{\sqrt{\beta}} \tag{10-30}$$

Since the mid-frequency overall gain of the two-stage amplifier without feedback is equal to $(g_m R)^2$, then it is apparent that for stability the overall gain must be less than $1/\beta$, inside the feedback loop.

10–9. Gain and phase margin

To graphically determine the stability of an amplifier, it is merely necessary to show that $|\, A\beta \,|$ is less than unity when the overall or loop phase angle approaches $0°$, and plots of $A\beta$ magnitude, usually in decibels, and of phase angle, may be used directly. Such curves also allow determination of the closeness of approach of actual performance to the stability limits.

The *gain margin* is the decibel value of $A\beta$ at the frequency at which the phase angle of $A\beta$ is $0°$. If negative this indicates the decibel rise in gain which is theoretically permissible without oscillation. If positive the amplifier is unstable.

The *phase margin* is the angle of $A\beta$ at the frequency at which $A\beta$ has a value of zero decibels, or unity magnitude.

The desirable magnitude of gain and phase margins varies with the application, but it is usual to require at least 10 db of gain and $30°$ of phase margin to take care of unavoidable shifts due to component variation. Figure 10–10 illustrates these criteria, showing a high-range plot for an amplifier with a gain margin of 8.2 db and a phase margin of $36°$, the amplifier being stable. Various combinations of RC circuits may be employed in the feedback loop or in the coupling networks to reduce the high-frequency response if further gain margin is considered desirable.

It should be noted that the frequency at which the gain and phase margins are controlled and measured is far outside the region of flat response of the amplifier, and thus far beyond the normally used range. This shows the necessity for control of phase and gain well beyond the operating band width in feedback amplifiers, and indicates that reduced distortion and increased stability have been purchased at the expense of problems associated with greater required band width.

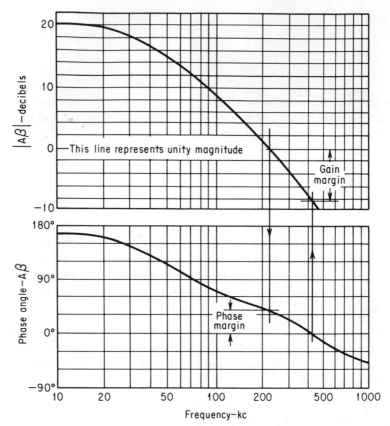

Fig. 10–10. Plot of high-frequency values of $A\beta$, showing gain and phase margin.

10–10. Direct-coupled amplifiers

The reactance of the coupling capacitor is the limiting factor in the amplification of very low frequencies. The low-frequency range of amplifiers can be extended to zero frequency by elimination of the coupling capacitor in circuits called *direct-coupled* or *d-c amplifiers*.

Without a coupling capacitor, the input grid or base element is placed at the potential of the anode or collector of the previous stage. This can be designed for by placing the appropriate voltage on cathode or emitter, to provide proper bias levels, but these voltages become cumulative and large in multi-stage amplifiers. The circuits are also sensitive to stability of the supply voltages, since the amplifier is unable to distinguish between a 1 mv signal and a 1 mv change in a base-emitter supply potential.

Changes in tube characteristics with voltage or time, or transistor parameters with temperature, are other causes of instability and drift in d-c amplifiers. Occasionally attempts are made to balance such changes by employment of a static balance tube, as in Fig. 10–11. Such a circuit is successful in many vacuum-tube voltmeters where frequent manual adjustments can be made to balance out the zero drift, but employment of such a device in sensitive amplifiers requiring long-time stability is not satisfactory, because of difficulties of matching dynamic characteristics. Negative feedback circuits have done most to solve the problems associated with the stable d-c amplifier.

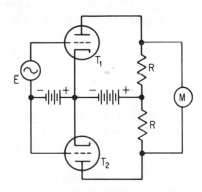

Fig. 10–11. Balanced d-c amplifier.

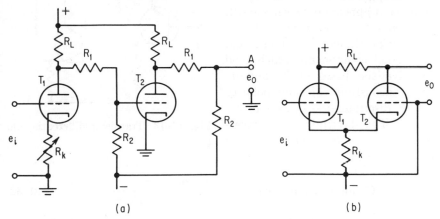

(a)   (b)

Fig. 10–12. (a) Resistance-coupled amplifier; (b) cathode-coupled d-c amplifier.

Resistance-coupled and cathode-coupled amplifiers, as in Fig. 10–12, are commonly employed as circuit elements, with and without feedback. In the resistance-coupled form of Fig. 10–12(a) the d-c voltage levels of successive stages are adjusted through choice of R_1 and R_2 and the use of positive and negative power supplies. By adjustment of R_k it is possible to bring the output potential at A to zero or ground with zero input. There is then a loss of gain through the voltage-dividing effect of R_1 and R_2, but this may reduce the gain only by a factor of two or three, and is a price which must be paid for achieving control of the internal d-c voltage levels in the amplifier. With well-regulated power supplies, the output drift may be only a few millivolts per hour, and occasional manual adjustment will cancel this.

The cathode-coupled amplifier at Fig. 10–12(b) uses a regulated power supply and a double triode. The gain with identical triodes is

$$A = \frac{\mu R_L}{2r_p + R_L} \tag{10-31}$$

The simplicity of the circuit, plus the stability gained through the negative feedback from the cathode resistor, makes it a desirable circuit form.

A more useful form of the balanced circuit is shown as the *differential amplifier* of Fig. 10–13. The input is applied between 1 and 2, and the output appears between 3 and 4. The circuit is sensitive only to differential changes in input, and any signal components which tend to drive the bases of T_1 and T_3 simultaneously in the same polarity will be discriminated against in the output. This discrimination is measured by the common-mode rejection ratio as

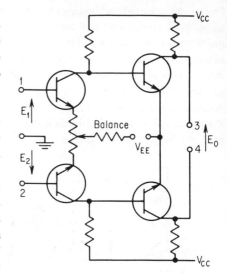

Fig. 10–13. Transistor differential amplifier.

$$\text{Common-mode rejection} = \frac{E_o \text{ for } E_1 = E_1; E_2 = 0}{E_o \text{ for } E_1 = -E_2} \tag{10-32}$$

Noise or hum reaching both terminals is therefore reduced in this ratio. Shifts in base-emitter junction voltage due to temperature changes will also be discriminated against, providing the transistors enjoy equivalent temperature situations. Since T_1, T_3 and T_2, T_4 are simultaneously being driven over the same portions of their dynamic curves, the compensation is better than can be achieved with the one static tube of Fig. 10–11. Negative feedback may be added to further stabilize these circuits.

Drift of output as a function of time is the limiting factor on performance of these basic amplifiers. Drift voltages may be considered as variations in d-c bias on the first stage of an amplifier, and residual drift is frequently defined in terms of a voltage, which, if placed on the input of the first stage, will produce the same change in output as is given by the drift. A *drift figure* for an amplifier is usually stated as the *equivalent input volts change per hour of operation*.

10–11. Chopper amplifiers

An obvious solution to the drift problem in direct-coupled amplifiers is to chop or modulate the slowly varying input signals into a form of a-c, amplify this with a conventional a-c amplifier, and rectify the output back to a slowly varying or d-c form. Such a system is shown in Fig. 10–14. The usual mechanical chopper employs a polarized a-c magnet to operate the switch arm and contacts, thus performing the switching in synchronism with the a-c supply. The input is connected to the amplifier only one-half of the time, and, for a 60-period switch rate, the input is sampled 60 times per second.

In order that the sampling accurately reflect the input, or give good reproduction of changes in input voltage, many samples must be taken per cycle of input, or the sampling frequency must be large with respect to the frequency of variation of the input. This is a fundamental limitation, and is particularly serious if 60 cycle a-c is used to supply the chopper. To provide for higher input frequencies the mechanical chopper is occasionally supplied with 400 cycle power. Transistors are also used as switches, and these devices permit removal of most frequency limitations on chopper amplifiers.

As indicated in the circuit diagram, the peak-to-peak amplitude of the amplifier input will equal the input voltage during the half cycle in which the chopper switch is open, and any change in the input voltage during this half period will not be indicated except as an average. To provide this average the input is supplied through a low-pass RC filter, composed of R_1 and C_1, which removes all frequencies above possibly one-tenth of the chopper frequency. The output is rectified by diode D, and harmonics of the chopping frequency are removed by the R_3C_3 filter at the output. Thus the band width is limited to about one-tenth of the chopping frequency, or six cycles for 60 cycle choppers. The diode D is sometimes replaced by additional contacts on the chopper reed, making a synchronous-rectifier chopper.

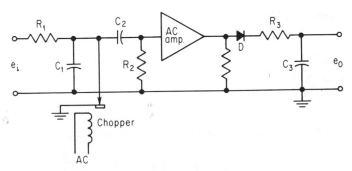

Fig. 10–14. Chopper-modulated amplifier.

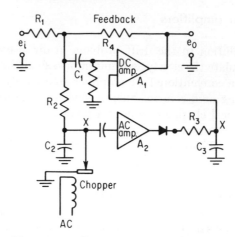

Fig. 10–15. Chopper-stabilized amplifier.

Considerably greater overall stability is possible in the *chopper-stabilized d-c amplifier*, employing negative feedback. The circuit of Fig. 10–15 uses a chopper a-c amplifier of gain A_2, inside a feedback loop, at the same time the higher-frequency components are amplified directly in a d-c amplifier, of gain A_1. Since these higher frequencies do not go through the chopper, the band width limitation imposed by the chopper frequency does not apply.

Any drift in output is fed back through R_4, and being of very slowly changing value, charges C_2 through R_2, the RC constants being chosen for long time constant. The voltage on C_2 is chopped, amplified in the a-c amplifier, rectified, filtered, and applied as additional input to the d-c amplifier as a drift-correcting voltage. This input cancels the equivalent input drift voltage of the d-c amplifier and brings the drift output voltage back nearly to zero. At the same time, the higher-frequency components are passed through C_1 directly into the d-c amplifier.

If e_d is the drift voltage of the d-c amplifier, then the output without the stabilizing amplifier is

$$e_o = A_1 e_d$$

where A_1 is the gain of the d-c amplifier. With the circuit of Fig. 10–15, and an a-c amplifier gain of A_2, the output for drift frequencies will be

$$e_o = A_1 A_2 e_d$$

while the output for all frequencies passing through C_1 and the d-c amplifier only will be

$$e_o = A_1 e_d$$

This places the driftless a-c amplifier in series with the d-c amplifier for slowly varying drift voltages, reduces the drift by the factor $1/A_2$, and brings the output back to near zero. Drifts of only a few microvolts per hour are possible in well-designed amplifiers.

10–12. Transistor choppers

As a result of the high cutoff resistance and the low saturation resistance, the transistor is a close approximation to the mechanical chopper of the previous section. When the base circuits are supplied by an input square wave of amplitude sufficient to drive the transistor between cutoff and saturation, the circuit of Fig. 10–16(a) switches T_1 and T_2 alternately off and on, chopping the input V_1 and providing an alternating input to the primary of the output transformer. The value of the output will differ from the input by the amount of the saturation voltage. While this may be made small by selection of suitable transistor types, it is desirable to match the transistors for this service to secure balanced output.

The circuit of Fig. 10–16(b) is an analogue of the single-reed or half-wave chopper. When the square-wave base input drives T_1 on, it turns T_2 off. Since T_1 is in series with the input and T_2 in parallel, the signal will then be passed to V_2. On the other half cycle of square wave, T_1 is turned off, disconnecting the input, and T_2 is in saturation, short-circuiting the output. With matched transistors, the collector-emitter saturation voltage in one case compensates for that in the reverse situation, and the output V_2 is closely equal to V_1.

Since the square-wave switching frequency can be chosen for each application, and made ten or more times the highest signal frequency, such choppers have attractive advantages. Phototransistors have also been employed in similar circuits, the light from a flashing gas-discharge lamp being used to replace the square-wave switching circuit.

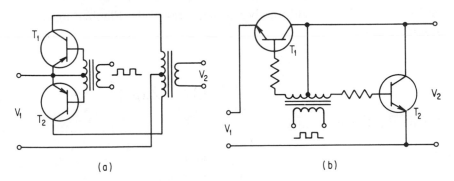

(a)   (b)

Fig. 10–16. Transistor chopper circuits.

10–13. The operational amplifier

One of the most common usages of the stabilized d-c amplifier is in an *operational amplifier*, capable of performing the basic mathematical operations of addition, subtraction, differentiation, and integration in analogue computers. This performance is achieved by a form of feedback amplifier, as in Fig. 10–17, wherein the d-c amplifier utilizes any stable high-gain form of the circuits described.

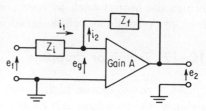

Fig. 10–17. The operational amplifier.

The amplifier has an input element Z_i and a feedback element Z_f, which are usual R, L, or C elements or combinations, where

$$e_R = iR, \qquad e_L = L\frac{di}{dt} = Lpi, \qquad e_C = \frac{1}{C}\int i\,dt = \frac{i}{Cp}$$

the elements then being referred to as $Z_i(p)$, $Z_f(p)$ where the $p = d/dt$ notation is used.

Assuming the current into the amplifier is negligible, then $i_1 = i_2$, and

$$\frac{e_1 - e_g}{Z_i(p)} = \frac{e_g - e_2}{Z_f(p)} \tag{10–33}$$

The amplifier has an internal gain A given by

$$A = -\frac{e_2}{e_g}$$

assuming an inherent odd number of phase reversals. Eliminating e_g from Eq. 10–33 gives

$$e_2 = -\left[\frac{Z_f(p)}{Z_i(p)}\right]\frac{e_1}{1 + \dfrac{1}{A}\left[1 + \dfrac{Z_f(p)}{Z_i(p)}\right]} \tag{10–34}$$

If the gain A is made large so

$$|A| \gg \left|1 + \frac{Z_f(p)}{Z_i(p)}\right|$$

then

$$e_2 = -\frac{Z_f(p)}{Z_i(p)} e_1 \qquad (10\text{--}35)$$

This equation indicates that the input and output voltages are related as the negative of $Z_f(p)/Z_i(p)$, or the ratio of the selected impedances.

If, for example, $Z_f(p) = R_f$, $Z_i(p) = R_i$, then

$$e_2 = -\frac{R_f}{R_i} e_1 \qquad (10\text{--}36)$$

and e_2 represents e_1 multiplied by a constant R_f/R_i, with the sign changed.

If $Z_f(p)$ is made a resistor R_f and $Z_i(p)$ a capacitor C_i, then

$$e_2 = -R_f C_i p e_1 \qquad (10\text{--}37)$$

and the output of the amplifier is the derivative of the input voltage, multiplied by a constant and with the sign changed. If $R_f = 1$ megohm, $C_i = 1\ \mu f$, then the $R_f C_i$ factor becomes unity.

Further, if $Z_f(p)$ is a capacitor C_f, and $Z_i(p)$ a resistor R_i, then

$$e_2 = -\frac{1}{R_i C_f} \frac{e_1}{p} \qquad (10\text{--}38)$$

and the output is equal to the negative of the integral of the input, multiplied by a constant $1/R_i C_f$.

Several input voltages may be simultaneously operated upon in the circuit of Fig. 10–18. If A is again very large

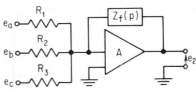

Fig. 10–18. Summing amplifier.

$$-e_2 = \frac{Z_f(p)}{R_1} e_a + \frac{Z_f(p)}{R_2} e_b + \frac{Z_f(p)}{R_3} e_c$$

If $R_1 = R_2 = R_3$, then

$$-e_2 = \frac{Z_f(p)}{R_1} (e_a + e_b + e_c) \qquad (10\text{--}39)$$

and the output represents a summation of the inputs.

Various combinations of R and C may be employed as $Z_i(p)$ and $Z_f(p)$, leading to a considerable variety in the mathematical operations which may be performed.

10–14. Transistor operational amplifier

Similar operations may be performed using transistor amplifiers, and emphasizing the basic principle that the transistor is a current-operated device. The circuit of Fig. 10–19 uses direct-coupled transistor circuits with an overall current gain A_i. The amplifier is connected through a feedback operational impedance $Z_f(p)$ to the common terminal or ground, and the input is shunted with a resistor R. It is assumed that the input resistance of

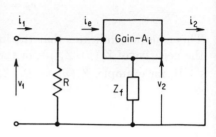

Fig. 10–19. Transistor operational amplifier.

the amplifier is very low, and that the output load is essentially a short circuit.

Under these assumptions the circuit shows that $v_1 = v_2$, and

$$(i_1 - i_e)R = (i_e - i_2)Z_f(p) \qquad (10\text{–}40)$$

By design there is an inherent odd number of phase reversals, or

$$-A_i = \frac{i_2}{i_1} \qquad (10\text{–}41)$$

Using the above relations it is possible to write

$$\frac{i_2}{i_1} = -\frac{R}{Z_f(p)}\left[\frac{1}{1 + \dfrac{1}{A_i}\left(1 + \dfrac{R}{Z_f(p)}\right)}\right] \qquad (10\text{–}42)$$

This equation is of the same form as Eq. (10–34). If A_i is made very large, or

$$A_i \gg \left| 1 + \frac{R}{Z_f(p)} \right|$$

then

$$i_2 = -\frac{R}{Z_f(p)}\, i_1 \qquad (10\text{–}43)$$

is the result.

If $Z_f(p)$ is a resistance, the amplifier is obviously a scale and sign changer. If $Z_f(p) = Lp$ for an inductance, then

$$i_2 = -\frac{R}{Lp}\, i_1 = -\frac{R}{L}\int i_1\, dt \qquad (10\text{–}44)$$

and the circuit is an integrator. If $Z_f(p)$ is a capacitance, then

$$i_2 = -RCpi_1 = -RC\frac{di_1}{dt} \qquad (10\text{–}45)$$

and the circuit is a differentiator.

10–15. Voltage regulators using d-c amplifiers

The d-c amplifier also is employed in circuits which stabilize the output voltage of rectifiers supplying d-c voltages for electronic circuits. Basic forms of these circuits, Fig. 10–20 (a) and (b), are known as shunt regulators, and Fig. 10–20(c) as a series form.

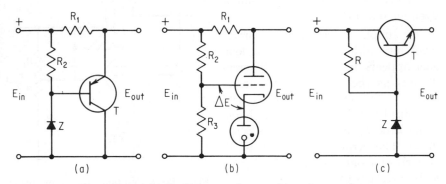

Fig. 10–20. (a), (b) Shunt regulators; (c) series regulator.

In Fig. 10–20(a) a constant-voltage Zener diode Z is used in series with a resistor R_2. Thus any change in input voltage E_{in} from the rectifier will appear across R_2, as base input to the transistor T, and making the emitter more positive. For the indicated PNP transistor the collector current increases, and this current produces a greater drop in R_1, this tending to subtract from the increased E_{in}, and stabilizing E_{out}. The transistor carries only a shunt current, and not the current transmitted to the load. Such shunt circuits are most useful for loads requiring currents comparable to the transistor rating, and have the advantage of being short-circuit proof, since an output short circuit simply unloads the transistor.

The tube circuit of Fig. 10–20(b) is similar in operation. A difference or error voltage ΔE is developed between the R_2, R_3 connection and the cathode which has its voltage fixed by a constant voltage gas tube (VR tube). If E_{in} increases then ΔE increases and makes the grid more positive to cathode, raising the anode current and increasing the voltage drop in R_1. Since $E_{out} = E_{in} - R_1 I$, then E_{out} does not vary as much as E_{in}, or the output voltage has been stabilized.

In the circuit at Fig. 10–20(c), the transistor is a series losser. Basically the circuit is an emitter-follower. An increase in E_{in} appears across R in series with Z, and changes the base voltage in such a direction as to reduce the emitter current, or raise the voltage drop across T. Since this drop is subtracted from the increased E_{in}, the output voltage change is decreased or the output stabilized. Such a circuit cannot tolerate short circuit, since an output short will place the total voltage of E_{in} across T, resulting usually in destruction.

Essentially these circuits are all feedback devices, in which output is compared to input, and further improvement in sensitivity is possible by inclusion of additional amplification inside the feedback loop. Such increase in sensitivity also provides extremely low values of ripple and of dynamic output resistance.

A simple vacuum-tube circuit involving additional feedback loop gain appears in Fig. 10–21. Therein T_1 acts as the variable series losser element. The cathode of T_2 is held at a fixed potential by the discharge (VR) tube T_3, or by a suitable Zener diode. The error signal input to T_2 is derived from the tap on R_1, R_2, and represents the difference between a part of the load voltage and the reference element drop.

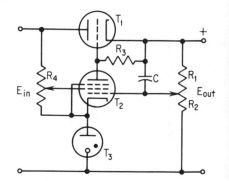

Fig. 10–21. Voltage regulator using a d-c amplifier.

If E_{out} increases, the grid of T_2 becomes more positive, increasing the anode current and the drop through R_3. The grid of T_1 becomes more negative and the resistance of T_1 is increased. Thus any increase in E_{out} creates an additional voltage drop in T_1 to oppose the input voltage increase. A decrease of input E_{in} causes the circuit to operate in reverse fashion, thus stabilizing E_{out}. In effect the circuit compares the voltage across R_2 with the constant voltage across T_3 and adjusts the resistance of T_1 to keep E_{out} constant.

The capacitor C effectively increases the gain of the circuit to ripple in the output, and this action makes the circuit a useful addition to the filtering action of the supply.

The dynamic output resistance of the regulator may be computed by assuming all voltage changes as small, making the linear equivalent circuit applicable for the tubes. The input to T_2 is then

$$E_{g2} = \frac{R_2}{R_1 + R_2} E_{out} = GE_{out}$$

If small changes only are considered, then $\Delta E_{g2} = G\Delta E_{out}$. The gain of the pentode is $A_2 = g_{m2}R_3$, after neglecting the minus sign, and so the change in voltage at the grid of T_1 is

$$\Delta E_{g1} = A_2 G \, \Delta E_{out} \tag{10-46}$$

Since the transconductance of T_1 is defined as $g_{m1} = \Delta I_p/\Delta E_{g1}$, then

$$\Delta I_p = g_{m1} A_2 G \, \Delta E_{out} \tag{10-47}$$

The effective output resistance of the regulator is then

$$R_s = \frac{\Delta E_{out}}{\Delta I_p} = \frac{1}{g_{m1} A_2 G} \tag{10-48}$$

High A_2 gain is desirable and this is usually obtained by use of a sharp cutoff pentode.

The amplification factor of T_1 is

$$\mu_1 = -\frac{\Delta E_b}{\Delta E_{g1}}$$

and using Eq. 10–47

$$\Delta E_b = -\mu_1 A_2 G \, \Delta E_{out} = \Delta E_{in} - \Delta E_{out} \tag{10-49}$$

from which

$$\Delta E_{out} = \frac{\Delta E_{in}}{1 + \mu_1 A_2 G} \tag{10-50}$$

Thus the change in output voltage is equal to the change in input divided by $1 + \mu_1 A_2 G$. The sensitivity is defined as the output change per unit input change or

$$S = \frac{\Delta E_{out}}{\Delta E_{in}} = \frac{1}{1 + \mu_1 A_2 G} \tag{10-51}$$

and high μ_1 and gain A_2 are important.

Problems

10-1. With feedback an amplifier gives an output of 10.5 v with an input of 1.12 v. When feedback is removed it requires 0.3 v input for the same output. Find the value of β, and of the gain without feedback. Input and output in phase, and β real.

10-2. An amplifier has a gain of 20 db and an output of 100 v with 10 per cent distortion. If feedback is to be used to reduce the distortion to 1.5 per cent, what value of β should be used, and what will be the new gain if A and β are real?

10-3. Connect a 1-megohm resistor across resistor R_2 of Fig. 9-42. Add feedback to the amplifier by connecting the input signal return lead to a tap on the 1-megohm resistor to provide 16 per cent feedback. If the tube has $\mu = 70$, $r_p = 66{,}000$ ohms, and $C = 0.1$ μf, $R_1 = R_2 = 100{,}000$ ohms, calculate the gain and phase shift at 100 cycles.

10-4. (a) Neglecting the reactance of C, develop an expression for gain in terms of tube and circuit constants, for the circuit of Fig. 10-22.

(b) Show that β is equal to the sum of the current and voltage feedback values of β.

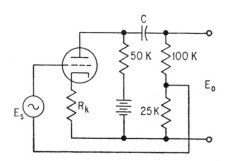

Fig. 10–22.

10-5. In Fig. 10-4(c), the resistors are $R_s = 100$ ohms, $R_L = 10{,}000$ ohms. The transistor has $h_{ie} = 1700$ ohms, $h_{re} = 5.0 \times 10^{-4}$, $h_{fe} = 44$, $h_{oe} = 22$ μmhos.

(a) Compute the gain without feedback, or $R_E = 0$.

(b) Repeat (a), using $R_E = 1000$ ohms.

(c) Calculate R_{ie} and R_{oe} for both cases.

10-6. For the circuit of Fig. 10-22, with $R_k = 2000$ ohms, $\mu = 22$, $g_m = 3000$ μmhos, show that β is equal to the sum of the voltage and current feedback β values.

10-7. In the circuit of Fig. 10-22, with the parameters of Problem 10-6, compute the gain and percentage of feedback.

10-8. An amplifier for a vacuum-tube voltmeter is to employ feedback, and must have an overall gain of 60. If the guaranteed accuracy is to be 1 per cent, and if internal gain changes of 12 per cent are found probable without feedback, determine the value of β required for stability, and the gain before feedback is added.

10-9. In Fig. 10-4(a), $R_k = 2000$ ohms, $\mathbf{Z}_L = 40{,}000$ ohms, and the tube is a 6AU6 pentode, with appropriate screen supply. Find the gain. Connect the grid return directly to cathode to remove the feedback and recompute the gain, assuming the same Q point.

10-10. The circuit of Fig. 10-5(a) is used with half of a 12AU7 triode with $\mu = 20$, $r_p = 7700$ ohms, $Z_L = 40{,}000$ ohms, $R_1 + R_2 = 250{,}000$ ohms. Specify the values of R_1 and R_2 needed to produce an overall gain of 5 at 1000 cycles, C being neglected.

10-11. In Fig. 10-6(a), R_1 = 250,000 ohms, R_2 = 25,000 ohms, Z_L = 50,000 ohms resistance, C = 0.01 μf, and the tube has μ = 35, r_p = 22,000 ohms. Plot a Nyquist diagram for the circuit.

10-12. An RC amplifier of three identical stages has f_1 = 18 cycles, f_2 = 140 kc for each stage. If the internal gain is −450, and β = 0.2, plot the Nyquist diagram, and determine the f_1' and f_2' values for the overall amplifier.

10-13. Prove that the gain of the amplifier of Fig. 10-12(b) is given by Eq. 10-31, assuming identical tubes.

10-14. For the circuit of Fig. 10-17, Z_i = 1 megohm, Z_f = 0.2 μf. For an input e_i = 0.3t, determine the output voltage as a function of time, if A is very large.

10-15. Repeat Problem 10-14, if Z_f is composed of 1 μf in parallel with 1.2 megohm resistance, if A = 500.

10-16. In Fig. 10-18, R_1 = 0.2 megohm, R_2 = 1.3 megohms, R_3 = 0.75 megohm, and Z_f is a 0.5-μf capacitor. The inputs are e_1 = 0.8 sin 377t, e_2 = 60t, e_3 = 1.2 v. Plot the output wave over 1/60 second.

10-17. In Fig. 10-23, the tubes have μ = 20, r_p = 8000 ohms, and the current through the meter M is zero for e_i = 0. Find the current through the instrument per volt of input.

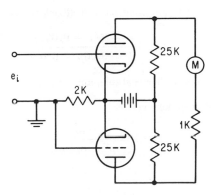

Fig. 10–23.

10-18. A 2N206 transistor with r_e = 20 ohms, r_b = 600 ohms, r_c = 1.8 megohms, h_{fe} = 47, is used in the circuit of Fig. 10-5(c). The source resistance is 200 ohms, R_L = 50,000 ohms. Specify R to provide 16 db feedback.

10-19. For the circuit of (b), Fig. 10-6, the tubes are the two halves of a 12AX7. Capacitance C and the coupling capacitance are 1.0 and 0.1 μf respectively. The cathode resistors are 2500 ohms each and all other resistors are 50,000 ohms. The second tube's cathode is adequately bypassed. Draw the Nyquist diagram for the circuit, assuming C_g for the second stage is 150 pf.

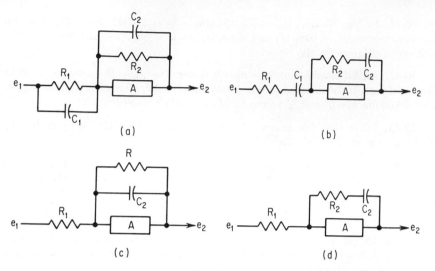

Fig. 10–24.

10-20. Determine the relation of e_2 to e_1 for each of the operational circuits of Fig. 10-24, in terms of the operator p.

10-21. A given feedback amplifier has a feedback factor given by

$$A\beta = \frac{-25(1 + 0.05p)}{1 + 0.20p + 0.02p^2}$$

Determine whether the amplifier is stable, and state limiting conditions.

10-22. A feedback amplifier has

$$A\beta = \frac{45}{p^2 + 3p + 1}$$

Is the amplifier stable?

References

1. Black, H. S., "Stabilized Feedback Amplifiers," *Elec. Eng.*, **53,** 114 (1934).

2. Bode, H. W., *Network Analysis and Feedback Amplifier Design.* D. Van Nostrand Co., Inc., New York, 1945.

3. Goldberg, E. A., "Stabilization of D-C Amplifiers," *RCA Rev.*, **11,** 296 (1950).

4. Learned, V., "Corrective Networks for Feedback Circuits," *Proc. I.R.E.*, **32,** 403 (1944).

5. Loftin, D. H., and White, S. Y., "Cascaded Direct-Coupled Tube Systems Operated from Alternating Current," *Proc. I.R.E.*, **18,** 669 (1930).

6. Lynch, W. A., "The Stability Problem in Feedback Amplifiers," *Proc. I.R.E.*, **39,** 1000 (1951).

7. Mayer, H. F., "Control of the Effective Internal Impedance of Amplifiers by Means of Feedback," *Proc. I.R.E.*, **27,** 213 (1939).

8. Nyquist, H., "Regeneration Theory," *Bell Syst. Tech. Jour.*, **11,** 126 (July 1932).

9. Ragazzini, J. R., Randall, R. H., and Russell, F. A., "Analysis of Problems is in Dynamics by Electronic Circuits," *Proc. I.R.E.*, **35,** 444 (1947).

10. Shea, R. F., *et al., Principles of Transistor Circuits.* John Wiley & Sons, Inc., New York, 1953.

11. Terman, F. E., "Feedback Amplifiers," *Electronics*, **10,** 15 (January 1937).

12. Valley, G. E., Jr., and Wallman, H., *Vacuum Tube Amplifiers.* McGraw-Hill Book Co., Inc., New York, 1948.

13. Williams, A. J., *et al.*, "D-C Amplifier Stabilized for Zero and Gain," *Trans. AIEE*, **67,** 47 (1948).

Class A and B Amplifiers with Large Signals | 11

Large input signals to transistor or vacuum tube are required if appreciable power output is to be obtained. The dynamic characteristics are nonlinear for wide input swings, and because of the nonlinear operation, equivalent circuits cannot usually be employed, and graphical analysis is used. The method is here applied to large-signal low- or audio-frequency amplifiers where fidelity and low distortion are of paramount interest. Class A operating conditions are often specified to obtain minimum distortion with reasonable power output. Push-pull circuits and feedback reduce distortion, and make higher power Class AB and B operation possible.

11–1. Output circuits

In the usual amplifier circuit of Fig. 11–1(a), the direct current I_b flows through the resistor R_L with a resultant power loss which serves no useful purpose. This power loss reduces the efficiency of circuit operation, and requires removal of the heat. In most applications it is hardly to be expected that the value of the available load R_L will be that which will provide a suitable load for the tube.

The circuits in Fig. 11–1(b) and (c) eliminate the d-c power loss and also provide means of adjusting the actual load R to the desired value R_L. The performance of the circuit is possible through the impedance-matching properties of a transformer. Because the transformer primary usually has negligible d-c resistance, the average anode or collector voltage will also be raised.

The transformer having a primary to secondary turns ratio $a = N_1/N_2$ presents to the tube an *apparent a-c load* R_L. Ideally the transformer will

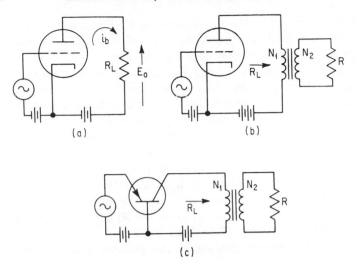

Fig. 11–1. Output circuits for power amplifiers.

have small losses and the voltages and currents are related as

$$a = \frac{N_1}{N_2} = \frac{V_1}{V_2} = \frac{I_2}{I_1}$$

$$V_1 = \frac{V_2 I_2}{I_1} \tag{11–1}$$

The impedance seen from the primary side is $\mathbf{Z}_1 = \mathbf{V}_1/\mathbf{I}_1$ and

$$\mathbf{Z}_1 = \frac{\mathbf{V}_1}{\mathbf{I}_1} = \frac{\mathbf{V}_2 \mathbf{I}_2}{\mathbf{I}_1^2} = \frac{a^2 \mathbf{V}_2}{\mathbf{I}_2}$$

The secondary load is $\mathbf{Z}_2 = \mathbf{V}_2/\mathbf{I}_2$ and then

$$\mathbf{Z}_1 = a^2 \mathbf{Z}_2 \tag{11–2}$$

which for the circuit under discussion becomes

$$R_L = a^2 R$$

As an example, a loudspeaker of 8 ohms resistance may provide a load of 5000 ohms to an amplifier output circuit by use of a transformer whose turns ratio a is

$$a = \sqrt{5000/8} = 25$$

The primary of the transformer, considered as lossless or *ideal*, would present negligible resistance to the d-c component I_b, and would appear as a 5000 ohms load to the a-c component I_p. For graphic analysis of the circuit, the d-c load line would be vertical from E_{bb}, the a-c load line through the Q point having a slope fixed by a^2R.

The ideal-transformer concept is convenient in determining the power capabilities of a tube and circuit, and actual transformers can be built to approach the ideal characteristics. A well-designed transformer should have low iron loss, and a high primary reactance at even the lowest frequencies in order to represent a satisfactory load at the low-frequency end of the operating range. The leakage inductance should be small to provide good high-frequency response, since it tends to resonate with transformer capacities and create a peak in the response at some high frequency. Well-designed transformers for the audio range may be found with power efficiencies ranging up to 85 and 90 per cent, but many models will also be found near the 50 per cent level.

Direct plate current flowing in the primary produces a saturating flux in the iron, and reduces the primary inductance. The load reflected into the tube circuit at low frequencies is then reduced, causing increased distortion. Circuits are available to prevent such saturation, or transformers may be built with air gaps in the magnetic circuit to alleviate the difficulty.

11-2. Power relations

An amplifier is essentially a frequency converter, changing d-c power into a-c power. The efficiency of the conversion process is called the *plate-circuit efficiency* and is defined as

$$\eta_p = \frac{\text{a-c power output}}{\text{d-c power input}} \times 100\% \tag{11-3}$$

where average power is ordinarily understood. Equation 11-3, using tube notation, then becomes

$$\eta_p = \frac{I_p^2 R_L}{E_{bb} I_b} \times 100\% \tag{11-4}$$

where R_L is the equivalent resistance through which the alternating current I_p flows. The power supplied by the source provides the a-c output, the d-c power losses in the load resistor, or the primary of the output transformer, and the power P_p representative of the energy losses in the tube or transistor. If a tetrode or pentode tube is used, the additional loss as heat at the screen grid must be included as part of the input.

The power input to the output circuit must be supplied by the d-c source, so that by the conservation of energy the average power in the circuit will be distributed according to

$$\text{power input} = \text{a-c power output} + \text{losses},$$

$$\left. \begin{aligned} E_{bb}I_b &= I_p^2 R_L + \text{losses} \\ E_{cc}I_c &= I_c^2 R_L + \text{losses} \end{aligned} \right\} \tag{11–5}$$

The losses comprise those in the d-c resistance of the load, and the internal loss of the transistor or tube. The internal loss is found from the device input, less the signal output or

$$\text{Internal loss} = P_d = E_b I_{bs} - I_p^2 R_L$$

$$= E_{cc}I_{Cs} - I_c^2 R_L$$

where I_{bs} and I_{Cs} are d-c or average currents with signal present. The quantity P_d is called the *dissipation* of the tube or transistor.

If at some instant there is zero input signal and consequently no a-c output, the entire input to the device must be internally dissipated. Designs must be based on the worst conditions to be encountered, and so the tube or transistor selected for Class A service must be capable of dissipating the amount of power loss expected with zero applied signal. As the a-c output increases, the internal loss then decreases and the device runs cooler.

It is customary to state a maximum value of plate dissipation for a vacuum tube, to ensure that the anode operating temperature will not be excessive. This means that a vacuum tube is rated in terms of its allowable losses, not in terms of its possible output, as is customary for electrical machinery—a very fundamental difference.

For a transistor the maximum internal or collector loss is also stated as a rating, but it will be a function of the cooling properties of the tran sistor mounting or *heat sink*, and the ambient operating temperature as well, since the allowable rise of temperature above ambient is much smaller for transistors than for vacuum tubes.

The operating condition imposes a maximum on the operating efficiency. For Class A operation, and the theoretically linear plate characteristics of Fig. 11–2, the input swing should be such as to drive the grid only to zero volts, at the positive maximum. The negative maximum may drive the plate current to zero, since the theoretical curves are linear. With a transformer-coupled load, the d-c load line is vertical, and the Q point may be placed halfway between $I_{\max}$ and zero current. This implies that

$$\frac{I_{\max} - I_{\min}}{2} = \sqrt{2}I_p = I_m = I_b$$

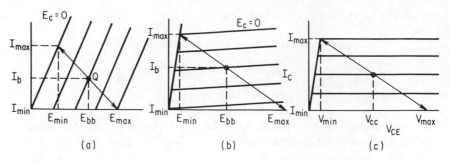

Fig. 11–2. Idealized characteristics: (a) triode; (b) pentode; (c) transistor.

Equation 11–4 can then be written, for the theoretical triode, as

$$\text{theoretical } \eta_p = \frac{50I_m^2 R_L}{E_{bb}I_m}\% = \frac{50I_m R_L}{E_{bb}}\% \qquad (11\text{–}6)$$

For large values of load, the plate voltage will be driven nearly to zero on the positive current swing, or $I_m R_L$ will approximate E_{bb}, so that the maximum theoretical efficiency for a transformer-coupled Class A amplifier, either tube or transistor, is 50 per cent. Because of distortion caused by the actual curved tube characteristics it is rarely possible to exceed 25 per cent for vacuum tubes, in practice. The transistor, having much greater linearity at low collector voltages, can be driven nearer zero collector voltage, and transistor Class A efficiencies as high as 49 per cent have been claimed.

11–3. Determination of amplitude distortion

Output voltage or current wave forms may be readily obtained by graphical plotting from the plate or collector characteristics, and analyzed by conventional methods for harmonics generated by nonlinearity of the characteristics. However, various ordinates of the waves may be obtained directly from the load line, and plotting of the wave form avoided.

A relation between output and input may be obtained by developing an equation for the dynamic curve of tube or transistor. About a given operating or Q point, the dynamic curve can be expressed by a power series, derived as a Taylor's series, in terms of variations of voltage or current from the operating point. The following equation is of this type:

$$i_c = a_o + a_1 e_i + a_2 e_i^2 + a_3 e_i^3 + a_4 e_i^4 + \cdots \qquad (11\text{–}7)$$

where the current i_c and voltage e_i are variational components around the Q point. It can be seen that if only the first two terms on the right are used, the dynamic curve is approximated by a straight line; if the third term

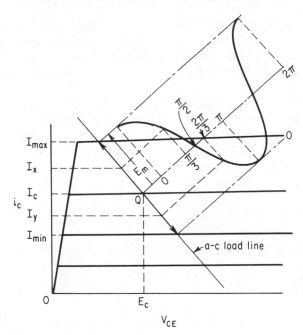

Fig. 11–3. Calculation of distortion from the transistor load line.

is added, the approximation is that of straight line plus a parabola. Closer approximation to the actual dynamic curve is obtained by addition of higher powers.

By reference to Fig. 11–3, it can be seen that if the applied signal e_i is zero, then operation is at the Q point, $i_c = I_C$, and $a_o = I_C$. Considering the input to the tube or transistor as sinusoidal,

$$e_i = E_m \cos \omega t$$

then the output current can be written as

$$i_c = I_C + a_1 E_m \cos \omega t + a_2 E_m^2 \cos^2 \omega t + a_3 E_m^3 \cos^3 \omega t + a_4 E_m^4 \cos^4 \omega t + \cdots$$

$$(11\text{–}8)$$

By use of trigonometric identities for multiple angles and by combining the resultant coefficients into a new set, Eq. 11–8 may be written as

$$i_c = I_C + A_o + A_1 \cos \omega t + A_2 \cos 2\omega t + A_3 \cos 3\omega t + A_4 \cos 4\omega t + \cdots$$

$$(11\text{–}9)$$

For the purposes of this analysis it may be reasoned that the higher-order harmonics will be small, and harmonics above the fourth dropped with small error; this does not invalidate the principle illustrated by the analysis. Now if the amplitudes of the harmonic components are to be determined, and the distortion computed, the constants of Eq. 11–9 must be evaluated. For the determination of the five constants shown, five equations may be written if the value of i_c is known for five instants in time.

The load line for the amplifier can be drawn as in Fig. 11–3. With the indicated signal amplitude, E_m, five values of current can be found at five instants spaced in time over the positive and negative half cycles. These instants are most easily chosen as $\omega t = 0$, with current designated I_{max} when the input voltage is at positive maximum; $\omega t = \pi/3$ with a current designated I_x when the input is at one-half the maximum; $\omega t = \pi/2$ with current I_C at zero input; $\omega t = 2\pi/3$ with current I_y at input one-half the negative maximum; and $\omega t = \pi$ with current I_{min} when the input is at negative maximum.

Substitution of these values of time and current into Eq. 11–9 yields five equations:

$$
\begin{aligned}
\omega t = 0° \qquad & I_{max} = I_C + A_0 + A_1 + A_2 + A_3 + A_4 \\[2mm]
\omega t = 60° \qquad & I_x = I_C + A_0 + \frac{A_1}{2} - \frac{A_2}{2} - A_3 - \frac{A_4}{2} \\[2mm]
\omega t = 90° \qquad & I_C = I_C + A_0 \qquad\quad - A_2 \qquad\quad + A_4 \\[2mm]
\omega t = 120° \qquad & I_y = I_C + A_0 - \frac{A_1}{2} - \frac{A_2}{2} + A_3 - \frac{A_4}{2} \\[2mm]
\omega t = 180° \qquad & I_{min} = I_C + A_0 - A_1 + A_2 - A_3 + A_4
\end{aligned}
\qquad (11\text{–}10)
$$

Elimination among these five equations results in the following expressions for the amplitudes of the various components:

$$A_0 = \tfrac{1}{6}(I_{max} + I_{min}) + \tfrac{1}{3}(I_x + I_y) - I_C \qquad (11\text{–}11)$$

$$A_1 = \tfrac{1}{3}(I_{max} - I_{min}) + \tfrac{1}{3}(I_x - I_y) \qquad (11\text{–}12)$$

$$A_2 = \tfrac{1}{4}(I_{max} + I_{min}) - \tfrac{1}{2}I_C \qquad (11\text{–}13)$$

$$A_3 = \tfrac{1}{6}(I_{max} - I_{min}) - \tfrac{1}{3}(I_x - I_y) \qquad (11\text{–}14)$$

$$A_4 = \tfrac{1}{12}(I_{max} + I_{min}) - \tfrac{1}{3}(I_x + I_y) + \tfrac{1}{2}I_C \qquad (11\text{–}15)$$

It is possible to define percentage distortion due to a particular harmonic as the ratio of the harmonic amplitude to that of the fundamental times 100 per cent, or

$$D_2 = \frac{A_2}{A_1} \times 100\%, \qquad D_3 = \frac{A_3}{A_1} \times 100\%, \qquad D_4 = \frac{A_4}{A_1} \times 100\%$$

The total harmonic distortion is defined as the ratio of the effective value of all harmonics to that of the fundamental, or

$$D = \frac{\sqrt{A_2^2 + A_3^2 + A_4^2 + \cdots}}{A_1} \times 100\% \tag{11-16}$$

The distortion present in the output of a triode or transistor is predominantly due to the second harmonic; if it is desired to neglect all higher harmonics as small, Eq. 11–9 may be written as

$$i_C = I_C + C_0 + C_1 \cos \omega t + C_2 \cos 2\omega t$$

By use of a three-point voltage-current-time table, the values of the amplitude coefficients can then be obtained as

$$C_0 = \tfrac{1}{4}(I_{\max} + I_{\min}) - \tfrac{1}{2}I_C \tag{11-17}$$

$$C_1 = \tfrac{1}{2}(I_{\max} - I_{\min}) \tag{11-18}$$

$$C_2 = \tfrac{1}{4}(I_{\max} + I_{\min}) - \tfrac{1}{2}I_C \tag{11-19}$$

These equations lead to some saving in time if harmonics of order higher than two are not important in the output. For pentodes and beam tubes, the third harmonic is usually the most important, so that Eqs. 11–11 to 11–15 must be resorted to.

For harmonics up to the nth, a schedule of time, voltage, current may be set up with $(n + 1)$ points taken from the load line, preferably at equal input voltage increments.

11–4. Intermodulation distortion

Input wave forms derived from speech or music, and pulses or other irregular waves are made up of a large number of harmonics, and rarely is the input to an amplifier a single-frequency sinusoid. If the curvature of the dynamic characteristic is appreciable and two or more signal frequencies are simultaneously applied to the amplifier input, a form of distortion known as *intermodulation* may result. This type of distortion adds frequencies in the output which are not harmonically related to the input frequencies.

Assume that the dynamic characteristic can be expressed by the first three terms of Eq. 11–7, higher-order terms being neglected for simplicity. Then

$$i_c = a_o + a_1 e_i + a_2 e_i^2 \tag{11-20}$$

If an input consisting of two non-harmonically related frequencies, ω_1 and ω_2, is introduced, as

$$e_i = E_1 \sin \omega_1 t + E_2 \sin \omega_2 t$$

then Eq. 11–20, with $a_o = I_C$, becomes

$$i_c = I_C + a_1(E_1 \sin \omega_1 t + E_2 \sin \omega_2 t) + a_2(E_1 \sin \omega_1 t + E_2 \sin \omega_2 t)^2$$

$$(11\text{–}21)$$

After expansion and introduction of identities including

$$\sin \omega_1 t \sin \omega_2 t = \tfrac{1}{2}[\cos (\omega_1 - \omega_2)t - \cos (\omega_1 - \omega_2)t]$$

the relation for current becomes

$$\left.\begin{aligned}
i_c = {}& I_C + \frac{a_2}{2}(E_1^2 + E_2^2) + a_1 E_1 \sin \omega_1 t + a_1 E_2 \sin \omega_2 t \\
& - \frac{a_2 E_1^2}{2} \cos 2\omega_1 t - \frac{a_2 E_2^2}{2} \cos 2\omega_2 t \\
& + a_2 E_1 E_2 \cos (\omega_1 - \omega_2)t - a_2 E_1 E_2 \cos (\omega_1 + \omega_2)t
\end{aligned}\right\} \quad (11\text{–}22)$$

The first line of the result includes a modified steady-state term, and the amplified input signal; the second line represents second-order distortion, and the third line represents additional distortion as the sum and difference frequencies of the input. If other frequencies are also present in the input then additional sum-and-difference terms appear, so that analysis on the basis of two input frequencies is indicative of the general situation.

Although these intermodulation frequencies may have small amplitude, they produce background noise which is extremely objectionable in audio service. Thus the elimination of this form of nonlinear distortion provides incentive for the design of truly linear amplifiers, or to the improvement of linearity with negative feedback.

11–5. Maximum power output—pentodes and triodes

Amplifiers supplying appreciable power output are driven over considerable ranges on their dynamic curves. The distortion then generated and the possible power output are both functions of the load assigned to the amplifier. Use of the condition $R_L = r_p$ will furnish maximum possible power for a given input signal, but the amplitude distortion produced with this load will usually be greater than is considered allowable. Higher values of load which permit greater driving voltages may raise the power output, and may increase or decrease the distortion. As used, loads for triodes are usually in the range of two to four times the value of the plate resistance, and a small fraction of the plate resistance for pentodes and beam tubes.

The maximum percentage of distortion allowed is arbitrary, since it is dependent on subjective factors. Usually a maximum of 5 per cent dis-

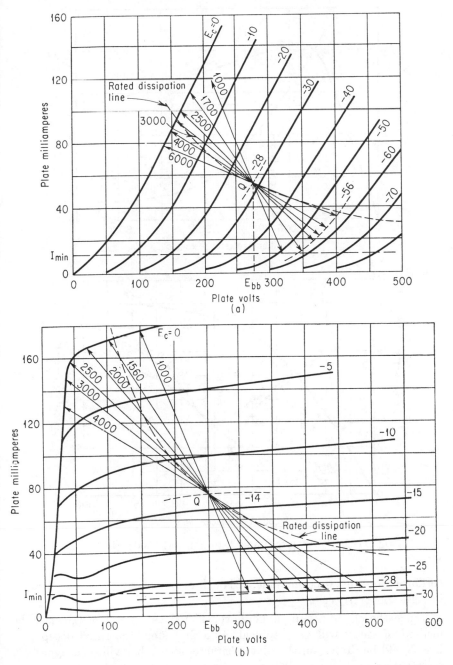

Fig. 11–4. Graphical determination of power output: (a) triode, P_d rated 15 w., E_{bb} max 275 v, $\mu = 5.8$, $r_p = 1700$ ohms; (b) beam tetrode, P_d rated 19 w, E_{bb} max $= 250$ v, $g_m = 6000$ μmho, $r_p = 22{,}500$ ohms.

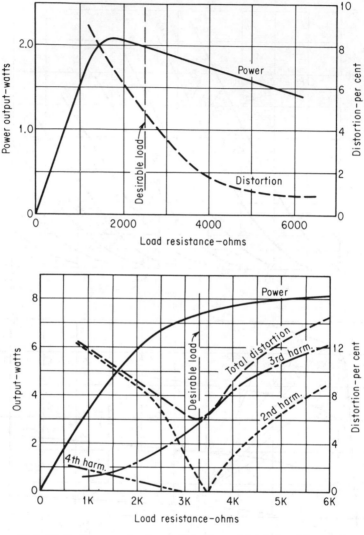

Fig. 11–5. Power output and distortion: (a) triode; (b) tetrode.

tortion is considered permissible, although only 1 or 2 per cent is tolerated in high-fidelity service.

Since the electron tube is being considered as a nonlinear device, the method of study will be graphical. As a first step, the rated dissipation line should be drawn on the plate characteristics; this will be a hyperbola representing

$$E_{bb}I_b = P_d \tag{11-23}$$

TABLE 17. DETERMINATION OF OPTIMUM LOAD—DATA FOR FIG. 11-5(b)

Beam tetrode of Fig. 11-4(b)

R_L ohms	I_{max} ma	I_{min} ma	I_x ma	I_y ma	A_1	I_p ma	Power watts	D_2 %	D_3 %	D_4 %	Total Harm. %
1000	177	15	122	38	82	58	3.4	11.6	1.2	1.8	11.8
1560	171	15	121	39	79	56	4.9	10.1	1.6	1.2	10.3
2000	166	15	120	39	77	54	5.9	8.8	2.3	0.8	9.1
2500	158	16	119	39	74	52	6.8	6.8	3.9	—	7.8
3000	146	16	117	40	69	49	7.2	2.9	5.8	—	6.5
4000	130	17	113	40	62	44	7.8	−2.9	8.7	—	9.2
5000	120	18	109	41	57	40	8.0	−6.5	10.7	—	12.5

where P_d is the rated dissipation of the tube. It is assumed that $E_b = E_{bb}$, since only transformer-coupled output circuits are used for high power output. Any Q point must lie on or below this hyperbola, to avoid exceeding the plate dissipation rating. For maximum output, E_{bb} will be chosen as the highest-rated plate supply voltage, and the Q point will be fixed on the hyperbola at the value of I_b given by Eq. 11–23.

Beam tetrodes are most often used as power amplifiers, and this discussion will employ the tetrode of Fig. 11–4(b). As a second step choose a value of I_{min}, so that operation will not carry into the nonlinear characteristics at low plate current. A horizontal line at the I_{min} value will serve as a limit of operation for negative swings. For Class A operation the maximum extreme of the other end of the load line will be $E_c = 0$.

The first experimental load line should pass through the $E_c = 0$ line near the knee of the curve. Calculate the slope and load resistance and draw a set of load lines for load values from one-half to twice the first load. Then compute the power output for each line, and calculate the percentages of the several harmonics, and the total harmonic content.

For triodes the first line may be drawn with a slope such that it intersects the I_{min} line at a value of E_c equal to twice the E_c value at the Q point. Other load lines are then drawn, and grid swings used which will drive the grid to either $E_c = 0$ at the positive peak, or to I_{min} at the negative peak, as determined by which of these limits is reached first.

The calculated results from the load lines appear in Table 17 and Fig. 11–5(b). A choice of load can be made from the data, and for the tetrode this might be 3300 ohms. The total-harmonic minimum near that load is due to the fact that the second harmonic is zero. For loads above this value it reverses in phase and rises again. From Eq. 11–13 the second harmonic goes to zero when

$$I_b = \tfrac{1}{2}(I_{max} + I_{min})$$

This value will occur for a load line drawn in such a way that the Q point falls at a value of current exactly halfway between I_{max} and I_{min}.

The choice of load has been made to give the largest power output with the least distortion. Higher load would increase the power only slightly, but would rapidly increase the distortion.

11–6. Transistor power performance

Similar methods may be employed to determine power output and distortion with the transistor. Particular importance must be attached to the determination of the collector dissipation and temperature. Since the maximum operating temperature is about 85°C for germanium and 200°C for silicon, the temperature difference between collector and surrounding ambient will be small. Thus radiation cannot be of importance as a cooling means, and conduction must be relied upon to remove the

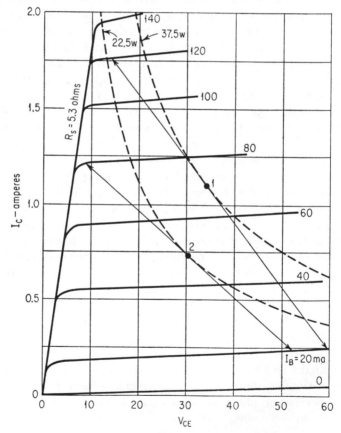

Fig. 11–6. Power output of silicon power transistor.

heat dissipated in the collector. By mounting the collector element in good thermal contact with the case, and then placing the case in good contact with a large metal mass or *heat sink*, it is possible to provide reasonable cooling.

The location of the $E_{cc}I_C = P_d$ hyperbola on the collector characteristics then becomes of first importance, since the allowable dissipation is a function of ambient temperature. Thus the designer needs to determine the environment under which the power transistor will operate as his first requirement. In Fig. 11–6 two hyperbolas are drawn for a silicon power transistor, for 37.5 watts dissipation at 25°C ambient and 22.5 watts at 75°C.

The transistor of the example is rated $V_{CE} = 60$ v maximum, and using this rating and the 37.5 watt dissipation curve, a Q point at (1) seems suitable, if the base current is not to be driven below about 20 ma where distortion becomes apparent in the curves. This load line is found to represent a resistance of 30 ohms, and calculated performance data are given in Table 18.

T<small>ABLE</small> 18.

	Load 1	Load 2
R_L	30 ohms	44 ohms
V_{max}	60 v	52 v
V_{min}	14 v	9 v
A_1	23.0 peak	21.5 peak
V_C at Q	34 v	30 v
A_2	1.5 peak	0.25 peak
D_2	6.5%	1.1%
Power output	8.8 w	5.3 w
Power input	37.5 w	22.5 w
Power efficiency	23.5%	23.3%
Input power	5.0 mw	1.94 mw
Power gain	1760	2730
Power gain, db	32.4	34.3

A second load line is drawn for the 22.5-watt dissipation condition through the Q point selected at (2), being limited in driving range by the curvature of the $I_B = 80$ ma characteristic, as well as the $I_B = 20$ ma minimum. Data for this 44-ohm load line are also presented in the table, the output being reduced.

Input circuit conditions for the common-emitter circuit may be determined from the base characteristics presented in Fig. 11–7. The load line for point (1) has been transferred point-by-point to this figure and

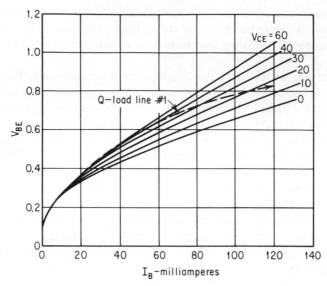

Fig. 11–7. Input characteristic for transistor of Fig. 11–6.

appears as the dashed line. For a driver of rather high impedance (approaching a constant-current source) the load line curvature due to nonlinear input resistance would have little effect, but for a low-resistance driver additional distortion would be introduced. Input rms voltage and current quantities may be calculated by previous methods, and for load line (1) are $I_b = 31.8$ ma, $V_{be} = 0.157$ v, so that the input power is 5.0 mw. The power gain then is

$$\frac{8.8}{5.0 \times 10^{-3}} = 1760 = 32.4 \text{ db}$$

It is apparent from Fig. 11–7 that the Q-point bias is $V_{EB} = 0.68$ v, $I_B = 70$ ma. Maintenance of this bias is critical, since a shift in Q point will change the dissipation, and may cause the maximum dissipation rating of the transistor to be exceeded. Constant-current bias may not be practical, but the stabilizing circuits previously discussed are useful.

A simple equivalent circuit for a power transistor appears in Fig. 11–8(a). The primed resistance elements are present due to the ohmic resistance of the transistor electrodes, since they may be appreciable in effect at high currents. The unprimed resistances are those of the junctions, as usual. The emitter junction resistance r_e is inversely proportional to current as previously discussed, and for high currents may be negligible, thereby also removing C_e from the circuit.

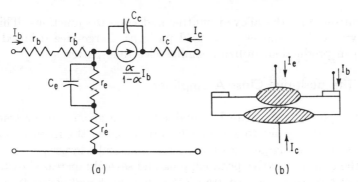

Fig. 11–8. (a) Equivalent circuit for a power transistor; (b) cross-section of alloy junction power transistor.

The common-base circuit provides no current gain, and this contradicts the purpose of power amplification. While the common-collector form has a high input resistance, it has a low power gain. These reasons leave the common-emitter circuit most favored for power amplification, and the current gain is then

$$\mathbf{A}_i \cong \frac{a}{1 - a} = h_{fe}$$

so that the power gain becomes approximately

$$\text{P.G.} \cong h_{fe}^2 \frac{R_L}{r_b' + r_b}$$

A limit on increasing load resistance to increase gain is set by the maximum rated voltage of the transistor. Thus the load resistance cannot be allowed to exceed a value

$$R_L = \frac{V_m^2}{8P_o}$$

for a Class A amplifier.

Another limiting phenomenon on peak voltage is that of *punch-through*. As has been previously discussed, the base layer thickness is a function of collector voltage, and at a high collector voltage the collector effect may extend completely through the base layer, producing an effective short circuit from collector to emitter, with consequent high current. Although the effect is nondestructive, it does mean that the transistor is inoperative above this limiting voltage value.

Power transistor construction is frequently concentric. Figure 11–8(b) illustrates a cross-section, showing the base contact as a ring on the base plate, surrounding the alloyed emitter and collector junctions. This produces symmetry of current and field patterns. Large-area diffused types are also in production, utilizing similar electrode patterns.

11-7. The push-pull Class A amplifier

Higher power output can be obtained from a given tube or transistor by moving the Q point to a higher bias position on the rated dissipation line. This permits a larger positive input swing, and a larger power output, but at the cost of negative peak clipping and severely increased distortion. By use of two tubes or two transistors in a *push-pull* connection, as in Fig. 11–9, much of the distortion can be canceled and a power output obtained which is greater than twice that of one device operating under normal Class A conditions. For pentodes or beam tubes, a screen supply and bypass capacitor would be added.

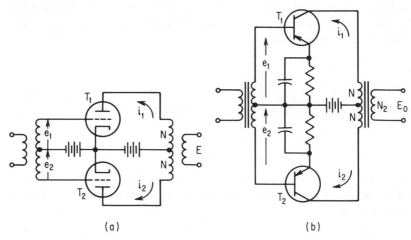

(a)   (b)

Fig. 11–9. (a) Triode push-pull amplifier; (b) transistor push-pull amplifier.

The circuit will be analyzed using a common form of notation, so that the result will be characteristic of the circuit, and applicable to either tube or transistor. It will be assumed that the tubes or transistors of each circuit have identical characteristics. The current in the output circuit will be related to the input voltage as

$$i = I_o + a_1 e_s + a_2 e_s^2 + a_3 e_s^3 + a_4 e_s^4 + \cdots \qquad (11\text{--}24)$$

By reference to the figure, if a voltage $e = E_m \sin \omega t$ is applied to the primary of the input transformer, the individual input voltages from the secondary are

$$e_1 = E_2 \sin \omega t$$

$$e_2 = E_2 \sin (\omega t + \pi)$$

because the transformer secondary constitutes one continuous winding, tapped at the center for the bias return. The output current of T_1 can then be written as

$$i_1 = I_{o1} + a_1 E_2 \sin \omega t + a_2 E_2^2 \sin^2 \omega t + a_3 E_2^3 \sin^3 \omega t + \cdots$$

and that of device T_2 as

$$i_2 = I_{o2} + a_1 E_2 \sin (\omega t + \pi) + a_2 E_2^2 \sin^2 (\omega t + \pi)$$
$$+ a_3 E_2^3 \sin^3 (\omega t + \pi) + \cdots$$

By use of trigonometric identities in terms of multiple angles

$$\left.\begin{aligned}
i_1 &= I_{o1} + B_o + B_1 \sin \omega t - B_2 \cos 2\omega t + B_3 \sin 3\omega t \\
&\qquad\qquad - B_4 \cos 4\omega t + \cdots \\
i_2 &= I_{o2} + B_o + B_1 \sin (\omega t + \pi) - B_2 \cos 2(\omega t + \pi) \\
&\qquad + B_3 \sin 3(\omega t + \pi) - B_4 \cos 4(\omega t + \pi) + \cdots
\end{aligned}\right\} \qquad (11\text{–}25)$$

From trigonometry

$$\left.\begin{aligned}
\sin (\omega t + \pi) &= - \sin \omega t \\
\cos 2(\omega t + \pi) &= \cos 2\omega t
\end{aligned}\right\} \qquad (11\text{–}26)$$

and similarly for all even and odd harmonics, so that i_2 can be written as

$$i_2 = I_{o2} + B_0 - B_1 \sin \omega t - B_2 \cos 2\omega t - B_3 \sin 3\omega t - B_4 \cos 4\omega t + \cdots$$
$$(11\text{–}27)$$

The primary of the output transformer is one continuous winding tapped at the center, and since the currents have positive directions assumed as shown, the magnetizing force acting on the transformer core is proportional to $N(i_1 - i_2)$.

With linear magnetic action assumed, the secondary output voltage E_o will be proportional to the ampere turns, or

$$E_o = 2K(B_1 \sin \omega t + B_3 \sin 3\omega t + B_5 \sin 5\omega t + \cdots) \qquad (11\text{–}28)$$

Since all even and odd harmonics will have algebraic signs determined by Eq. 11–26, then Eq. 11–28 shows that the push-pull connection with matched tubes or transistors will eliminate from the output all even

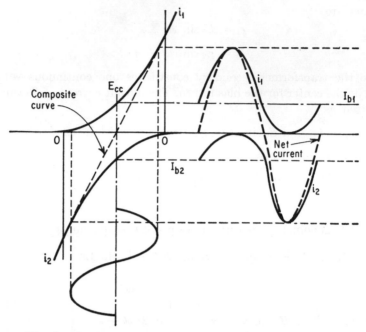

Fig. 11–10. Use of transfer curves to explain push-pull action.

harmonics as well as even-order intermodulation frequencies. This effect is also illustrated graphically in Fig. 11–10, by use of the dynamic transfer curve of each tube, plotted in subtractive relation, and used to derive a *composite transfer curve* for the push-pull combination.

Transistors or triodes, with predominantly even-harmonic distortion, may be operated in this way to give low distortion and increased power output. From Fig. 11–5(b) it can be seen that increased power output is possible by operation of pentodes or beam tubes with larger loads, but with a penalty in increased second-harmonic distortion. Push-pull operation of pentodes cancels this second-harmonic, leaving only the odd-harmonic distortion, and a higher load may thus be profitably used on pentodes or beam tubes as well.

The total primary load into which the tubes or transistors work is that reflected from the secondary, as

$$R_L = \left(\frac{2N}{N_2}\right)^2 R \qquad (11\text{–}29)$$

where N is the number of turns in one half of the primary, and an ideal transformer is assumed. The "per-tube" or "per transistor" load is obviously one-fourth of R_L.

Cancellation of d-c fluxes in the output transformer core allows use of less iron, and a cheaper transformer. Any ripple remaining in the supply voltage will also cancel, reducing possible hum in the output. This permits use of a power supply with less filter than is needed for the preceding small-signal amplifiers.

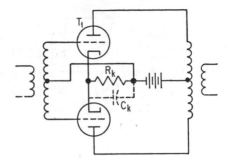

Fig. 11-11. Grid bias by cathode resistor in push-pull amplifier.

A cathode or emitter bias resistor may be used as in Fig. 11-11. Without bypass C_k, the current through R_k is

$$i_k = i_1 + i_2$$

and the voltage drop across R_k is

$$e_k = R_k(2I_o + 2B_o + 2B_2 \cos 2\omega t - 2B_4 \cos 4\omega t + \cdots) \quad (11\text{-}30)$$

Here the even harmonics remain, and are of such phase as to produce negative feedback. If the tubes or transistors are not matched, the odd harmonics will be only partially suppressed, and the odd-harmonic drop across R_k will produce positive feedback and increase the distortion. Since dynamically matched tubes or transistors are not usual, it is advisable to employ a cathode or emitter bypass capacitor.

Using the bypass capacitor, the bias voltage is

$$E_{cc} = (2I_o + 2B_o)R_k$$

Since B_o is a function of signal amplitude, the Q point will be fixed only if B_o is small with respect to I_o. This condition is satisfied in Class A operation, and the bias will be constant at the value $2I_oR_k$. In Class AB, the second harmonic and B_o increase due to operation into the curved characteristics. The plate current swing and power output must then be limited when using cathode bias, to prevent distortion due to shift of the Q point. Fixed bias permits normal output.

Since the circuit reduces nonlinearity and distortion, it is interesting to examine an equivalent circuit derived from the usual linear tube equivalents, as in Fig. 11-12. The equivalent generators are in series, and since the loads are equal, the circuit partakes of the form of a bridge, and the line connecting the generator mid-points and the load may be removed, giving Fig. 11-12(b). The power output may be written for the circuit as

$$P = \left[\frac{2\mu E_g}{2r_p + (2N/N_2)^2 R}\right]^2 \left(\frac{2N}{N_2}\right)^2 R \quad (11\text{-}31)$$

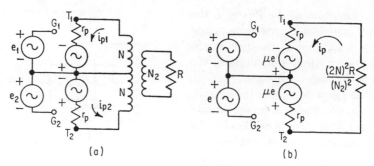

Fig. 11–12. Derivation of the equivalent circuit for the push-pull amplifier.

Examination of this equation shows that maximum power output would be obtained with a reflected load equal to $2r_p$. Experiment shows that permissible loads, based on distortion considerations, do approximate this value. This matching of loads, in combination with the linearization produced by the push-pull connection, allows greater power output from given devices with decreased distortion.

Unfortunately, for pentodes or beam tubes a matched load will be too large from the standpoint of odd-harmonic generation caused by operating around the knee of the curves, and lower loads will be found necessary for low distortion.

11–8. The Class AB push-pull amplifier

By further increasing the Q-point bias and raising the anode or collector voltage, keeping the dissipation at the rated value, the load line becomes longer or larger output voltage swings are possible, with further power increases resulting. The tubes or transistors may be cut off for portions of the input cycle, but the even-harmonic distortion so generated is canceled by the push-pull connection. Such extended operation is described as Class AB.

Particularly for vacuum tube operation, the subscript 1 is used, as in Class AB_1, to indicate that no grid current flows at any time in the cycle. For even greater output, larger input swings may be used; the designation AB_2 indicates that grid current flows at the peaks of the input cycle. The driving amplifier then is called upon to furnish power to the grid circuits during the positive peaks and must have low impedance, if distortion of the input wave form is not to occur. The impedance of the driver reflected into the grid circuit can be reduced if a step-down transformer is used to the grids of the Class AB_2 tubes. The transformer reduces the voltage by the turns ratio, but it reduces the reflected impedance by the square of the turns ratio.

11-9. The Class B push-pull amplifier

If the bias be increased to approximate cutoff, the operation changes
to Class B. Because of the increased length of upward swing possible on
the load line, higher power output is obtained than is possible for Class
A or AB operation. The negative half cycle is completely cut off, but the
even-harmonic distortion created is again canceled by the push-pull
connection of the amplifier.

Operation of the Class B push-pull amplifier may be explained by
reference to Fig. 11-13. The dynamic input-output characteristic of tube
B has been plotted upside down to show the subtractive nature of the
relationship. The value of bias obtained by extending the linear portion
of the dynamic curve to the zero axis is called the *extended-cutoff* voltage.
The composite transfer characteristic is then drawn by adding algebrai-
cally the current values at each input voltage. The result will be nearly
linear for most tubes or transistors.

Application of a sinusoidal input in push-pull to the two tubes, A and
B, causes tube A to conduct on the positive half of the input cycle, and

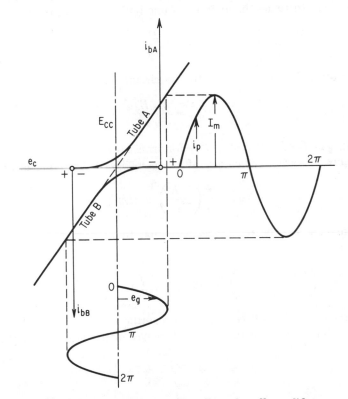

Fig. 11-13. Operation of Class B push-pull amplifier.

tube B to conduct on the negative half. Since the composite transfer characteristic is linear, the current pulses will be sinusoidal in shape; the output current wave, being the sum of the two pulses, will appear as the original sinusoidal input.

The linearity of the composite transfer curve permits drawing an analogy between the tube or transistor operating in Class B and a linear diode rectifier. By utilizing the current relationships developed in Chapter 5, it can be seen that the alternating value of the output current wave of Fig. 11–13 is

$$I_{\mathrm{rms}} = \frac{I_m}{\sqrt{2}}$$

The total a-c power output then is

$$P_o = \frac{I_m^2 R'}{2} \tag{11–32}$$

where R' is the reflected per-tube or per-transistor load (one-fourth the load reflected to the primary of the transformer). The total d-c current input is equal to twice the average of one half sine wave, then

$$I_{\mathrm{d-c}} = \frac{2I_m}{\pi}$$

and the total d-c power input to the circuit is

$$P_{\mathrm{d-c}} = \frac{2I_m E_{\mathrm{d-c}}}{\pi} \tag{11–33}$$

where $E_{\mathrm{d-c}}$ is E_{bb} for tubes or E_{CC} for transistors.

The output-circuit efficiency of a linear Class B amplifier is then

$$\eta_p = \frac{\pi}{4} \left(\frac{I_m R'}{E_{\mathrm{d-c}}} \right) \times 100\%$$

The term $I_m R'$ can be recognized as equal to $(E_{\mathrm{d-c}} - E_{\min})$ or $(E_{\max} - E_{\mathrm{d-c}})$. So

$$\eta_p = \frac{\pi}{4} \left(\frac{E_{\mathrm{d-c}} - E_{\min}}{E_{\mathrm{d-c}}} \right) \times 100\% = \frac{\pi}{4} \left(1 - \frac{E_{\min}}{E_{\mathrm{d-c}}} \right) \times 100\% \tag{11–34}$$

The minimum value of $E_{\min}$ is zero regardless of size of load, and consequently the maximum *theoretical* efficiency of a Class B amplifier is

$$\eta_p = \frac{\pi}{4} \times 100\% = 78.5\%$$

This is a notable increase over the efficiency possible for Class A amplifiers, and is responsible for the widespread use of Class B push-pull operation for high-power output.

From the relations above, it is possible to write the a-c power output in terms of the direct-current input as

$$P_o = \frac{\pi^2 I_{\text{d-c}}^2 R'}{8} \tag{11-35}$$

where $I_{\text{d-c}}$ is again the total current taken from the source. If the a-c output is small, the input d-c power is likewise reduced, and this accounts for the high efficiency of the Class B amplifier. Since the power input is large only for large signals, the power output and dissipation must be calculated for maximum signal, rather than for zero signal as in a Class A amplifier. The peak loss which will determine the dissipation rating required will occur for outputs near or at the maximum.

To avoid the necessity of a fixed supply for biasing normal power triodes to cutoff, tubes that operate at extended cutoff with zero bias voltage have been designed for Class B service. This implies that a signal will drive the grid positive during the whole of its half cycle; grid current flows over the whole cycle and provides a much more constant load for the driver amplifier than is possible when grid current flows only in pulses at the peaks of the cycle. An extended linear region and relatively sharp cutoff have also been designed into the dynamic characteristic of zero-bias tubes. The linearity of the dynamic curve is necessary, since with only one tube operating at a time, distortion due to nonlinearity in one tube cannot be canceled by nonlinear distortion in the other tube except near cutoff, where the composite curve differs from the dynamic curves.

Since Class B conditions allow greater power output for a given dissipation rating, its use with transistors is especially attractive. The analysis can be carried somewhat further and the collector dissipation for both transistors written as

$$P_d = \frac{2 I_m E_{CC}}{\pi} - \frac{I_m^2 R'}{2} \tag{11-36}$$

Taking the derivative with respect to I_m and setting the result to zero establishes a condition for maximum collector loss as

$$I_m = \frac{2}{\pi} \frac{E_{CC}}{R'}$$

There will be a theoretical limit to the collector current given by $I_m' = E_{CC}/R'$,

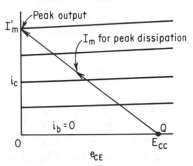

Fig. 11–14. Demonstrating ideal conditions for peak dissipation and peak output.

as shown in Fig. 11–14. The signal giving maximum loss is therefore that which produces a swing I_m related to this theoretical I'_m as

$$\frac{I_m}{I'_m} = \frac{2}{\pi} = 0.637$$

and the load line relations are indicated in the figure.

The maximum dissipation will then be given by

$$P_d = \frac{2}{\pi^2} \frac{E_{CC}^2}{R'} = 0.20 \frac{E_{CC}^2}{R'} \tag{11–37}$$

at a total d-c current value of

$$I_{\text{d-c}} = \frac{4}{\pi^2} \frac{E_{CC}}{R'} = 0.41 \frac{E_{CC}}{R'} \tag{11–38}$$

The efficiency at maximum loss will be 50 per cent. Using these relations, it is possible to select a transistor with a suitable loss rating for a given output.

A typical transistor Class B anplifier, driven by a pair of emitter-follower stages, is shown in Fig. 11–15. The emitter follower provides a low input resistance to the Class B base circuits, and permits direct coupling, thereby avoiding problems associated with coupling capacitors.

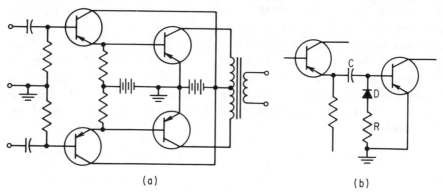

(a)   (b)

Fig. 11–15. Class B push-pull amplifier and driver.

In Fig. 11–15(b) is shown a portion of the driving circuit. The asymmetrical base current taken by one of the Class B transistors in Fig. 11–15(a) causes a d-c voltage component to appear across C, thereby upsetting the base bias. The diode and R provide a circuit which gives a symmetrical load on the driver stage, and also provides a constant load into which the emitter follower works, reducing loading distortion.

11-10. Crossover distortion

Transistor characteristics are not ideal, and if operated exactly at cutoff in Class B, they will introduce *crossover distortion*, due to the non-linear transfer curve near zero current. For small input signals neither Class B transistor will produce an output. As the signal gets larger, current flows only near the peak of the input cycle, and the output wave form has the shape indicated in Fig. 11–16. For very large signals the effect may become minimal.

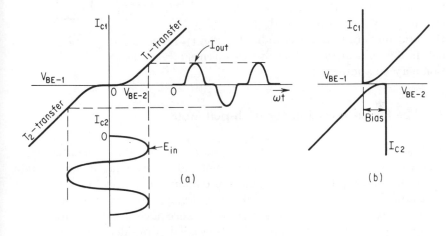

Fig. 11–16. Cross-over distortion.

The same problem arises in over-biased Class B tube amplifiers, and is avoided by the use of extended cutoff bias. In order to produce the same sort of linear composite transfer curve achieved by use of extended cutoff with tubes, Class B transistors are usually given a small forward bias, resulting in a shift of the transfer curves as in Fig. 11–16(b). The result is a more linear output relation.

11-11. Transistor amplifiers with complementary types

The requirement for equal input voltages of opposite phase in push-pull amplifiers can be eliminated by use of a selected pair of transistors, an *NPN* and a *PNP*, or complementary types. For such a combination, as in Fig. 11–17, a signal of one polarity will simultaneously drive the base of one unit into the operating region and the base of the second unit beyond cutoff. Thus a common input will give Class B performance. The need for center-tapped transformers is removed, and loads of suitable impedance may be directly connected without a transformer.

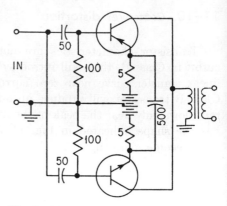

Matched power transistors intended for complementary symmetry service are available. It should be noted that their characteristics may not be perfectly matched over the entire dynamic range, and Class B operation does not cancel individual unit nonlinearities; thus distortion may be appreciable.

Fig. 11–17. Push-pull operation by complementary symmetry.

11–12. Phase inversion for push-pull input

Except for the case of complementary symmetry with transistors, it is necessary to have two equal voltages in 180° phase relation as the input for push-pull amplifiers, and circuits producing such voltages are known as *phase inverters*. Center-tapped transformers are usual in transistor circuits, but are avoided in tube service, because of cost and poor frequency response at the high impedance levels needed. Consideration will therefore be given to the tube types of circuits, but the similarity to the transistor circuits is apparent, and similar analysis is possible.

Most circuits can be classified as either *phase-splitting* or *phase-reversing*, and may differ in performance from the ideal, which would preserve exact voltage balance and phase opposition over a desired frequency range. A widely used phase reverser is shown in Fig. 11–18. Input E_s is supplied directly to tube T_1, with input to T_2 supplied by the voltage drop across the cathode resistor R_k. The grid voltages are

$$\mathbf{E}_{g1} = E_s - (I_1 - I_2) R_k$$

$$\mathbf{E}_{g2} = - (I_1 - I_2) R_k$$

The two tubes are identical, and usually $R_1 = R_2$, but the output voltages $\mathbf{E}_1$ and $\mathbf{E}_2$ will not be equal in magnitude because of the indicated inequality of inputs. The output voltages will be in the ratio

$$\frac{\mathbf{E}_1}{\mathbf{E}_2} = \frac{[r_p + R_2 + (\mu + 1) R_k] R_1}{(\mu + 1) R_k R_2} \tag{11–39}$$

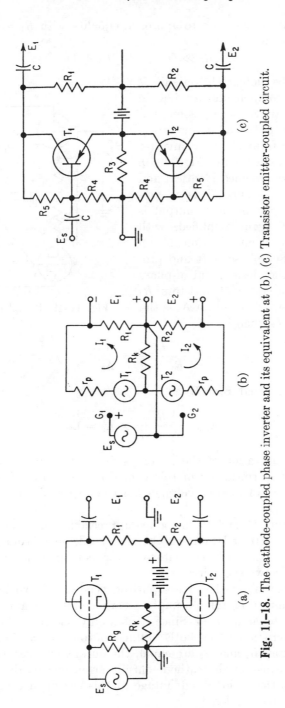

(c)

(b)

(a)

Fig. 11-18. The cathode-coupled phase inverter and its equivalent at (b). (c) Transistor emitter-coupled circuit.

If the output voltages are to approach equality with $R_1 = R_2$, then it is necessary to make

$$R_k \gg (r_p + R_2)/(\mu + 1) \qquad (11\text{–}40)$$

which can be done. The circuit is simple and components are low in cost, but with $R_1 = R_2$ some unbalance of outputs may occur.

A second form of phase inverter is the *paraphase* circuit of Fig. 11–19. The tubes are assumed identical and $R_1 + R_2 = R_3$. Tube T_1 is an amplifier, but a portion of its output is selected and again amplified, with the consequent introduction of an additional 180° phase shift and production of the desired out-of-phase voltages. The ratio of resistors R_1 and R_2 is selected so that if $\mathbf{A}_2$ is the gain of tube T_2, then

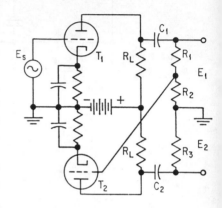

Fig. 11–19. Paraphase inverter.

$$\frac{R_2}{R_1 + R_2} = \frac{1}{\mathbf{A}_2} \qquad (11\text{–}41)$$

with the result that $\mathbf{E}_1 = \mathbf{E}_2$ as

$$\mathbf{E}_1 \times \frac{R_2}{R_1 + R_2} \times \mathbf{A}_2 = \mathbf{E}_2$$

Balanced operation of the circuit is predicated upon a knowledge of the gain $\mathbf{A}_2$ and constancy of this gain throughout the life of the tube. Some unbalance of the two voltages must be expected if the gain changes in tube T_2.

If capacitors C_1 and C_2 introduce appreciable phase shift at low frequencies, the 180° relation will be disturbed, since voltage $\mathbf{E}_1$ passes through only one such capacitor-resistor combination, whereas $\mathbf{E}_2$ is acted upon by two such circuits.

Phase inverters of the phase-splitting type are shown in Fig. 11–20. For the vacuum tube this is simply a cathode-follower amplifier with an additional plate-circuit load. Since it uses only one tube, any changes in tube characteristics affect both voltage outputs in a similar manner; thus, if resistors R_1 and R_2 are equal, the output voltages will always be balanced. Because of the cathode-output arrangement, the gain will be small; this is the major disadvantage of this circuit in comparison with those previously considered.

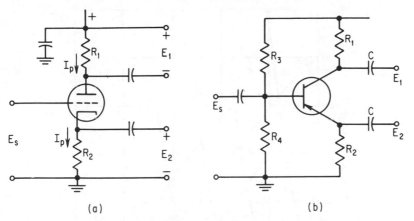

Fig. 11–20. Split-load forms of phase inverters.

The gain for either output can be computed as

$$A = \frac{E_1}{E_s} = \frac{\mu R_1}{r_p + R_1 + (\mu + 1) R_2} \qquad (11\text{–}42)$$

If $R_1 = R_2$, the outputs are inherently balanced. It is apparent that degenerative feedback with $\beta = 0.5$ is present in this circuit, and consequently the gain stability is high.

11–13. Amplifiers with reactive loads

All analyses of large-signal amplifiers have so far been made with resistive loads. As shown below, it is desirable to avoid reactive loads because of potential large-signal distortion, but transformer reactances in portions of a frequency range may be unavoidable. Owing to the angle between current and voltage in reactive loads, the plate current does not have the same value for increasing plate voltages that it has for decreasing voltages; and the load line, when plotted, becomes some form of ellipse, varying from the straight line for purely resistive loads to a circle for purely reactive loads.

A reactive load decreases the permissible grid-signal voltage, since the elliptical load line may carry the operating point into the region of low plate current and thereby introduce distortion. This effect is illustrated for the large grid voltage used in drawing the load line in Fig. 11–21. This elliptical load line is drawn for a load of $3200 + j2400$ ohms, the grid-signal voltage being 40 v peak. No method exists, except a laborious point-by-point plot of the wave form, by which an analysis for distortion may be made when operation is in the nonlinear region of the tube characteristics with a reactive load.

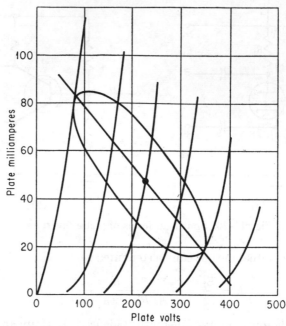

Fig. 11–21. Load line for a reactive load on an amplifier.

That the curve is an ellipse for a reactive load is shown by the fact that load circuit voltage and current expressions are, respectively

$$e_o = E_o \sin \omega t$$

and

$$i_p = I_m \sin (\omega t + \Phi)$$

These constitute the parametric equations of an ellipse.

Problems

11-1. (a) Determine the value of load to be used with a 2A3 tube operating in the circuit of Fig. 11-22, if the power output is to be the greatest obtainable under Class A conditions and distortion is to be less than 8 per cent. The Q point is to be at $E_{cc} = -50$, $I_b = 50$ ma, and L is large.

(b) If L has a resistance of 1000 ohms, what value of E_{bb} must be used?

(c) Plot curves of power output and per cent distortion against load.

Note: Try load lines for values of $R_L = 1000, 1500, 2000, 3000,$ and 5000 ohms.

11-2. A 6L6 tube in the circuit of Fig. 11-23, with transformer ratio $N_1/N_2 = 10$, is operated at $E_{bb} = 250$ v, $E_{cc} = -12$ v, and $E_{c2} = 250$ v, with $R_L = 20$ ohms. Find the fundamental power output, plate-circuit efficiency, per cent second and third harmonic, with an input of 10 v peak value.

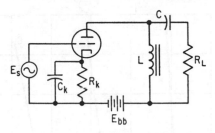

Fig. 11–22.

11-3. (a) Find the fundamental power output, plate-circuit efficiency, and plate dissipation for a 2A3 tube operating with $E_b = 200$ v, and $E_{cc} = -30$ v, $E_s = 25$ v peak, with a series load of 3000 ohms.

(b) Find the value of E_{bb} needed to supply the circuit of (a).

(c) Repeat (a) and (b) if the load is shunt-fed through a choke of zero d-c resistance.

11-4. (a) A 6L6 tube is used in the circuit of Fig. 11-23. If R_L is 10 ohms, find the reflected primary load and transformer turns ratio required to obtain maximum possible power output with less than 10 per cent total second- and third-harmonic distortion. The voltage E_{bb} is 250, screen voltage is 250, I_b is to be 65 ma, and $I_{min} = 10$ ma.

(b) Plot curves of power output, and per cent total distortion against reflected primary load.

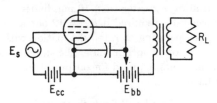

Fig. 11–23.

11-5. The transistor whose characteristics appear in Fig. 11-24 is to be operated in the common-emitter circuit at $V_{CE} = 30$ v, $I_B = 4$ ma. The maximum collector voltage rating is 60 v. Plot power output, second- and third-harmonic distortion in per cent against load.

11-6. Using a 6L6 tube in the circuit of Fig. 11-23, with $E_{cc} = -20$ v, $E_{bb} = 250$, $E_{c2} = 250$, and $R_L = 500$ ohms, and assuming that the transformer is ideal and that the tube is to work into a load of 7000 ohms with $E_s = 5.3$ rms, 1000 cycles, find from the characteristics:

(a) I_b flowing.

(b) Transformer turns ratio required.

(c) Fundamental power output.

(d) Plate-circuit efficiency.

(e) Per cent total second and third harmonics.

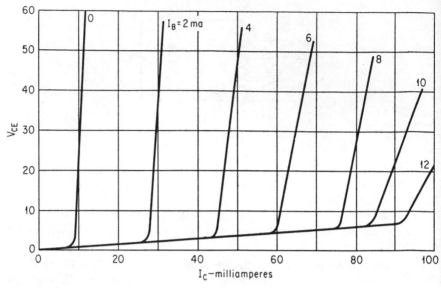

Fig. 11–24.

11-7. The 6L6 has a rated plate dissipation of 19 w. Using the tube in the circuit of Fig. 11-23 with an effective primary load of 4000 ohms with $E_{bb} = 350$ and $E_{c2} = 250$ v, and assuming that the transformer is ideal, the grid is never positive, and the plate current is always greater than 10 ma, find:

    (a) Transformer turns ratio required if $R_L = 12$ ohms.

    (b) Q point with tube operating at rated dissipation with zero signal.

    (c) Maximum possible power output under the stated conditions.

    (d) Value of E_s in rms volts required for output of (c).

    (e) Per cent total harmonics.

11-8. One half of a 12AX7 and a 6L6 are to be used in a two-stage amplifier to supply 7.5 w to a 10-ohm load. A 250-v plate supply is available, and cathode bias is to be used on both tubes. The first stage is resistance-coupled to the 6L6, and the operating frequency range is to be 100 to 5000 cycles.

Design the complete circuit for high efficiency and low amplitude and frequency distortion. The input signal required is to be 0.5 v or less.

11-9. Determine the value of all coefficients of the harmonic series up to A_7, in terms of $I_{max}, I_x, I_y, I_r, I_s, I'_r,$ and I'_s, where I_r and I_s are taken at points of one-third and two-thirds peak voltage, respectively, and I'_r and I'_s are the corresponding values for negative input voltage.

11-10. For the transistor of Fig. 11-6, with a Q point at $I_B = 60$ ma, $V_{CE} = 30$ v, select sufficient load lines to plot a curve of power output against load resistance, and determine that load giving the maximum power output without driving I_B below 20 ma. Compute the efficiency, and second- and third-harmonic percentages for the load giving maximum power.

11-11. For the load found in Problem 11-10, determine the db power gain and find the base bias conditions needed.

11-12. Prove the statement following Eq. 11-30 that the cathode-bias voltage drop will have even-harmonic voltage components that will produce negative feedback.

11-13. Two transistors of the type of Fig. 11-6 are used in push-pull. With $V_{CE} = 25$ v, $I_B = 60$ ma, determine the load (collector-to-collector) giving maximum power output.

11-14. A certain triode tube may be considered as having linear characteristics expressed by

$$i_b = 0.003(5e_c + e_b) \text{ amp}$$

(a) For Class A operation, $E_b = 300$ v, $E_c = -30$ v, find power output, efficiency, and d-c power input for a signal of 30 v peak, and load of 500 ohms.
(b) Find value of load giving maximum power output under conditions of (a).

11-15. A push-pull tube circuit is operating Class B with a plate-to-plate load of 5000 ohms. The d-c milliammeter in the common anode circuit reads 212 ma for a steady sinusoidal signal. What is the a-c power output? If the anode-voltage supply is 1560, what are the plate-circuit efficiency and plate dissipation?

11-16. A pair of 6L6 tubes is to supply 8 w to a loudspeaker of 16 ohms resistance. The push-pull stage is to be driven by a phase-splitting, cathode-anode-output type of phase inverter. The plate supply for all tubes is 250 v. Design the complete circuit, giving all values of circuit constants, and specify the grid driving voltage required for the phase inverter if it uses a 12AX7 tube.

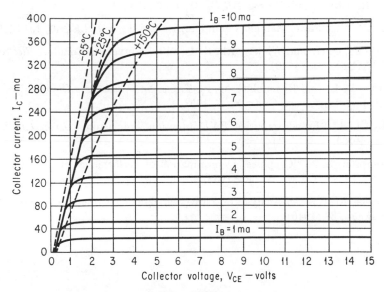

Fig. 11–25.

11-17. A transistor of the type of Fig. 11-24 is operated with a load of $20 + j30$ ohms, with $E_{CC} = 30$ v and $I_B = 4$ ma. For a peak input current of 2 ma, plot the load-line diagram.

11-18. Using the transistor of Fig. 11-25, calculate the maximum power output in Class A for a transformer-connected load of 20 ohms, with $V_{CE} = 8$ v. At the operating point the collector current is 120 ma.

11-19. Determine the per cent second harmonic when the transistor of Problem 11-18 is driven by a sine signal of 4 ma peak, around the specified Q point, and with $R_L = 50$ ohms, transformer-coupled.

11-20. Two transistors having the characteristics of Fig. 11-25 are used in a Class B push-pull circuit with $V_{CC} = 12$ v, $R' = 20$ ohms, $i_{B \text{ max}} = 10$ ma. Determine the power output, the input power, and the required collector dissipation rating for the transistors.

References

1. Armstrong, L. D., and Jenny, D. A., "Behavior of Germanium Junction Transistors at Elevated Temperatures and Power Transistor Design," *Convention Record, I.R.E.*, Part 6, 22 (1953).

2. Ebers, J. J., and Moll, J. L., "Large Signal Behavior of Junction Transistors," *Proc. I.R.E.*, **42**, 1761 (1954).

3. Espley, D. C., "The Calculation of Harmonic Production in Thermionic Valves with Resistive Loads," *Proc. I.R.E.*, **21**, 1439 (1933).

4. Hall, R. N., "Power Rectifiers and Transistors," *Proc. I.R.E.*, **40**, 1512 (1952).

5. McProud, C. G., and Wildermuth, R. T., "Phase Inverter Circuits," *Electronics*, **13**, 47 (December 1940).

6. Riddle, R. L., and Ristenblatt, M. P., *Transistor Physics and Circuits*. Prentice-Hall, Inc., Englewood Cliffs, N. J., 1958.

7. Saby, J. S., "Fused Impurity *PNP* Junction Transistors," *Proc. I.R.E.*, **40**, 1358 (1952).

8. Thompson, B. J., "Graphical Determination of Performance of Push-Pull Amplifiers," *Proc. I.R.E.*, **21**, 591 (1933).

9. Wheeler, M. S., "An Analysis of Three Self-Balancing Phase Inverters," *Proc. I.R.E.*, **34**, 67 (1946).

Resonant-Load Amplifiers with Large Signals | 12

Large signal radio-frequency amplifiers are employed with resonant load circuits in the generation of power for the transmission of radio signals and for industrial purposes. To obtain high power efficiency and high power output, operation is usually in the Class B or C modes. The resultant wave form distortion can be reduced by resonant filters, if desired.

In such operation, d-c power is converted to radio-frequency power by tubes or transistors acting as synchronous switches; d-c power is supplied in pulses to a resonant load circuit, in synchronism with the voltage across the load. After supplying a pulse of energy to the load, the switch disconnects the source and load, and the energy stored in the load continues in free oscillation. This action is frequently compared with that of supplying pulses of energy to a pendulum, the pendulum swinging free at its own rate for most of its cycle.

Transistors as yet have not been developed for very large power output, and so analysis will here be carried out largely as related to the tube. The methods are general, however, and can be applied to the transistor whenever desirable.

12–1. Class C operation

All Class B and C amplifiers operate with discontinuous current, and a method of analysis is necessary which allows for an arbitrary angle of conduction in each cycle. It is usual to operate a radio-frequency power amplifier with a resonant load circuit, as in Fig. 12–1. The resistance R is coupled

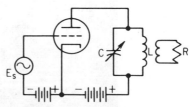

Fig. 12–1. Power amplifier with resonant load.

into the circuit inductively, and represents the output load. The resonant circuit will also act as a filter which responds only to the desired band of frequencies. It will be assumed that this circuit is resonant at the frequency of the input source, E_s.

The bias voltage will ordinarily be set to two or more times the cutoff value for Class C operation. The input signal E_s should be of sufficient amplitude to drive the grid considerably positive on the positive peak. The action as a synchronous switch is then illustrated in Figs. 12–2 and 12–3.

It is assumed that the circuit has been in operation for a time such that the LC circuit has stored energy and is developing a sinusoidal voltage in series with the anode source E_{bb}. The anode voltage will then appear as e_b, oscillating from some high value due to $E_{bb} + \hat{E}_L$, where $\hat{E}_L$ is the peak of the load voltage, to some minimum value, $E_{bb} - \hat{E}_L$. The dashed cutoff line may then be drawn as $- e_b/\mu$. As the grid input, e_c, rises above

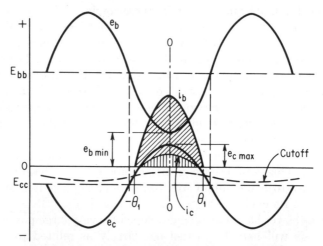

Fig. 12–2. Synchronous switch operation with resonant load.

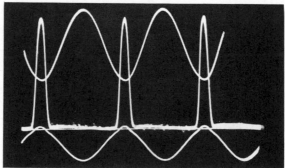

Fig. 12–3. Current and voltage relations in a Class C amplifier.

the cutoff line at an angle shown as $-\theta_1$, the tube conducts and connects the source and load, and current flows. When e_c crosses the zero voltage line and goes positive at an angle $-\theta_2$, a current i_c begins to the grid. Both anode and grid currents reach maximum at the time of most positive voltage, and, with a resonant or resistive load, the anode voltage will be minimum at that instant. During the latter half of the pulse, these events are repeated in reverse order, with the switch action disconnecting tube and load at angle θ_1.

Wave forms may be as shown, although if current saturation had been reached at the peak of the input pulse, the anode current wave would have been flattened, as a result of attraction to anode or grid of all electrons emitted from the cathode. In the case of the transistor, this situation would be reached at collector saturation. Thus it is not inherent that the shape of the current pulse should bear any particular relation to the wave shape of the input voltage.

The switch connects the d-c source to the oscillatory circuit only for a short interval of length $2\theta_1$. In this interval sufficient energy must be supplied to the resonant circuit to replenish all losses and power output, and to keep the circuit in oscillation until the next cycle of input power.

The power lost in the tube is $e_b i_b$, on an instantaneous basis. The losses may be reduced, or the efficiency raised, by (1) increasing the bias and driving voltages, thereby shortening the current pulse, or (2) decreasing the minimum anode voltage by increase of load impedance. Although application of (1) is feasible, it may force the tube or transistor into saturation without gain in output, or it will increase the driving power requirement, since the grid current will then flow at an increased value of a-c grid voltage. Method (2) is also possible, but it is found that if the minimum anode voltage falls below the maximum grid voltage, the grid current rises rapidly; if saturation is then reached, the more positive grid robs the anode of electrons, reducing the anode current and cutting power output.

It is usually found that maximum output occurs near the condition of equality between minimum anode voltage and maximum grid voltage.

12–2. Current and voltage wave forms in Class C operation

When an attempt is made to choose Class C operating conditions, it is found that the following variables must be specified: d-c anode voltage, load impedance, grid bias, and the a-c input or driving voltage. The dependent variables, θ_1, and the anode loss, are not directly determinable. Only the maximum anode loss and the maximum anode voltage are fixed by the tube ratings.

Because of the discontinuous nature of conduction, the study of Class C performance must be bassed on a knowledge of the wave forms of the current pulses. In Fig. 12–2 it can be seen that anode current is cut off until the grid voltage, expressed as

$$e_c = E_{cc} + \hat{E}_g \cos \theta \qquad (12\text{–}1)$$

equals cutoff. In this relation $\hat{E}_g$ represents the peak value of the a-c grid-voltage wave. The cosine wave is chosen for the symmetry which it contributes.

The anode current then flows for an angle of conduction $2\theta_1$, less than 180°. The plate voltage is expressible as

$$e_b = E_{bb} - \hat{I}_1 R_L \cos \theta \qquad (12\text{–}2)$$

where R_L is the resonant impedance of the tuned circuit load, and I_1 is the peak value of the fundamental component of anode current. For triodes the cutoff voltage is $e_c = -e_b/\mu$, and the above relations allow computation of the bias which, for a given input voltage, will produce anode current cutoff at a desired angle θ_1 as

$$E_{cc} = -\frac{E_{bb}}{\mu} - \left(\hat{E}_g - \frac{\hat{I}_1 R_L}{\mu} \right) \cos \theta_1 \qquad (12\text{–}3)$$

The term $\hat{I}_1 R_L$ is recognizable as $\hat{E}_o$. It is thus possible to control the conduction angle.

The analysis will be made in terms of a triode, but is equally applicable to beam tubes and pentodes. It should be noted that cutoff for such tubes is determined by $-E_{c2}/\mu_2$, where μ_2 is the grid-screen amplification factor.

It is possible to employ the *constant-current* curves, as in Fig. 12–4, to obtain instantaneous values of grid and anode currents. Wave forms of these currents may be plotted, although the current values may be used directly to calculate performance data.

Equation 12–1 may be solved for $\cos \theta$, and used in Eq. 12–2 to give

$$e_b = E_{bb} + \frac{E_{cc}\hat{E}_o}{\hat{E}_g} - \frac{\hat{E}_o}{\hat{E}_g} e_c \qquad (12\text{–}4)$$

Since $\hat{E}_o$ and $\hat{E}_g$ are peak values and E_{bb} and E_{cc} are constants, this relation between instantaneous anode and grid voltages is represented by a straight line. Thus the operation line of Fig. 12–4 would be fixed by two points of tube operation, or drawn with a slope equal to $-\hat{E}_o/\hat{E}_g$.

A Q point may then be chosen as one point on the operation line. For the example, this may be selected at 2000 anode volts, -370 v bias as twice cutoff, as indicated on the two-times-cutoff locus. A higher bias value might lead to higher efficiency; this is a design variable subject to experiment.

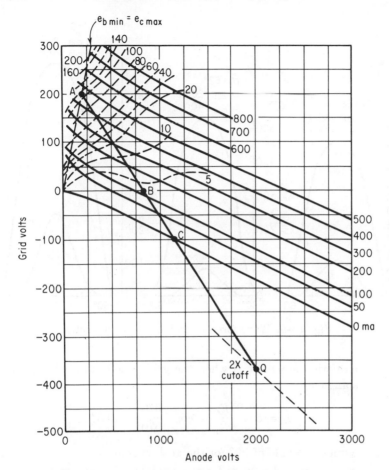

Fig. 12–4. Constant-current curves. Solid, i_b; dashed, i_c.

A second point on the operation line may be taken as the point of equality of maximum grid voltage and minimum anode voltage. To demonstrate the method, take $e_{g\,max} = e_{b\,min} = +200$ v and mark this as A. Criteria for the selection of this value will be discussed later. The operation line is then drawn between A and Q, the line containing all pairs of e_c and e_b operating values. The selection of A has fixed $\hat{E}_g = 570$ v and $\hat{E}_o = 2000 - 200 = 1800$ v. Noting point C at zero plate current, it can be seen that the anode current pulse starts when the anode voltage reaches 1150 v, or when $\hat{E}_o \cos \theta_1 = 2000 - 1150 = 850$ v. The half angle of conduction is then

$$\theta_1 = \cos^{-1} \frac{850}{1800} = 62°$$

and the full anode pulse length will be 124°.

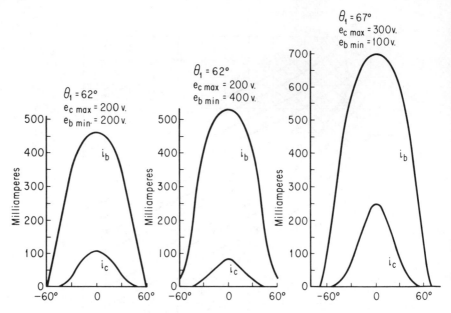

Fig. 12–5. Wave forms of grid and plate current.

Grid conduction starts at B when the grid is zero and going positive. Calling this angle θ_2

$$\theta_2 = \cos^{-1}\frac{E_{cc}}{\hat{E}_g} = \cos^{-1}\frac{370}{570} = 49.5°$$

giving a conduction angle of 99° for the grid current.

Values of current and voltage for any angle can be read from the operating line by laying off points corresponding to values of $\hat{E}_o \cos\theta$, for desired increments of θ. Taking intervals of 10° provides the data of Table 19, with the wave forms plotted in Fig. 12–5.

Operation lines for two other sets of $e_{b\,\min}$ and $e_{c\,\max}$ have been used to obtain Fig. 12–5(b) and (c). The curves of Fig. 12–5(c) indicate the broadened character of the anode wave, and the peaked grid current expected when the maximum grid voltage exceeds the minimum anode voltage. The result is an increase in anode loss, since high values of anode current occur at voltages well above the minimum. The driving power also rises as a result of the large values of grid current.

By graphical integration it is possible to compute the average values of i_b and i_c, from which the anode and grid power inputs can be found; the trapezoidal rule is applicable to the situation. If the base of an area under a curve $y = f(x)$ be divided, between a and b, into intervals of

TABLE 19. DATA FROM OPERATION LINE OF FIG. 12–4

$$\mu = 11 \qquad e_{b\ min} = 200 \text{ v}$$
$$E_{bb} = 2000 \text{ v} \qquad e_{c\ max} = 200 \text{ v}$$
$$E_{cc} = -370 \text{ v} \qquad \hat{E}_{g} = 570 \text{ v}$$

θ	0°	10°	20°	30°	40°	50°	60°	63°
$\cos \theta$	1.00	0.985	0.940	0.866	0.766	0.643	0.500	0.342
$\hat{E}_{o} \cos \theta$	1800	1770	1690	1560	1380	1160	900	610
$E_{bb} - \hat{E}_{o} \cos \theta$	200	230	310	440	620	840	1100	1190
i_b, ma	460	450	415	350	230	120	10	0
i_c, ma	110	95	75	35	10	0	0	0

uniform length Δx, then

$$\int_{a}^{b} y \, dx = \Delta x \left(\frac{y_0}{2} + y_1 + y_2 + \cdots + y_{n-1} + \frac{y_n}{2} \right) \qquad (12\text{--}5)$$

If 10° intervals are taken, then $\Delta x = \pi/18$ radians. Since

$$I_b = \frac{1}{2\pi} \int_{-\pi}^{\pi} i_b \, d\theta$$

with y_0 taken for $\theta = 0°$, and $y_n = 0$, the value of I_b becomes

$$I_b = 2 \times \frac{1}{2\pi} \times \frac{\pi}{18} \left(\frac{y_0}{2} + y_1 + y_2 + \cdots + y_{n-1} \right) \qquad (12\text{--}6)$$

The coefficient 2 is present because the current ordinates cover only one half of the conduction cycle under cosine symmetry.

A similar method may be used to arrive at the average value of the grid current, I_c.

It is also possible to employ a Fourier expansion to arrive at the peak value of the fundamental a-c component as

$$\hat{I}_1 = \frac{2}{\pi} \int_{0}^{\theta_1} i_b \cos \theta \, d\theta \qquad (12\text{--}7)$$

The integral is the area under a curve whose ordinates are expressed as $i_b \cos \theta$. If successive products of i_b and $\cos \theta$ are taken at 10° intervals, and if y_0' is the value of the product at 0°, y_1' at 10°, and so on, then

$$\hat{I}_1 = \frac{1}{9} \left[\frac{y_0'}{2} + y_1' + y_2' + \cdots + y_{n-1}' \right] \qquad (12\text{--}8)$$

Similar methods would also give the value of I_{g1}.

The results of such calculations from the data of Table 19 are presented in Table 20.

TABLE 20. CALCULATED VALUES FROM FIG. 12–5

	(a)	(b)	(c)
E_{bb}	2000 v	2000 v	2000 v
E_{cc}	−370 v	−370 v	−370 v
$e_{c\ max}$	+200 v	+200 v	+300 v
$e_{b\ min}$	+200 v	+400 v	+200 v
θ_1	62°	62.5°	67°
$\hat{E}_g$	570 v	570 v	670 v
$\hat{E}_o$	1800 v	1600 v	1800 v
I_b	100 ma	114 ma	174 ma
I_c	15 ma	11 ma	33 ma
$\hat{I}_1$	180 ma	206 ma	303 ma
$\hat{I}_{g1}$	28.5 ma	21 ma	65 ma

12–3. Power considerations in Class C amplifiers

On the assumption that the current components have been evaluated it is possible to determine certain power relationships. For instance, the power input to the circuit from the plate source is

$$P_{\text{in}} = E_{bb}I_b \tag{12–9}$$

and the power output to the load, with a tuned load of resonant resistive impedance R_L assumed, is

$$P_{\text{out}} = \frac{\hat{I}_1^2 R_L}{2} \tag{12–10}$$

for the fundamental component. The plate dissipation is then simply

$$P_d = P_{\text{in}} - P_{\text{out}}$$

and the plate-circuit efficiency is given by

$$\eta_p = \frac{\hat{I}_1^2 R_L}{2E_{bb}I_b} \times 100\% \tag{12–11}$$

In the grid circuit all power is supplied by the a-c driving-source generator E_s. Part of this power is used to *charge* the bias source, since the direct grid current is directed into the positive terminal. This power loss is

$$P_c = E_{cc}I_c \tag{12–12}$$

and if the bias is obtained from a grid leak, then

$$R_g = \frac{E_{cc}}{I_c}$$

The power input to both the grid and bias supply is

$$P_g = \frac{1}{2\pi} \int_{-\pi}^{\pi} i_c \hat{E}_g \cos\theta \, d\theta \qquad (12\text{–}13)$$

The pulse of grid current occurs during a very small portion of the cycle near the peak of the grid-voltage wave, so that during the pulse interval the value of cosine θ approximates unity. The above integral may then be simplified to

$$P_g = \frac{\hat{E}_g}{2\pi} \int_{-\pi}^{\pi} i_c \, d\theta$$

However

$$I_c = \frac{1}{2\pi} \int_{-\pi}^{\pi} i_c \, d\theta$$

and thus the power input to the grid circuit can be approximated as

$$P_g \cong \hat{E}_g I_c \qquad (12\text{–}14)$$

where I_c is the average or d-c value of grid current, which is ordinarily metered in such amplifiers. This approximation usually holds as a rough rule of thumb.

The power gain given by the tube is the ratio of a-c power output to a-c power input to the grid circuit, or

$$\text{Power Gain} \cong \frac{\hat{I}_1^2 R_L}{2 \hat{E}_g I_c} \qquad (12\text{–}15)$$

This is an important economic criterion of amplifier performance, since input power is expensive by reason of the amount of equipment needed to generate that power. Tetrodes and pentodes excel over triodes in this respect.

Since tubes are rated in terms of allowable internal losses, a slight improvement in efficiency may make a major addition to output. This relationship can be seen if the output be expressed as

$$P_{\text{out}} = \frac{\eta_p \times \text{dissipation}}{1 - \eta_p} \qquad (12\text{–}16)$$

Efficiency is therefore of prime importance.

Power calculations resulting from the three operating conditions of Table 20 are given in Table 21.

TABLE 21. POWER OUTPUT AND EFFICIENCY FROM FIG. 12–5

	(a)	(b)	(c)
I_b	100 ma	114 ma	174 ma
$\hat{E}_o$	1800 v	1600 v	1800 v
I_c	15 ma	11 ma	33 ma
$\hat{E}_g$	570 v	570 v	670 v
$\hat{I}_1$	180 ma	206 ma	303 ma
$\hat{I}_{g1}$	28.5 ma	21 ma	65 ma
R_L	10,000 ohms	7770 ohms	5940 ohms
Power input	200 w	228 w	348 w
Power output	162 w	165 w	272 w
Plate loss	38 w	63 w	76 w
η_p	81%	72.5%	78.5%
Grid driving power	8.5 w	6.3 w	22 w
θ_1	62°	62.5°	67°
θ_2	49.5°	49.5°	56.5°
Grid loss	3.0 w	2.2 w	9.9 w
Power gain	19.1	26.2	12.4

12–4. Optimum operating conditions

The results of the preceding section, though permitting calculation of Class C performance for assumed conditions, fail to answer the fundamental question: What values of load impedance, grid driving voltage, and bias will give maximum output for a given anode loss? To provide answers, a procedure based on the graphical methods of the preceding sections is ordinarily used.

With increase in excitation, the grid becomes more positive at its peak. If the maximum grid voltage exceeds the minimum anode voltage, the grid momentarily becomes the most positive electrode and the grid current rises abruptly. As a result the grid-excitation power increases, but the efficiency and plate current fail to increase in proportion to the increase in driving power. The effect on grid and plate currents of allowing the maximum grid voltage to exceed the minimum anode voltage is illustrated in Table 21, which confirms that equality of these voltages gives higher efficiency, and lower proportionate grid driving power, than when the amplifier is overdriven.

Thus when operating conditions are chosen as a preliminary to drawing an operating line, it is common practice to choose $e_{c\,\text{max}} = e_{b\,\text{min}}$. By selecting a Q point consistent with tube ratings and then locating a few points where this condition of equality holds on the long-dash locus in Fig. 12–4, a set of operating lines may be drawn. After running through a set of calculations as for Tables 19, 20, and 21, it should be possible to select desirable values of $\hat{E}_g$, R_L, and E_{cc} to give optimum performance.

12–5. The linear Class B amplifier

The amplifier of Fig. 12–6 can be adjusted to Class B conditions by bringing the bias voltage to cutoff. Under this bias the angle of anode current conduction is 180° and a definite performance analysis is possible, although the graphical methods of preceding sections can also be applied. If the tuned circuit has reasonably high Q (usually 10 or above) and if the

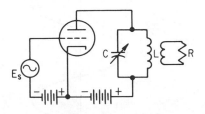

Fig. 12–6. The Class B amplifier with tuned load.

dynamic transfer characteristic is reasonably linear over the range of operation, the anode current pulses will approximate half-sinusoids, and the harmonic voltages across the resonant load circuit will be small.

In order to calculate performance in terms of power output, anode dissipation, efficiency, and desirable loads, Everitt (Ref. 1) has devised an analytical method based on the equation showing the anode current in a vacuum tube as functionally related to the electrode voltages. That is

$$i_b = f(\mu e_c + e_b)$$

Under an assumption that such a relationship is linear, the functional expression becomes

$$i_b = g_p(\mu e_c + e_b) + C \tag{12–17}$$

If a curve be drawn with cutoff at the origin, C is zero. From the relation that $\mu = g_m r_p$, the above becomes

$$i_b = g_m \left(e_c + \frac{e_b}{\mu}\right) \qquad i_b \geqq 0 \tag{12–18}$$

This relation between i_b and the composite voltage $e_c + e_b/\mu$ results in the straight line characteristic of Fig. 12–7, with slope given by g_m. The actual characteristic may be slightly curved near zero, but this curvature has negligible effect on the overall value of the current pulse. Effects of curvature of the characteristic due to saturation at the upper end of the curve can be neglected, since Class B operation is of a nature to avoid driving the grid positive to that extent, usually due to the requirements of linearity imposed.

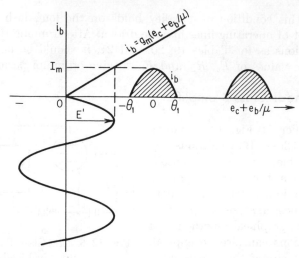

Fig. 12–7. The Class B amplifier with linear relation between i_b and $e_c + e_b/\mu$.

For all negative values of the composite voltage the current is zero. The load is tuned to the frequency of E_s, has resonant impedance R_L, and offers negligible impedance to all harmonics and to direct current. Applied to the linear characteristic of Fig. 12–7 is the composite voltage with peak of E', given by

$$E' = E_{cc} + \hat{E}_g + \frac{E_{bb} - \hat{I}_1 R_L}{\mu} \qquad (12\text{–}19)$$

where $\hat{E}_g$ and $\hat{I}_1$ are peak values of grid input voltage and fundamental frequency a-c plate current, as before. For Class B operation the bias will be adjusted to $E_{cc} = - E_{bb}/\mu$ and thus

$$E' = \hat{E}_g - \frac{\hat{I}_1 R_L}{\mu} \qquad (12\text{–}20)$$

This expresses the peak value of the composite voltage; written as a cosine function, the composite voltage is $e_c + e_b/\mu = E' \cos \theta$, and Eq. 12–18 becomes

$$i_b = g_m E' \cos \theta \qquad (12\text{–}21)$$

under the assumed Class B conditions, giving the pulses of Fig. 12–7.

Because of the linear assumption, the plate-current pulses will be half sinusoids. These pulses may be expressed in terms of a Fourier series as

$$i_b = I_b + \hat{I}_1 \cos \theta + \hat{I}_2 \cos 2\theta + \hat{I}_3 \cos 3\theta + \cdots \qquad (12\text{–}22)$$

By the usual methods the coefficient of the fundamental-frequency term may be found as

$$\hat{I}_1 = \frac{2}{\pi} \int_0^{\pi/2} i_b \cos\theta \, d\theta$$

in view of the symmetry of the cosine pulse.

Performing the integration, and using Eq. 12–20, it is possible to write

$$\hat{I}_1 = \frac{g_m E'}{2} = \frac{g_m \hat{E}_g}{2} \left(\frac{1}{1 + R_L/2r_p} \right) \tag{12–23}$$

This is the peak of the fundamental anode current component. The output voltage E_o in rms value is

$$E_o = \frac{g_m \hat{E}_g R_L}{2\sqrt{2}} \left(\frac{1}{1 + R_L/2r_p} \right) \tag{12–24}$$

The d-c component of anode current may be found by averaging the half-sine pulse over the full cycle, or

$$I_b = \frac{1}{2\pi} \int_0^{2\pi} i_b \, d\theta = \frac{g_m E'}{\pi} \int_0^{\pi/2} \cos\theta \, d\theta = \frac{g_m E'}{\pi} = \frac{g_m \hat{E}_g}{\pi} \left(\frac{1}{1 + R_L/2r_p} \right) \tag{12–25}$$

The average value of the anode current is proportional to the amplitude of the input signal voltage.

The power output to the load impedance R_L is

$$P_{\text{out}} = \frac{g_m^2 \hat{E}_g^2 R_L}{8} \left(\frac{1}{1 + R_L/2r_p} \right)^2 \tag{12–26}$$

Maximizing this expression shows that the greatest power output will be obtained if $R_L = 2r_p$. This may not necessarily be the load which will meet the linearity assumptions, however, as will be shown in the next section.

The power efficiency may be found by use of Eqs. 12–25 and 12–26, giving

$$\eta_p = \frac{E_o^2/R_L}{I_b E_{bb}} \times 100\% = \frac{\pi}{4} \frac{\sqrt{2} E_o}{E_{bb}} \times 100\% \tag{12–27}$$

The Class B linear amplifier with resonant load has a power efficiency which is proportional to the input signal, and approaches 78.5 per cent as $\sqrt{2} E_o$ or the peak voltage across the load approaches E_{bb}. Usual working values of efficiency are 55 to 65 per cent.

The plate loss is the difference between input and output, or

$$P_d = E_{bb}I_b - E_o^2/R_L = I_b \left(E_{bb} - \frac{\pi^2 I_b R_L}{8} \right) \quad (12\text{--}28)$$

Following Eq. 11–38 the anode loss is a maximum when

$$I_b = \frac{4}{\pi^2} \frac{E_{bb}}{R_L} \quad (12\text{--}29)$$

indicating that the maximum loss does not necessarily occur at maximum signal.

Equation 12–24 shows that the output voltage E_o is a linear function of the input voltage E_g, since the tube parameters are constants under the linear assumption, and near constants in practice. Such an amplifier is a *Class B linear amplifier*, and may be used to amplify inputs of varying amplitude, such as are encountered with modulated radio-frequency signals. Because such a wave may have certain cycles with peaks twice the normal or steady-state value, it is customary to establish the operating conditions so that the steady-state value is determined by radio-frequency input peaks slightly less than one-half the design input maximum. This limitation prevents the peak signals from driving the tube into the saturation region, and insures maintenance of the desired linear relation between input and output voltage.

12–6. Graphical analysis for the Class B linear amplifier

The analytical method of the preceding section establishes the linear nature of the Class B amplifier, but does not give an answer to the question of proper driving voltage, since it is not possible to ascertain the closeness of approach to saturation. The graphical method of Section 12–2 may also be used, and does allow approximation of the proper input. An example will be given, using the characteristics of Fig. 12–8, for a tube with $\mu = 20$.

The *diode line* for $e_{b\,min} = e_{c\,max}$ was previously used as a limiting locus, but in Class B service it is usually not desirable to drive the tube to this condition, because of the approach to saturation and loss of linearity. High grid currents may also introduce distortion in the driving circuits. It is usually considered good Class B design to limit the grid drive so that the value of $e_{b\,min}$ is one and one-half to two times $e_{c\,max}$, and a limit of twice $e_{c\,max}$ is drawn as a locus in Fig. 12–8. It can be seen that this avoids most of the nonlinearity in the spacing of grid current lines.

The tube has a rated anode dissipation of 300 watts, and a Q point is chosen at $E_{bb} = 3000$ v, $E_{cc} = -155$ v, giving $I_{bo} = 0.100$ amp. As a first trial the grid will be driven 75 v positive, and this locates A on the locus for $e_{c\,max} = 75$ v, $e_{b\,min} = 150$ v. Immediately it follows that $\hat{E}_g =$

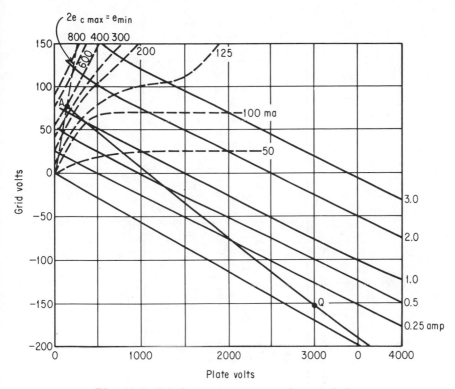

Fig. 12–8. Triode constant-current characteristics.

230 v, $\hat{E}_o = 2850$ v. The methods of the previous sections may be followed, leading to computation of input, output, and losses as tabulated in Table 22. Also assembled for comparison in Table 23 are calculations using the methods of Sections 12–5 and 11–9.

It appears that while these more idealized methods give reasonably close correlation on current values, the outputs are optimistic and the losses pessimistic, the latter being a critical error. This is to be expected, however, since both of these analytical methods assume zero distortion, and it is apparent that the particular load and grid-input conditions actually force the tube into near saturation. This can be readily seen in a flattened anode current wave if the i_b data of the table are plotted. The value of g_m is also not constant over the operating range, and this introduces an error.

The graphical method also contributes considerable data on input power requirements. While only 8.8 watts average drive are called for, a peak power of 90 watts is required. A reasonably large input power source is therefore needed, if good voltage regulation and input wave form are to be obtained.

TABLE 22. CALCULATIONS FROM FIG. 12–8

θ	0°	10°	20°	30°	40°	50°	60°	70°	80°	90°	100°
Cos θ	1.00	0.985	0.940	0.866	0.766	0.643	0.500	0.342	0.174	0.0	−0.174
$\hat{E}_o \cos \theta$	2850	2810	2680	2470	2190	1830	1430	975	500	0.0	−500
$E_{bb} - \hat{E}_o \cos \theta$	150	190	320	530	810	1170	1570	2025	2500	3000	3500
i_b	1.1	1.06	1.0	0.9	0.75	0.60	0.40	0.30	0.18	0.10	0.03
i_c	0.4	0.3	0.12	0.07	0.05	0	—	—	—	—	—
$i_b \cos \theta$	1.1	1.03	0.94	0.78	0.58	0.28	0.20	0.10	0.03	—	−0.004
$i_c \cos \theta$	0.4	0.29	0.12	0.06	0.04	0	—	—	—	—	—
$i_c \hat{E}_o \cos \theta$	90	65	27	13	8.5	0	—	—	—	—	—

TABLE 23. COMPARISON OF METHODS, CLASS B LINEAR AMPLIFIER

$$\mu = 20 \qquad E_{bb} = 3000 \text{ v}$$
$$\text{average } g_m = 15,000 \ \mu\text{mhos} \qquad E_{cc} = -155 \text{ v}$$
$$R_L = 5740 \text{ ohms}$$

	Table 22	Section 12–5	Section 11–9
I_{bo}	0.100 amp		$I_m = 1.1$ amp
I_{bs}	0.328	0.338 amp	0.350 amp
I_c	0.041		
$\hat{I}_1$	0.496	0.532	0.550
I_1	0.350	0.376	0.388
$\hat{I}_{g1}$	0.079		
I_g	0.056		
P_g	8.8 w		
Input	984 w	1028 w	1050 w
Output	707 w	810 w	860 w
Plate loss	277 w	218 w	190 w

12–7. Resonant load circuits

Both Class B and C radio-frequency power amplifiers have been studied in operation with resonant loads. The resistive impedance R_L presented by such loads is an important factor in the performance of the amplifiers, and the proper value of R_L should be achieved. The load circuit must also provide selectivity, or be of a Q value high enough that its impedance at harmonic frequencies is negligible, since the load is often expected to serve as a filter circuit.

In Section 9–19 the factor of merit, Q, was defined. Since

$$Q = \frac{\omega L}{R} = \frac{\omega L I^2}{R I^2} = \frac{E_o I}{R I^2} \qquad (12\text{–}30)$$

where ωL is the inductive reactance of the parallel circuit, R is the effective resistance considered as in series with L, I being the current flowing therein, and E_o is the effective voltage across the load. For $R \ll \omega L$, or reasonable Q, then $E_o \cong \omega L I$. It is apparent that

$$Q = \frac{\text{Volt-amperes}}{\text{Watts}} \qquad (12\text{–}31)$$

or Q is the ratio of the oscillating volt-amperes to the power being supplied to R. Since the power is extracted throughout the cycle but the input occurs only for a short pulse, it is necessary to maintain the circulating volt-amperes large in order to keep the oscillatory action going, or to maintain a sinusoidal wave form across the circuit. As an analogy, the energy extracted from a pendulum during its swing must be small compared to the energy stored in the bob; otherwise the motion of the pendulum is affected.

A desirable minimum for tank circuit Q has been found to approximate 10. Values much less may lead to insufficient selectivity, or unsatisfactory waveforms.

The tuned circuit can be designed from the specification for Q and the load impedance desired. In view of the power definition

$$R_L = \frac{E_o^2}{P_{\text{out}}} \qquad (12\text{--}32)$$

This desired load is the resonant impedance of the tank circuit, or

$$R_L \cong \frac{\omega L}{\omega C R}$$

$$X_C = \frac{E_o^2}{Q P_{\text{out}}} \qquad (12\text{--}33)$$

after which

$$X_L = X_C \left(\frac{Q^2}{Q^2 + 1} \right) \qquad (12\text{--}34)$$

which completes the specification of the required L and C values.

Final adjustment of the load to exact resonance is accomplished by *tuning* or varying either L or C until the maximum impedance or unity power factor condition is reached. This is usually indicated by *tuning for the dip* in the reading of the anode d-c ammeter, as in Fig. 12–9. To take the Class B linear amplifier as an example, Eq. 12–25 stated that

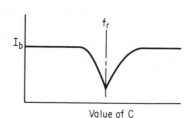

Fig. 12–9. Variation of d-c plate current through resonance, for Class B or Class C amplifiers.

$$I_b = \frac{g_m \hat{E}_g}{\pi} \left(\frac{1}{1 + R_L/r_p} \right) \qquad (12\text{--}35)$$

For reasonable values of Q, the impedance of the tuned circuit will increase rapidly as resonance is approached, reaching a maximum $= R_L$ at resonance. Equation 12–35 then states that when the load is in resonance, the direct plate current will have a dip or minimum as shown in Fig. 12–9. This same variation of I_b with tuning is observed in Class C as well as

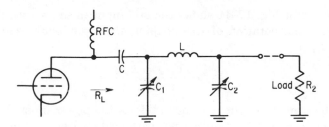

Fig. 12–10. Pi-network output circuit.

Class B amplifiers, and serves as a satisfactory tuning indicator. The circuit may also be tuned for maximum E_o value.

A common modification of the simple resonant tank circuit is the π network of Fig. 12–10. Here RFC is a shunt supply circuit for the anode current, and the impedance of the radio-frequency choke will be very high. Capacitor C is low in reactance and blocks the d-c anode voltage from the tuned circuit. As normally used, the output power is supplied to an antenna load, R_2, of 50 to 75 ohms, whereas the load presented to the tube, R_L, will approximate several thousand ohms. Capacitor C_2 will then be considerably larger than C_1, to provide the appropriate impedance match with $R_L > R_2$. Choosing Q as greater than 10, the design follows as

$$X_{C1} = \frac{R_L}{Q}, \quad X_{C2} = \sqrt{\frac{R_L R_2}{Q^2 + 1 - R_L/R_2}}$$

$$X_L = \frac{R_L}{Q^2 + 1}\left(\frac{R_L}{X_{C1}} + \frac{R_2}{X_{C2}}\right)$$

An added advantage for the circuit is that C_2, a large capacitance, is shunted across the load and provides a low impedance path for harmonics, thus helping to filter the output current.

12–8. The grounded-grid Class C power amplifier

The reasons of electrostatic shielding and stability which make the grounded-grid amplifier desirable for receiving also make it desirable for power-amplifier purposes. General operation as a Class C amplifier can be analyzed by the methods just presented, but a certain amount of consideration needs to be given to the manner of power input and output to the circuit.

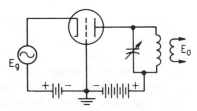

Fig. 12–11. Grounded-grid Class C amplifier.

The circuit of Fig. 12–11 shows the grid input in series with the plate circuit. With the notation of this chapter, the input power supplied by generator E_g is

$$P_{\text{in}} = \frac{\hat{E}_g \hat{I}_g}{2} + \frac{\hat{E}_g \hat{I}_1}{2} \qquad (12\text{–}36)$$

The first term on the right is recognizable as the power input due to the grid current; this will be required no matter what form of circuit is employed. The second term is seen to be an additional power term due to flow of plate current through the signal generator, and is a factor peculiar to this circuit.

The a-c power available in the plate circuit is

$$P_p = \frac{\hat{E}_g \hat{I}_1}{2} + \frac{\hat{E}_p \hat{I}_1}{2} \qquad (12\text{–}37)$$

in view of the fact that generator E_p, representing the equivalent tube action of the amplifier, is in series with E_g, the source generator. The first term on the right is recognizable as the additional input term of Eq. 12–36, the second term being the amplified output. Therefore the additional power is not lost but is added to the power developed in the circuit and made available to the load.

12–9. Frequency multipliers

The Class C amplifier, because of the large harmonic content in its plate current, is often employed as a frequency multiplier, usually as a doubler or tripler. The load in the plate circuit will then be tuned to resonance at the desired multiple of the input frequency, and will be assumed to present a resistive impedance R_L at that multiple frequency and negligible impedance at other frequencies.

In effect the grid causes the tube, as a synchronous switch, to supply energy to the tank circuit as the plate voltage swings down to a minimum. As the tank circuit oscillates at twice the grid frequency or another multiple thereof, there is no current pulse at the time of succeeding voltage minimums until the next positive grid swing. It is therefore necessary to supply sufficient energy to cause the tank circuit to carry over between pulses. The situation is shown in Fig. 12–12.

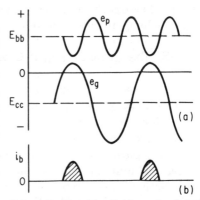

Fig. 12–12. (a) Grid and plate voltages of a Class C frequency doubler; (b) plate current pulses.

It can be seen that the angle of conduction should approximate, and be no longer than, the time of a half cycle of the output voltage. For doubling service, this condition fixes the angle of $2\theta_1$ at 90° or less. This limitation requires a high value of bias and a large grid excitation voltage. Tetrodes or pentodes make excellent multipliers because they may be easily over-biased, and a large grid drive can be readily obtained.

12–10. Neutralization of triode amplifiers

In Chapter 8 it was pointed out that a triode in a circuit such as that of Fig. 12–13 might regenerate or oscillate when the plate load circuit

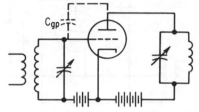

happens to be inductive, on account of the energy fed back from the plate circuit to the grid circuit in the internal C_{gp} capacity. For receiving applications the trouble was overcome by use of pentode tubes which reduce C_{gp} to negligible values. In the generation of large amounts of power at radio frequencies there are still many applications for which triode tubes

Fig. 12–13. Triode amplifier with tuned load.

are preferred, and it becomes necessary to develop a means of eliminating or neutralizing the energy feedback through the internal tube capacity. The difficulty is present only where grid and plate circuits are tuned to the same frequency, since if the energy fed back finds no impedance in the grid circuit, it cannot develop a voltage to be reamplified through the tube. Consequently, frequency doublers are not susceptible to oscillation difficulties.

If the anode load could be maintained resistive or capacitive, energy would not be fed back in proper phase; but with tuned circuits as loads, it is impractical to expect that they will always be maintained on the capacitive side of resonance.

Hazeltine developed the circuit of Fig. 12–14(a) to overcome the trouble. The output coil is tapped at some convenient point, usually the center, and the lower end of the coil is connected back to the grid through a small capacitance C_N.

It is desired that the equivalent plate-circuit generator μE_g at Fig. 12–14(b) produce no voltage in the grid circuit between G and K. The grid G is capacitively coupled to P through C_{gp}, but this coupling may be balanced by connection of the grid through a capacitance C_N to a point N, of opposite phase to that of the anode. Since C_{gp} is usually of the order of a few picofarads, C_N will also be of the same order of magnitude.

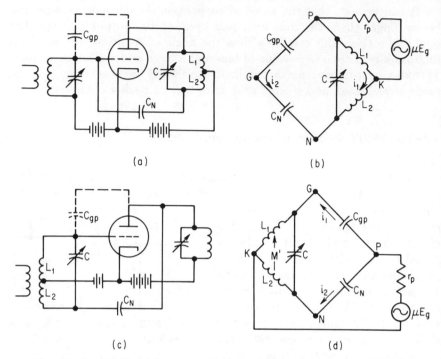

Fig. 12–14. (a) Hazeltine neutralizing circuit; (b) its equivalent; (c) Rice neutralizing circuit; (d) its equivalent.

The neutralizing circuit comprises a rather uncommon form of bridge wherein the source voltage μE_g is connected across one arm and coupled into a second bridge arm through capacitance C, aided somewhat by the effects of the mutual inductance between L_1 and L_2. For the circuit to operate so that zero voltage appears between G and K requires phase and magnitude equality of the voltages of points G and K with respect to N. If the L_1, L_2, C resonant circuit is of reasonable Q or if M is large, the currents flowing in L_1 and L_2 are equal, and points P and N will be of opposite phase with respect to K. Then, from the circuit, if the potentials of G and K are to be of equal phase and magnitude with respect to N,

$$\frac{-ji_2/\omega C_{gp}}{-ji_2/\omega C_N} = \frac{j\omega L_1 i_1}{j\omega L_2 i_1}$$

or the balance conditions are

$$\frac{C_N}{C_{gp}} = \frac{L_1}{L_2} \tag{12–38}$$

If the assumptions on Q or M are not fully met, so that P and N are not of exactly opposite phase, it may be found impossible to neutralize the circuit irrespective of the adjustment of C_N. This condition is occasionally met in practice.

Rice devised the circuit of Fig. 12–14(c), in which the grid coil is split and the neutralizing voltage introduced into the two coil halves. The equivalent circuit, drawn at (d), appears as a more ordinary form of bridge until it is realized that the equivalent plate-circuit generator must produce zero volts across one arm of the bridge, between G and K.

Consideration of the tuned circuit of (d) shows that it is excited by a current i_1 at one end, flowing through L_1, and a current i_2 at the other end, flowing through L_2. In a resonant circuit the circulating current in L and C is equal to Q times the exciting current. The circulating current due to i_1 would be Qi_1, and that due to i_2 would be Qi_2, but these circulating currents must be in opposite directions. To make the net circulating current zero would require that $i_1 = i_2$; and if

$$L_1 = L_2$$

then

$$C_{gp} = C_N$$

If the net circulating current is zero, no voltage can be produced between G and K because of the equivalent plate generator μE_g. The circuit is said to be neutralized, and the above pair of equations become balance conditions.

Adjustment of these circuits is usually carried out by balancing for absence of the reverse effect, namely, absence of energy feed from grid to plate. This balance is effected by supplying grid excitation but removing the anode voltage, that is, by eliminating the electronic action within the tube but leaving the electrostatic effect of C_{gp}. If the circuits are unbalanced, energy will be supplied to the plate tank from the grid circuit through the neutralizing circuit or C_{gp}. By searching for energy in the tank circuit with a sensitive detector coupled to the plate coil, it is possible to find the adjustment of C_N which reduces transfer of energy from grid to plate to a negligible amount. This same adjustment will then neutralize a transfer of energy in the reverse direction, or the bridge has been balanced.

Neutralization of a push-pull radio-frequency amplifier is simple, since the output tank circuit is already split into two halves, and only two capacitors need be supplied. A typical circuit is shown in Fig. 12–15.

Transistor neutralization to reduce feedback internal to the transistor may be carried out in similar fashion. However, the neutralizing capacitor will usually be shunted with a resistor, since the mutual impedance is not strictly capacitive.

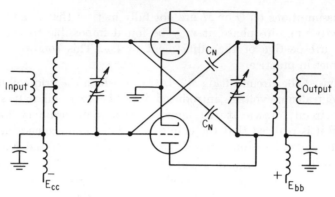

Fig. 12–15. Neutralized triode power amplifier.

12–11. Power sources for power amplifiers

Although anode-voltage sources have been shown in the circuit diagrams as batteries, such usage is not economical. Actual high-power amplifiers are usually supplied by high-voltage rectifiers from a-c lines. A filter is introduced to bring the ripple down to an acceptable figure.

The bias sources may be of three types: rectifier-filter combinations, cathode resistors, or grid-leak bias. Combinations of several of these are also employed. The first type is usually employed in some form so that cutoff bias at least will always be present. In the event of failure of this bias supply, relays should remove the anode voltage to prevent overheating of tubes by the high currents which would flow in the unbiased tube.

Cathode resistors are wasteful of d-c power and are employed only in units of small power input. Grid-leak bias, the cheapest form, utilizes the d-c grid current which flows in the grid circuit, to provide negative bias, as in Fig. 12–16. The value of resistor required is readily obtained by Ohm's law as

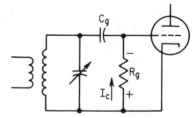

Fig. 12–16. Grid leak bias.

$$R_g = \frac{E_{cc}}{I_c}$$

where I_c is taken as the expected direct grid current. The capacitor C_g is present to prevent the d-c voltage developed across R_g from being short-circuited by the tuned circuit. Its reactance should be small at the operating frequency.

Grid-leak bias cannot be used on the linear Class B amplifier when amplifying a modulated or varying input, since the bias would then vary, and proper performance requires cutoff bias at all times.

Problems

12-1. A parallel-resonant circuit of $Q = 20$ is composed of L and R in series, in parallel with a value of $C = 27$ pf to tune the circuit to 10 mc. It is excited by a current whose waveform is specified as follows:

$$i = 0.41 + 1.62 \sin 2\pi \times 10^7 t + 0.45 \sin 4\pi \times 10^7 t$$

where the current is in amperes. Find the ratio of E_1 to E_2 for the frequencies present.

12-2. A Type 833-A triode, with $\mu = 35$ and $r_p = 3000$, is operated as a Class B linear amplifier with $E_b = 2500$, $\hat{E}_g = 90$, $E_{cc} = -70$, $\theta_1 = 90°$, $e_{bmin} = 300$, and has a tuned plate load of 4000 ohms. Find I_b, I_1, output, plate input, and plate-circuit efficiency.

12-3. The Type 810 triode is rated as follows as a Class B linear amplifier: $\mu = 36$, $r_p = 6500$, maximum $E_{bb} = 1200$, maximum plate dissipation $= 85$ w. A tuned load circuit of $Q = 12$ is used at a frequency of 5 mc. For optimum operating conditions, find:

(a) Bias voltage, E_{cc}.
(b) Plate current, I_b.
(c) The resonant impedance of the tuned circuit.
(d) The a-c voltage across the load.
(e) The effective value of E_g required.
(f) A-c power output.
(g) Power input.
(h) Plate efficiency.

12-4. Using the constant-current curves for the 75T tube as given in Appendix A, plot the wave forms of grid current, plate current, and plate voltage if $E_{bb} = 1000$ v, $E_{cc} = -200$ v, $e_{b\,min} = 100$, $e_{c\,max} = +100$. Find the angles of conduction for grid and plate currents.

12-5. Characteristics for the 304-TH triode are shown in Fig. 12-17. One such tube is operated with $E_{bb} = 2000$ v, $E_{cc} = -200$ v, and $e_{bmin} = e_{c\,max}$ at $+300$ v. Compute:

(a) I_b and I_c.
(b) The output power.
(c) The plate circuit efficiency.
(d) The power gain.
(e) The circuit elements for the plate load with $Q = 15$.
(f) Plate dissipation.

12-6. Repeat Problem 12-5 but with $e_{b\,min} = 200$ v and $e_{c\,max} = 100$ v. Compare results with Problem 12-5.

12-7. Two tubes having the characteristics of Fig. 12-4 are operated in parallel with 1500 plate volts, bias at three times cutoff, and $e_{b\,min} = e_{c\,max} = 200$ v. The tube filaments take 5 v and 6 amp each, and a-c and d-c power to supply the transmitter costs 2 cents per kilowatt-hour.

(a) Find the power required to drive the grid circuit of this amplifier.

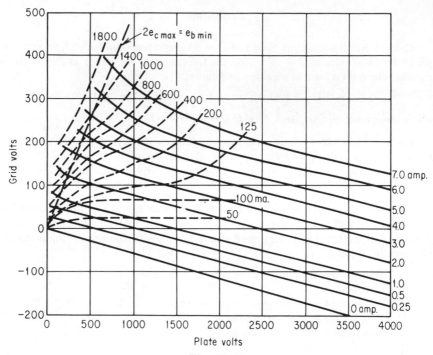

Fig. 12–17.

(b) If the transmitter is operated 20 hr per day, find the annual power bill for supplying this amplifier.

(c) What is the power cost per kilowatt-hour of radio-frequency output?

12-8. A 304-TH tube (characteristics in Fig. 12-17) is rated at 2000 plate volts, 0.600 plate amperes, 0.125 grid amperes, and 300 w plate dissipation. With a bias of −200 v, choose operating conditions and design the tank circuit (Q loaded = 12) to give a power output of 750 w to the load. Find the power gain.

References

1. Everitt, W. L., "Optimum Operating Conditions for Class-C Amplifiers," *Proc. I.R.E.*, **22,** 152 (1934).

2. ——, "Output Networks for Radio-Frequency Amplifiers," *Proc. I.R.E.*, **19,** 725 (1931).

3. Everitt, W. L., and Spangenberg, K., "Grid Current Flow as a Factor in the Design of Vacuum-Tube Power Amplifiers," *Proc. I.R.E.*, **26,** 612 (1938).

4. Mouromtseff, I. E., and Kozanowski, H. N., "Analysis of the Operation of Vacuum Tubes as Class-C Amplifiers," *Proc. I.R.E.*, **23,** 752 (1935).

5. Thomas, H. P., "Determination of Grid Driving Power in Radio Frequency Power Amplifiers," *Proc. I.R.E.*, **21,** 1134 (1933).

Oscillators | 13

Oscillators are the generating circuits for radio frequencies, and stability of frequency is the most rigid requirement on oscillator design and performance. The operation of most radio systems is almost completely dependent on stable oscillators in both transmitter and receiver.

Almost any oscillator circuit can be made stable if it is operated in a vacuum, at constant temperature, with unchanging components and tubes or transistors, supplied by constant voltages—and if no power be taken from the circuit. The real stability problem arises in attempting to obtain reasonable power output from oscillators placed under normal environments, and constructed with practical components.

This chapter will develop the general conditions necessary for generation of oscillations, and will discuss a few of the usual circuits. Generators for extremely high frequencies will be studied in Chapter 21.

13–1. Feedback requirements for oscillation

An oscillator may be studied as a form of feedback amplifier, in which special requirements are placed on A and β. In the circuit of Fig. 13–1, the feedback voltage supplies the entire amplifier input, or

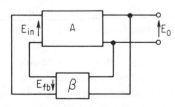

Fig. 13–1. Basic feedback oscillator.

$$\mathbf{E}_{fb} = \mathbf{E}_{in} = \beta\mathbf{E}_o = \beta A\mathbf{E}_{in}$$

from which

$$(1 - A\beta)\mathbf{E}_{in} = 0 \qquad (13\text{–}1)$$

If output is to be obtained then $\mathbf{E}_{in} \neq 0$; therefore for $\mathbf{E}_{in}$ to exist and for the circuit to produce an output, the above equation requires that

$$1 - \mathbf{A\beta} = 0$$

or

$$\mathbf{A\beta} = 1 \tag{13-2}$$

This is the Barkhausen criterion for oscillation. The expression emphasizes two basic requirements for oscillation: that the gain, frequency, and phase shifts must be such that

$$\mathbf{A\beta} = 1 \tag{13-3}$$

or *the overall loop gain be unity*, and that the

$$\text{phase shift of } A = - \text{ phase shift of } \beta \tag{13-4}$$

or *the overall phase shift around the loop be zero*, or a multiple of 2π.

The requirement of unity loop gain forces the circuit to adjust its amplitude of operation or gain $\mathbf{A}$ to an appropriate value. In starting of oscillation, it may be assumed that an initial switching surge occurs in the output circuit. A voltage resulting from this disturbance is fed back to the input circuit, will be amplified, and will appear at the output. This larger output is again fed back to the input, and the process is repeated. With the increasing amplitudes present in this process, the gain A will begin to decrease as the amplifier works into the saturation or cutoff regions of the characteristics. When A reaches a value which satisfies Eq. 13-3, the growth stops, and a steady-state oscillation continues. Since $|\beta|$ can never exceed unity, then $|A|$ must always $\geqq$ unity.

The limitation of amplitude by operation into the cutoff and saturation regions implies distortion of output current. However, if the load be a resonant circuit with a high Q, the filtering action of the circuit will limit the resonant tank current predominantly to the fundamental. Thus purity of output wave form is a function of circuit Q. Since the voltage fed back will be derived from the resonant circuit voltage or current, then it is only the fundamental which will be fed back, and consequently the condition of $\mathbf{A\beta} = 1$ will be met for the fundamental frequency.

Equation 13-4 requires that the circuit adjust its frequency of oscillation so that the reactances in the amplifier and β network will produce the correct phase shifts. For good frequency stability, the feedback network should have a rapid variation of phase with change in frequency. Thus only a small frequency shift is required to correct a phase angle change due to component or power supply variation.

If the oscillator has a resonant circuit load, then the Q of the circuit determines the phase shift per cycle of frequency variation. Figure 9–32 illustrates the phase variation of a resonant circuit. The steepness of the curve near f_r is a function of Q, and for very large Q the slope

$d\theta/d\omega$ approaches infinity. Therefore, high Q in the resonant load circuit is favorable to good wave form and to improved frequency stability as well.

Most oscillators operate by reason of feedback from output to input; the manner in which the feedback is achieved is the differentiating factor between the various forms of oscillator circuits. Negative resistance or two-terminal oscillators, treated in the latter part of the chapter, represent a different method of achieving oscillations.

13–2. Circuit requirements for oscillation

Figure 13–2 illustrates a basic form of oscillator circuit, as employed with a resonant circuit as a load. The circuit may be analyzed to determine the necessary circuit conditions which must be met for oscillation to occur.

The load impedance for (a) is

$$Z_L = \frac{Z_3(Z_1 + Z_2)}{Z_1 + Z_2 + Z_3} \tag{13–5}$$

Considering the transistor as in the common-emitter circuit, the voltage gain is

$$\mathbf{A}_{ve} \cong \frac{-aZ_L}{r_e + (1-a)(r_b + Z_s)}$$

The impedance in the base circuit is

$$Z_s = \frac{Z_2(Z_1 + Z_3)}{Z_1 + Z_2 + Z_3} \tag{13–6}$$

so that the gain for the circuit may be expressed as

$$\mathbf{A}_{ve} = \frac{-aZ_3(Z_1 + Z_2)}{(Z_1 + Z_2 + Z_3)[r_e + r_b(1-a)] + (1-a)Z_2(Z_1 + Z_3)} \tag{13–7}$$

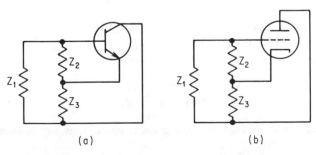

(a)   (b)

Fig. 13–2. General resonant-load oscillator circuit.

The circuit obviously provides feedback and

$$\beta = \frac{Z_2}{Z_1 + Z_2}$$

if the feedback due to the common internal resistance r_e be neglected as small compared to the external voltage fed back.

The overall loop gain then is

$$A\beta = \frac{-a}{1-a}\left[\frac{Z_2 Z_3}{(Z_1 + Z_2 + Z_3)\left(r_b + \dfrac{r_e}{1-a}\right) + Z_2(Z_1 + Z_3)}\right] \qquad (13\text{--}8)$$

It will now be assumed that the coupling and load impedances are reactive, that is $Z_1 = jX_1$, $Z_2 = jX_2$, $Z_3 = jX_3$. Then

$$A\beta = \frac{-a}{1-a}\left[\frac{-X_2 X_3}{j(X_1 + X_2 + X_3)\left(r_b + \dfrac{r_e}{1-a}\right) - X_2(X_1 + X_3)}\right] \qquad (13\text{--}9)$$

For oscillations to occur requires that $A\beta = 1$, or be real, so that *the reactive term must be zero*, or

$$X_1 + X_2 + X_3 = 0 \qquad (13\text{--}10)$$

The circuit therefore will oscillate at the frequency at which the X_1, X_2, X_3 circuit is resonant. Using Eq. 13–10 in Eq. 13–9, and noting that $X_2 = -(X_1 + X_3)$, then under oscillation conditions

$$A\beta = \frac{a}{1-a}\frac{X_3}{X_2} \qquad (13\text{--}11)$$

The loop gain must be positive, and therefore reactances X_2 and X_3 must be of the same sign, or the same type of reactance. Because of Eq. 13–10, it is apparent that X_1 must a reactance of opposite sign and type to X_2 and X_3.

Since **Aβ** must equal unity for oscillation to continue, and must be greater than unity for oscillations to start, it is evident that Eq. 13–11 states a *minimum value for the theoretical gain* $a/(1-a)$ as

$$\frac{a}{1-a} = \frac{X_2}{X_3} \qquad (13\text{--}12)$$

Thus we have established certain general conditions for resonant circuit oscillators.

13-3. Basic oscillator circuits

It is now possible to apply these circuit criteria in the study of conventional oscillator circuits. All these circuits will employ tuned circuits for energy storage, since they will operate essentially as Class C devices. Feedback will be provided through a reactance equivalent to X_1, giving an input voltage derived from the output of the circuit.

The *Hartley circuit* of Fig. 13-3(a) and (b) is one of the oldest and most popular forms of oscillators. The reactances of the previous discussion are identified, and feedback occurs through the capacitor X_1. The position of the tap between the two parts of the inductor determines the magnitude of the feedback and is not critical in location. The power supply is connected *in shunt* with the tuned circuit, and high-frequency currents are prevented from using the power supply as a return path by insertion of the high-reactance radio-frequency choke L in series.

The *Colpitts circuit* of Fig. 13-3(c) and (d) is the inverse of the Hartley oscillator, with the feedback through the inductive reactance X_1. The capacitors X_2 and X_3 are usually made equal as a matter of convenience, as their ratio is not critical.

The circuit at (e) is more complex. Tuned circuits are used in both plate and grid circuits, and are usually shielded from each other. These circuits represent X_2 and X_3, with the feedback occurring through the grid-plate capacity of the tube as X_1. This means that both tuned circuits must be tuned on the inductive side of resonance for oscillations to occur. The circuit of highest Q will have the most rapid change of phase with frequency, therefore it will control the oscillator frequency. Since the anode circuit is ordinarily loaded by an external load, whereas the grid circuit supplies only the input losses, it is usually the grid circuit which is of higher Q and fixes the frequency. The anode tank will then tune broadly, and may be used to adjust to desired value of output, or to change the loading on the oscillator. This circuit is designated as a *tuned-grid-tuned plate oscillator*.

The circuit of (f) is a further modification, with only the output or collector circuit tuned. Feedback is provided by mutual coupling between the collector circuit and the base. This is a *tuned collector* circuit; the vacuum tube version would be a *tuned-plate oscillator*.

Some form of bias proportional to input is shown in these circuits. Class C operation is desired, but if a fixed bias beyond cutoff were used, no initial starting pulse of current could ever flow, and oscillations would not build up. With grid-leak bias proportional to input, there is no bias until oscillation starts. An output circuit pulse appears, this induces an input pulse, the oscillation builds up to a maximum and the bias develops in proportion.

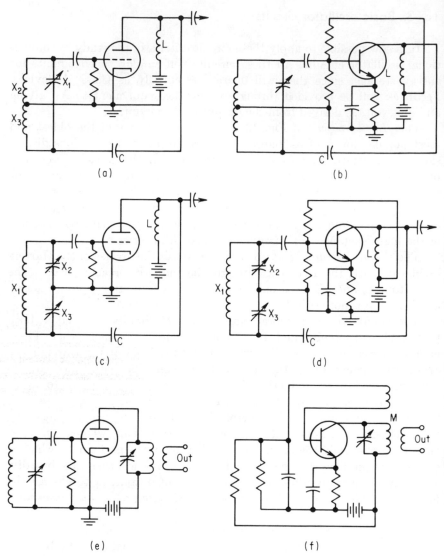

Fig. 13–3. (a), (b) Hartley oscillator; (c), (d) Colpitts oscillators; (e) tuned-plate-tuned grid; (f) tuned collector.

For improved frequency stability, it is customary to follow an oscillator with a Class A *buffer amplifier* so that no appreciable load is introduced into the oscillator frequency-determining circuit. The Class A stage is then arranged to drive a Class C amplifier from which power output may be derived. The buffer amplifier isolates the oscillator from changes in loading which might affect the frequency of oscillation. Use of regulated supply voltages also helps to stabilize the transistor or tube parameters which are liable to affect the frequency, as coupled-in effects on the resonant load circuit.

13-4. The electron-coupled circuit

A means of incorporating a buffer amplifier within the oscillator tube itself is shown in Fig. 13-4 as an *electron-coupled circuit,* for use with tetrodes or pentodes. The cathode, grid, and screen constitute a triode Hartley oscillator with one difference, namely, the radio-frequency grounding of the screen instead of the cathode. The screen thus acts as a shield between the triode oscillator and the anode and load circuit. Electrons from the triode region pass through the screen and reach the anode, which serves as a collector electrode, and this alternating plate current sets up voltages in the output. In a tetrode or pentode the anode voltage has negligible effect on the anode current, and changes in anode voltage due to the load circuit have only slight effect on the μ and r_p of the tube, which enter into the frequency-determining reactances, thus giving improved frequency stability over the unbuffered oscillator. Changes in μ and r_p caused by supply voltage variation can also be nullified by proper selection of potentials, since changes in anode voltage have an opposite effect on frequency to changes in screen voltage, over a reasonable range.

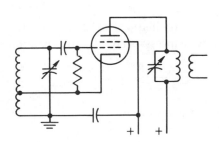

Fig. 13-4. Electron-coupled Hartley oscillator.

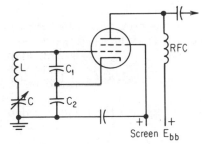

Fig. 13-5. Clapp modification of the electron-coupled Colpitts circuit.

The circuit is said to be electron coupled because the coupling between input or resonant frequency-determining circuit and the output or load is through the electron stream. Although shown as a Hartley, any of the basic oscillator circuits may be used.

Figure 13-5 illustrates a version of the Colpitts circuit as an electron-coupled oscillator. Capacitor C is ordinarily used to tune the circuit to operating frequency, as a matter of convenience.

13–5. Effect of device parameters on frequency

The circuit of Fig. 13–6 is the equivalent circuit for the Colpitts transistor oscillator of Fig. 13–3(d). The influence of transistor parameters on frequency can be determined, at least as an approximation.

The use of the equivalent circuit assumes linearity of performance and sinusoidal currents, whereas actual oscillators operate in Class C with variation of parameters and somewhat distorted wave forms. However, as a means to qualitative understanding of the interrelated circuit effects, the use of the equivalent circuit seems justified.

Resistor R represents resonant circuit losses as well as the load coupled into the circuit. Reference to Fig. 13–2 shows that

$$Z_1 = R + j\omega L$$

$$Z_2 = -j/\omega C_1$$

$$Z_3 = -j/\omega C_2$$

Substitution in Eq. 13–8, for the necessary oscillatory conditions of a general resonant-load oscillator, leads to

$$A\beta = \frac{a/(1-a)}{R\omega^2 C_1 C_2\left(r_b + \dfrac{r_e}{1-a}\right) + \omega^2 L C_2 - 1 + j\left\{\left[\omega^3 L C_1 C_2 - \omega(C_1 + C_2)\right]\left(r_b + \dfrac{r_e}{1-a}\right) - R\omega C_2\right\}}$$

$$(13\text{–}13)$$

It has been established that $A\beta = 1$ for oscillations to occur, and this requires that the reactive term of the above expression equal zero. Therefore

$$\left[\omega^2 L C_1 C_2 - (C_1 + C_2)\right]\left(r_b + \frac{r_e}{1-a}\right) - R C_2 = 0$$

which leads to the frequency-determining equation as

$$f = \frac{1}{2\pi}\sqrt{\frac{1}{\dfrac{L C_1 C_2}{C_1 + C_2}}\left[1 + \frac{R C_2}{(C_1 + C_2)\left(r_b + \dfrac{r_e}{1-a}\right)}\right]} \qquad (13\text{–}14)$$

The effective capacity of the two tuning capacitors is $C = C_1 C_2/(C_1 + C_2)$, so that the frequency of oscillation is due to the resonant circuit, modified by the effect of the load and the transistor parameters.

The transistor parameters are functions of emitter current and temperature, so that shift of the operating point or a change of ambient conditions will change the oscillation frequency. The dependence of frequency on load is indicative of the need for Class A buffer amplifiers, which extract no power or present no load to the oscillator.

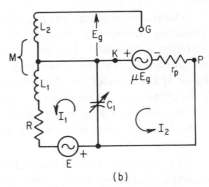

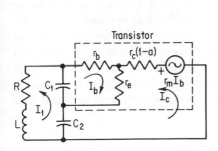

Fig. 13–6. Colpitts oscillator equivalent circuit using a transistor.

Fig. 13–7. Tuned-plate oscillator equivalent circuit.

The vacuum-tube tuned-plate oscillator, with equivalent circuit as in Fig. 13–7, can be analyzed in similar fashion, resulting in an expression for the frequency of oscillation as

$$f = \frac{1}{2\pi} \sqrt{\frac{1}{L_1 C_1}\left(1 + \frac{R}{r_p}\right)} \tag{13–15}$$

The frequency of oscillation will be that of the resonant circuit, modified by the tube parameter r_p, and the load as reflected in R. Both of these circuit parameters may vary and affect the frequency.

Another factor affecting frequency stability of oscillators is the effect of temperature on the inductance and capacity of the tuned circuit. Inductors are particularly sensitive, but the effect may be compensated by the use of special capacitors which vary in capacitance inversely as the temperature effect on the inductance, maintaining a constant LC product over a reasonable temperature range. Inductors have positive temperature coefficients of inductance, so the compensating capacitor should have a negative temperature coefficient of capacity. High values of tuning capacitance are also helpful, since this results in a higher circuit Q, and a greater $d\theta/d\omega$ or phase change per cycle near resonance.

13–6. Piezoelectric crystals

It has been mentioned that effects of temperature on inductors and capacitors are factors in frequency drift of oscillators. These changes frequently amount to more than 10 parts per million per degree change. It is desired that oscillator frequencies be maintained within a very few cycles per megacycle, and while stability of that order can be reached with well-designed temperature-compensated circuits, they are expensive to build.

The resonant circuit of an oscillator can be replaced with a mechanically vibrating *piezoelectric crystal*, whereupon a great increase in frequency stability is obtained. In such crystals, if mechanical stresses are applied on two opposites faces, electrical charges appear on some otheɪ pair of faces. If the stresses are changed fron compression to tension, the electrical polarity reverses. The converse effect is also present; that is, if electrical charges are placed on two opposite crystal faces by applying a potential, a mechanical strain and change in dimensions is produced between two other opposite faces.

For quartz, the piezoelectric material most commonly used for frequency control, the crystal is hexagonal in cross section. If the axes are designated as in Fig. 13–8, so-called *X*- and *Y*-cut crystals are obtained by slicing sections from the crystal parallel to the crystal blanks shown. These sections are then ground, lapped, and etched to the thickness needed for a given frequency of vibration.

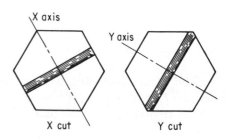

Fig. 13–8. Quartz crystal cuts—*Z* axis normal to page.

A voltage applied to electrodes positioned on appropriate crystal faces will cause the crystal to vibrate, with large amplitude at the natural frequency. These mechanical resonances depend only on the crystal dimensions and the type of mechanical movement permitted to the crystal. Since quartz is a very stable material, the frequency of mechanical oscillation of such a bar is likewise very stable.

Vibrations may take place in thickness, in bending, and in shear. Crystal design, cutting, and mounting involve the selection of dimensions such that only one of these modes will yield a resonant frequency in the range of desired operation.

The resonant frequency of a given crystal is a function of temperature. It may have either a positive or a negative temperature coefficient, depending on the crystal cut. By proper orientation of the axes at which the crystal cut is made, a zero-temperature-coefficient crystal is obtainable, the so-called GT cut, which is essentially constant in frequency over the range 0°-100°C. The AT and CT cuts also have zero coefficients but over much smaller operating ranges, as shown in Fig. 13–9.

Crystals are mounted by clamping between metal electrodes, or by having the electrodes electroplated on the crystal faces. The mounted crystal is enclosed in a container, frequently evacuated to eliminate mechanical damping due to the air.

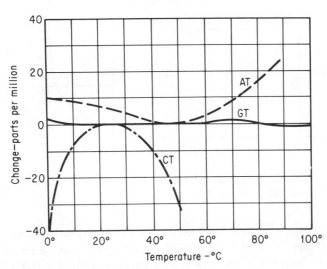

Fig. 13–9. Frequency change versus temperature for crystal cuts.

A crystal appears as if it were an electrical circuit of configuration shown in Fig. 13–10. Capacitance C_h represents the shunting capacitance which arises between the electrodes. Parameters R, L, and C represent values analogous to the mechanical properties of the crystal alone. The circuit properties of a crystal are due to its very high ratio of mass to elastance (equivalent to a high L/C ratio), and to a very high ratio of mass to damping (equivalent to a high Q). The latter may be in the order of 10,000 to 30,000, with values up to 500,000 for specially treated crystals mounted in vacuum. The crystal has series-resonant and antiresonant frequencies which lie very close together, as shown in Fig. 13–10(c). These curves are justified by writing the reactance expression for the crystal as

$$jX = \frac{-j(\omega^2 LC - 1)}{\omega(C + C_h)\left(\dfrac{\omega^2 LCC_h}{C + C_h} - 1\right)} \qquad (13\text{–}16)$$

Since the ratio of C_h to C may be 100 or more, it can be seen that the series resonance or zero due to the numerator is almost at the frequency of the pole or antiresonance due to the denominator.

Crystals can be made with fundamental frequencies ranging from about 4 kc to 10 mc. For frequencies above 10 mc, the quartz plates become very thin and fragile; it is possible, however, to manufacture crystals to accentuate harmonic modes, thus raising the upper limit to 100 mc or more.

The stability of frequency possible with zero-temperature-coefficient crystals and stabilized supply voltages may be of the order of 1 to 10

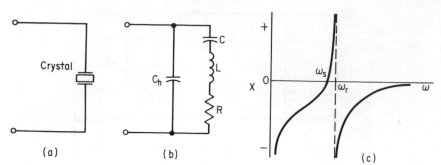

Fig. 13–10. (a) Crystal circuit symbol; (b) equivalent electrical circuit; (c) reactance curve for crystal.

cycles per megacycle over long periods of time. Crystals designed for and operated under laboratory-controlled conditions will show changes of less than 0.1 cycle per million cycles, and such crystal-oscillator circuits are frequently used for measurement of time to high degrees of precision.

13–7. Crystal oscillators

Since a crystal acts as an electrical resonant circuit, it is only natural that it be employed as the frequency-determining circuit for an oscillator. Several circuit forms are shown in Fig. 13–11. The *Pierce* oscillator in Fig. 13–11(a) and (c) utilizes the crystal as a parallel resonant feedback circuit. Basically it is a Hartley oscillator, and the cathode connection is obtained between the choke and grid leak. Its value lies in the lack of need for any other tuned circuit.

The circuit at Fig. 13–11(b) is a tuned grid-tuned plate oscillator with the grid circuit replaced by the crystal, which then becomes the frequency-determining element because of its high Q. Feedback is through the internal C_{gp} capacitance of the tube. Pentodes are desirable for use in this

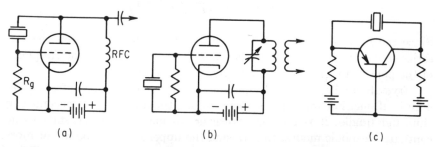

Fig. 13–11. (a) Pierce oscillator; (b) tuned-plate crystal oscillator; (c) transistor form of Pierce oscillator.

service because the low grid voltage required for their drive reduces the a-c voltage across the crystal and minimizes heating. In pentodes with very complete internal shielding, it may be necessary to shunt a small capacity between grid and anode to provide sufficient feedback to permit oscillation. The anode circuit must be tuned on the inductive side of resonance to set up the phase conditions necessary for proper feedback and oscillation.

The effect of plate-load tuning on frequency is largely a result of the change of C_{in} of the tube due to load phase-angle conditions. The crystal circuit and the tube input is shown in Fig. 13–12, with the effective capacitance then being

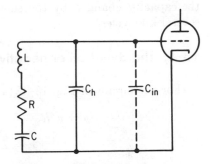

$$C_e = \frac{C(C_h + C_{in})}{C + C_h + C_{in}}$$

Fig. 13–12. Quartz crystal in the grid circuit.

For resonance, with the high Q due to the crystal, it is possible to use the relation

$$\omega = \sqrt{\frac{1}{L_e}\left[\frac{C + C_h + C_{in}}{C(C_h + C_{in})}\right]} = \sqrt{\frac{1}{L_e C}\left(1 + \frac{C}{C_h + C_{in}}\right)} \quad (13\text{–}17)$$

The parameter which is varied by tube or load changes is C_{in}. Since C is always very small in a crystal, it is not possible for changes in C_{in} to have much effect on the resonant frequency.

This statement may be supported by reference to the values for a typical crystal, resonant at 474 kc, as

$$L = 3.66 \text{ h} \qquad C_h = 5.76 \text{ pf}$$

$$C = 0.0316 \text{ pf} \qquad R = 4518 \text{ ohms}$$

For a triode, C_{in} may be assumed as 30 pf. Then the resonant frequency is

$$\omega_1 = \sqrt{\frac{1}{LC}}\,(1 + 0.000884).$$

If it now be assumed that a change in load causes C_{in} to change by 10 per cent (a large change) to a new value of 33 pf, then

$$\omega_2 = \sqrt{\frac{1}{LC}}\,(1 + 0.000816)$$

Taking the ratio of the frequencies

$$\frac{f_1}{f_2} = \sqrt{\frac{1.000884}{1.000816}} = 1.000033$$

This equation indicates that the 10 per cent change in C_{in} has caused a shift of 0.0033 per cent in frequency. At 474 kc this represents a change of 15.6 *cycles*. A simple resonant circuit at the same frequency, in which the capacity changed by the same percentage, would shift frequency by several kilocycles.

13–8. The dynatron or negative-resistance oscillator

For the circuit of Fig. 13–13(a), it is possible to write

$$i_R = e/R, \qquad\qquad i_C = C\,de/dt,$$

$$e = L\,di_L/dt$$

from which the circuit differential equation may be formed as

$$LC\frac{d^2i_L}{dt^2} + \frac{L}{R}\frac{di_L}{dt} + i_L = 0 \qquad\qquad (13\text{--}18)$$

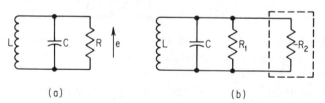

(a)   (b)

Fig. 13–13. Basic negative-resistance oscillator.

This equation has a solution

$$i_L = K\epsilon^{[-(1/2RC)+j\omega]t} \qquad\qquad (13\text{--}19)$$

where

$$\omega = \sqrt{\frac{1}{LC} - \frac{1}{4R^2C^2}}$$

Equation 13–19 is that of a decaying transient, which might follow an initial switching pulse. If an oscillation is to build up in such a circuit, instead of decaying, the real term of the exponent must be positive, and this is possible only if R is made negative.

By connecting across the circuit a device to introduce a *negative resistance,* $- R_2$, as in Fig. 13–13(b), or to supply energy, the total resistance of the circuit can be made negative, providing $| R_2 | < R_1$. Several tube or transistor circuits are available to introduce the negative resistance, one being the *dynatron,* shown in Fig. 13–14(a). Such a circuit is also referred to as a *two-terminal oscillator,* since connection is made to only two points on the tuned circuit.

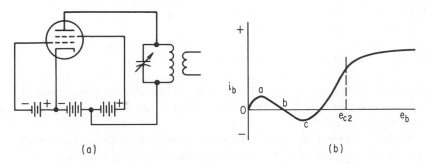

Fig. 13–14. (a) the dynatron oscillator; (b) plate characteristic for a tetrode, with negative-resistance region.

In Fig. 13–14(b), the g_p of the tetrode is represented by the slope of the i_b, e_b curve, and a region of negative plate conductance or resistance appears between a and c. As has been previously discussed, this negative slope is due to secondary emission from the anode when the screen is more positive than the anode. Operation in this region supplies a negative resistance, which may satisfy the conditions for oscillation. If operation is restricted to the region abc, good wave forms may be obtained. Because of variability of the secondary emission, the frequency stability is not great.

If the circuit resistance is negative, then amplitude will continue to build up. As the operation passes the points a and c, the negative resistance decreases, and amplitude will stabilize at the condition at which $| R_2 | = R_1$, or the net circuit resistance is zero. The frequency will then be given by $\omega = \sqrt{1/LC}$.

It may be reasoned that if oscillations are to build up in the tuned circuits of the feedback types of oscillators, the resistance of these circuits must also be negative during the transient buildup, and zero during the steady state. This is the normal condition, but for purposes of analysis, it has here seemed more desirable to stress the feedback conditions rather than the presence of negative resistance in such circuits.

13–9. Phase-shift oscillators

A *phase-shift oscillator* is shown in Fig. 13–15. No tuned circuit is required, but because of the lack of filtering action, the wave form may be nonsinusoidal. If the amplitude is kept low, a good sinusoid may be obtained. The circuit oscillates at a frequency at which the tube (or transistor) provides a phase shift of 180°, and the external circuit between

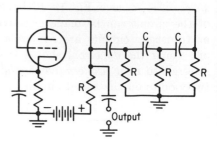

Fig. 13–15. Phase-shift oscillator.

anode and grid provides an equal shift. The circuit is therefore a feedback oscillator, controlled by the phase angle of the *RC* network. Because of the complexity of this network, the oscillator is not well suited to variable-frequency use.

A phase-shift circuit which overcomes these difficulties is the resistance-capacitance oscillator of Fig. 13–16. Fundamentally this circuit is a two-stage feedback amplifier employing positive feedback for phase shift and oscillation, and negative feedback for amplitude limitation and improvement of wave form.

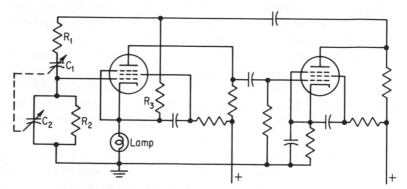

Fig. 13–16. Resistance-capacitance phase-shift oscillator.

Positive feedback is provided by coupling the output back to the input through R_1, C_1, R_2, C_2. Oscillation will occur at a frequency of $1/(2\pi\sqrt{R_1R_2C_1C_2})$ cycles per second. Ordinarily C_1 and C_2 are simultaneously varied for supplying variable output frequencies.

Negative feedback, which limits operation to the linear part of the tube characteristics to provide good wave form, is provided by R_3 and the small tungsten-lamp cathode resistor. For low output the current fed back to the lamp is small and its resistance is low, making the negative feedback low. If the output tends to increase, the lamp current increases, changing the lamp resistance and increasing the negative feedback. As a result the output amplitude stabilizes at a substantially constant value that does not overload the tubes. Excellent output wave form is possible, as is demonstrated by the use of this circuit in laboratory oscillators where very low distortion of wave form is required.

Problems

13-1. For the Colpitts oscillator of Fig. 13–3(c), derive the frequency of oscillation equation.

13-2. A certain tube has $\mu = 12$, $r_p = 6500$ ohms, and is used in a tuned-plate oscillator at a frequency of 1.5 mc, with a resonant circuit Q of 25. If $L_1 = 100\ \mu h$, determine the resistance loading, and the capacity required for resonance.

13-3. Because of a plate voltage change, the r_p of the tube in Problem 13–2 changes to 5000 ohms. Find the percentage of frequency shift.

13-4. Develop the frequency relation for the Hartley transistor oscillator of Fig. 13–3(b), neglecting the effect of the bias circuit.

13-5. A Colpitts oscillator uses an inductor of 37 μh, each tuning capacitor has 300 pf capacity, $r_p = 15,000$ ohms, and L has series resistance such that Q of the circuit $= 15$. Find the value which μ must have for oscillation to take place, and the frequency of oscillation. Assume Class A operation.

13-6. In Fig. 13–15 the triode has $r_p = 70,000$ ohms. If $R = 30,000$ ohms and $C = 0.002\ \mu f$, find the frequency if oscillations occur, and the value of μ required.

13-7. In Fig. 13–17, neglecting the reactance of C, find the gain required from each stage if the circuit is to oscillate, and the frequency of oscillation. $C_1 = 0.1\ \mu f$, $L_1 = 0.15h$, $R_3 = 20,000$ ohms, g_m of each triode $= 2500\ \mu mho$.

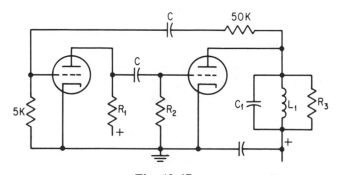

Fig. 13–17.

13-8. A crystal has the following analogous electrical values: $L = 250h$, $C = 0.04$ pf, $R = 1800$ ohms, and $C_h = 8$ pf. Find the frequency of oscillation when used in the grid circuit of a tube having $g_m = 2000$ μmho, $C_{gk} = 5$ pf, $C_{gp} = 3$ pf, with a resistive load of 27,000 ohms.

13-9. Show that the phase-shift conditions are such that oscillations will occur in the circuit of Fig. 13–16 when $\omega = \sqrt{R_1 R_2 C_1 C_2}$.

13-10. Derive the frequency relation for the oscillator of Fig. 13–18.

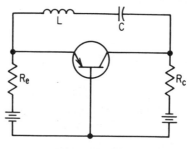

Fig. 13–18.

References

1. Cady, W. G., "The Piezo-Electric Resonator," *Proc. I.R.E.*, **10**, 363 (1922).

2. Dow, J. B., "A Recent Development in Vacuum Tube Oscillator Circuits," *Proc. I.R.E.*, **19**, 2095 (1931).

3. Heising, R. A., *Quartz Crystals for Electrical Circuits—Their Design and Manufacture*. D. Van Nostrand Co., Inc., New York, 1946.

4. Llewellyn, F. B., "Constant Frequency Oscillators," *Proc. I.R.E.*, **19**, 2063 (1931).

5. Lo, A. W., *et al.*, *Transistor Electronics*. Prentice-Hall, Inc., Englewood Cliffs, N. J., 1955.

6. Mason, W. P., "Low Temperature Coefficient Quartz Crystals," *Bell Syst. Tech. Jour.*, **19**, 74 (1940).

7. Terman, F. E., *et al.*, "Some Applications of Negative Feedback with Particular Reference to Laboratory Equipment," *Proc. I.R.E.*, **27**, 649 (1939).

Modulation Processes | 14

A continuous sine wave conveys no information. In order to transmit information by the usual a-c wave form, it is necessary to vary the characteristics of the wave in some manner. This variation of the wave, in order to transmit information, is called *modulation*.

Essentially the modulation process is one of frequency translation, in which the information-carrying frequencies are translated to higher or lower frequency bands, one or more of which become the desired output. An understanding of the process and its effects is of utmost importance in the study of electronic systems.

One of the most common uses of modulation is in radio transmission where the frequency of the usual audio or informational signal is not suited to direct radiation. By modulation, the information is translated to a suitable frequency and radiated. At the receiving end of the circuit, a reverse process of translation or *demodulation* is employed to strip the information from the transmitted frequency. This process will be studied in Chapter 15.

14–1. Fundamentals of modulation

Whenever an alternating voltage is written

$$e = A \cos (\omega t + \theta)$$

the concept of a phasor rotating with time may be associated therewith, with the instantaneous voltage magnitude represented by a projection of that phasor on the j axis.

Certain fundamentals in the use of rotating phasors to describe alternating currents and voltages are frequently submerged and lost through repetitive study of constant-frequency electrical systems. If the angle is considered as one of the characteristics of a sinusoidal wave which may be varied in the modulation process, it becomes necessary to re-examine the usage of the rotating-phasor concept in the light of this possible variation of angle. This will not invalidate the accepted usage of the concept for constant-frequency systems.

Consider the angular position of the rotating phasor defined as some angle θ with respect to a fixed reference. This angle is a function of time, since the phasor is assumed in rotation. Angular velocity is $\omega = d\theta/dt$, from which

$$\theta = \int \omega \, dt + \theta_o$$

showing that the instantaneous position of the phasor is a function of all preceding values of angular velocity. Since $\omega = 2\pi f$, then

$$f = \frac{1}{2\pi} \frac{d\theta}{dt} \tag{14-1}$$

becomes a fundamental definition of frequency. This is of the nature of an instantaneous frequency.

An alternating voltage may be accurately defined as

$$e = A \cos \theta = A \cos \left[\int \omega \, dt + \theta_o \right] \tag{14-2}$$

The constant of integration is the phase angle. There then appear two parameters of an a-c wave which may be varied or modulated. These are the amplitude, A, and the angle, resulting in two basic types of modulation:

I. *Variation of amplitude A with time, resulting in amplitude modulation* (AM).

II. *Variation of the angle with time, resulting in the general case of angle modulation.* There are two subtypes, namely:

(a) Variation of $\int \omega \, dt$ with time, producing *frequency modulation* (FM).

(b) Variation of the phase angle θ_o with time, giving *phase modulation* (PM).

For case I, the angular velocity ω is a constant with value ω_c, the so-called carrier frequency. Use of Eq. 14-2 then gives

$$e = A \cos (\omega_c t + \theta_o) \tag{14-3}$$

which is the ordinary expression for an a-c voltage, and as such confirms the general approach which led to Eq. 14-2. If the signal carrying the information is

$$e_m = E_m \cos \omega_m t$$

the amplitude A should vary as

$$A = E_c + k_a E_m \cos \omega_m t = E_c\left(1 + \frac{k_a E_m}{E_c'} \cos \omega_m t\right) \qquad (14\text{–}4)$$

The complete amplitude-modulated voltage is then written as

$$e = E_c(1 + m_a \cos \omega_m t)\ \cos \omega_c t \qquad (14\text{–}5)$$

where the constant phase term θ_0 has been dropped as of no importance in this process. The proportionality constant, k_a, relates the variation of amplitude and the maximum signal E_m. The modulation frequency ω_m is ordinarily small with respect to ω_c, the carrier angular frequency.

The *modulation factor* is

$$m_a = \frac{k_a E_m}{E_c} \qquad (14\text{–}6)$$

When multiplied by 100 per cent this becomes the *modulation percentage*. In usual amplitude-modulation systems it is not desirable for $k_a E_m$ to be greater than E_c, or for the modulation percentage to exceed 100 per cent.

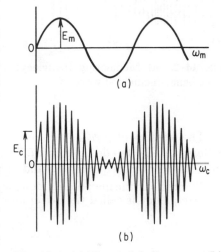

Fig. 14–1. (a) The modulating wave; (b) the amplitude-modulated wave.

For case II(a), that of frequency modulation, the angular velocity ω is made to vary in accordance with the amplitude of the modulating signal, as

$$\omega = \omega_o + k_f E_m \cos \omega_m t \qquad (14\text{–}7)$$

where $f_o = \omega_o/2\pi$, is called the *center frequency*, ω_m is the modulation angular frequency, and k_f is the degree of frequency variation determined by the amplitude of the modulating signal. By use of Eq. 14–2

$$e = E_c \sin \int (\omega_o + k_f E_m \cos \omega_m t)\ dt + \theta_o$$

$$= E_c \sin\left(\omega_o t + \frac{k_f E_m}{\omega_m} \sin \omega_m t\right) \qquad (14\text{–}8)$$

the constant of integration θ_o being dropped as a constant angle.

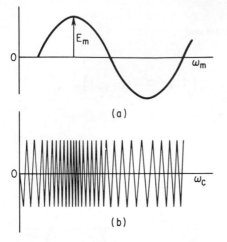

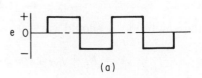

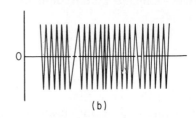

Fig. 14–2. (a) Modulating frequency; a frequency-modulated wave.

Fig. 14–3. Square wave at (a), phase-modulating a radio-frequency wave at (b).

The coefficient $k_f E_m$, when divided by 2π, is called the *frequency deviation*, and often designated Δf. This is the deviation in cycles per second from the center frequency f_o, and is proportional to amplitude E_m.

The ratio of the maximum frequency deviation to the maximum modulation frequency is called the *deviation ratio*, as

$$\delta = \frac{\Delta f}{f_m} = \frac{k_f E_m}{\omega_m} \tag{14–9}$$

Finally, the frequency-modulated wave can be written as

$$e = E_c \sin (\omega_o t + \delta \sin \omega_m t) \tag{14–10}$$

In a frequency-modulated wave the frequency deviates from the center frequency ω_o in accordance with the amplitude of the modulating signal. The deviation is independent of the modulating frequency, and the modulated wave is of constant amplitude at all times.

Another coefficient, the *modulation index*, is occasionally used and defined as

$$m_f = \frac{k_f E_m}{\omega_m} = \frac{\Delta f}{f_m} \tag{14–11}$$

For case II(b), that of phase modulation, ω is assumed constant at ω_o, and the result of Eq. 14–2 given the form

$$e = E_c \sin (\omega_o t + \varphi)$$

For the phase modulation case of the general class of angle modulation, the angle φ may be given a time variation as

$$\varphi = \varphi_o + k_p E_m \cos \omega_m t \qquad (14\text{–}12)$$

where k_p is the proportionality constant that relates phase angle variation with signal amplitude. Then

$$e = E_c \sin (\omega_o t + \varphi_o + k_p E_m \cos \omega_m t)$$

Defining the *phase deviation* as

$$\varphi_d = k_p E_m \qquad (14\text{–}13)$$

and neglecting the constant phase angle φ_o, the general expression for a phase-modulated wave is

$$e = E_c \sin (\omega_o t + \varphi_d \cos \omega_m t) \qquad (14\text{–}14)$$

Since both frequency and phase modulation are types of angle modulation, the similarity between Eq. 14–10 for frequency modulation and Eq. 14–14 for phase modulation should not be surprising. The equations differ in the coefficients δ and φ_d, and in a 90° shift in the modulation phase angle. The basic difference lies in the coefficients:

$$\text{FM:} \quad \delta = \frac{k_f E_m}{\omega_m} \qquad\qquad \text{PM:} \quad \varphi_d = k_p E_m$$

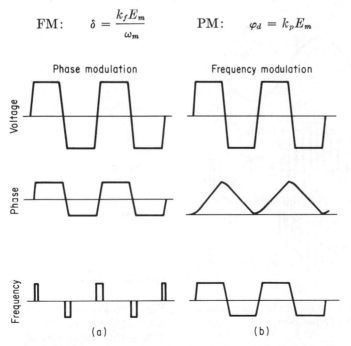

Fig. 14–4. Differences between phase and frequency modulation.

Therefore δ is an inverse function of the modulating frequency, whereas φ_d is independent of modulating frequency. Because of the similarity between these two forms of angle modulation, it is relatively easy to convert from one form to the other, and this is the principle of the Armstrong type of frequency modulation.

14–2. Frequency and power spectra in amplitude modulation

In the preceding section an expression for an amplitude-modulated wave was written as

$$e = E_c(1 + m_a \cos \omega_m t) \cos \omega_c t \qquad (14\text{–}15)$$

By trigonometric identity

$$\cos (\omega_m t) \cos (\omega_c t) = \tfrac{1}{2} \left[\cos (\omega_c + \omega_m)t + \cos (\omega_c - \omega_m)t \right]$$

so that an amplitude-modulated wave can be expressed as

$$e = E_c \cos \omega_c t + \frac{m_a E_c}{2} \cos (\omega_c + \omega_m)t + \frac{m_a E_c}{2} \cos (\omega_c - \omega_m)t \qquad (14\text{–}16)$$

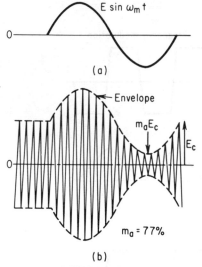

Fig. 14–5. Amplitude modulation with $m = 77$ per cent.

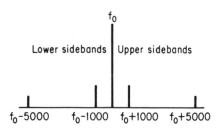

Fig. 14–6. Frequency spectrum of a carrier amplitude modulated at 1000 and 5000 cycles, simultaneously.

A wave that is amplitude-modulated by a single frequency actually consists of three frequencies. One is the original carrier frequency, ω_c, and the other two represent the sum and difference of the carrier and modulation frequencies.

The carrier envelope produced by amplitude modulation appears in Fig. 14–5. Such a wave is not the result of simple addition of carrier and modulation frequencies, but occurs because of the *product* of two trigonometric functions appearing in Eq. 14–15.

The frequency represented by the sum of carrier and modulation frequencies is called the *upper side frequency*; that resulting from the difference is the *lower side frequency*. For modulation by the complex wave forms of speech or music, a great many such side frequency pairs will exist, one pair for each frequency component; these groups of side frequencies are called *side bands*.

The band width required for transmission of an amplitude-modulated radio-frequency signal is equal to twice the highest modulating frequency. Figure 14–6 shows the frequency spectrum resulting from simultaneous modulation of a carrier with 1000 cycles and 5000 cycles.

Certain power relations can be developed for sinusoidal modulation. From Eq. 14–16 it is apparent that the amplitude of either side band is $m_a/2$ times the carrier amplitude. Power is proportional to the square of voltage, so that

$$\text{Carrier power} = \frac{KE_c^2}{2}$$

$$\text{Total side band power} = 2\frac{Km_a^2E_c^2}{8} = \frac{m_a^2}{2} \times \text{carrier power}$$

The total power in a modulated wave is

$$P = \frac{KE_c^2}{2}\left(1 + \frac{m_a^2}{2}\right) \tag{14–17}$$

so that at 100 per cent modulation the side band power is 50 per cent of carrier average power, and the total power is 150 per cent of carrier average power.

On positive modulation peaks the amplitude of the wave doubles so that the instantaneous peak power is then four times the carrier average value. Amplifiers that are to handle modulated voltages must be designed to handle such peak voltages.

The carrier is a uniform amplitude sinusoid, so that in a sense it represents a power waste. Systems have been devised for removing the carrier, or of removing one side band and the carrier, resulting in a saving of power and equipment and a reduction of band width. Such systems will be discussed later.

14–3. Frequency spectrum in frequency modulation

It was shown in Section 14–1 that a frequency-modulated wave could be written as

$$e = E_c \sin (\omega_o t + \delta \sin \omega_m t)$$

This expression is of the form $\sin (a + b)$, and can be expanded as

$$\sin (\omega_o t + \delta \sin \omega_m t) = \sin (\omega_o t) \cos (\delta \sin \omega_m t)$$

$$+ \cos (\omega_o t) \sin (\delta \sin \omega_m t) \quad (14\text{–}18)$$

These complex functions can be evaluated by means of Bessel functions, where

$$\cos (\delta \sin \omega_m t) = J_o(\delta) + 2J_2(\delta) \cos 2\omega_m t + 2J_4(\delta) \cos 4\omega_m t$$

$$+ 2J_6(\delta) \cos 6\omega_m t + \cdots \quad (14\text{–}19)$$

$$\sin (\delta \sin \omega_m t) = 2J_1(\delta) \sin \omega_m t + 2J_3(\delta) \sin 3\omega_m t$$

$$+ 2J_5(\delta) \sin 5\omega_m t + 2J_7(\delta) \sin 7\omega_m t + \cdots \quad (14\text{–}20)$$

The J_n's are Bessel functions of the first kind and order n, and are defined by an infinite series given by

$$J_n(\delta) = \sum_{k=0}^{\infty} \frac{(-1)^k}{k!(k+n)!} \left(\frac{\delta}{2}\right)^{n+2k} \quad (14\text{–}21)$$

Values of $J_n(\delta)$ are tabulated in various mathematical tables and a brief table is given in the Appendix.

By use of

$$\sin a \cos b = \tfrac{1}{2} \left[\sin (a + b) + \sin (a - b) \right]$$

$$\cos a \sin b = \tfrac{1}{2} \left[\sin (a + b) - \sin (a - b) \right]$$

and of Eqs. 14–19 and 14–20, the frequency-modulated wave becomes

$$e = E_c \{ J_o(\delta) \sin \omega_o t + J_1(\delta)[\sin (\omega_o + \omega_m)t - \sin (\omega_o - \omega_m)t]$$

$$+ J_2(\delta)[\sin (\omega_o + 2\omega_m)t + \sin (\omega_o - 2\omega_m)t]$$

$$+ J_3(\delta)[\sin (\omega_o + 3\omega_m)t - \sin (\omega_o - 3\omega_m)t]$$

$$+ J_4(\delta)[\sin (\omega_o + 4\omega_m)t + \sin (\omega_o - 4\omega_m)t] + \cdots \} \qquad (14\text{--}22)$$

A frequency-modulated wave is composed of a center frequency $\omega_o/2\pi$, and an infinite set of side frequencies, each pair spaced by an amount equal to the modulating frequency. The amplitudes of the various side frequencies are determined by the Bessel coefficients.

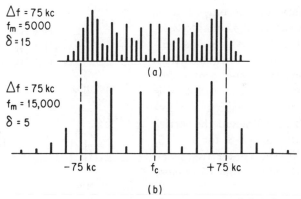

Fig. 14–7. Frequency spectrum of frequency-modulated waves.

In theory, a frequency-modulated signal will have a frequency spectrum of infinite width. Fortunately, the J_n coefficients decrease rather rapidly and the series converges, so that the band width required for good transmission becomes finite. Because of the inverse relation of δ to f_m, the low modulating frequencies have more side frequencies of importance than do the higher modulating frequencies. As shown in Fig. 14–7, the greater number of significant but close-spaced frequencies occupies about the same band width as does the signal of fewer but wider-space side frequencies for the higher modulating frequency. In general, it may be concluded that almost all side frequencies needed for good reproduction of wave form will lie in the range $\pm\Delta f$, except for δ values below 10. For these lower deviation values the high modulation frequencies will produce significant side bands beyond Δf, but these high frequencies contain low energy if speech or music are being transmitted. Thus these side frequencies may not modulate widely and the Δf range may not be seriously limiting. For FM broadcasting the Δf range is usually ± 75 kc, but receiver band widths are designed for ± 100 kc, giving some coverage of the side frequencies beyond Δf.

The function J_0 becomes zero or has roots at values of δ equal to 2.40, 5.52, 8.65, 11.79, 14.93, $\cdots$, as indicated in Fig. 14–9. At those values of deviation ratio the center frequency does not exist, and this is one reason for not calling the frequency with J_0 coefficient the carrier frequency. In Fig. 14–8, for $\delta = 15$, $\Delta f = 75,000$, the center frequency term is small, since δ at 15 is close to the root at 14.93.

In this discussion of frequency modulation, the amplitude of the wave, E_c, remains constant, and the deviation of frequency from the center is a function of the amplitude of the modulating signal. This point is clear if it is remembered that δ is a function of modulating signal amplitude.

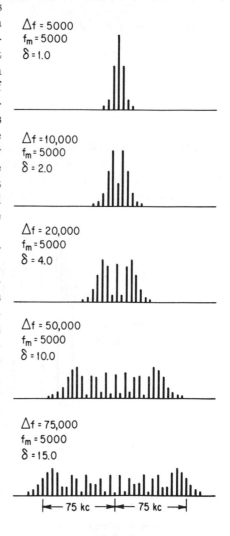

Fig. 14–8. Spectra of FM waves, showing effect of changing frequency deviation.

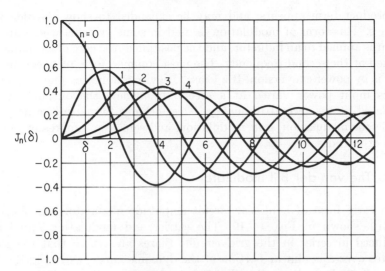

Fig. 14–9. Bessel functions.

14–4. Amplitude modulation principles

Amplitude modulation may be accomplished by any process whereby an output wave is a result of the *product* of two input waves. Two general methods are available for achieving this product; one involves a nonlinear relation between voltage and current in a circuit device, the second permits use of a circuit having a linear relation between input and output power.

A transistor or vacuum tube will have a nonlinear volt-ampere relation as

$$i = a_o + a_1 e_s + a_2 e_s^2 + \cdots \qquad (14\text{–}23)$$

and if a two or more frequency input be applied as

$$e_s = E_1 \sin \omega t + E_2 \sin \beta t$$

then modulation and side bands will appear in the output current as a result of the $\sin \omega t \sin \beta t$ term caused by expansion of the second power term in the series.

A linear form of modulation causes a current of one frequency to pass through an impedance whose magnitude is varied at a second frequency; then the voltage across the impedance is

$$\mathbf{E} = I_m \sin \omega t \times Z \sin \beta t$$

The product term appears, and may be expanded to show the side frequencies. This form of modulation is used in some systems where an a-c current is applied to an inductor, and the position of the core of the inductor is varied at the second frequency. The most common form of linear modulation is by power conversion. If a Class C device amplifying one frequency has its input power varied at a second frequency, the output will be modulated at the second frequency. This includes forms known as plate or collector modulation, grid modulation, and screen or suppressor modulation of tetrodes.

14-5. The van der Bijl modulator

An early form of nonlinear circuit amplitude modulator was the van der Bijl, shown in Fig. 14-10. The carrier and modulating signal are introduced in series in the grid circuit. Biases are set so that the tube operates over a nonlinear portion of the dynamic curve, as in Fig. 14-11. The peak carrier voltage plus the peak modulating voltage will just carry the tube to cutoff.

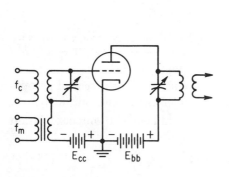

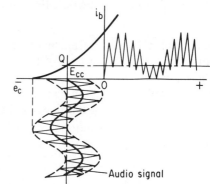

Fig. 14-10. The van der Bijl modulator.   **Fig. 14-11.** Operation of the van der Bijl modulator.

Applying signals of

$$e_s = E_c \cos \omega_c t + E_m \cos \omega_m t \qquad (14\text{-}24)$$

to a characteristic expressed by Eq. 14-23 gives

$$i = I_o + a_1 E_c \cos \omega_c t + a_1 E_m \cos \omega_m t + a_2 E_c^2 \cos^2 \omega_c t$$

$$+ a_2 E_m^2 \cos^2 \omega_m t + 2 a_2 E_c E_m \cos \omega_m t \cos \omega_c t.$$

which may be transformed to

$$i = I_o + \frac{a_2(E_c^2 + E_m^2)}{2} + a_1 E_c \cos \omega_c t + a_1 E_m \cos \omega_m t$$

$$+ \frac{a_2 E_c^2}{2} \cos 2\omega_c t + \frac{a_2 E_m^2}{2} \cos 2\omega_m t$$

$$+ a_2 E_c E_m \cos (\omega_c + \omega_m)t + a_2 E_c E_m \cos (\omega_c - \omega_m)t. \qquad (14\text{--}25)$$

The direct current is changed in value, the original input frequencies are present, and new frequencies comprising the side frequencies and second-harmonic distortion terms have appeared.

The current flows through the tank circuit, resonant at $f_c = \omega_c/2\pi$. The tank is assumed to have a high resonant resistance, R, to f_c and nearby frequencies, and negligible impedance to d-c and all other frequencies. If it be required that $\omega_c \gg \omega_m$, the voltages appearing across the tank circuit are

$$e_L = iR = a_1 E_c R \cos \omega_c t + a_2 E_c E_m R \cos (\omega_c + \omega_m)t$$

$$+ a_2 E_c E_m R \cos (\omega_c - \omega_m)t \qquad (14\text{--}26)$$

It is apparent that these terms represent the carrier and upper and lower side frequencies, and that the nonlinear circuit has accomplished amplitude modulation.

Should the tuned circuit have too high a Q value, its impedance may fall at the frequencies of some of the higher side bands, and this will lower the effective percentage modulation for those frequencies; this is known as *side-band clipping.*

The side frequencies and the second-harmonic terms are present because of, and are proportional to, the coefficient a_2. This coefficient is the rate of change of slope, or the curvature, of the transfer characteristic in the operating region. High a_2 values will increase the per cent modulation, but will increase the distortion. Also the dynamic curve becomes more linear with increased load resistance, and a_2 falls; thus for high modulation the load must be low, which reduces power output. Because of the low output and low possible modulation percentage, the circuit is not often used, but was presented here as an illustration of the nonlinear circuit method of modulation.

14–6. Modulated Class C amplifier

A common application of the linear method of modulation varies the power input to a tube or transistor in accordance with the modulating signal.

Assume a Class C amplifier with the input circuit driven by a source of power at carrier frequency f_c. In Class C operation the driving voltage can be increased until saturation conditions are reached, and further increases in input fail to give proportionate output increases. This situation is illustrated in Fig. 14–12(a), which relates the output alternating current in the resonant tank to the grid driving voltage, for several values of supply voltage.

The operation of the Class B linear occurs as shown, up to the point of saturation. For Class C operation the input E_g is further raised to give operation in saturation, as shown by the dashed line at E_{g1}. Replotting of data taken for E_{g1} gives the curve of Fig. 14–12(b). This curve indicates that a linear relation between output tank current and plate supply voltage can be expected in a Class C amplifier driven into saturation.

If the plate supply voltage is then made to vary at a rate slow with respect to a cycle of the carrier frequency, the alternating tank current will vary linearly with E_b, and the envelope of variation will be that of the modulating signal. A sufficiently long linear region of the curve

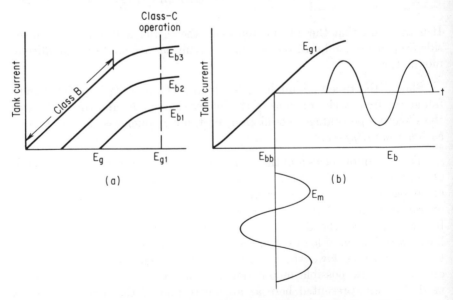

Fig. 14–12. (a) I_{tank} vs E_g for a class C amplifier; (b) I_{tank} vs E_b for a saturated amplifier.

is assumed to exist, as shown in Fig. 14–12(b).

A circuit for providing the desired variation of E_b at the modulation rate is shown in Fig. 14–13. The *modulated amplifier* is that portion of the circuit supplied with carrier signal E_c, and the *modulator* is the circuit supplying the modulating signal E_m. In this case the modulator is a Class B amplifier supplying the modulating signal in series with E_{bb}. The total voltage supplied to the modulated amplifier is

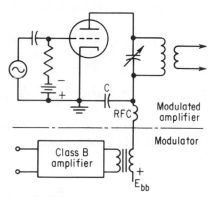

Fig. 14–13. Plate modulation by a class B modulator.

$$E_b = E_{bb} + E_m \cos \omega_m t$$

From Fig. 14–12(b), for 100 per cent modulation it is necessary that $E_m = E_{bb}$, so that

$$E_b = E_{bb}(1 + m \cos \omega_m t) \qquad (14\text{–}27)$$

is a more useful form of the expression. Examination of this equation indicates that should m exceed the value 1.0, or the modulation percentage exceed 100 per cent, then E_b becomes negative at intervals. Obviously, zero current would flow and a gap of zero output would appear. This phenomenon would cause transient damping currents in the output tank, and transmission of signals at frequencies somewhat off the expected carrier frequency, creating interference to adjacent radio channels.

Two design factors are important in setting up a plate modulator. These are the plate loss to be expected in the Class C modulated amplifier, and the value of load into which the modulator works. The latter value is especially important if a Class B audio amplifier is employed as modulator.

The average value of the plate current when averaged over a cycle of the carrier frequency has two components under linear modulation as

$$I_b' = I_b + m I_b \cos \omega_m t$$

If modulation is linear, then the cosine term contributes nothing to a time average over a cycle of f_m, and a d-c ammeter reads I_b independent of the value of m. If nonlinear effects enter, the average of I_b' becomes different from I_b, and this discrepancy is usually taken as an indication of improper operation.

The plate-circuit input is

$$P_{in} = \frac{1}{2\pi} \int_0^{2\pi} E_{bb}(1 + m \cos \omega_m t)I_b(1 + m \cos \omega_m t)d\omega_m t$$

$$= E_{bb}I_b + \frac{m^2}{2} E_{bb}I_b \tag{14-28}$$

The d-c source can supply only the I_b component of plate current, so the remainder of the power input is obtained from the output of the modulator, or

$$P_{out\ modulator} = \frac{m^2}{2\eta} E_{bb}I_b \tag{14-29}$$

where η is the decimal efficiency of the modulator output transformer. The term $m^2 E_{bb}I_b/2$ represents power input to the modulated amplifier for the side band.

The power output *to the tank circuit* as determined by the Class C amplifier efficiency η_p is

$$P_{out} = \eta_p E_{bb}I_b \left(1 + \frac{m^2}{2}\right)$$

since the efficiency is approximately constant over the modulation cycle. The plate loss of the modulated amplifier is then

$$P_d = P_{in} - P_{out} = E_{bb}I_b \left(1 + \frac{m^2}{2}\right)(1 - \eta_p) \tag{14-30}$$

indicating that the loss increases with m. Thus it is necessary to choose tubes such that in the unmodulated condition they will be operating at only 67 per cent of rated dissipation. Since 100 per cent modulation is not constantly reached for voice or music, this percentage reduction in dissipation may be somewhat decreased for that service.

The impedance into which the modulator-transformer secondary works can be readily calculated. It represents a resistance given by

$$R_b = \frac{\text{modulation component of secondary voltage}}{\text{modulation component of secondary current}}$$

$$= \frac{m E_{bb} \cos \omega_m t}{m I_b \cos \omega_m t} = \frac{E_{bb}}{I_b}. \tag{14-31}$$

The modulator transformer can then be designed to present the proper plate-to-plate load to the modulator tubes.

14–7. Grid-bias modulation

A Class C amplifier driven by a carrier-frequency source at f_c, and given a sufficiently high load impedance, will develop a linear relation between the fundamental component of anode current and the grid bias voltage. If the bias then be made to vary at frequency f_m, modulation of plate-circuit output will be achieved in a circuit such as Fig. 14–14. The basic difference between this method and the van der Bijl modulator can be seen by comparison of the currents in Figs. 14–11 and 14–15. The van der Bijl circuit varies the amplitude of a continuous direct current (Class A) whereas the grid-bias method has a plate current of discontinuous pulses (Class B or C).

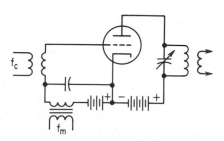

Fig. 14–14. Grid-bias modulator.

The tube is operated as a Class C amplifier, with a bias greater than cutoff. The circuit operates through changing the current conduction angle at the f_m rate. The tube operation varies from an underexcited low efficiency Class C amplifier with no modulation to a higher efficiency mode approximating Class B on modulation peaks, and then practically complete cutoff on negative peaks.

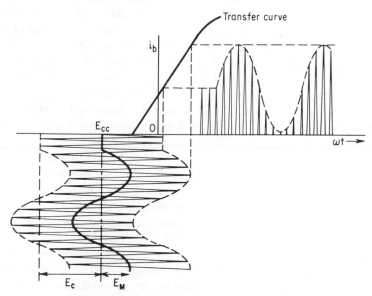

Fig. 14–15. Grid-bias modulation.

These changes in conduction angle cause changes in plate-circuit efficiency. Under carrier only, or zero modulation conditions, the power output will be one fourth the peak value and the voltage peak across the load will be one half the supply voltage; $e_{b\ min}$ will thus be high and the efficiency of the order of 30 per cent. On negative modulation peaks the tube is driven to almost complete cutoff and output nears zero. On positive peaks the output voltage peak approaches the supply voltage and the efficiency doubles to near 60 per cent. The additional power required for the side bands of the modulated wave is supplied by changes in circuit efficiency, shifting greater or lesser amounts of power between the load and the tube losses. For this reason grid-bias modulation is sometimes called *efficiency modulation*.

Because of the low carrier-only level of efficiency, the dissipation ratings for a given power output must be higher than for plate modulation. This requirement is conterbalanced by the fact that less modulator power is needed for the grid-bias system. Circuit adjustment is more difficult for the latter system, however, due to the critical values needed for bias, carrier driving voltage, and the magnitude of the load.

14–8. Other forms of amplitude modulation

Modulation of the suppressor-grid voltage of tetrodes is a satisfactory means of efficiency modulation, and values of m up to 0.9 can be achieved with reasonably low distortion. The suppressor grid is negatively biased to a point which reduces the efficiency to about 30–35 per cent. This lowers the possible power output, since the output to be expected under normal Class C operation will be reached only on modulation peaks, when the efficiency approaches 60-70 per cent. Suppressor modulation is easier to adjust than is grid-bias modulation because the bias and signal voltages are in two independent circuits, reducing interaction.

Grid-bias and plate modulation may be combined in a form known as *cathode modulation*. A transformer with tapped secondary is connected in the cathode lead as output for the modulator. A portion of the modulating voltage is selected from the taps and introduced into the grid circuit, whereas the full secondary voltage is applied in the anode circuit. The power required for modulation, and the performance and efficiency, is intermediate to that of the two primary forms of modulation.

To modulate tetrodes it is found necessary to simultaneously modulate both screen and anode through circuits such as Fig. 14–16. The circuit at Fig. 14–16(a) reduces the anode voltage to the desired screen voltage, but wastes modulating power in the resistor R. The multiple secondary transformer at Fig. 14–16(b) provides proper voltages to both screen and anode, for simultaneous modulation.

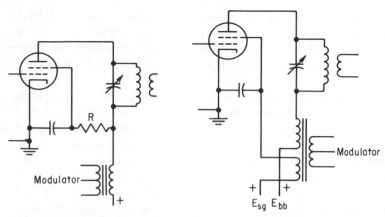

Fig. 14–16. Simultaneous plate and screen modulation for tetrodes.

14–9. AM-SSB systems

The carrier in amplitude modulation conveys no information and may be considered a waste of power. It is possible to suppress the carrier and transmit the side bands only in a *suppressed-carrier* (SC) system, also called a *double-side-band* or DSB system.

It is also apparent that the second side band conveys redundant information (overlooking frequency-selective fading in the ionospheric transmission path which might remove one side band), and the space occupied by an AM wave in the frequency spectrum might be halved if one side band only were transmitted without carrier. The result is an AM-SSB-SC system, more generally referred to as SSB transmission.

The carrier must be reintroduced at the receiver for such systems, and should be synchronized with the original oscillator to avoid distortion. Lack of exact synchronism produces a slight shift in each frequency component of the modulation; for voice operation this is considered tolerable since it is the amplitude rather than the exact frequency which gives sounds a particular meaning. It is still found that the reintroduced carrier must be within a few cycles of the original carrier to preserve intelligibility.

Two major methods are used at present to separate the side bands and carrier. Both systems employ a *balanced modulator* to remove the carrier from the desired signal, and this circuit will be discussed in the next section. The *phasing method* of SSB generation develops two sets of side bands without carrrier, but with the side bands out of phase. Addition or subtraction of the side-band sets then removes the upper or lower side band as desired. This method can be employed at radio frequencies as high as a few megacycles.

The *filter* method generates the side bands without carrier, then discards one side band by use of a narrow-band filter. Many filters of satisfactorily narrow pass band with flat response are suited only to low frequencies, so that separation of the side bands is usually carried out in the range of 20 kc to 5 mc. The output side band is then translated to the transmission frequency by a process known as heterodyning, to be discussed in Chapter 15.

The lowest frequency component of the unwanted side band is separated from its counterpart in the wanted side band by twice the lowest modulating frequency. This may require the filter to separate two signals differing by only 40 cycles, at a base frequency of kilocycles or megacycles. This is a severe requirement on either method of SSB generation, since the desired wanted to unwanted side-band ratio may be as high as 30-50 db. This can be accomplished, but simpler circuits cut off the modulation pass band at about 200 cycles, by a high-pass filter, so that a 400-cycle difference exists between the nearest frequencies, thus making the filter requirements less severe.

14-10. The balanced modulator

A circuit usually employed to remove the carrier from the side bands in an AM signal is the *balanced-modulator* of Fig. 14-17.

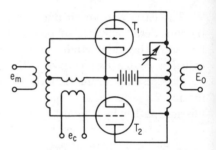

It may be assumed that operation takes place over the curved portion of the transfer characteristic of the two identical tubes. Considering a-c components only, then

Fig. 14-17. Balanced modulator.

$$i_p = a_1 e_g + a_2 e_g^2 + \cdots \qquad (14\text{-}32)$$

The modulation voltage introduced on the grid of T_1 is $E_m \sin \omega_m t$, and on the grid of T_2 is $-E_m \sin \omega_m t$. A carrier frequency voltage is introduced in the common lead to cathode, so that the input of T_1 is

$$e_{g1} = E_m \sin \omega_m t + E_c \sin \omega_c t$$

and that of T_2 is

$$e_{g2} = -E_m \sin \omega_m t + E_c \sin \omega_c t$$

Using Eq. 14-32, the a-c anode currents are

$$i_{p1} = a_1 E_m \sin \omega_m t + a_1 E_c \sin \omega_c t + a_2 E_m^2 \sin^2 \omega_m t$$

$$+ 2a_2 E_m E_c \sin \omega_m t \sin \omega_c t + a_2 E_c^2 \sin^2 \omega_c t + \cdots \qquad (14\text{-}33)$$

$$i_{p2} = -a_1 E_m \sin \omega_m t + a_1 E_c \sin \omega_c t + a_2 E_m^2 \sin^2 \omega_m t$$

$$- 2a_2 E_m E_c \sin \omega_m t \sin \omega_c t + a_2 E_c^2 \sin^2 \omega_c t + \cdots \qquad (14\text{-}34)$$

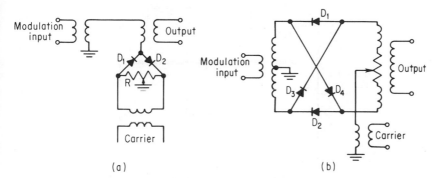

Fig. 14–18. Other forms of balanced modulators, using diodes.

The secondary voltage on the output transformer is proportional to the difference of the two primary currents, and is given by

$$e_o = 2k(a_1 E_m \sin \omega_m t + 2a_2 E_m E_c \sin \omega_m t \sin \omega_c t) \qquad (14\text{–}35)$$

The tuned circuit at the output, resonant to ω_c or the original carrier frequency, will be sufficient to reject the modulation term, ω_m, provided that $\omega_c \gg \omega_m$. The remaining term may then be transformed to

$$E_o = 2ka_2 E_m E_c [\cos(\omega_c - \omega_m)t - \cos(\omega_c + \omega_m)t] \qquad (14\text{–}36)$$

which consists solely of the side bands of an AM wave.

Resistance modulation may also be used for balanced modulation to remove the carrier, as in Fig. 14–18. In (a) the two diodes alternately are conducting and open at carrier-frequency rate; thus the output is caused to vary as

$$E_o = I_m \cos \omega_m t \times R_d \cos \omega_c t$$

and this product term produces modulation as

$$E_o = \frac{I_m R_d}{2} [\cos(\omega_c + \omega_m)t + \cos(\omega_c - \omega_m)t] \qquad (14\text{–}37)$$

which is the expected side-band pattern without carrier.

The circuit at Fig. 14–18(b) is a more elaborate form which can be shown to switch the modulation input at the carrier-frequency rate, again giving side bands without carrier, providing the carrier balance control is properly set. This form is very commonly used in carrier telephony.

14–11. SSB by the phasing method

Generation of an SSB signal by the phasing method requires two balanced modulators and two 90° phase-shift networks, one giving a constant

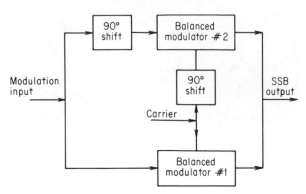

Fig. 14–19. Block diagram of phasing method of *SSB* generation.

phase shift over the modulating frequency range, the other providing a 90° shift only over the range of carrier frequencies expected.

As in Fig. 14–19, the modulation frequencies are fed to the two balanced modulators, to one directly and to the other through the 90° phase shift network for the modulating frequencies. The carrier is likewise supplied to the two modulators in quadrature. The outputs of the two modulators, consisting of side bands only, are then added or subtracted, to give either the upper or lower side band as output.

The inputs to the two modulators are

	(1)	(2)
Modulation	$E_m \sin \omega_m t$	$E_m \cos \omega_m t$
Carrier	$E_c \sin \omega_c t$	$E_c \cos \omega_c t$

It may again be assumed that the modulators have parabolic characteristics given by

$$i = a_1 e_s + a_2 e_s^2 \qquad (14\text{--}38)$$

For modulator (1) the two inputs are

$$e_{s1} = E_m \sin \omega_m t + E_c \sin \omega_c t$$

$$e_{s2} = -E_m \sin \omega_m t + E_c \sin \omega_c t$$

Using these inputs, and assuming an output circuit resonant to ω_c, the output of the balanced modulator is given as

$$E_{o1} = 2ka_2 E_m E_c [\cos (\omega_c + \omega_m)t - \cos (\omega_c - \omega_m)t] \qquad (14\text{--}39)$$

For modulator (2) the two inputs are

$$e_{s1}' = E_m \cos \omega_m t + E_c \cos \omega_c t$$

$$e_{s2}' = -E_m \cos \omega_m t + E_c \cos \omega_c t$$

and again using Eq. 14–38, the output of the second modulator may be written as

$$E_{o2} = 2ka_2 E_m E_c [\cos (\omega_c + \omega_m)t + \cos (\omega_c - \omega_m)t] \qquad (14\text{--}40)$$

If the outputs of the two modulators are added

$$E_{o1} + E_{o2} = K a_2 E_m E_c \cos (\omega_c + \omega_m)t \qquad (14\text{--}41)$$

and the upper side band is obtained. The subtraction of the outputs gives the lower side band as

$$E_{o2} - E_{o1} = K a_2 E_m E_c \cos (\omega_c - \omega_m)t \qquad (14\text{--}42)$$

The modulating frequency phase shifter is required to have a constant 90° shift and constant insertion loss over the frequency range of the modulating input. Physically this is best achieved by introducing a phase shifter in each branch, with a constant 90° difference between their outputs over the required frequency range. The attenuation difference can also be held approximately constant. A simple form of such a circuit is shown in Fig. 14–20.

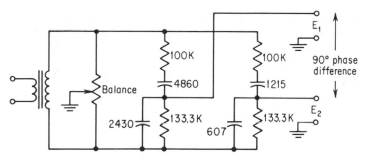

Fig. 14–20. Audio phase-shift network, range 300–3000 cycles.

14–12. Filter method of SSB generation

The filter method of generating a single-side-band signal is simple, but the design of the filter is not. As has been pointed out, it is necessary to provide a filter cutoff on one side which will separate signals differing by only twice the lowest modulation frequency. Circuits have been designed, however, using powdered-iron-core inductors, quartz crystals as resonators, or mechanical resonant systems, which perform satisfactorily in this regard.

A block diagram of the system appears in Fig. 14–21. The filter may be adjusted to select either upper or lower side band as desired. After

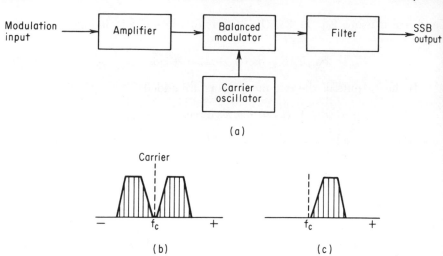

(a)

(b) (c)

Fig. 14–21. (a) Filter generation of *SSB*; (b) output of balanced modulator; (c) output after filter.

filtering, the desired output frequency is obtained by frequency multiplication.

The response curve for a mechanical resonator filter, operating at 455 kc, is shown in Fig. 14–22, as an example. This unit employs elastances (capacity) or spring elements, and masses (inductance) in an assembly analogous to an electrical filter circuit. However, the Q of mechanical elements is ordinarily much higher than is possible with inductors, and sharper cutoff and frequency response is possible with the mechanical system.

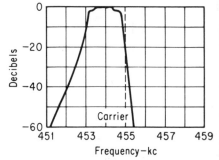

Fig. 14–22. Response of mechanical filter at 455 kc.

Since filter elements cannot have infinitely steep cutoff slopes, it is customary to place the filter cutoff so that the carrier frequency position is possibly 20 db below the level of the wanted side band. Thus in Fig. 14–22, the value of f_c would be 455 kc. This causes some attenuation of the lower frequencies of the wanted side band, but insures greater attenuation of the undesired band. As shown, frequencies below 200 cycles would be attenuated, but these frequencies are not important for understandable speech and their loss is usually unnoticed. By so placing the f_c position, a modulation frequency of 200 cycles in the unwanted side band is attenuated 35 db with respect to the wanted band, and this is the order of suppression usually desired.

14–13. FM by reactance variation

Variation of the inductance or capacitance in the tuned circuit of an oscillator at the desired modulation rate will produce frequency modulation of the oscillator frequency. Mechanical means of variation cannot follow the frequencies used, but it is possible to employ a tube or transistor as a variable reactance, which when shunted across the oscillator tank circuit will vary the reactance of the circuit at the desired rate. One form of reactance-tube circuit is shown in Fig. 14–23(a), the variable reactance appearing across the A, A terminals when these terminals are shunted across an a-c voltage source.

Operation of the circuit may be determined by reference to Fig. 14–23(b), in which the tube is replaced with its current-source equivalent. The current $\mathbf{I}$ is

$$\mathbf{I} = \frac{\mathbf{E}}{R - j/\omega C} + g_m \mathbf{E}_g + \frac{\mathbf{E}}{r_p} \tag{14–43}$$

The grid voltage is $\mathbf{E}_g = \mathbf{E}R/(R - j/\omega C)$ so that

$$\mathbf{I} = \frac{(1 + g_m R)\mathbf{E}}{R - j/\omega C} + \frac{\mathbf{E}}{r_p}$$

The term involving r_p will be negligible for the usual pentode. The impedance appearing at the A, A terminals then is equivalent to a resistance and capacitance in parallel, or

$$\mathbf{Z}_{A,A} = \frac{R}{1 + g_m R} - \frac{j}{\omega C(1 + g_m R)} \tag{14–44}$$

If it be required that $1/\omega C \gg R$, then this impedance is due to an effective capacitance

$$C_e = C(1 + g_m R) \cong g_m R C \tag{14–45}$$

The capacitance appearing at the A, A terminals is a function of the g_m of the tube, and this parameter can be varied by the grid bias. If the bias be controlled by the modulating signal, the effective capacitance can be varied at the modulation rate.

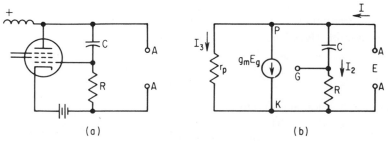

Fig. 14–23. (a) Reactance-tube circuit; (b) equivalent circuit.

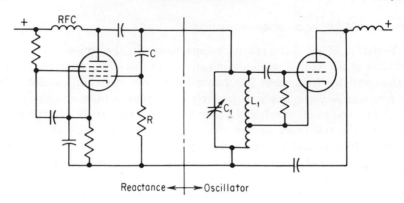

Fig. 14–24. Application of a reactance tube to an oscillator.

If this reactance tube is connected across the tuned tank of an oscillator, as in Fig. 14–24, the output frequency can be swung through a frequency range, in accordance with the modulating signal. Linearity of frequency deviation vs grid-bias voltage can be secured by limiting the change in bias to a few volts. The effective value of g_m under modulation may be written as

$$g_m = g_e(1 + k_f E_m \cos \omega_m t)$$

The oscillator frequency will then be

$$\omega = \frac{1}{\sqrt{L_1[C_1 + RCg_e(1 + k_f E_m \cos \omega_m t)]}} \tag{14–46}$$

The center frequency with zero modulation will be

$$\omega_o = \sqrt{\frac{1}{L_1(C_1 + RCg_e)}} \tag{14–47}$$

The frequency shift due to modulation can be expressed as a ratio to ω_o, or

$$\frac{\omega}{\omega_o} = \sqrt{\frac{1}{1 + \dfrac{k_f E_m \cos \omega_m t}{1 + C_1/RCg_e}}} \tag{14–48}$$

The frequency shift will be small, and the above may be expanded by the binomial theorem. Only the first two terms need be retained to give

$$f \cong f_o\left[1 - \frac{k_f}{2(1 + C_1/RCg_e)} E_m \cos \omega_m t\right] \tag{14–49}$$

which is a frequency-modulated wave with

$$m_f = -\frac{k_f E_m}{2(1 + C_1/RCg_e)} \tag{14–50}$$

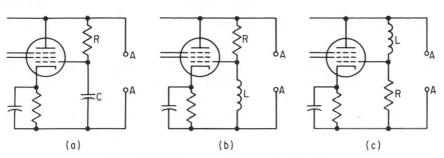

(a)   (b)   (c)

Fig. 14–25. Three reactance-tube circuits.

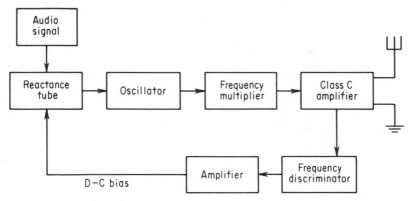

Fig. 14–26. Block diagram of an FM transmitter.

Three other basic reactance-tube circuits are illustrated in Fig. 14–25. The circuits at Fig. 14–25(a) and (c) appear as inductive, and that at Fig. 14–25(b) as capacitive.

The stability of the center frequency is dependent on the stability of the oscillator and reactance tube, and will not usually meet channel tolerances which allow ± 2 kc at 100 mc. It is customary to utilize a frequency stabilizing system, one example being shown in Fig. 14–26 in block form. The path from audio signal to reactance tube, oscillator, multiplier, and output Class C amplifier is as indicated. A portion of the output is sampled and applied to a circuit called a *frequency discriminator*, which gives a d-c output voltage proportional in amplitude and polarity to the instantaneous shift of the modulated wave from the center frequency. This d-c voltage is then averaged and applied as additional bias to the grid of the reactance tube, so as to shift the average frequency in a direction to correct any error or drift from center.

The above method employs a tuned circuit in the discriminator as the standard against which frequency is compared. Another method compares the output frequency against that of a crystal oscillator, and the difference frequency is amplified, rectified, and averaged before being applied as a d-c correction bias for the reactance-tube modulator.

14–14. The Armstrong FM system

An FM wave differs from a PM wave by reason of the deviation ratio, which is an inverse function of f_m. The Armstrong system, an early frequency-modulation method, operates on the audio signal with a weighting network so that the modulating signal amplitude becomes inversely proportional to frequency. By phase-modulation with this signal, it is possible to generate a synthetic FM wave. Since the original generator is crystal-controlled, the center frequency will be stable.

It may be seen from Fig. 14–9 that the Bessel coefficients for $\delta < 0.5$ exist only for $n \leq 2$. Replacing δ with φ_d, and for $\varphi_d < 0.5$, $n \leq 2$, Eq. 14–22 can be written

$$e = E_c\{J_o(\varphi_d)\cos\omega_o t + J_1(\varphi_d)[\sin(\omega_o + \omega_m)t - \sin(\omega_o - \omega_m)t]$$
$$+ J_2(\varphi_d)[\sin(\omega_o + 2\omega_m)t + \sin(\omega_o - 2\omega_m)t]\} \quad (14\text{--}51)$$

If φ_d is small, then J_2 will be small, and this PM wave will appear as the AM wave of Eq. 14–16, with the carrier shifted 90° with respect to the side bands. Thus an amplitude-modulated wave may be produced, the carrier removed in a balanced modulator, and the side bands recombined with a 90° shifted carrier, the result being a PM wave. If, then, the modulating frequency is given an amplitude which varies inversely with fre-

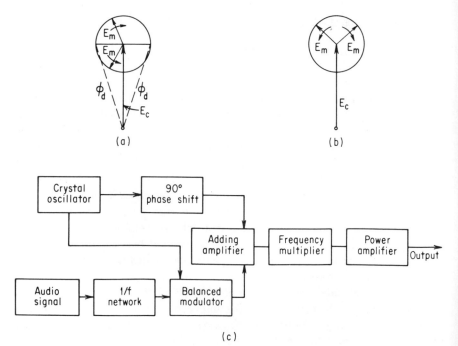

Fig. 14–27. (a) PM; (b) AM; (c) the Armstrong system.

quency, or φ_d replaced with δ, the wave becomes a frequency-modulated one.

Figure 14–27 illustrates the result. At Fig. 14–27(a) the two side frequency phasors rotate in unison but in opposite directions, and the sum of the carrier and side bands causes the carrier to change phase by the angle φ_d. It will be noted that the phase relation of carrier and side frequencies is at 90° with respect to the AM situation at Fig. 14–27(b); in the latter case only the amplitude of the carrier is varied, and not the phase.

In the block diagram at Fig. 14–27(c), the audio signal is weighted and applied to the balanced modulator with the carrier oscillator output. The output E_B then consists only of side frequencies, E_B, and these are recombined with the shifted carrier in the adding amplifier. The whole process is performed at low frequency, and a high degree of frequency multiplication is used to produce the desired frequency deviations of thousands of cycles.

14–15. Amplification of modulated signals

It would appear that amplitude modulation at a low signal level, followed by power amplification to raise the power level, would provide a saving in power and cost over the high-level AM methods discussed. If such amplification is undertaken with a Class C amplifier, and the amplifier is operating into saturation as it should for high efficiency, large variations in input voltage will have only small effect on the output, or the modulation would be stripped off the carrier.

However, it was shown that the output of the Class B radio-frequency amplifier was a direct function of input voltage, so that such a circuit will amplify an amplitude-modulated signal properly. Such circuits are called Class B linear amplifiers, and are widely used, particularly to raise the power level of SSB signals originally generated at low level.

There is no such problem in amplification of FM signals, since the amplitude is constant. Class C amplifiers, at high efficiency, are used to raise the power level of such signals.

14–16. AM versus FM with respect to interference

Noise signals, created by atmospheric static or manmade electrical discharges, create reception problems for weak radio signals. Such noise signals are essentially amplitude-modulated, and if a receiver is designed for reception of FM signals, and made insensitive to amplitude variations, such spasmodic interference can be largely eliminated. Thus FM has a major advantage over AM for noisy channel use, particularly in the mobile service.

Interference between two simultaneously received signals on the same or adjacent channels is also a major difficulty in some radio reception. In this respect FM has advantages over AM, as may be seen from Fig. 14–28. In Fig. 14–28(a) one signal, as represented by a phasor A, rotates about point 0. A second signal of amplitude B is received simultaneously, so that the sum voltage applied to the receiver input is R. As phasor B rotates through its cycle, the amplitude of R will change greatly; thus the input to the receiver is varied in amplitude by signal B, and in an AM receiver the B signal may cause appreciable amplitude interference with A even though B is quite small.

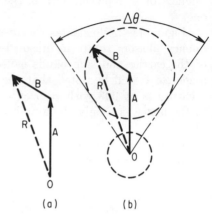

Fig. 14–28. Effect of interference between two FM signals.

If signal A be of constant amplitude and frequency-modulated, as in Fig. 14–28(b), and an interfering FM signal B be added, the resultant input to the receiver will be R. Vector B will rotate about the end of A, and the resultant R will vary in amplitude and also in relative phase angle. For the relative amplitudes as shown, the variation $\Delta\theta$ approximates 1 radian, as indicated by the extent of the circle locus. Even if the two signals are equal in amplitude, the phase-angle variation cannot be much greater, although the amplitude variation would then be so severe that AM reception would be impossible.

An FM receiver can be made insensitive to amplitude variations of reasonable magnitude by clipping all signals to a common low level; this effect might be indicated in the diagram by reducing the resultant signal always to an amplitude fixed by the small circle with center at O. Very considerable amplitude variations, due either to amplitude modulation on the signal or to amplitude variation of R caused by the interfering signal, can be removed. The voltage effective on the receiver would then be of amplitude fixed by this small dashed circle, but varying about $\pm \frac{1}{2}$ radian in phase angle with respect to vector A. If, however, the original frequency modulation causes its phase angle to vary through $2\pi\Delta f/f_m$ radians per cycle, or 10π radians for $\Delta f = 75,000$ cycles and $f_m = 15,000$ cycles, it can be seen that the phase-angle variation of $\pm \frac{1}{2}$ radian due to interference is quite small. If $f_m = 150$ cycles for the same value of Δf, then the desired signal phase variation would be 500π radians, still further reducing the effect of the interference.

The effect of the interfering signal can be reduced under certain, but not all, circumstances by widening the frequency band or increasing Δf. E.H. Armstrong is credited with development of the FM system, and with demonstrating that increased band width of signal does reduce interference when the signal is definitely above the noise level.

14–17. Pulse modulation systems

In addition to the modulation methods discussed, in which modulation by sinusoidal signals has been assumed, there are other systems in which the modulation of a radio-frequency carrier may be by short pulses. The simplest of these is the conventional telegraph, whereby information is transmitted by a code of dots and dashes, or by turning the carrier on and off, as a limiting case of amplitude modulation. Code pulses are also sent by frequency modulation wherein a symbol (mark) is transmitted at one frequency and the space between symbols is sent at a second frequency. This is a form of modulation known as frequency-shift telegraphy.

Most pulse systems are based on sampling of the information signal amplitude at periodic intervals, usually about twice the maximum frequency present, or about 8000 times per second for voice transmission. They transmit a very short pulse of radio-frequency carrier for each sample, with the pulse characteristics varied in some manner proportional to the signal amplitude at the sampling instant.

Multiplex operation may also be employed, in which pulses due to other messages are inserted and transmitted between the pulses of the first message. This requires a synchronized message distributor at the receiver to sort the individual pulses into the proper channels. Synchronism is usually obtained by transmitting a synchronizing pulse at regular intervals.

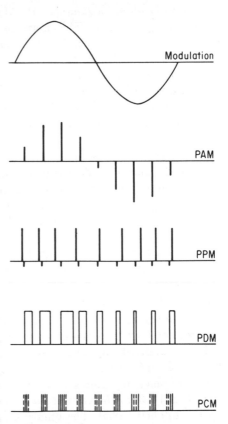

Fig. 14–29. Forms of pulse modulation.

Four common pulse systems are illustrated in Fig. 14–29, and are:

Pulse-amplitude modulation (PAM), in which the modulating signal is sampled at the basic rate, usually $1/2f_m$, where f_m is the maximum value, and the amplitude of the modulation determines the amplitude of the transmitted pulse. The band width will be great for exact pulse wave form, but may be reduced by a low pass filter, thereby somewhat rounding the pulses. As long as the amplitude at the pulse intervals is preserved, no distortion will be introduced.

Pulse-position modulation (PPM), is a form in which the timing or position of the pulse is varied around a fixed mean value and conforms to the signal amplitude at the time of sampling. That is, a positive signal may set the pulse ahead, a negative signal will set the pulse behind the reference time. In reception the pulse shape received is not important, the time of arrival being the only information necessary for interpretation of the signal.

Pulse-duration modulation (PDM), varies the pulse length or duration around a fixed value. This may be done by shifting either the leading or trailing edge, or both, as a function of the sampled amplitude. Greater channel band width is required than for PAM, and design must be co-ordinated to prevent overlap of the variable length pulses in multiplex use. The reception of such a wave is simple, since the information can be recovered from the demodulated pulses by passing them through a low pass filter having a pass band equal to that of the modulation frequency range.

Pulse-code modulation (PCM), translates the sampled amplitude data into a code, and the code is transmitted as a succession of pulses and spaces. The system enjoys greater freedom from noise and interfering signals than is possible with most other pulse systems. This freedom arises from the fact that it is merely necessary to determine that a pulse was or was not transmitted, and it is not necessary to measure any characteristic of the received wave form. If the signal has sufficient amplitude, it is possible to operate circuits at the receiver which will regenerate the original pulse, free from noise. This permits ready use of repeater stations for long distance transmission, without cumulative effects on the wave form or information.

The magnitude of each sample of the modulating signal is measured and rounded off into one of a set of quantized levels, which are the only values permitted to the system. These levels are finite in number and furnish the information for assembly of the pulses as a code group. Quantization of the sample may be accomplished in a form of cathode-ray tube, as in Fig. 14–30. A horizontal sheet beam of electrons is deflected vertically by the applied signal. The binary digital code is used, with the presence of a pulse indicated by a 1, absence by a 0. Thus

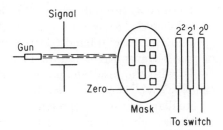

Fig. 14-30. Quantizing tube for PCM system (three-pulse group, eight level system).

	2^2	2^1	2^0
7 =	1	1	1
6 =	1	1	0
5 =	1	0	1
4 =	1	0	0
3 =	0	1	1
2 =	0	1	0
1 =	0	0	1
0 =	0	0	0

is the code for the eight level, three-bit mask shown. Portions of the sheet of electrons pass through appropriate holes in the mask and reach the vertical collecting electrodes behind each column of holes. The signal is quantized by the vertical deflection of the beam, and the mask holes. By sequential switching of the electrodes, the beam or signal may be sampled at the desired frequency, and the code pulses assembled into the required serial pulse groups. Thus each pulse transmitted indicates by its location in the code group, the presence of a particular power of two in the signal amplitude sample.

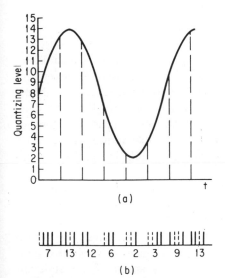

Fig. 14-31. Pulse quantizing and coding in PCM.

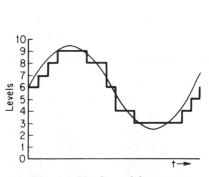

Fig. 14-32. Quantizing error.

The above three digit or *bit* code permits quantizing a signal into 2^3 or eight levels. An n bit code would raise this to 2^n levels, with a corresponding increase in band width required because of the increased number of pulses transmitted. Figure 14–31 illustrates a wave quantized into 16 levels, with the resultant pulse groups shown in Fig. 14–31(b). The start time for each code group is a fact known to both transmitter and receiver by auxiliary timing equipment.

Errors can be introduced by insertion of an extra pulse by noise, but this must occur at a precise time, and will not be frequent. A pulse may also be dropped due to a fading signal or interference. Various more-elaborate codes are available to provide methods of self-checking for errors. Should such a system indicate that an error has occurred, the equipment then asks the transmitting station to repeat the offending code group.

In receiving there will be a small random noise in the decoded signal, due to the finite and limited number of quantizing levels. This noise will have a maximum value equal to one half a quantizing level, as shown in Fig. 14–32. For lower frequency modulation, where the sampling rate is greater per cycle of modulation, this error would not appear as great.

The band width is obviously proportional to the sampling rate $2f_m$, to the number of quantizing levels or bits per code group, and to the number m of messages multiplexed on one channel if this feature is added. For good pulse wave form the band width requirements of the circuits can then be found by the methods of Section 9–14.

14–18. Information content and channel capacity

It may be assumed that the cost of a given system for transmission of information is proportional to the band width required. A system requiring a given band width may be justified, however, if it can be shown that the information transmittable per unit time is greater than for some other narrower band system. A measure of the information content of signals, and the relation to band width or channel requirements is an economic necessity in the selection of optimum modulation and transmission methods.

There are three signal characteristics which must be included in such a measure: the frequency band required, the time needed for transmission, and the system requirements for recognition of levels of signal intensity.

Speech is our most usual method of information exchange. As a continuous function its band width is equal to the difference between maximum and minimum frequency components present. Its speed of transmission is limited by the human vocal chords, and its range of intensity variation may be 1000:1 or 30 db. Thus speech postulates a system of limited band width but very large intensity range.

Signals coded into pulses may be found to have much different requirements. The band width for perfect pulse reproduction is theoretically infinite, but the number of recognizable signal levels may be reduced to two. Thus pulse transmission is a system requiring wide band width, but very limited requirements for recognition of signal levels.

Approximations may be made in these methods, which reduce the system requirements. It is found, for instance, that the ear can recognize only changes in intensity which approximate twice the power; these steps of just-audible intensity change may be taken as 2.5 db. For a signal-intensity ratio of 30 db, it is then sufficient that we recognize only about 12 levels. Naturalness or fidelity may be lost, but intelligibility will not be damaged. Thus requirements on the overall speech system are reduced.

Likewise, for pulse systems we may use PCM where the only characteristic of a pulse which must be recognized is its presence. The band width may then be greatly reduced with degradation of pulse shape, but without much loss in information transmitted.

Sensitivity of the several systems to noise or random signals must also be considered, since this will control the rate of information accurately received, and determine the power level required for transmission. Such sensitivity to noise is much greater for speech, where we are attempting to recognize a large number of intensity levels, than it is for pulses where we note only the presence or absence.

It is apparent that measures of information content of a signal, rate of information transmittal, and efficiency of use of channel band width, would be very helpful in system design. Such measures are available in a portion of our science known as *information theory*.

The measure of information quantity is defined by the number of possible values, states, or levels which a signal may have in a basic interval of the signal. This number of states or levels is defined as the equivalent number of ideal on-off signals, or binary digits, which would be required if it were to be so transmitted. That is, the *quantity of information* in a basic signal interval is

$$I_o = \log_2 L \qquad (14\text{--}52)$$

where the unit of I_o is the *bit* (*bi*nary dig*it*) and L is the number of states or levels distinguished by the receiver.

As an example, consider speech which has been sampled at 2.5 db levels, as discussed above. There would be 12 such volume levels in the 30 db dynamic range covered by the voice and recognized by the receiver. The information content of speech would then be *defined* as

$$I_o = \log_2 12 = 3.58 \text{ bits}$$

For a teletypewriter code in which five digit positions are represented by holes punched in the transmission tape, there are $2^5 = 32$ possible states of information per basic interval, or per code. This provides for the 26 letters of the alphabet plus start, stop, shift and other control signals. The quantity of information per basic interval is then

$$I_o = \log_2 32 = 5 \text{ bits}$$

The quantity of information transmitted per unit time is the *information rate* in bits per second. For speech, we have already mentioned that signals should be sampled at a rate equal to twice the highest frequency component present (thus providing at least one pulse for each half cycle), and this provides a measure of the number of speech intervals present. Although speech may contain frequencies up to 6000 cycles, it is found that intelligibility is maintained even when the frequency band is limited to 250-3000 cycles per second, as is done in telephony. With 12 distinguishable levels and $2750 \times 2 = 5500$ basic intervals per second, the rate of transmission of speech information is

$$I = 5500 \log_2 12 = 19,700 \text{ bits/sec}$$

For the teletypewriter code, the usual transmission speed is 60 five-letter words per minute. Allowing an additional space code for each word gives a rate of six codes per second. Then

$$I = 6 \log_2 32 = 30 \text{ bits/sec}$$

It is of interest to analyze a television signal in a similar manner. It may be assumed that the eye can distinguish 10 gradations of light intensity. The quantity of information contained in a given picture element or dot is

$$I = \log_2 10 = 3.32 \text{ bits per picture element}$$

There are 525 lines per frame, and it may be assumed that resolution and circuit band width is such that each line will have about 500 identifiable dots. There are 30 frames per second, so that the number of picture elements or dots per second is

$$n = 525 \times 500 \times 30 = 7.875 \times 10^6$$

and the information rate then is

$$I_o = 7.875 \times 10^6 \log_2 10 = 2.62 \times 10^7 \text{ bits/sec}$$

We may reason from the above that teletypewriter service transmits information slowly, but requires only a narrow frequency band. Speech is of intermediate speed with moderate band width requirements, and television transmits information at a high rate, but requires a wide frequency channel.

It is found that the capacity of a channel to transmit information is a function not only of band width, but also of *signal-to-noise ratio*, expressed as S/N. Noise power is ordinarily assumed to be uniformly distributed over the received band, or is said to be "white" in character. The problem is to estimate the probability of being able to distinguish a given number of levels or states in the presence of noise.

Assume that in a stated band width there is a noise power of N watts, and a signal power of S watts. The received power is then $S + N$ watts, or proportional to $\sqrt{S + N}$ volts, and we are attempting to receive this in the presence of $\sqrt{N}$ volts of noise. A signal less than the noise will not usually be distinguishable, whereas a signal $\sqrt{S}$ greater than $\sqrt{N}$ will probably be separable. The number of distinct states or levels which can be distinguished, *on the average*, may be taken as proportional to the ratio of the voltages, or

$$L = \frac{\sqrt{S + N}}{\sqrt{N}} = \sqrt{1 + S/N} \tag{14–53}$$

The maximum information available in a basic interval of the signal is then

$$I_o = \log_2 \sqrt{1 + S/N} = \tfrac{1}{2} \log_2 (1 + S/N) \tag{14–54}$$

We have already assumed that the number of basic information intervals per second is twice the frequency band width or $2B$. The total information which can be transmitted in time T over a noisy channel of band width B is then

$$I_T = BT \log_2 (1 + S/N) \tag{14–55}$$

This result, which relates the information transmitted to the band width of the channel, the time available for transmission, and the signal-to-noise ratio, is called the *Hartley-Shannon law*. As originally suggested in 1928 by Hartley it had the form BT, but this was modified to the above form many years later by Shannon, to include the effect of signal-to-noise ratio.

It may be seen that the total information can be increased by widening the band, allowing greater time for transmission, or increasing the signal-to-noise ratio. The latter increase may be very expensive in terms of equipment complexity or power, because of the exponential increase rate.

Equation 14–55 shows that it is possible to receive a signal and information even though S is less than N, or the signal is apparently buried in the noise. This is the subject of major efforts in the communication art, but will not be gone into here except to indicate that such reception may be possible by slowing down the rate of transmission, or increasing T or the time of transmission, or by so coding the information as to require a much greater band width for transmission.

Speech, when transmitted by double-side-band AM, occupies a band twice its own frequency range. It therefore requires a large S/N for successful reception, and this is well known. Part of the advantage of DSB over SSB is in the double transmission of the side band information, or the in-built redundancy of the system. An advantage of SSB, even though the band width has been narrowed, is in the avoidance of interference from the AM carrier, a factor not related to the channel capacity.

When speech is transmitted by FM means, the band width may be enlarged indefinitely by change of deviation ratio. It has been shown that such enlargement reduces the sensitivity of the system to noise interference, or permits lower S/N ratios.

It has already been mentioned that the reception of pulse transmission, and of PCM in particular, is possible with high accuracy in severe noise interference. It is now apparent that the ability to receive such signals is fundamentally a result of the greatly increased band width required for transmission of the pulses.

It must also be remembered that the frequency spectrum is limited, and system designers are always under pressure to fit their systems into finite frequency channels, or face trade-offs in performance against the limitation of the frequency spectrum. Thus ideal design results can rarely be achieved in practice.

Problems

14-1. If a voltage of form

$$e = E_a(1 + m \sin \omega_m t) \sin \omega_c t$$

is applied to a resistor R, find the power dissipated. If $m = 0.35$, find the power dissipated by each of the frequency components present.

14-2. An amplitude-modulated wave has a carrier frequency of 1000 cycles and a modulation-signal frequency of 100 cycles. Plot waves of the individual frequencies present over one cycle of the 100-cycle wave and add point by point, obtaining a modulated wave. The amplitudes are $E_c = 100$ v, $E_m = 50$ v. Show how the modulation percentage might be measured on a cathode-ray oscilloscope.

14-3. A modulated wave is expressed by the equation

$$e = 25(1 + 0.27 \cos 1250t + 0.18 \cos 3000t) \cos 10^7 t$$

State all frequencies present, and give the amplitudes of m for each frequency.

14-4. In Fig. 14–33 the force F moves the slider between the 45- and 55-per cent points on the resistor at a rate of 6 times per second. Write the expression for the voltage E_o, and state all frequencies present.

14-5. An amplitude-modulated carrier of 2.5 megacycles is 60 per cent modulated at 10,000 cycles. Write the expression for the voltages appearing across a

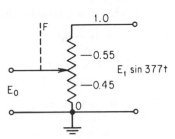

Fig. 14-33.

resonant circuit, tuned to 2.5 megacycles, and having Q of 5, through which this current flows. What is the value of m_a for the voltage across the circuit? Repeat for a tuned circuit of $Q = 150$. $L = 4$ microhenrys in both cases.

14-6. An amplitude-modulated Class C amplifier has a plate efficiency of 76 per cent and a carrier power input of 1000 w.

(a) What modulator power output will be required for 90 per cent modulation?

(b) If the modulated amplifier operates at 2250 plate volts, what ratio will be required for a transformer to couple a Class B modulator requiring 7500 ohms plate-to-plate load into the Class C modulated amplifier?

(c) If the transformer of (b) is 78 per cent efficient, find the power output of the modulator tubes for 90 per cent modulation.

14-7. A plate-modulated Class C amplifier takes 200 ma at 2000 v on the plate, and has a carrier output of 250 w. The modulator is transformer-coupled and uses tubes operating in Class A with $\mu = 20$, $r_p = 1000$, desired output impedance = 1500 ohms, and plate efficiency of 35 per cent when producing 100 per cent modulation.

(a) What transformer turns ratio is required?

(b) What is the modulator tube power output required for 100 per cent modulation, if the modulation transformer is perfect?

(c) What per cent modulation will be obtained with 30 v rms grid input to the modulator?

(d) What is the total average d-c power required by both modulator and modulated amplifier at 100 per cent modulation?

(e) What should be the plate-dissipation rating of the modulated amplifier?

14-8. A plate-modulated amplifier operating at 2000 plate volts has a rated plate dissipation of 100 w. When it is operated at 100 per cent amplitude modulation and full allowable input, the radio-frequency output to the tank circuit is 467 w.

(a) Find the unmodulated carrier power output.

(b) Determine the value of plate current taken by the modulated amplifier.

(c) A Class B modulator has an output impedance of 7500 ohms. What transformer ratio is required to couple this to the above modulated amplifier if the transformer is 92 per cent efficient? (Consider shunting effect of loss.)

(d) What power output must the Class B tubes supply for 100 per cent modulation?

14-9. A van der Bijl modulator with a transfer characteristic expressed by

$$i_b = I_b + a_1 e_g + a_2 e_g{}^2$$

has as an input voltage given by

$$e = 10 \sin 2.5 \times 10^6 t + 3 \sin 12 \times 10^3 t$$

(a) Write the expression for the output current.

(b) If this current flows through a parallel-resonant circuit tuned to a frequency of $(2.5 \times 10^6)/2\pi$, and with a Q of 6, find the voltages present across the circuit. The circuit inductance is 200 μh.

14-10. What is the ratio of the peak power required in a single-side-band signal to that in a double-side-band plus carrier signal, both carrying equal intelligence at 100 per cent modulation?

14-11. A wave with peak amplitude of 100 v and frequency of 100 megacycles is frequency-modulated at 10,000 cycles with a frequency deviation of 75 kc. Find the amplitude of the center frequency and all side frequencies up to the sixth. Plot to scale as a line diagram.

14-12. A frequency-modulated broadcasting station is assigned a frequency channel of 92.1 to 92.3 megacycles.

(a) What is the maximum permissible value of δ for a modulating frequency of 5000 cycles?

(b) For this modulating frequency, how many side-band frequencies could be permitted to exist on each side of the center frequency?

(c) Plot a line diagram of amplitudes of all side bands which will fill the channel.

14-13. Find expressions for the resistance and inductance produced at the A,A terminals by the circuit of Fig. 14-25(a). Neglect r_p.

14-14. Find expressions for the resistance and capacity produced at the A,A terminals by the circuit of Fig. 14-25(b). Neglect r_p.

14-15. Find expressions for the resistance and inductance produced at the A,A terminals by the circuit of Fig. 14-25(c). Neglect r_p.

14-16. In the reactance-tube circuit of Fig. 14-24, the g_m of the reactance tube can be varied over the range of 800 to 2000 μmho. With $f_c = 500$ kc, and C chosen as 2 pf, what value should R have if it is desired to shift the frequency over a range of ± 7.5 kc? The capacity C_1 is 25 pf.

14-17. The relation between modulating voltage and frequency deviation produced may be found by varying the voltage and noting the values of voltage at which the center-frequency amplitude becomes zero. Explain why this may be done.

14-18. The reactance-tube circuit of Fig. 14-25(b) is connected to a Hartley oscillator operating at 10 megacycles (before the modulator is connected). With $R = 10,000$ ohms and $L = 10 \times 10^{-6}$ h, what frequency deviation will be produced if the g_m of the reactance tube is changed from 300 to 1200 μmho?

14-19. A sine wave of 1000 cycles and 7 v peak is sampled 9000 times per second, by a quantizing system which recognizes 1 v levels. Write the binary code representation of the pulse groups for a PCM system to transmit one cycle of the above wave.

14-20. A wirephoto picture of size 5 × 7 inches is scanned at a rate of 100 lines per inch, with equal horizontal resolution; we assume that we can see 12 density gradations. Determine the S/N ratio in db required for the channel, of band width 1200 cycles, if the picture is transmitted in 10 seconds.

References

1. Armstrong, E. H., "A Method of Reducing Disturbances in Radio Signaling by a System of Frequency Modulation," *Proc. I.R.E.*, **24**, 689 (1936).

2. Black, H. S., *Modulation Theory*, D. Van Nostrand Co., Inc., New York, 1953.

3. Carson, J. R., "Notes on Theory of Modulation," *Proc. I.R.E.*, **10**, 57 (1922).

4. Crosby, M. G., "Frequency Modulation Noise Characteristics," *Proc. I.R.E.*, **25**, 472 (1937).

5. ———, "Reactance-Tube Frequency Modulators," *R C A Rev.*, **5**, 89 (1940).

6. Dome, R. B., "Wide-Band Phase-Shift Networks," *Electronics*, **19**, 112 (December 1946).

7. Everitt, W. L., "Frequency Modulation," *Trans. A.I.E.E.*, **59**, 613 (1940).

8. Goldman, S., *Information Theory*, Prentice-Hall, Inc., Englewood Cliffs, N. J., 1953.

9. Hartley, R. V. L., "Relations of Carrier and Sidebands in Radio Transmission," *Proc. I.R.E.*, **11**, 34 (1923).

10. ———, "Transmission of Information," *Bell System Tech. J.*, **7** (July 1928).

11. Jahnke, E., and Emde, F., *Tables of Functions*. Dover Publications, Inc., New York, 1945.

12. *Proceedings of the I.R.E.*, Special issue on single side band, **44**, 1661–1914 (1956).

13. Reich, H. J., "The Use of Vacuum Tubes as Variable Impedance Elements," *Proc. I.R.E.*, **30**, 288 (1942).

14. Roder, H., "Amplitude, Phase, and Frequency Modulation," *Proc. I.R.E.*, **19**, 2145 (1931).

15. Schwarz, M., *Information, Transmission, Modulation, and Noise*. McGraw-Hill Book Co., New York, 1959.

16. Shannon, C. E., "A Mathematical Theory of Communication," *Bell System Tech. J.*, **27**, (July and October 1948).

Demodulation | 15

Now that the modulation of a radio-frequency wave has been studied, it is necessary to discuss the fundamental process of *demodulation* or *detection*, whereby the modulated wave may be translated back to the component frequencies in order to recover the original information. The semiconductor diode or vacuum diode are the usual devices involved.

Demodulators for amplitude modulation are usually classed as (a) *small-signal*, or *square-law* detectors, and (b) *large signal*, or *linear* detectors. The square-law detector operates by reason of the curvature of the volt-ampere characteristic of the diode. The linear detector operates with signals of several volts or more and in a manner similar to that of the diode rectifier with RC filter, wherein the volt-ampere characteristic may be assumed linear over the conducting region.

Demodulators for frequency-modulated signals are designed to be insensitive to amplitude variation, to reduce noise and static interference, and utilize circuits which convert frequency variations into amplitude variations.

15–1. Square-law demodulation

For small values of the changing or signal voltage e_s, the dynamic curve of a triode (or diode) is of the form shown in Fig. 15–1, and can be expressed by the usual Taylor's series

$$i_p = a_1 e_s + a_2 e_s^2 + a_3 e_s^3 + a_4 e_s^4 + \cdots \tag{15-1}$$

For a limited range of signal the terms of higher degree than the second may be neglected. Note that coefficient a_1 is a function of the slope of the curve, and a_2 is the rate of change of slope. The effectiveness of the

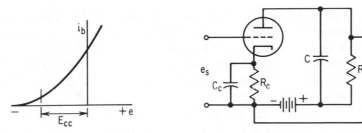

Fig. 15–1. Square-law demodulator.

demodulation will be shown to depend on the magnitude of a_2. The bias therefore is used to set the Q point near cutoff, where the curvature of such characteristics is greatest.

If the signal voltage is derived from an AM wave, then

$$e_s = E_c(1 + m_a \cos \omega_m t) \cos \omega_c t$$

and the resultant plate current expression is

$$i_p = a_1 E_c \cos \omega_c t + a_1 E_c m_a \cos \omega_m t \cos \omega_c t$$
$$+ a_2 E_c^2 (1 + 2m_a \cos \omega_m t + m_a^2 \cos^2 \omega_m t) \cos^2 \omega_c t \quad (15\text{–}2)$$

which can be transformed to a complex expression involving many frequencies:

$$i_p = \frac{a_2 E_c^2}{2} + \frac{a_2 E_c^2 m_a^2}{4} + a_1 E_c \cos \omega_c t + a_2 E_c^2 m_a \cos \omega_m t$$

$$+ \frac{a_1 E_c m_a}{2} \left[\cos (\omega_c - \omega_m)t + \cos (\omega_c + \omega_m)t \right]$$

$$+ \frac{a_2 E_c^2}{2} \left(1 + \frac{m_a^2}{2}\right) \cos 2\omega_c t + \frac{a_2 E_c^2 m_a^2}{4} \cos 2\omega_m t$$

$$+ \frac{a_2 E_c^2 m_a}{2} \left[\cos (2\omega_c - \omega_m)t + \cos (2\omega_c + \omega_m)t \right]$$

$$+ \frac{a_2 E_c^2 m_a^2}{8} \left[\cos 2(\omega_c - \omega_m)t + \cos 2(\omega_c + \omega_m)t \right] \quad (15\text{–}3)$$

In the output circuit it is possible to find all these frequencies, identifiable as a d-c term, the original carrier, the modulation frequency, the original side frequencies, the second harmonic of the carrier and of the modulation frequencies, the side frequencies on the second harmonic of the carrier, and additional side frequencies on the second carrier harmonic due to the second harmonic of the modulation. If higher-order terms had been present in Eq. 15–1, then higher-order terms would appear in the above, and the actual frequency spectrum would be extremely involved. However, the coefficients a_3, a_4, a_5, $\cdots$, become progressively smaller so no terms of quantitative significance have been overlooked.

All the terms except the repeated carrier and side frequencies contain the coefficient a_2, and are a result of the product term. Since modulation was a process in which a product term was formed, it would appear that modulators may also be demodulators, and this is true.

In the plate circuit of the triode in Fig. 15–1, capacitor C has a low reactance compared to R at f_c, and a high reactance at f_m. Then all frequencies which approximate f_c or higher will be bypassed around the load R. The voltage appearing across R will be

$$e_o = \frac{a_2 E_c^2 R}{2}\left(1 + \frac{m_a^2}{2}\right) + a_2 E_c^2 m_a R \cos \omega_m t + \frac{a_2 E_c^2 m_a^2 R}{4} \cos 2\omega_m t \qquad (15\text{–}4)$$

The d-c term will be removed or blocked by the capacitor C_1. The modulation frequency, as the desired output, will be passed on for further amplification through this capacitance, but the second harmonic of the modulation also passes with the desired signal, and represents a distortion term proportional to m_a^2.

In early modulation systems, it was not possible to modulate the signal fully, and such detectors were satisfactory for m_a small. Today, with high values of m_a usual in radio broadcasting, the distortion is considered undesirable and the square-law demodulator is not often used.

15–2. Linear diode demodulation

A diode in series with a large load resistor may be represented by a linear volt-ampere characteristic as given in Fig. 15–2(a). If an amplitude-modulated wave be applied, rectification will occur, and the original modulation may be recovered as a variation of the average value of the output voltage. The average current may be obtained as

$$I_{\text{av}} = \frac{1}{2\pi} \int_{-\pi/2}^{\pi/2} \frac{E_c}{r_d + R}\left(1 + m_a \cos \omega_m t\right) \cos \omega_c t$$

where r_d is the diode internal resistance. The current is zero over the portion of the carrier cycle in which the applied voltage is negative. Then

$$I_{\text{av}} = \frac{E_c}{\pi(r_d + R)} + \frac{m_a E_c \cos \omega_m t}{\pi(r_d + R)} \qquad (15\text{–}5)$$

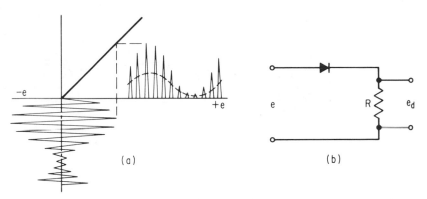

Fig. 15–2. Linear diode detection.

The rectification process has recovered a direct component and a current changing in proportion to the original modulation. This current will produce the output voltage across R, and since $m_a E_c = k_a E_m$, then

$$e_d = \frac{E_c R}{\pi (r_d + R)} + \frac{k_a E_m R \cos \omega_m t}{\pi (r_d + R)} \qquad (15\text{–}6)$$

and the original modulation has been recovered without distortion terms.

In the square-law detector the output modulation term was proportional to E_c and E_m. In the case of the linear detector, the demodulated signal is independent of carrier strength, depending only on E_m.

The simple circuit of Fig. 15–2(b) is inefficient since only about one third of the input voltage is available in the output due to the $1/\pi$ coefficient. In addition to the current terms present in Eq. 15–5, there will be a carrier-frequency component present in the load, as well as harmonics of the carrier frequency, as in the load in any half-wave rectifier. To improve the operational efficiency and to filter out these high-frequency currents, it might be suggested that a capacitor be connected across the load. Experiment indicates the result of addition of a capacitor as successful, with increased output. However, additional consideration indicates that the circuit is now that of a diode operating into an RC filter, and the above analysis will no longer be valid.

15–3. Analysis of the linear envelope detector

When a filter capacitor is added across the resistance load of a diode detector, the circuit becomes that at Fig. 15–3(a). The capacitor C charges to the peak of each carrier-frequency cycle, and discharges slowly through R on the negative half cycle, the voltage across C and the load tending to follow the *envelope* of the modulated wave.

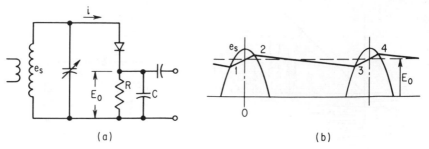

Fig. 15–3. Addition of capacity to the linear diode detector.

The situation is similar to that of the half-wave rectifier with RC filter, but the earlier analysis neglected the resistance of the diode. In detector diodes the internal resistances are higher and performance is influenced by the ratio R/r_d, so that further analysis is necessary.

In the circuit of Fig. 15–3, the capacitor C charges in series with the diode resistance r_d, whenever the applied voltage e_s exceeds the voltage across C. Conduction starts at some point 1 in Fig. 15–3(b) and continues to 2, the voltage across the RC load rising in some manner as indicated by the line between these points. At 2 the source voltage at carrier frequency is falling faster than the voltage across C can change, e_c becomes larger than e_s, and diode conduction ceases. The capacitor C then discharges through R, which is large with respect to r_d, so that the voltage falls slowly to 3 at which point conduction starts again and the cycle is repeated.

The variation of voltage over the interval 1, 2, 3, 4, is small and occurs at carrier frequency. The variation may be neglected, and it will then be assumed that the voltage across C is E_o, a constant over a few cycles of carrier frequency, but a variable over a cycle of modulation frequency. In other words, $f_c \gg f_m$.

It may be assumed that the volt-ampere characteristic of the diode is linear as shown in Fig. 15–4. An amplitude-modulated wave is applied to the circuit as

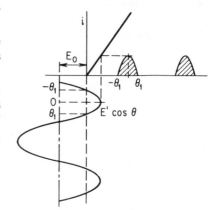

Fig. 15–4. Operation of the linear diode with RC load.

$$e_s = E_c(1 + m_a \cos \omega_m t) \cos \omega_c t$$

The voltage across the *diode* will be biased by the amount E_o, as indicated in Fig. 15–4, and current will flow for less than 180°, or only when the diode anode is positive with respect to the cathode. Because of the discontinuous nature of conduction, methods of analysis similar to those used for the Class B linear amplifier must be developed.

The voltage across the diode, is then

$$e_d = E_c(1 + m_a \cos \omega_m t) \cos \omega_c t - E_o$$

which, for the carrier frequency cycle illustrated in Fig. 15–4, may be written more conveniently as

$$e_d = E' \cos \theta - E_o \tag{15-7}$$

This expression implies that for a few cycles of f_c the term $E_c(1 + m_a \cos \omega_m t)$ is approximately constant. The current in the circuit can be written from the volt-ampere curve as

$$i = \frac{e_d}{r_d} \qquad e_d > 0 \tag{15-8}$$

$$i = 0 \qquad e_d < 0$$

so that

$$i = \frac{1}{r_d}(E' \cos \theta - E_o) \tag{15-9}$$

during the conduction interval. The average of this current over a carrier-frequency cycle may be designated I_o and determined as

$$I_o = \frac{1}{\pi r_d}(E' \sin \theta_1 - E_o \theta_1) \tag{15-10}$$

after noting that the conduction limits are $-\theta_1$ and $+\theta_1$.

From the figure it is apparent that

$$\cos \theta_1 = \frac{E_o}{E'} \tag{15-11}$$

The detected voltage which appears across the load, under the assumption that the carrier component is bypassed by C, is

$$RI_o = E_o = \frac{E'R}{\pi r_d}(\sin \theta_1 - \theta_1 \cos \theta_1) \tag{15-12}$$

Substituting for E', the load voltage may then be written as

$$E_o = \frac{RE_c}{\pi r_d}\left[(\sin \theta_1 - \theta_1 \cos \theta_1) + m_a(\sin \theta_1 - \theta_1 \cos \theta_1) \cos \omega_m t\right] \tag{15-13}$$

The first term on the right is independent of time and is a direct voltage, dependent on the magnitude of E_c. The second term varies at modulation frequency, has an amplitude proportional to E_m, and indicates recovery of the original modulating signal. Demodulation has occurred without distortion in a manner similar to that discussed in the preceding section, but with coefficients dependent on functions of θ_1, a result of the discontinuous conduction through the diode.

From Eq. 15–11

$$E_o = E' \cos \theta_1$$

and this may be used in Eq. 15–12 to yield

$$\frac{R}{r_d} = \frac{\pi}{\tan \theta_1 - \theta_1} \tag{15–14}$$

The ratio R/r_d is a function of choice of diode and load. From this information the designer may then determine θ_1 from Table 24 or Fig. 15–5. Other circuit parameters are then readily determined. Since R/r_d is a constant of the circuit, the angle of conduction θ_1 is also a constant for that circuit. This is true irrespective of the degree of modulation or the amplitude of E_c applied.

If the load resistance R were infinite, then the capacity C would charge to the peak value of E', the average value of load voltage E_o would equal the peak value of E', and this output could not be exceeded, or the *detection efficiency* would be maximum. It is convenient to define the ratio of E_o actually obtained to the value E' which might theoretically be obtained, as the detection efficiency, η_d. That is,

$$\eta_d = \frac{E_o}{E'} = \cos \theta_1 = \frac{R}{\pi r_d} (\sin \theta_1 - \theta_1 \cos \theta_1) \tag{15–15}$$

TABLE 24. LINEAR-DIODE DETECTOR FUNCTIONS

$\dfrac{R}{r_d}$	θ_1 (degrees)	η_d	$\dfrac{R_i}{R}$
∞	0	1.00	0.500
1751	10	0.985	0.509
210.8	20	0.940	0.538
58.4	30	0.866	0.594
22.3	40	0.766	0.685
9.85	50	0.643	0.839
4.59	60	0.500	1.113
2.06	70	0.342	1.693
0.735	80	0.174	3.495
0.0	90	0.0	∞

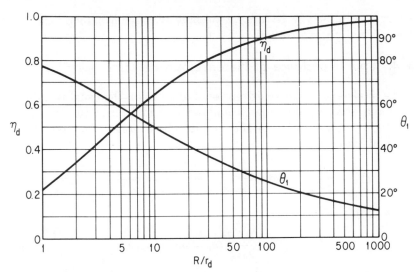

Fig. 15–5. Efficiency and conduction angle as a function of R/r_d.

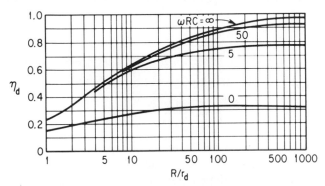

Fig. 15–6. Variation of efficiency as C is increased.

If the detection efficiency of the linear-diode circuit is computed by use of Eq. 15–6, then

$$\eta_d = \frac{1}{\pi\left(\dfrac{1}{R/r_d} + 1\right)} \qquad (15\text{–}16)$$

and this relation is plotted for $\omega RC = 0$ in Fig. 15–6, for comparison with the detection efficiency achieved by envelope detection, with the bypass capacitor. It is also possible to compute the detection efficiency for values of capacitance intermediate to the $\omega RC = 0$ and the $\omega RC = \infty$ curves, to illustrate the beneficial effect of envelope detection. Since the ratio R/r_d will usually be large, especially with semiconductor diodes, the efficiency will always be high.

15–4. Input impedance of the envelope detector

The diode and load circuit represent a shunt on the usual tuned-circuit source and absorb power therefrom, and it is of interest to determine the magnitude of this loading of the circuit. The average input power to the diode and load is

$$P_{in} = \frac{1}{2\pi} \int_{-\pi}^{\pi} ei \, dt = \frac{1}{2\pi} \int_{-\theta_1}^{\theta_1} \frac{E' \cos \theta (E' \cos \theta - E_o)}{r_d} \, d\theta$$

in view of Eq. 15–9. Then

$$P_{in} = \frac{(E')^2}{2\pi r_d} (\theta_1 - \sin \theta_1 \cos \theta_1) \tag{15–17}$$

The effective input resistance of the diode and load is equal to the resistance which would dissipate P_{in} with the same voltage applied. Since E' is a peak value

$$R_i = \frac{(E')^2}{2P_{in}} = \frac{\pi r_d}{\theta_1 - \sin \theta_1 \cos \theta_1} \tag{15–18}$$

By use of Eq. 15–14, it is possible to obtain

$$\frac{R_i}{R} = \frac{\tan \theta_1 - \theta_1}{\theta_1 - \sin \theta_1 \cos \theta_1} \tag{15–19}$$

This function is evaluated in Table 24 and plotted in Fig. 15–7. With usual circuit design employing R/r_d values of 50 or more, it can be seen that R_i/R is relatively independent of R/r_d values. Once R is selected

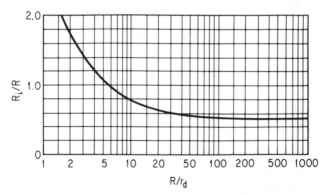

Fig. 15–7. Loading effect of the diode detector.

and R_i obtained, the performance of the amplifier and tuned circuit supplying the diode can be obtained.

For large values of R/r_d the equivalent load resistance of the diode tends toward $0.5R$ in the envelope detector. In the linear-diode detector this load appears as equal to $2R$.

15–5. Amplitude distortion in envelope detectors

The RC product of the diode load determines the rapidity with which the voltage across the load can change. If the voltage does not change rapidly enough to follow the modulation envelope, then amplitude distortion will be introduced. This effect occurs only as the modulation envelope is decreasing, since at that time C must discharge through R and the time constant is large. On the increasing portions of the envelope the capacitance is charged through r_d (usually much smaller than R), and the time constant is not limiting.

The maximum permissible value of C depends on the highest modulation frequency and the maximum modulation percentage, since if C is too large, the voltage E_o will not fall fast enough between cycles to follow a declining modulation envelope. If the value of C is too small, the output voltage will be reduced or the efficiency lowered because of insufficient charge storage to maintain the voltage between successive carrier cycles.

The difficulty is most serious at the instant at which the rate of change of the modulation envelope is greatest; the rate of discharge of C must be less than the slope of the modulation envelope for the highest modulation frequency. For an amplitude-modulated signal the rate of change of the modulation envelope is

$$\frac{de}{dt} = \frac{d}{dt} \left[E_c(1 + m_a \cos \omega_m t) \right] = -E_c m_a \omega_m \sin \omega_m t \qquad (15\text{–}20)$$

The capacitor C can discharge from some voltage E according to

$$e_c = E\epsilon^{-t/RC}$$

so that

$$\frac{de_c}{dt} = -\frac{E}{RC}\epsilon^{-t/RC} = -\frac{e_c}{RC}$$

Since the modulation envelope appears across C,

$$\frac{de_c}{dt} = -\frac{E_c(1 + m_a \cos \omega_m t)}{RC} \qquad (15\text{–}21)$$

In order that the voltage across C may follow the variation of the modulation envelope, the rate of fall of the envelope must be less than the rate of fall of the discharge voltage across C; the critical condition which will just permit following the changes in envelope voltage can be stated as

$$E_c m_a \omega_m \sin \omega_m t = \frac{E_c(1 + m_a \cos \omega_m t)}{RC}$$

$$RC = \frac{1}{\omega_m}\left(\frac{1 + m_a \cos \omega_m t}{m_a \sin \omega_m t}\right) \tag{15-22}$$

Maximizing the right side with respect to t gives

$$\cos \omega_m t = -m_a, \qquad \sin \omega_m t = \sqrt{1 - m_a^2}$$

Consequently the maximum value of the load time constant which will still permit the modulation envelope to be followed is

$$RC \leqq \frac{1}{\omega_m} \frac{\sqrt{1 - m_a^2}}{m_a} \tag{15-23}$$

showing that the circuit parameters are limited by the maximum modulation frequency and the modulation percentage. Even though the time constant must approach zero for 100 per cent modulation in the above, practice shows that distortion is not excessive if the maximum value of RC does not exceed $1/\omega_m m_a$.

A second form of amplitude distortion results when a complete diode-detector circuit is used, as in Fig. 15–8(a). Here R_1 and C_1 serve the functions previously discussed, while C_2 blocks the d-c component from the following amplifier, and R_2 serves as a volume or gain control. The result insofar as the diode is concerned is that the d-c and a-c circuit impedances are different, the a-c resistance being the smaller and due to R_1 and R_2 in parallel, the reactance of C_2 being neglected.

A modulation component of current will exist in the diode circuit, along with the d-c component due to E_c. The negative peak of the a-c component of current should never exceed the direct current, since such

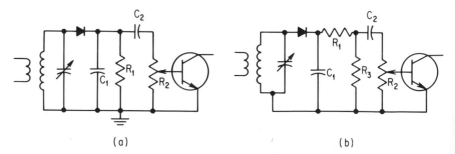

(a)   (b)

Fig. 15–8. Distortion reduction in the diode envelope detector.

action would lead to zero current, negative currents being impossible in the diode. The a-c wave form would then be *clipped* on the negative peak.

From Eq. 15–13 it is possible to write the ratio of the peak of the a-c voltage in the diode output to the d-c voltage as

$$\frac{\text{Peak } E_{a-c}}{E_{d-c}} = \frac{(\text{Peak } I_{a-c}) \, | \, Z_m \, |}{I_{d-c} R_1} = m_a \qquad (15\text{–}24)$$

From the reasoning above, the maximum value for the ratio (peak I_{a-c}/I_{d-c}) is unity, if clipping is to be avoided. The maximum value for m, if clipping is to be avoided, is

$$\text{Max } m_a = \frac{| \, Z_m \, |}{R_1} \qquad (15\text{–}25)$$

which for the circuit of Fig. 15–8(a), becomes

$$\text{Max } m_a = \frac{R_2}{R_1 + R_2} \qquad (15\text{–}26)$$

This would make it seem desirable to lower R_1 to raise the maximum m_a value, but to do so will lower the detection efficiency and increase the effect of possible nonlinearity of the diode. The designer is led to a compromise as at Fig. 15–8(b), where an attempt is made to equalize the d-c and a-c load values by introducing a resistor R_1 in series with the a-c load. This expedient sacrifices some output voltage, but additional gain is easily obtained to compensate. It can then be stated that

$$\text{Max } m_a = \frac{R_1 + R_2 R_3/(R_2 + R_3)}{R_1 + R_3} = \frac{1}{1 + R_3^2/(R_1 R_2 + R_1 R_3 + R_2 R_3)}$$

$$(15\text{–}27)$$

which can be made to approach unity by making R_1 large and R_3 small, without serious effects on the detection efficiency.

With a large input signal to minimize zero distortion in semiconductor diodes, and a large R/r_d to linearize the diode curve, it is possible to hold the distortion to one or two per cent in envelope detectors.

15–6. Automatic gain control (AGC)

In radio reception the strength of the received signal varies, both from station to station, and from instant to instant because of changes in the path of propagation. To provide nominally constant output power, it is desirable to vary the gain or amplification in the radio receiver, in inverse proportion to the strength of the received signal. Circuits for this purpose are called *automatic gain control* (AGC), or *automatic volume control* (AVC).

A measure of the strength of the received carrier is available in the d-c voltage output from the detector diode, given by Eq. 15–13 as

$$e_{d-c} = \frac{E_c R}{\pi r_d}(\sin\theta_1 - \theta_1\cos\theta_1)$$

It is possible to separate this voltage from the modulation by an *RC* filter, with time constant long with respect to the lowest modulation frequency, and designated R_3, C_3 in Fig. 15–9. The d-c voltage so obtained may be applied as a bias to vary the gain of amplifiers ahead of the detector.

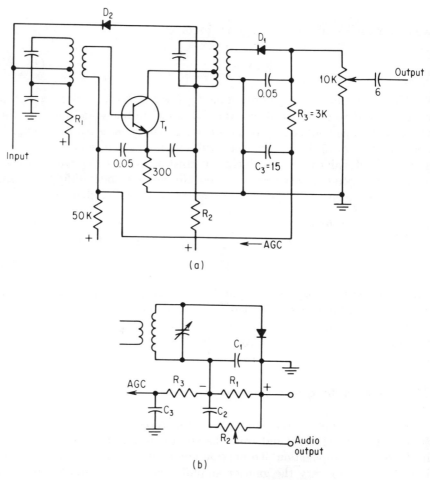

Fig. 15–9. Simple AVC systems. (capacities in μf.)

In transistor amplifiers several currents or voltages might be varied to provide change in gain, but the most desirable seems to be I_E. For a typical NPN transistor, the curve of Fig. 15–10 shows the range of gain change available. In Fig. 15–9(a), the negative voltage from D_1 changes the base bias of T_1 and reduces the emitter current with increasing signal strength. As the emitter current is reduced, various parameters change; h_{fe} and the internal gain fall, and h_{ie} and h_{oe} change and impedance mismatches result which further reduce the overall gain.

In the vacuum-tube circuit of Fig. 15–9(b), the negative voltage from the detector is applied as grid bias to one or several variable-mu amplifier stages, reducing the g_m and thereby dropping the overall gain.

A strong carrier signal produces a large d-c voltage, which makes a large reduction in gain. A weak received signal produces only a small control voltage, and allows higher amplifier gain. Thus the level of signals at the detector is held somewhat constant, and Fig. 15–11 shows the improvement to be expected. Since the control must always allow a slight change to obtain a working bias voltage, it is impossible for the system to produce absolute constancy of detector output. Improvement is proportional to the number of amplifier stages under control, usually two to four in most receivers.

The system as shown will reduce the strength of all signals, even the extremely weak ones. To remedy this, a separate diode may be used to isolate the detection function from the AGC. By an additional bias or threshold, this second diode may be held from conducting until a certain signal level is reached. Thus full gain is available for weak signals, and as shown in Fig. 15–11, considerable improvement in constancy of output is possible.

To provide additional control action on extremely strong signals, the shunting diode, D_2, of Fig. 15–9(a), is used. At normal signal levels, D_2 is back biased by the difference of voltage drops across R_1 and R_2.

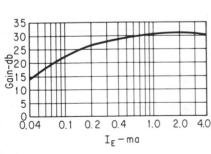

Fig. 15–10. Gain vs I_E for 2n168 transistor.

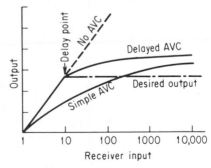

Fig. 15–11. Operation of a receiver with AVC.

As the normal AGC circuit operates, the collector current of T_1 is reduced, lowering the drop across R_2 and at a predetermined level D_2 becomes conducting, constituting a low-impedance shunt across the first transformer and drastically reducing the gain. This system is excellent for control of high signal strengths, in the range in which emitter current cannot be further reduced.

15–7. Dynamic rectification characteristics

It is sometimes convenient to determine envelope-detector performance from *rectification characteristics*, one family being given in Fig. 15–12 for a vacuum diode. These curves are experimentally determined and show the relation between E_o and I_o for various values of applied carrier. Load lines may then be superimposed to show the relation between E_o and I_o for any load R and rms carrier voltage. From this value of rms unmodulated carrier voltage, a Q point is determined. When the impressed carrier is modulated, the point of operation moves up and down along the load line. If the a-c load is appreciably different from the d-c load R, then operation is along an a-c line drawn with appropriate slope through the Q point fixed by the amplitude of the unmodulated carrier.

Such a line is drawn dashed through a Q point fixed by a 100,000-ohm d-c load and an rms carrier voltage of 15 v. It is assumed that the d-c load [R_1 of (b), Fig. 15–9] is shunted by a volume control R_2 of 100,000 ohms, isolated by a large capacity C_2. Thus the a-c load line has a slope determined by a 50,000-ohm load.

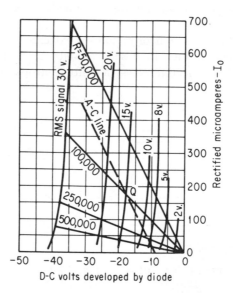

Fig. 15–12. Rectification characteristic.

It may be seen that the a-c load line reaches zero current before the applied a-c voltage reaches zero; that is the current reaches zero when the a-c rms voltage reaches 6 v. A 100 per cent amplitude-modulated wave would have a radio-frequency value varying from zero to 30 v, for the situation under discussion. The a-c load line indicates that the anode current would be zero for all values of radio-frequency voltage less than 6 v peak, thus showing the effects of negative peak clipping. For lower percentages of modulation, the voltage will not fall to such low values, and the distortion will not be present. This result corresponds with the previous analytical discussion.

15–8. The product detector

Transmission of SSB signals is an attractive method because of the saving in radio-frequency power made possible by elimination of the carrier, and by the fact that the frequency band required for transmission is one half that needed for DSB, or double-side-band AM signals. For reception of SSB signals, it is necessary to introduce a carrier at a frequency within a few cycles of the original value, and this is most often done with the *product detector* of Fig. 15–13. The process of detection of SSB signals is more nearly one of modulation.

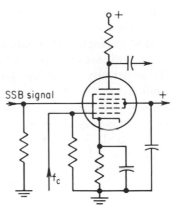

Fig. 15–13. Product detector for *SSB* reception.

A five-grid or *pentagrid* tube is used because of the shielding it provides between the signal and local oscillator supplying the carrier; this shielding improves the carrier frequency stability. The reintroduced carrier is supplied to grid 1, and the SSB signal to grid 3. The local carrier oscillator causes the electron stream to vary at the oscillator frequency, and the single-side-band signal then varies this sinusoidally-varying stream in accordance with the signal. The output current appears as a product of the input frequencies; this is similar to the impedance modulation mentioned in Section 14–4. Since the modulation process requires a product of two frequencies, the necessary condition for modulation is present in the product detector, and the new carrier is modulated by the received side band. The desired output is the original modulating frequency, present in the detector output as the difference frequency of ω_c and the side band.

Grids 2, 4, and 5 serve as screen and suppressor as in conventional pentodes. The value of the pentagrid structure lies in the independence of bias adjustments and signal levels for the two grids, to give the greatest output of the product term.

15–9. Electronic voltmeters

The proportionality between an a-c input voltage and a direct output current that is inherent in rectification and demodulation processes has furnished an operating principle for many types of laboratory instruments called *vacuum-tube voltmeters*. These range in complexity from simple diode rectifiers to large amplifier-rectifier combinations covering wide frequency ranges, and have had very extensive development. Only a few basic types will be discussed here.

The simplest form is that of the diode rectifier and series resistance of Fig. 15–14(a). The operation follows the laws of the half-wave rectifier, and I_{d-c} as read is proportional to the *average* value of the applied voltage. The circuit imposes a load of $2R$ on any apparatus to which it is connected, so that ordinarily R should be high.

If a capacitor is connected across R as indicated by the dotted lines, the sensitivity improves (efficiency rises), as was true for the diode demodulator. The I_{d-c} reading is proportional to the *peak* of the applied voltage. By choice of semiconductor diodes of small size and low capacitance, it is possible to extend the frequency range of such voltmeters up to hundreds of megacycles. The accuracy of such diode voltmeters is good over a long period of time and depends largely on stability of R.

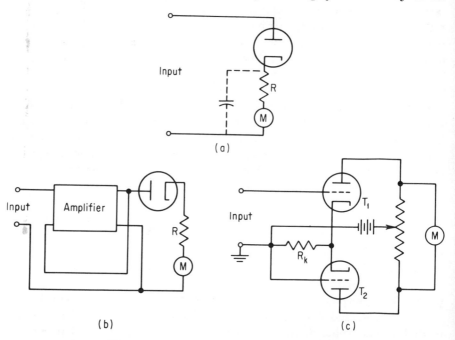

Fig. 15–14. Vacuum-tube voltmeter circuits.

The variation at Fig. 15–14(b) incorporates a feedback-stabilized amplifier ahead of a diode detector. By using considerable feedback it is possible to stabilize the gain of the system, and it is possible to measure a-c voltages as small as a few microvolts in this manner.

The form at Fig. 15–14(c) is popular where minimum-scale values of 2 or 3 v are satisfactory. It is considered that T_2 will compensate T_1 for changes in power-supply voltages. This effect may be thought of as due to the independence of a Wheatstone bridge from source changes, since the circuit can be seen as a bridge. The tap on the load resistor may be adjusted for initial balance, after which meter M reads the unbalance current and is calibrated in terms of a-c input.

An important factor in using any electronic meter on waves which are not truly sinusoidal is to determine what *function* of the input wave is actually being measured. Until this is known, readings may be meaningless.

A second factor which must be considered is the frequency range for which a particular instrument is designed. These vary from simple audio instruments good up to 10,000 or 20,000 cycles to high-frequency instruments giving accurate readings to hundreds of megacycles.

15–10. Demodulation of FM signals

The demodulation or detection of frequency-modulated signals in order to recover the transmitted information poses a special problem, since the original information signal is usually made up of varying amplitude waves, and these must be recovered from the frequency-modulated signal and reproduced as amplitude variations. If the noise-reduction properties of frequency modulation are to be exploited, it is also necessary that this detector be insensitive to changes in amplitude. If that is accomplished, then the only varying property of the incoming signal is frequency, and non-frequency-modulated noise and interfering AM signals will have no effect on the output.

One means for removing amplitude variations is by use of a limiter, or an amplifier giving substantially constant output for all input signals above a given level. The limited signal may be applied to a circuit which will change frequency variations to amplitude variations, for the demodulation process. One form is that of a tuned circuit, where the variation of amplitude against frequency inherent in the slope of a shoulder of a resonant curve will give FM detection. In Fig.

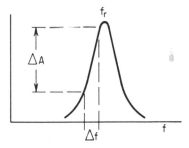

Fig. 15–15. Tuned-circuit slope detector for FM signals.

15–15 a signal having a frequency variation is applied to a circuit resonant at a frequency f_r slightly different from the center frequency of the FM wave. As the frequency varies, an amplitude-modulated voltage is available across the tuned circuit. This method, though simple, is not generally satisfactory because of the curvature present in the slopes of tuned circuits.

A second form of detector is the frequency discriminator. The circuit is sensitive to amplitude variation and must be preceded by an amplitude limiter. A third detector is of the ratio type, which, when properly adjusted, is insensitive to amplitude variations and requires no limiter. The gated-beam tube is also a means of accomplishing frequency discrimination without the complications of the limiting operation.

15–11. The amplitude limiter

The discriminator circuit in the FM system will give satisfactory noise rejection only when an amplitude limiter is used ahead of the discriminator.

One such limiter is an amplifier in which the input signal exceeds the voltage needed to drive the tube or transistor between saturation and cutoff, thus giving constant output for all signals above the limiting level. As a limiter, the pentode circuit of Fig. 15–16 employs only grid-leak bias. When the input swings the grid positive, the grid current through R_g creates a bias. In effect the zero axis of the wave is shifted downward until the positive radio-frequency peaks drive the grid just sufficiently positive to cause enough grid current to maintain the required bias. Consequently the positive peaks of signal are fixed or clamped at zero.

Because of low anode and screen voltage, cutoff occurs at a small negative voltage, and negative peaks are clipped. The output thus swings between zero and cutoff, and is independent of amplitude variations which exceed these limits.

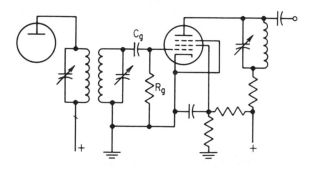

Fig. 15–16. Amplitude limiter.

If the $R_g C_g$ time constant of the grid circuit is too long, it is possible for sudden amplitude changes, such as noise pulses, to drive the grid more positive than normal and to produce an amplitude plate-current variation before the bias has time to adjust itself to the required level. Time constants in the order of one or two microseconds are used in the grid circuit so that the circuit can respond to sudden pulses.

The circuit may limit at inputs of the order of 5 to 10 v rms, and operates best with sharp-cutoff, high-g_m pentode tubes. Limiter performance is shown in Fig. 15–17. As the input signal becomes large enough to saturate the limiter, the receiver output due to noise drops. Grid current flows during limiting, and may be measured to indicate proper limiter operation, and the strength of the received signal. For most tubes it is found that 300 to 500 μamp of grid current is sufficient for proper limiting action.

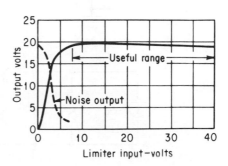

Fig. 15–17. Limiter performance.

15–12. The frequency discriminator

The conversion of frequency variations to amplitude variations in FM reception is handled in a discriminator circuit, which employs properties of the doubly-tuned transformer. Consider the amplifier at Fig. 15–18(a), with its equivalent circuit at Fig. 15–18(b). The primary and secondary are resonant, or $\omega_r L_1 = 1/\omega_r C_1$, and $\omega_r L_2 = 1/\omega_r C_2$. By neglecting r_p of the pentode as large, Thevenin's theorem allows the circuit to the left of terminals a, a to be replaced as in Fig. 15–18(c), where the generator is

$$\mathbf{E} = -\frac{jg_m \mathbf{E}_g}{\omega C_1} \qquad (15\text{–}28)$$

The resistance R_d is the loading produced by rectifier diodes later to be introduced into the circuit. The secondary resistances can be combined as

$$R_s = R_2 + \frac{1}{\omega^2 C_2^2 R_d} \qquad (15\text{–}29)$$

The Q of the primary is

$$Q_1 = \frac{\omega_r L_1}{R_1}$$

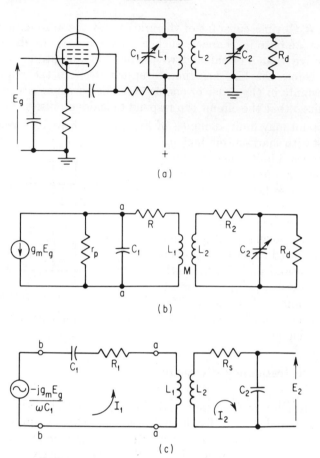

Fig. 15–18. Equivalent circuits for doubly-tuned amplifier.

and that of the secondary

$$Q_2 = \frac{\omega_r L_2}{R_s} = \frac{\omega_r L_2}{R_2 + 1/\omega_r^2 C_2^2 R_d} \tag{15–30}$$

The input impedance at terminals b, b is

$$\mathbf{Z}_{1i} = \mathbf{Z}_{bb} = \mathbf{z}_i - \frac{\mathbf{z}_r^2}{\mathbf{z}_o}$$

Using the fractional frequency deviation δ and the equations developed in Section 9–24 for the doubly-tuned circuit, it is possible to determine $\mathbf{Z}_{bb}$ as

$$\mathbf{Z}_{bb} = \frac{\omega_r L_1}{Q_1} (1 + j2Q_1\delta) + \frac{\omega_r^2 k^2 (1 + \delta)^2 L_1 L_2}{(\omega_r L_2/Q_2)(1 + j2Q\delta)}$$

Such circuits are usually designed for $Q_1 = Q_2 = Q$. It is reasonable to neglect δ with respect to unity, so that the input impedance of the circuit becomes

$$Z_{bb} = \frac{\omega_r L_1}{Q}\left[\frac{(1 + j2Q\delta)^2 + k^2Q^2}{1 + j2Q\delta}\right] \tag{15-31}$$

The input impedance at terminals a, a of Fig. 15–18(c) can be similarly built up as

$$Z_{a,a} = z_i - \frac{z_r^2}{z_o} = j\omega_r L_1(1 + \delta) + \frac{\omega_r^2 k^2(1 + \delta)^2 L_1 L_2}{(\omega_r L_2/Q_2)(1 + j2Q\delta)}$$

After again neglecting δ with respect to unity

$$Z_{a,a} = j\omega_r L_1\left(1 - \frac{jk^2Q}{1 + j2Q\delta}\right) \tag{15-32}$$

The primary voltage E_1 at terminals a, a is then obtainable as

$$\mathbf{E}_1 = \frac{-jg_m\mathbf{E}_g}{\omega_r(1 + \delta)C_1}\frac{\mathbf{Z}_{aa}}{\mathbf{Z}_{bb}}$$

$$= g_m E_g Q\omega_r L_1\left[\frac{1 + j2Q\delta - jk^2Q}{(1 + j2Q\delta)^2 + k^2Q^2}\right]$$

and this can be simplified by dropping the usually negligible term jk^2Q, giving

$$\mathbf{E}_1 = g_m E_g Q\omega_r L_1\left[\frac{1 + j2Q\delta}{(1 + j2Q\delta)^2 + k^2Q^2}\right] \tag{15-33}$$

The secondary voltage $\mathbf{E}_2$ of the doubly-tuned circuit is given in Section 9–24 as

$$\mathbf{E}_2 = \frac{jg_m\mathbf{E}_g kQ^2\omega_r\sqrt{L_1 L_2}}{(1 + j2Q\delta)^2 + k^2Q^2} \tag{15-34}$$

Equations 15–33 and 15–34 provide the background information needed for study of the frequency discriminator of Fig. 15–19. The doubly-tuned circuit is used with the secondary operating into two diode rectifiers. The major difference from the amplifier circuit discussed above lies in the connection through C between the anode of the amplifier and the center point of the secondary. The amplifier preceding the tuned circuits is usually operated as a limiter; capacitor C blocks the d-c and has negligible reactance.

The circuit may now be considered qualitatively, to secure some understanding of the mode of operation before a quantitative analysis.

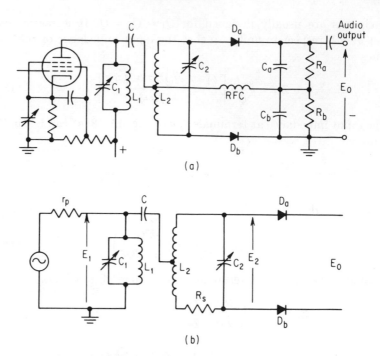

Fig. 15–19. The Foster-Seeley frequency discriminator.

It may be observed that at f_r, the resonant frequency where $\delta = 0$, the primary and secondary voltages become

$$\mathbf{E}_1 = g_m \mathbf{E}_g Q \omega_r L_1 \left(\frac{1}{1 + k^2 Q^2} \right) \tag{15–35}$$

$$\mathbf{E}_2 = j g_m \mathbf{E}_g k Q^2 \omega_r \sqrt{L_1 L_2} \left(\frac{1}{1 + k^2 Q^2} \right) \tag{15–36}$$

and $\mathbf{E}_2$ is in quadrature with $\mathbf{E}_1$. This leads to the resonant-frequency $(\delta = 0)$ diagram at Fig. 15–20(a).

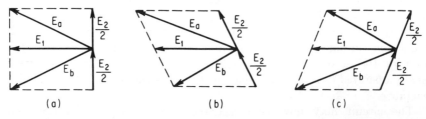

Fig. 15–20. Phasor diagrams illustrating the discriminator performance.

The voltages between the diode anodes and ground in Fig. 15–19(b) are, respectively,

$$\mathbf{E}_a = \mathbf{E}_1 + \frac{\mathbf{E}_2}{2} \tag{15-37}$$

$$\mathbf{E}_b = \mathbf{E}_1 - \frac{\mathbf{E}_2}{2} \tag{15-38}$$

and phasors representing these quantities appear in the diagram. In Fig. 15–19(a) of the circuit, the diode rectifiers are connected to provide an output $\mathbf{E}_o$ which is proportional to the difference of $|E_a|$ and $|E_b|$, and at resonance this magnitude difference is zero.

At frequencies above resonance the phasor diagram becomes that at Fig. 15–20(b), and below resonance that at Fig. 15–20(c). In each of these cases there is a magnitude difference between E_a and E_b, resulting in output voltage E_o. The polarity of this voltage will, however, be reversed in the two cases. It will be found that frequency deviations from resonance are translated into output amplitude variations in accordance with the curve of Fig. 15–21 and that over an appreciable frequency region this translation will be linear with frequency. A frequency-modulated wave will then produce a voltage E_o, of magnitude and polarity corresponding to the original modulating signal.

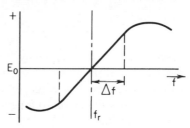

Fig. 15–21. The discriminator characteristic.

A quantitative analysis may be made of the circuit performance by writing the voltage between diode anodes and ground as

$$\mathbf{E}_a = \frac{g_m \mathbf{E}_g \omega_r L_1 Q \left(1 + j2Q\delta + j\frac{kQ}{2}\sqrt{\frac{L_2}{L_1}} \right)}{(1 + j2Q\delta)^2 + k^2 Q^2} \tag{15-39}$$

and

$$\mathbf{E}_b = \frac{g_m \mathbf{E}_g \omega_r L_1 Q \left(1 + j2Q\delta - j\frac{kQ}{2}\sqrt{\frac{L_2}{L_1}} \right)}{(1 + j2Q\delta)^2 + k^2 Q^2} \tag{15-40}$$

The output is E_o, and this voltage to ground appears as the difference of the *magnitudes* of E_a and E_b. If two new parameters are introduced as

$$Q\delta = X$$

and

$$kQ = k/k_c = K$$

then the magnitude difference appears as

$$| E_a | - | E_b | = \frac{g_m E_g Q \omega_r L_1}{\sqrt{(1 + K^2)^2 + 8X^2(1 - K^2 + 2X^2)}}$$

$$\times \left[\sqrt{1 + \left(2X + \frac{K}{2}\sqrt{\frac{L_2}{L_1}}\right)^2} - \sqrt{1 + \left(2X - \frac{K}{2}\sqrt{\frac{L_2}{L_1}}\right)^2} \right] \quad (15\text{--}41)$$

The ratio of the magnitudes of E_2 to E_1 at resonance is

$$\left| \frac{E_2}{E_1} \right| = kQ \sqrt{\frac{L_2}{L_1}} \quad (15\text{--}42)$$

and it is customary to design the transformer to give a value of 2 for this ratio, or 1:1 to each side of the secondary. For the usual case kQ is chosen equal to 1.5, so that $L_2/L_1 = 1.77$ in that case.

The value of Q may determined from the relation

$$Q = \frac{f_r}{2\Delta f}$$

where $2\Delta f$ is the frequency band over which approximate linearity is desired. Usual frequency deviations are $\pm$ 75 kc, but to allow for frequency drift of the signal a value of $2\Delta f = 200$ kc may be desirable. With an operating frequency of 10 megacycles, the value of $Q = 50$ is given by the above relation.

Since $kQ = k/k_c$ has been assumed equal to 1.5, then $k = 0.03$. Using the above values, one of the terms of Eq. 15–41 can be written as

$$\frac{K}{2}\sqrt{\frac{L_2}{L_1}} = \frac{1.5}{2}\sqrt{1.77} = 1.0$$

and the reason for choice of the parameters is apparent. The above values have been used to draw the performance curve of Fig. 15–22. The predicted curve shape is seen, with a linear region running over values of $Q\delta = \pm 0.4$.

High primary inductance will raise the output of the discriminator. However, L_1 is limited by L_2, which is fixed in its relation to L_1, and the size of L_2 is limited by the necessity of having a reasonable value of tuning capacity C_2. A value of $C_2 = 50$ pf, including stray capacity, is reasonable. The rest of the transformer design values can be obtained from the previously developed relations as

$$L_2 = 1/\omega_r^2 C_2 = 5.08 \ \mu h, \qquad L_1 = L_2/1.77 = 2.87 \ \mu h,$$

$$C_1 = 1/\omega_r^2 L_1 = 88.3 \ pf, \qquad Q_1 = Q_2 = Q = 50$$

$$kQ = 1.5, \text{ therefore } k = 0.03, \qquad M = k\sqrt{L_1 L_2} = 0.12 \ \mu h$$

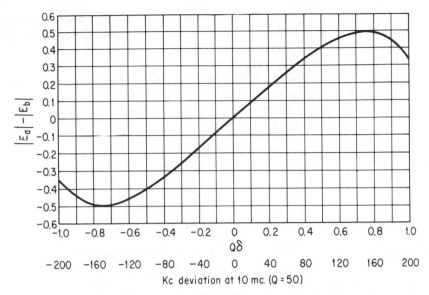

Fig. 15–22. Calculated discriminator performance.

Equation 15–41 shows that the output is proportional to E_g, the input amplitude. This result shows the necessity for limiting to precede the discriminator if amplitude-modulated signals or noise are to be rejected.

The demodulation of FM waves is achieved in two steps: (1) that of changing the FM wave to an amplitude variation, which is accomplished by the tuned circuit, and (2) the rectification of the amplitude varying wave by diodes which simultaneously take a difference of the two applied voltages to make the output zero at the center frequency.

15–13. The ratio detector for FM

Equation 15–41 shows that the differential voltage is affected by amplitude modulation if that is allowed to reach the detector. It may be shown that for a particular signal, undeviated, a d-c voltage of 10 v may appear across resistors R_a and R_b of Fig. 15–19(a), the polarities being opposite and E_o equal to zero. If the input frequency then deviates in such a way that the voltage applied to T_a increases and that to T_b decreases, the voltage across R_a may increase to $+ 15$ v and that across R_b may decrease to $- 5$ v. The output voltage is $+ 10$ v, or the difference between the two, with ground as reference.

A stronger signal may produce 15 v when undeviated. When it is deviated the same amount as before, the voltage across R_a becomes $+ 22.5$ v and that across R_b becomes $- 7.5$ v, and the output voltage is $+ 15$ v.

In both the above cases the frequency deviation gave rise to differing amplitudes of output, and thus the circuit responded to amplitude variations. However, it should be noted that in both cases the *ratio* of the voltage across R_a and R_b was the same, namely, 3:1. If a detector could be made to respond only to this ratio and not to respective magnitudes, then it would be insensitive to amplitude variations.

By the notation of the preceding section the two voltages E_a and E_b are each proportional to E_g, or

$$E_a = A E_g$$

and

$$E_b = B E_g,$$

and it may be found that the coefficients are related as

$$A - B = C,$$

where C is a constant for a given deviation. Consequently,

$$E_a - E_b = (A - B)E_g = CE_g, \tag{15–43}$$

and it may be seen, therefore, that the output differential voltage is a function of the input amplitude E_g. If, however, the ratio be taken as

$$\frac{E_a}{E_b} = \frac{A}{B}, \tag{15–44}$$

this ratio is independent of input-signal amplitude.

A circuit for obtaining the desired ratio is shown in Fig. 15–23, the main change from the discriminator being made by reversal of one diode so that D_1 and D_2 are now in series. The combination of R_2 and C_c has a long time constant of the order of 0.25 sec. The full secondary voltage is applied across this combination and results in a d-c output voltage E which is constant, irrespective of any amplitude modulation present, because of the large time constant.

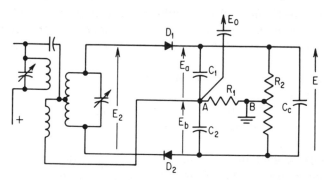

Fig. 15–23. The ratio detector for FM.

For an undeviated signal the voltages on C_1 and C_2 are equal, and no voltage appears across R_1. When frequency deviation takes place the unbalanced diode voltages charge C_1 and C_2 unequally, and point A shifts in potential. Point B is fixed in potential by the $R_2 C_c$ combination, and consequently a voltage appears across R_1. Since E is relatively fixed for a given signal, the sum of E_1 and E_2 must also be fixed, and it is then the ratio of E_1 to E_2 which changes at the frequency of the modulating signal. Thus, the circuit is called the *ratio detector*.

The circuit is considered somewhat critical to adjust for linear operation. It is useful for receivers, where the complexity and cost necessitated by the extra gain and limiter circuits of the discriminator type of FM detector cannot be justified.

15–14. The gated-beam tube as a limiter-discriminator

A further development in the detection of frequency-modulated signals is the *gated-beam tube*. This tube features a control characteristic which is step-shaped; that is, for a change of grid potential from negative to positive the plate current abruptly rises from zero to a sharply defined maximum value. Further increase in the positive grid potential causes no change in the plate current, as shown in Fig. 15–24. Such a characteristic is suited to limiting and removal of amplitude modulation and noise from FM signals.

The basic design is illustrated by Fig. 15–25. Electrons are attracted toward a positive accelerator electrode and pass through a slit in this electrode, forming a narrow beam. The beam passes between control grid electrodes in reaching a positive plate. When the control grid is positive, the electron beam reaches the plate without difficulty. When the grid voltage is made slightly negative, a few electrons are caused to turn back in front of the grid electrode; these increase the space charge in this region and cause other electrons to slow down or turn around, further increasing the space charge until this cumulative effect blocks the main electron

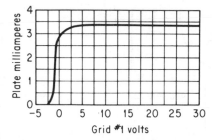

Fig. 15–24. Plate-current characteristic of the gated-beam tube.

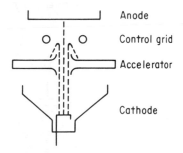

Fig. 15–25. Principle of the gated-beam tube.

stream and the current is cut off. Since the space charge is concentrated in the center of the beam, the returning low-speed electrons are caused to diverge and fall back to the accelerator, much as is the water in a fountain.

The operation of the tube approximates a gate being opened, or closed, and the transition condition being abrupt in terms of grid-voltage change required to produce it. This steepness of the characteristic is obtained by the removal of the returning electrons from the stream by the accelerator. If they were allowed to return toward the cathode they would increase the space charge near the cathode surface, reducing the outgoing current and flattening the characteristic.

The degree to which the gate function is achieved is illustrated in the curve of Fig. 15–24. The grid is biased to a point on the rising portion of the curve and passes the beam on the positive half cycles, rejects it on the negative half cycles. The bias is obtained from a cathode resistor, since the total cathode current remains nearly constant, the beam electrons simply being shifted from anode to accelerator. Since no RC circuits are required in the input, the limiting action is instantaneous, and impulse noise is more effectively rejected than in the case of the grid limiter. A circuit tuned to the signal frequency is used as an output load.

The tube has been designed to serve as a frequency discriminator as well as a limiter. If the plate is changed to a grid, the electron beam is passed to a second slit and a grid-anode system similar to the first. The general arrangement is illustrated in Fig. 15–26.

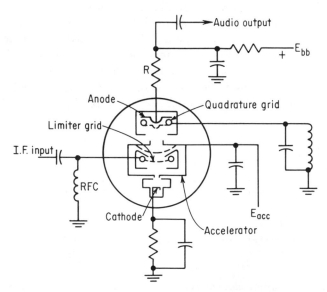

Fig. 15–26. The gated-beam tube in a frequency discriminator circuit.

The first grid passes limited-amplitude pulses of electrons through the slit in the second accelerator electrode. These electrons form a periodically varying space charge in front of the second control or *quadrature* grid. This space charge induces currents in the circuit of this quadrature grid; and since the magnitude of the induced current is proportional to the rate of change of space charge, the current in the tube and the voltage developed across the resonant circuit are in quadrature with the electron-beam pulses. The current is large enough to develop about 5 v across the tuned circuit— sufficient to operate the gate action set up by the quadrature grid and the anode. Thus, the action of the second gate lags behind that of the first gate.

For frequency-modulated signals the frequency of the induced quadrature-grid current may be above or below the resonant frequency of the tuned circuit. The voltage developed across the tuned circuit then varies in phase with change of frequency, and this causes a variation in the length of the period during which both gates are open. At the center frequency the two gates are coincidentally open for 90°. As the frequency varies, the coincidence period becomes less or more than 90° and the pulse of output current shortens or lengthens. As a result a discriminator characteristic is developed which is satisfactory for the usual frequency deviation of ±75 kc.

The tube is an efficient solution to the limiter-discriminator problem, and also has a number of other applications as a harmonic and square-wave generator, and in phase-angle measurements.

15–15. Frequency mixers and converters

Another type of circuit of interest is the frequency *converter* or *mixer*. Its function is that of translating or shifting a band of frequencies centering on f_1 so as to create a similar band of frequencies centering about some other frequency f_2. The process is usually carried out by a product demodulator.

The first signal grid of a pentagrid converter, as described in Section 15–8, will be supplied with a local oscillator frequency

$$e_1 = E_x \cos \omega_x t \qquad (15\text{–}45)$$

This signal will be of large amplitude, and cause the electron stream to vary at frequency f_x, swinging from near cutoff to reasonable amplitude. The band of frequencies to be shifted will usually comprise an amplitude-modulated carrier and side bands

$$e_2 = E_c \cos \omega_c t + \frac{m_a E_c}{2} \cos (\omega_c - \omega_m)t + \frac{m_a E_c}{2} \cos (\omega_c + \omega_m)t \qquad (15\text{–}46)$$

and will be supplied to the second signal grid. This signal on the second grid will further modulate the electron stream, producing a product term for all frequencies present. From the previously developed theory it is known that among the frequencies in the output, there will be

$$
\begin{array}{ll}
f_c & f_c - f_x \\
f_x & f_c - f_x - f_m \\
f_c + f_x & f_c - f_x + f_m \\
f_c + f_x - f_m & \\
f_c + f_m + f_x &
\end{array}
$$

The sum and difference terms will have amplitudes proportional to the product of the individual frequency-component amplitudes.

The frequencies in the left-hand column are not of interest now, and it is possible to separate them from the frequencies in the right-hand column, usually by a tuned-circuit filter. However, if the frequency f_x is so chosen that

$$f_c - f_x = f_k$$

where f_k is that of a desired new carrier, then it follows that the three terms on the right represent the original carrier and side bands translated to the new carrier frequency, f_k, giving

$$f_c - f_x = f_k \tag{15–47}$$

$$f_c - f_x - f_m = f_k - f_m \tag{15–48}$$

$$f_c - f_x + f_m = f_k + f_m \tag{15–49}$$

as the new carrier group. Thus, signals received on one frequency band may be translated and amplified at other and more desirable frequencies, before final demodulation and extraction of information content. This principle receives extensive use in complete radio systems, to be discussed.

In one form of pentagrid converter circuit, shown in Fig. 15–27(a), the local oscillator function is combined by using grid 1 as an input, to form a tuned-grid oscillator circuit with the cathode and grid 2 as an anode, operating at frequency f_x and modulating the electron stream at that frequency. Grids 3 and 5 constitute a screen system to shield grid 4, carrying the external signal e_2, as in the electrode system of the left tube in the figure.

A variety of pentagrid tubes and mixer transistors are available, and may be used with internal oscillator action or with a separate oscillator tube. In any case, the output at the new frequency is given by a *conversion transconductance*, g_c, where

$$g_c = \frac{I_p(f_k)}{E_c} \tag{15–50}$$

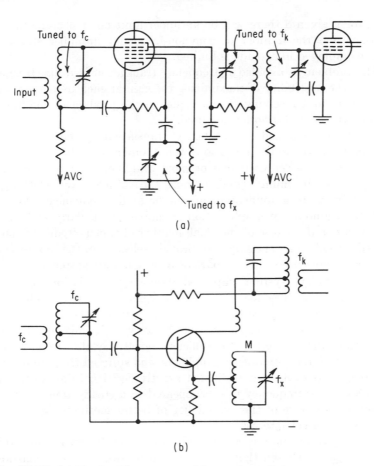

Fig. 15–27. (a) Pentagrid converter; (b) transistor frequency converter.

as a measure of the efficiency with which the input frequency is converted to the new frequency. The conversion gain then is

$$\mathbf{A}_c = g_c \mathbf{Z}_L \tag{15–51}$$

where $\mathbf{Z}_L$ is the impedance shown to the f_k component of anode current.

15–16. AM radio receiving systems

A basic limitation of the ultimate amount of amplification possible at a given frequency is the presence of positive feedback, usually unwanted but almost invariably present. It has been shown that if $A\beta = 1 + j0$, an amplifier will become an oscillator. Because of stray couplings, or other causes of feedback, it is impossible to make $\beta = 0$ for an amplifier.

Thus, for a given β there will be an upper limit on A if oscillation is not to occur, and the number of common-frequency amplifier stages which may be employed in cascade is limited.

The problem is avoided if frequency translation is utilized, since this provides the possibility of maximizing the gain at each frequency, with an overall gain in a receiving system equal to the product of the individual gains at the several frequencies used.

Before development of frequency translation systems, several simpler methods of radio reception were employed. The *radio-frequency amplifier* and *detector* used one or more amplifiers operating at the frequency of the incoming signal, to raise the voltage level. Detection was followed by more amplification at low or audio frequencies. Because of the limited amount of amplification available, particularly at high signal frequencies, and because of the small number of tuned circuits which could be used (usually one per stage) to provide selectivity, the radio-frequency amplifier is now used only as part of more complex systems.

The *heterodyne* system employed frequency translation, as discussed in Section 15–15. The local oscillator frequency, f_x, was made equal to f_c of the received signal, so that $f_c - f_x = f_k = 0$, and the output frequency indicated by Eqs. 15–47, 15–48, and 15–49 was f_m only, or the original modulation was recovered. For sufficient sensitivity the circuit had to be combined with radio-frequency amplifiers, and suffered the gain limitations mentioned above. Also, if f_x did not exactly equal f_c to an accuracy of a few cycles, a low frequency $f_c - f_x$ appeared as a steady tone or whistle in the output. Because of the availability of better methods the circuit now has only historical interest.

The *superheterodyne* is a more elaborate adaptation of the principle, in which f_x is so chosen that $f_c - f_x = f_k$ will always yield a constant frequency f_k called the *intermediate frequency*, since it is usually intermediate in value between f_c and f_m. A block diagram of such a receiving system appears in Fig. 15–28. The receiver ordinarily employs some signal- or radio-frequency amplification operating at f_c. The signal is then passed into a frequency converter which translates the signal and side bands into a new frequency group f_k, $f_k + f_m$, and $f_k - f_m$. Amplification in a fixed-tune amplifier at frequency f_k follows.

By reason of these translations in carrier frequency it is possible to use more overall gain than can be employed in the radio-frequency receiver alone. That is, if A_x is the maximum stable gain at any one frequency, it is possible, by utilizing this amount of gain at two frequencies in cascade, to raise the overall gain to A_x^2, avoiding instability and oscillation troubles.

Since the intermediate frequency is usually lower than the original signal frequency, the tuned circuits in the intermediate amplifier may be

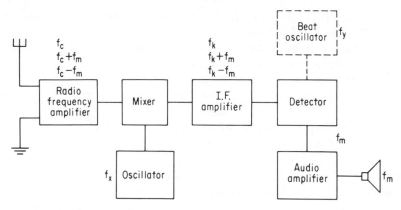

Fig. 15–28. Block diagram of the superheterodyne for AM reception.

made more selective (in terms of width in cycles) than could be done at signal frequency. It is common practice to couple the circuits with doubly-tuned transformers giving rather flat tops and steep sides to the frequency response curve of the intermediate-frequency amplifier. The improved selectivity at the lower frequency plus the large number of tuned circuits through which the signal must pass makes the super-heterodyne a highly selective system. For further improvement in selectivity, as well as image rejection discussed below, the process of frequency translation may be repeated to provide further gain and more tuned circuits at a still lower intermediate frequency, so that double- and triple-conversion systems are available.

After intermediate-frequency amplification, the signal is applied to a demodulator, usually an envelope or product detector, and the modulation frequency, f_m, is derived. It may be further amplified at an audio frequency before it reaches the final output device or loud speaker.

A continuous-wave or CW signal, broken into dots and dashes as for telegraph transmission, carries no amplitude information and would not give an output other than the d-c due to the carrier. To make the dots and dashes audible it is necessary to create an audio tone from the signals. A separate *beat-frequency oscillator* is used, as shown by the dashed lines, with frequency f_y differing from f_k by a few hundred or few thousand cycles. The resulting difference frequency due to modulation of f_k by f_y makes the dots and dashes audible at a tone suited to the operator's desires. Since f_k is the same for all signals, then f_y can be fixed and preset.

Because of the requirement that f_x shall be adjustable in such a way that f_k be constant for all received frequencies, the local oscillator frequency f_x must differ from each f_c by the amount of the intermediate frequency.

For a broadcast-band receiver, the radio-frequency circuits must tune from 1650 kc to 550 kc, a frequency ratio of 3:1. The oscillator, with the tuning capacitor ganged with the radio-frequency tuning capacitor for ease in tuning, and with the usual 455 kc intermediate frequency, must cover a frequency range of 2105 kc to 1005 kc, or a ratio of 2.09:1. It is also possible for the oscillator frequency to be lower than the received frequency, or to cover the range of 1195 kc to 95 kc, but this represents a tuning ratio of 12.57:1, an impossibly large range for usual tuning capacitors.

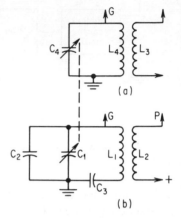

Fig. 15–29. Tracking system for superheterodyne oscillator tuning.

Circuits have been developed to allow use of identical tuning capacitors in tuning the radio-frequency and oscillator circuits over these differing tuning ranges. Such a circuit is shown in Fig. 15–29, with $C_1 = C_4$ as tuning capacitors, and L_1, C_2, and C_3 as alignment variables. Thus, the oscillator frequency can be given the correct value at three frequencies in the range, and will not deviate greatly at other points. These alignment frequencies are usually chosen as 600 kc, 1000 kc, and 1400 kc. Inductor L_1 is adjusted at 600 kc, C_3 at 1000 kc, and C_2 at the highest frequency.

Variable capacitors with the plates of the oscillator section especially shaped to provide the correct frequency variation with angle of rotation are also available.

The superheterodyne circuit was invented during World War I but was not widely adopted until after 1927; it is now the accepted standard circuit for radio receivers. The easy design for selectivity and high gain are reasons for this preference. A difficulty of the circuit is the presence of *image frequencies*, or the possible reception of two signals at one control setting. For any setting of the oscillator frequency, two signals differing by twice the intermediate frequency, can produce IF output. For instance, if the desired signal is at 545 kc, then the oscillator will be at 1000 kc with a 455 kc IF. A second signal at 1455 kc could also be received and would be called the image signal. By introducing additional selectivity at the signal frequency to lower the strength of the undesired signal, and the use of higher intermediate frequencies to separate the image further from signal frequency, it is possible to suppress these image responses.

15–17. FM receiving system

The receiving systems for FM usually employ the superheterodyne circuit; such a receiver is shown in block form in Fig. 15–30. Since most frequency-modulated signals are transmitted at center frequencies above 80 megacycles, the radio-frequency circuits will be designed for high-frequency reception. The IF must be high enough that the signal-frequency circuits can provide sufficient selectivity against the image frequency, and also must be chosen so that sufficient band width is available to pass bands of $2\Delta f$ frequency width. This requirement dictates IF frequencies usually in the range of 10 megacycles; that of 10.7 megacycles is one frequently employed.

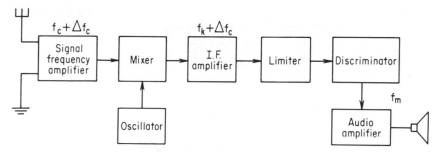

Fig. 15–30. Block diagram of a limiter-discriminator FM receiver.

Except for these modifications in frequency, the FM receiver follows the design of the AM type until the limiter circuit is reached. Here the amplitude modulation and amplitude varying noise are removed and the signal is passed to the discriminator. The output of the discriminator consists of the signal at frequency f_m, and is amplified further in the audio amplifier and applied to the loudspeaker.

15–18. Parametric converters and amplifiers

Frequency converters or initial amplifier stages at microwave frequencies must be low in internal noise, as defined in Section 8–21, if the weak signals encountered in radar or space communications are to be received. The output of such circuits includes the signal, thermal noise power $kT\Delta f$ from the antenna, and thermal and shot noise contributed by the amplifying device. The smaller the noise component introduced by the amplifier, the smaller will be the degradation of the signal-to-noise ratio of the output, and improvements here have major economic advantages in communications systems.

Research to develop converters or amplifiers with lower noise output than is present in our best tubes or transistors has led to several devices, among which is the *parametric amplifier*. This device is an energy converter which operates with nonlinear reactances or parameters, with the form employing the nonlinear solid-state capacitor to be considered here.

As an analogy, consider a resonant tuned circuit, including a capacitor whose plates may be mechanically moved, thus changing its capacitance. As indicated in Fig. 15–31, the capacitor plates are pulled apart at the voltage maximum, decreasing C and raising E because $E = q/C$ and the charge is unchanged. When the voltage E goes through zero the plates are returned to their original close spacing. Whenever the capacitance is decreased the voltage increases and voltage amplification is obtained.

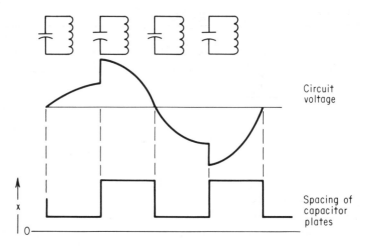

Fig. 15–31. Principle of the parametric amplifier.

The energy required to pull the plates apart against the attraction of the electric field is supplied or "pumped" into the circuit by an auxiliary source, and is stored in the electric field. Since the plates are pushed together at a time of zero charge or voltage, the energy is not returned to the pump but is ultimately transferred to the resonant circuit.

In this idealized situation it can be seen that the frequency of the energy pump f_p must be exactly twice, and in phase with, the signal frequency f_s. This is a situation difficult or impossible to achieve and is called the degenerate case. In practical situations, f_s may be somewhat different from $f_p/2$, and the signal and pump drift into and out of periods of favorable interaction, giving beats and somewhat less than the full theoretical gain.

Any nonlinear reactance which can be time varied may be employed to transfer the energy, but the device which made such systems possible was the voltage-variable capacitor, *varactor*, or solid-state diode. It has been previously shown that under reverse bias, the thickness of the depletion layer and its capacitance are nonlinear functions of the applied voltage.

The noise introduced by vacuum tubes and transistors is due to the inherent particle nature of current or charge flow. In a voltage-variable capacitor there is theoretically no noise because there is no flow of current, only a variation of the width of the space-charge region. With an equivalent circuit for the diode as in Fig. 15–32, it is seen that the diode is not perfect, and a small amount of thermal noise will be introduced by the small resistor R_b, the bulk resistance of the diode material. If the complication is warranted, this internal noise can be reduced by refrigeration of the diode to liquid nitrogen temperatures. The parallel resistance R_p is very large, and can be neglected.

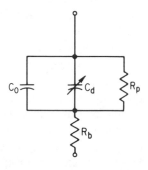

Fig. 15–32. Equivalent circuit of a voltage-variable diode.

A theoretical limitation on the speed with which this capacitor can be varied is imposed by the dielectric relaxation time, of the order of 10^{-13} sec. A practical limit appears, however, in the time constant $R_b C_o$, where C_o is the fixed capacitance of the diode and holder, of the order of 0.1 to 0.2 pf, and R_b will be an ohm or two. The upper limit on frequency is thought to be 30 to 60 gigacycles, at present.

In general, parametric amplifiers are frequency converters; they are amplifiers when the output is at the same frequency as the input. In the circuit of Fig. 15–33(a) the pump frequency f_p is twice the signal frequency f_s. Since E_p is made large with respect to E_s, the capacitance of the voltage-variable is swung at pump frequency, and when the two oscillations are in

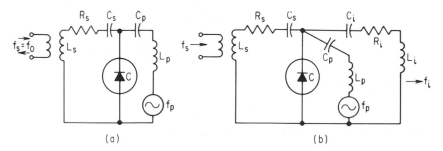

(a)   (b)

Fig. 15–33. (a) Synchronous parametric amplifier; (b) generalized amplifier.

proper phase relation, the signal builds up. Since exact equality of frequency or $f_p = 2f_s$ and the appropriate phase cannot be met in actuality, it is more convenient to allow $f_p \cong 2f_s$, and a difference frequency $f_i = f_p - f_s$ will appear at the output. This situation is illustrated in Fig. 15–34, and a pair of frequencies will appear for each f_s, leading to a complex spectrum. The sum frequency, $f_p + f_s$, will fall outside the amplifier pass band and can be neglected.

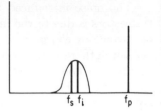

Fig. 15–34. Frequency relations in amplifier with $f_p \cong 2f_s$.

The phase and frequency limitations can be relaxed if we add an *idler* circuit $L_iC_iR_i$, as at Fig. 15–33(b), resonant at the difference frequency $f_i = f_p \pm f_s$. In effect, this idler circuit serves as an additional flywheel or energy reservoir, accepting energy from the pump or f_s circuit and storing it until needed, then releasing it at the proper time and phase to provide power gain in the signal circuit. In fact, with f_p differing greatly from f_s, power gain can be obtained only if the idler circuit is present.

The effect of the idler circuit can be demonstrated. The variable capacitance may be assumed to change as

$$\frac{1}{C} = \frac{1}{C_d} \sin \omega_p t \tag{15–52}$$

in step with the pump frequency. The current in the signal circuit is then

$$i_s = I_s \sin (\omega_s t + \varphi_1) \tag{15–53}$$

The voltage across C, due to this signal current, is then

$$v_C = \frac{1}{C} \int i_s \, dt = \frac{1}{C_d} \sin \omega_p t \int I_s \sin (\omega_s t + \varphi_1) \, dt$$

Obviously, this circuit is a modulator of the variable impedance form, and the result will show two side bands, as

$$v_C = \frac{I_s}{2\omega_s C_d} \left[\sin (\omega_p t + \omega_s t + \varphi_1) + \sin (\omega_p t - \omega_s t - \varphi_1) \right] \tag{15–54}$$

If we now require that

$$\omega_p = \omega_s + \omega_i \tag{15–55}$$

where $\omega_s = 1/\sqrt{L_s C_s}$ and $\omega_i = 1/\sqrt{L_i C_i}$, then

$$v_C = \frac{I_s}{2\omega_s C_d} \left[\sin (\omega_i t - \varphi_1) + \sin (2\omega_p t - \omega_i t + \varphi_1) \right]$$

The current in the idler circuit is

$$i_i = \frac{v_C}{R_i} = \frac{I_s}{2\omega_s C_d R_i} \sin (\omega_i t - \varphi_1) \tag{15–56}$$

the other side band component being so far from idler resonance as to result in negligible current.

This current i_i in the idler circuit will create an additional voltage across C as

$$\Delta v_C = \frac{1}{C} \int i_i \, dt = \frac{1}{C_d} \sin \omega_p t \int \frac{I_s}{2\omega_s C_d R_i} \sin (\omega_i t - \varphi_1) \, dt$$

$$= \frac{I_s}{4\omega_s \omega_i R_i C_d^2} \left[\sin (\omega_p t + \omega_i t - \varphi_1) + \sin (\omega_s t + \varphi_1) \right] \tag{15–57}$$

But Δv_C will then introduce an additional current component $\Delta i_s = \Delta v_C / R_s$ in the signal circuit. Neglecting the first frequency term above as far from signal frequency resonance, this additional current component is

$$\Delta i_s = \frac{I_s}{4\omega_s \omega_i R_i R_s C_d^2} \sin (\omega_s t + \varphi_1) \tag{15–58}$$

and this demonstrates the ability of the idler circuit to automatically produce the proper phase relations. This result is additive to the initial signal current, and gain has been obtained. Actually, it is apparent that the result is due to positive feedback, and the action can lead to instability and oscillation if not controlled.

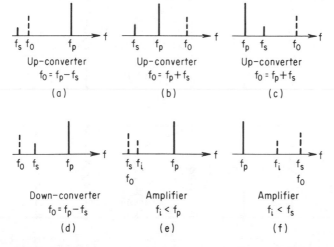

Fig. 15–35. Parametric amplifier forms giving power gain.

If the output frequency is chosen as $f_o > f_s$, the amplifier is known as an *up-converter*, and when $f_o < f_s$, it is known as a *down-converter*. Frequency relations leading to useful gain are shown in Fig. 15–35; other frequency combinations lead to attenuation situations.

For Fig. 15–35(b) and (c), with f_o higher than f_p and output taken from the idler tank, the up-converter is stable and the gain is the ratio f_o/f_s. If f_s is already in the microwave region, having the output at a significantly higher frequency to achieve high gain may pose circuit problems. In Fig. 15–35(a), the gain is $-f_o/f_s$, and the negative sign indicates a regenerative situation, or that the feedback is positive, with gain obtained at the cost of stability and band width. The theoretical gain of the down-converter at Fig. 15–35(d) is also f_o/f_s, but less than unity in this case. The circuit is regenerative and the gain may be large but unstable.

For the regenerative converters of Fig. 15–35(a) and (d), the pump frequency is the highest frequency in the system, and is $f_o + f_s$. The amplifiers in Fig. 15–35(e) and (f) achieve gain by regeneration or positive feedback, with the output being taken from the input tank as in the mathematical example above; the idler circuit must always be present.

15–19. Noise performance of the parametric amplifier

To study, in simple style, the noise figure of a parametric amplifier, consider the circuit of Fig. 15–36(a), with output f_o taken from the input tank. Resistor R_1 is the parallel result of losses in the f_s tank and the variable capacitor. Resistor R_a represents the antenna or signal source resistance

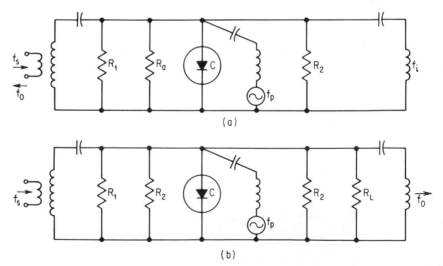

(a)

(b)

Fig. 15–36. Circuits for study of noise in parametric amplifiers.

as transformed by the coupled circuit. An approximation to the noise figure is

$$F = 1 + \frac{T}{T_o}\left(\frac{R_a}{R_1} + \frac{f_s}{f_i}\right) \tag{15–59}$$

where T_o is taken as the ambient 290°K and T is the operating temperature of the apparatus.

The unity term is the thermal noise of an antenna or generator at room temperature; the second term represents thermal noise due to the tank circuit plus the noise contribution of the idler tank; thus it is desirable to have a high idler frequency. This requires a high pump frequency since $f_p = f_s + f_i$. The noise figure equation for the stable up-converter is of similar form.

The down-converter is represented in Fig. 15–36(b) where R_L is the shunt resistance due to losses introduced at f_o by the coupled-in load. The noise figure is then

$$F = 1 + \frac{T}{T_o}\left(\frac{R_a}{R_1} + \frac{R_L f_s}{R_2 f_o}\right) \tag{15–60}$$

Since f_o is smaller than f_s in a down-converter, it will be necessary to compensate for this in the last term by very close coupling to the load, reducing the coupled-in effect of R_L. High regeneration due to positive feedback will be needed for useful gain, and a large ΔC will also be necessary.

In general, ΔC values of diodes will range up to 2.5 pf, and will usually be found larger in high reverse-voltage units. Silicon appears better than germanium, and graded junctions better than abrupt junctions. Usual pump voltages will operate the diode up to about one-half of the reverse voltage rating.

Problems

15-1. A diode and load have a characteristic

$$i, = 10^{-5}e_s + 3.5 \times 10^{-6}e_s^2$$

for small positive inputs. If an amplitude-modulated wave, having a carrier peak amplitude (unmodulated) of 2.5 v is modulated 75 per cent and applied to the diode, find all frequency components and their amplitudes across a load of 60,000 ohms. Also compute the per cent distortion introduced into the modulated signal.

15-2. A sinusoidal modulated signal is applied to the diode detector of Fig. 15–3, (a) with $R = 100,000$ ohms. If the per cent of modulation is varied for a carrier of 10 v, plot the variation of output against per cent modulation, using the chart for the 6H6 in Fig. 15–12.

15-3. A carrier voltage of 10 v rms is applied to the diode of Fig. 15–3(a). The load R is 250,000 ohms and the current I_o is 30 μamp.

(a) Find the efficiency of detection.

(b) Find the load the detector presents to the tuned circuit.

(c) What voltage is available for AVC use?

15-4. An amplitude-modulated wave of carrier peak value of 12 v, 10^6 cycles, with 65 per cent modulation, is applied to a linear-diode detector (Fig. 15–3)(a) with $R = 200,000$ ohms, $r_p = 27,000$, and $C = 150$ pf. Find the modulation-output voltage, the voltage available for AVC action, the detection efficiency, and the load which the circuit imposes on the tuned input circuit.

If the Q of the unloaded resonant circuit is 80, and the inductance is 20 μh, find the band width of the circuit when it is loaded with the diode detector.

15-5. In an envelope detector circuit, with $R = 250,000$ ohms and $C = 250$ pf, plot as a function of modulation frequency the highest value of m that can be employed without introduction of distortion due to inability to follow the modulation envelope.

15-6. A 6H6 diode is used in the circuit of Fig. 15–8(a). If $R_1 = 100,000$ ohms, $R_2 = 250,000$ ohms (tap at top), $C_1 = 50$ pf, and $C_2 = 0.05$ μf, with a carrier amplitude of 10 v at 1 megacycle frequency and modulation of 1200 cycles, find:

(a) The limiting modulation percentage above which distortion increases rapidly.

(b) The circuit changes that should be made to reduce this difficulty.

15-7. In the circuit of Fig. 15–8(a), $R_1 = 200,000$ ohms, $R_2 = 250,000$ ohms, $C_1 = 100$ pf, and $C_2 = 0.001$ μf. For the tap on R_2 at maximum find the highest permissible value of m if peak clipping is to be avoided.

15-8. (a) In the circuit of Fig. 15–8(a), $R_1 = 200,000$ ohms, $C_1 = 100$ pf, and $C_2 = 0.1$ μf. Plot a curve of the value of R_2 against the corresponding value of m which may be employed without peak clipping being present.

(b) If the circuit of Fig. 15–8(b) is used and $R_1 = 50,000$ ohms, again plot a curve of R_2 against the value of m that may be used without clipping distortion; $R_3 = 100,000$ ohms.

15-9. In Fig. 15–14(c) the tube is a 6SN7 with each triode unit having $\mu = 20$ and $r_p = 7700$ ohms. If $R_k = 1500$ ohms, the plate load is 50,000 ohms center-tapped, and the meter M has a resistance of 400 ohms, find the meter reading when 1.0 v rms is applied to the input circuit.

15-10. A resonant circuit of $Q = 50$ is used as a detector of FM waves. If the center frequency is 10 megacycles and the circuit is tuned so that the center frequency is placed below the resonant frequency where the power input is one-half the maximum, find the change in voltage across the resonant circuit for a frequency deviation of 50 kc above and below the center frequency if a constant $I = 50$ μa is applied.

15-11. A frequency discriminator follows a limiter having $g_m = 1000$ and operating at 10.7 megacycles. If the primary is tuned with a 50 pf capacitor, $Q_1 = Q_2 = 80$, find the output to the diodes in terms of volts per kilocycle deviation from the center frequency, using usual design parameters.

15-12. (a) Draw a block diagram of a superheterodyne circuit for AM reception with one radio-frequency amplifier, two intermediate-frequency stages, and one audio amplifier. If the received signal has a carrier of 950 kc, modulated at 2000 cycles, and the intermediate-frequency amplifier is turned to 455 kc, designate the frequencies present in each amplifier stage.

(b) If the oscillator frequency is above the signal frequency, what image frequency may cause interference?

15-13. Capacitor C_2 in Fig. 15–19 is chosen to be 50 pf. If the detection efficiency is 0.90, and $R_a + R_b = 250$ K, $Q_1 = Q_2$, determine an appropriate design for the input transformer for the discriminator to receive a band of ± 200 kc at a center frequency of 22 mc. By plotting a response curve, show whether the design will yield satisfactory linearity.

15-14. A single-side-band wave is applied to a frequency translator along with a single frequency $E_q \sin \omega_q t$. Show that the SSB signal may be raised or lowered in frequency by this method.

References

1. Aiken, C. B., "Theory of the Diode Voltmeter," *Proc. I.R.E.*, **26,** 859 (1938).

2. Foster, D. E., and Seeley, S. W., "Automatic Tuning, Simplified Circuits, and Design Practice," *Proc. I.R.E.*, **25,** 289 (1937).

3. Heffner, H., and Wade, G., "Gain, Bandwidth, and Noise Characteristics of the Variable Parameter Amplifier," *J. Appl. Phys.* **29,** 1321, (1958).

4. Herold, E. W., "The Operation of Frequency Converters and Mixers for Superheterodyne Reception," *Proc. I.R.E.*, **30,** 84 (1942).

5. Kilgour, C. E., and Glessner, J. M., "Diode Detection Analysis," *Proc. I.R.E.*, **21,** 930 (1933).

6. Manley, J. M., Rowe, H. E., "Some General Properties of Nonlinear Elements," *Proc. IRE.*, **44,** 904 (1956).

7. Marique, J., "Notes on the Theory of Diode Rectification," *Wireless Eng.*, **12,** 17 (1935).

8. *Proc. of the IRE.*, Special issue on single-side-band modulation. **44,** December, (1956).

9. Roder, H., "Theory of the Discriminator Circuit for AFC," *Proc. I.R.E.*, **26,** 590 (1938).

10. Ryder, J. D., *Networks, Lines, and Fields*, 2nd ed. Prentice-Hall, Inc., Englewood Cliffs, N. J. 1955.

11. Uhlir, A., Jr., "The Potential of Semiconductor Diodes in High-Frequency Communication," *Proc. IRE.*, **46,** 1099, (1958).

12. Wing, A. H., "On the Theory of Tubes With Two Control Grids," *Proc.IRE.* **29,** 121, (1941).

Wave-Shaping Circuits | 16

Another large group of circuits, concerned with the generation or handling of nonsinusoidal forms of voltage or current, remains to be considered. In these applications the ability of the transistor or vacuum tube to serve as an inertialess and almost resistance-less switch is considerably emphasized over the amplifying or linear properties of the device. Applications of this nature have become increasingly important with the development of television, radar, electronic computers, and pulse forms of transmission systems.

16–1. Response of RC and RL circuits

A series combination of R and C appears in Fig. 16–1; these might be the equivalents for more complex networks. If S is closed at $t = 0$, and v_o is the initial potential across C, then

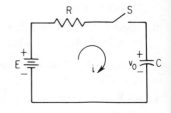

Fig. 16–1. Simple RC circuit.

$$Ri + \frac{1}{C} \int_0^t i \, dt + v_o = E$$

which has the well-known solution

$$i = \frac{E - v_o}{R} \epsilon^{-t/RC} \tag{16–1}$$

The potential across the capacitor is

$$v_C = E - Ri = v_o + (E - v_o)(1 - \epsilon^{-t/RC}) \tag{16–2}$$

528

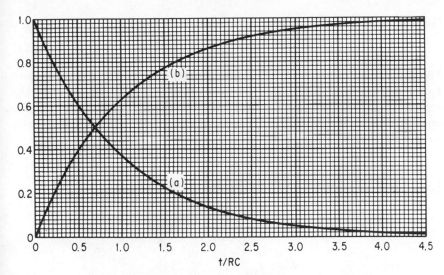

Fig. 16–2. (a) Value of $\epsilon^{-t/RC}$; (b) value of $1 - \epsilon^{-t/RC}$.

These equations contain the terms $\epsilon^{-t/RC}$ and $1 - \epsilon^{-t/RC}$, which appear in usual RC circuit analysis; plots of these functions are shown in Fig. 16–2. The term RC is the *time constant* of the circuit. For R in ohms and C in microfarads, the units of RC are microseconds.

At $t = 0$ the current is given by $i_o = (E - v_o)/R$, and at $t = \infty$ the current is zero. At $t = 0$ the capacitor potential is v_o, and at $t = \infty$ it is E. Between these limits the changes will occur according to the exponential curves, dependent only on RC. For this reason the curves are conveniently plotted in units of RC. It can be seen that in one time constant, a change of voltage or current in RC circuits will be 63 per cent completed, will be 88 per cent completed in two time constants, and may be considered fully completed in four time constants, when the variable will have reached 98 per cent of the value at infinite time.

The RL series circuit of Fig. 16–3 may be similarly treated. Upon closure of S, the circuit equation is

$$E = Ri + L\frac{di}{dt}$$

The current in L is zero at $t = 0$, so that

$$i = \frac{E}{R}(1 - \epsilon^{-Rt/L}) \qquad (16\text{–}3)$$

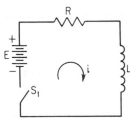

Fig. 16–3. Simple RL circuit.

Since $v_L = L\,di/dt$, the voltage across the inductance is

$$v_L = E\epsilon^{-Rt/L} \tag{16-4}$$

The same form of exponential relation appears as for the RC case, with L/R being the time constant. If R is in ohms and L in microhenrys, the units of L/R are microseconds. Again the full change of current or voltage can be considered complete in four time constants, a useful relation in estimating circuit performance.

16–2. Differentiation and integration by RC circuits

Summing the currents at A, Fig. 16–4, leads to

$$C\frac{d(e_i - e_o)}{dt} - \frac{e_o}{R} = 0$$

and using $p = d/dt$,

$$e_o = \frac{RCp}{1 + RCp}\, e_i \cong RCpe_i \tag{16-5}$$

the approximation holding if the time constant RC is small with respect to the smallest time increment in the input e_i. The output voltage e_o is then *proportional to the derivative of the input voltage.*

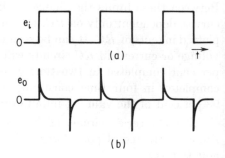

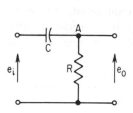

Fig. 16–4. An RC differentiating network.

Fig. 16–5. Output of a differentiating network with square-wave input.

An abrupt change in potential applied to the circuit appears instantaneously across the resistor, since the voltage across the capacity cannot change instantaneously. As C charges, the output potential across R falls.

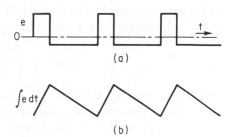

(a)

(b)

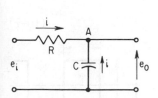

Fig. 16–6. An RC integrating network.

Fig. 16–7. Response of integrating network with rectangular input.

This is illustrated for a square wave input in Fig. 16–5. For large RC, the voltage across R could not reach zero during a cycle, and the output voltage would have a different form. It can be seen that if RC is made smaller, the output voltage would more nearly approach the ideal spike of the true derivative.

The circuit of Fig. 16–6 is useful as an integrator of the input voltage. Summing the currents at A

$$\frac{(e_i - e_o)}{R} - C\frac{de_o}{dt} = 0$$

which becomes

$$e_o = \frac{e_i}{1 + RCp} \cong \frac{1}{RCp}e_i \tag{16-6}$$

and the circuit *will integrate the applied voltage*, under the assumption that RC is long with respect to the largest time increment in the signal.

The output of a differentiating circuit is independent of the d-c level of the input, but the output of an integrating circuit must eventually attain a d-c level equal to that of the input. For this reason, a true integrating action is attained only for input signals having an average value of zero. The performance on such a signal is indicated in Fig. 16–7.

16–3. RC coupling circuits

The RC differentiating circuit of Fig. 16–5 appears as an element in the coupling network of usual RC amplifiers; its use therein must suppress differentiation if distortion is to be avoided. One may take the inverse of the assumptions that lead to Eq. 16–5, or assume that the differentiation will be minimized if RC is made large, in which case Eq. 16–5 becomes

$$e_o = \frac{RCp}{1 + RCp}\, e_i \cong e_i \qquad (16\text{–}7)$$

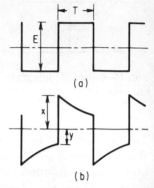

The output voltage will then be identical with the input, or no distortion is introduced.

The effect of the coupling circuit may be investigated further by application of a square wave to the input. A low frequency will be chosen, since if ωRC is large at that frequency it will be even larger at all higher frequencies. When such a wave is first applied there will be a transient extending over a few cycles, but this will be neglected here. After steady state is reached, as in Fig. 16–8, the amplitude of the jump of the output in Fig. 16–8(b) must equal the input jump in Fig. 16–8(a). This jump is composed of two parts, x above the axis and y below the axis. However,

Fig. 16–8. Response of an RC coupling circuit to a square wave.

$$x + y = E$$

where E is the peak-to-peak applied voltage.

It is apparent that

$$y = x\epsilon^{-T/RC}$$

so that

$$x = \frac{E}{1 + \epsilon^{-T/RC}} \qquad (16\text{–}8)$$

Between rise and fall points the curve is that of the exponential $e^{-t/RC}$.

The results of a choice of various time constants for the coupling network are shown in Fig. 16–9. A small time constant, as in Fig. 16–9(b), shows the differentiating tendency of the circuit. The figure reinforces the assumption that for an RC coupling network the time constant must be long, in fact 10 or more times the interval of the wave will be required. This confirms the result reached in Section 9–18 where the network was similarly studied.

The material of this section shows that application of a low-frequency square wave to an amplifier should indicate the form of coupling-circuit response in the output. Since the square-wave response is a more critical test than amplitude response to sinusoidal waves, the square wave is often used as an input in testing procedures.

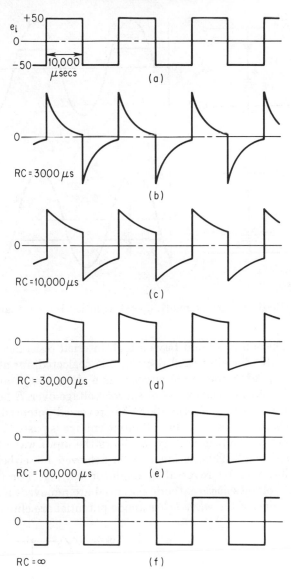

Fig. 16–9. Response of an RC coupling network as a function of the time constant of the network.

16–4. Clippers and limiters

One of the most important elements in the generation of nonsinusoidal wave forms is the *clipper*. A simple circuit, with its output wave form, is illustrated in Fig. 16–10. A diode in series with an emf is shunted across

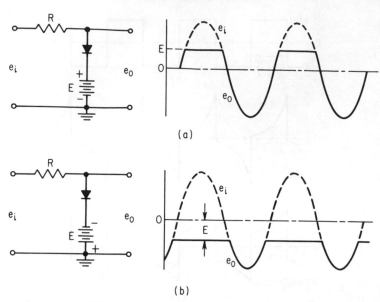

Fig. 16–10. Clipping circuits, operating at levels other than zero.

the circuit. The source should have a high internal resistance, represented here by R. If the diode forward resistance is neglected, for all values of e_i above the value of E the diode appears as a short circuit and voltage E appears as the output, the excess of source voltage over E being iR drop. For values of e_i less than E, the diode has reversed potential and is open. The iR drop is then zero, and the full input voltage is passed to the output.

Adjustment of the bias voltage E allows the input wave to be clipped at any desired level. This action can be achieved for either positive or negative half waves by reversal of diode or battery. For fixed cathode potential, all voltages *above* cathode potential are removed; for fixed anode voltage, all values of the wave *below* anode potential are clipped.

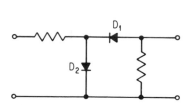

Fig. 16–11. Series-shunt limiting or clipping.

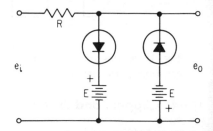

Fig. 16–12. Double-diode clipper for generating square waves.

The series-shunt form of Fig. 16–11 would completely eliminate all positive-going input voltages. Its action is an improvement over the previous circuits, since diode D_1 blocks the signal, and diode D_2 short circuits the signal to ground simultaneously. On the negative half cycle diode D_1 passes the signal, and D_2 appears open. Reversal of the diodes, or the addition of biases is possible as for previous circuits.

Square waves can be generated from sine waves of the desired frequency by clipping both positive and negative peaks. Such a clipper may use two oppositely-connected and oppositely-biased diodes, as in Fig. 16–12. The output will have finite rise time, which may be improved by doing the clipping at low level, amplifying, and clipping again, thus improving the squareness of the wave. A dual diode clipper operating at two different signal levels may be used to remove the noise components from received pulse signals, as indicated in Fig. 16–13.

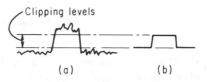

(a)   (b)

Fig. 16–13. (a) Received pulse; (b) signal after clipping.

Triode or transistor circuits can also be used for clipping or limiting, by driving these devices beyond cutoff and into saturation, as shown for the transistor limiter of Fig. 16–14. The input signal should be large compared to the voltage difference between cutoff and saturation. Resistor R limits the current on the positive swing.

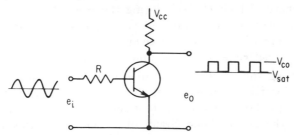

Fig. 16–14. Overdriven transistor for saturation and cutoff limiting.

16–5. Clamping circuits

The *clamping circuit* or *d-c restorer* is used in television and elsewhere, when it is necessary to insert a d-c component into a wave, following a-c amplification. A diode clamp is shown at Fig. 16–15(a), as an RC coupling circuit of *long time constant*, and a shunt diode. The source and diode should be of low resistance.

The diode reacts in the circuit whenever point A is positive, and the capacitor C charges through a low-time-constant circuit which includes

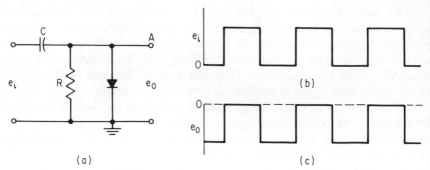

Fig. 16–15. Diode clamping circuit.

the resistances of source and diode. Consider the square wave of (b) applied at the instant the wave goes positive. Point A becomes positive and the diode connects point A to the zero-potential side of the circuit. The full applied voltage then appears across C, and the output is at zero as in Fig. 16–14(c).

When the input voltage falls to zero, the right side of C must instantaneously fall by the same amount, taking point A with it to a negative potential. If the RC time constant is very long, C cannot appreciably discharge in the negative interval, so that the potential of A remains of negative value. When the input rises, the output once more goes up to zero. Any charge which C loses during the negative long time-constant interval is immediately resupplied at the beginning of the low time-constant period. Therefore, if RC is large and the source and diode resistances are small, the positive peaks of the input are *clamped* at zero.

By reversing the diode it is possible to clamp the negative peaks at zero, and by insertion of bias potentials in series with the diode the circuit can be made to clamp at other potentials; one example is shown in Fig. 16–16. Since the grid-cathode circuit of a triode simulates a diode, it is possible to employ the input circuit of a triode for clamping purposes and the anode circuit for additional gain.

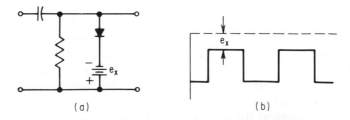

Fig. 16–16. Clamping at a value other than zero.

16–6. The ringing circuit for pulse generation

A ringing circuit employs a parallel RLC combination as in Fig. 16–17, with the resistance of L included in R. If the current in L at $t = 0$ is i_o, then

$$C \frac{dv}{dt} + \frac{1}{C} \int_0^t v \, dt + \frac{v}{R} + i_o = 0$$

$$p^2 v + \frac{1}{RC} pv + \frac{v}{LC} = 0 \qquad (16\text{–}9)$$

The roots of this equation are

$$p = -\frac{1}{2RC} \pm \sqrt{\frac{1}{4R^2C^2} - \frac{1}{LC}} \qquad (16\text{–}10)$$

The case of interest is that of *underdamping*, in which the radical becomes

$$\sqrt{\frac{1}{4R^2C^2} - \frac{1}{LC}} = j\sqrt{\frac{1}{LC} - \frac{1}{4R^2C^2}} = j\omega \qquad (16\text{–}11)$$

The solution of the differential equation then is

$$v = (K_1 \epsilon^{j\omega t} + K_2 \epsilon^{-j\omega t}) \epsilon^{-t/2RC} \qquad (16\text{–}12)$$

Noting that at $t = 0$ the voltage $v = 0$, and $dv/dt = -i_o/C$, the solution to the original equation is obtainable as

$$v = -\frac{i_o}{\omega C} \epsilon^{-t/2RC} \sin \omega t \qquad (16\text{–}13)$$

The result is oscillatory, at a frequency

$$f = \frac{1}{2\pi} \sqrt{\frac{1}{LC} - \frac{1}{4R^2C^2}} \qquad (16\text{–}14)$$

The circuit voltage is damped by the factor $\epsilon^{-t/2RC}$. If the losses are small, as required for the underdamped case, then the maximum energy stored in the inductor is transferred substantially without loss to the capacitor during the first fraction of a cycle. Thus

$$\frac{C v_{\max}^2}{2} = \frac{L i_o^2}{2}$$

and the peak voltage during the first half cycle will be

$$v_{\max} = -i_o \sqrt{\frac{L}{C}} \qquad (16\text{–}15)$$

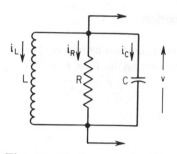

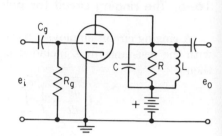

Fig. 16–17. Currents in the
RLC circuit.

Fig. 16–18. A ringing circuit.

In application, the oscillatory circuit is used as a plate load as in Fig. 16–18, the combination becoming a ringing circuit, since the *RLC* circuit is allowed to oscillate at its own natural frequency after being impulsively excited. The input e_i will be a high-amplitude square wave which will have its positive peak clamped at zero. During the positive half cycle the anode current will establish itself at i_o, and because of the damping introduced by the low plate resistance of the tube, the *RLC* circuit cannot oscillate. When the tube is cut off by application of the negative half cycle of the square wave, the *RLC* circuit is effectively disconnected and left free to oscillate or ring at its own natural frequency. This action is illustrated by the oscillogram of Fig. 16–19.

The circuit is an excellent source of *marker pips*, or pulses of short duration, obtained by clipping at a level equal approximately to the peak

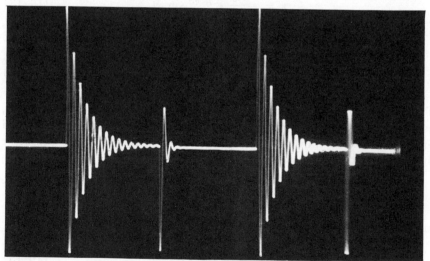

Fig. 16–19. Output voltage of a ringing circuit.

of the second cycle. This leaves a series of pips created by the peaks of the first cycles, and at a time set by the driving square wave.

The possibility of a resonant circuit somewhere in an amplifier breaking into a damped oscillation when excited by an impulse provides a means of checking amplifier high-frequency performance. By applying a square-wave the presence of an oscillatory condition, and its degree of damping, can be detected by the presence in the output of an oscillation following the abrupt change in voltage. An example of this is given in Fig. 16–20. An estimate of the frequency of this oscillation, and therefore the circuit probably at fault, can be made through knowledge of the square-wave fundamental frequency. Therefore square-wave amplifier testing provides a means of assaying amplifier response at both low and high frequencies.

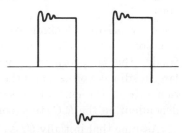

Fig. 16–20. Oscillations on an output square wave.

16–7. Blocking oscillators

Another circuit commonly used to generate short marker pips or pulses is the *blocking oscillator*. The basic circuit is usually that of a grid-tuned oscillator, with very large grid inductance, large coupling or M, and a rather low Q in the tuned circuit. The time constant of the $R_g C_g$ combination must also be long with respect to the time of a cycle of the resonant frequency.

During the initial half cycle the grid is driven strongly positive by reason of the close coupling between L_1 and L_2, and C_g rapidly charges to a high potential because of the grid current and the low resistance of the grid-cathode path. At the end of the first half cycle the grid is highly nega-

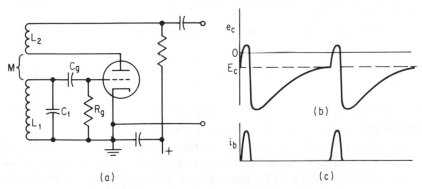

Fig. 16–21. Blocking oscillator operation.

tive or the tube has developed sufficient bias to cut itself off; although oscillations may continue in the LC circuit as a ringing circuit, the low Q prevents them from being of appreciable magnitude. Thus the output is one large but short current pulse, as shown in Fig. 16–21.

The interval between pulses or the repetition rate is controlled by the $R_g C_g$ time constant, since C_g must discharge through R_g down to a potential where the tube is no longer cut off before another output pulse may start.

A transistor blocking oscillator appears in Fig. 16–22. The circuit functions much like that for the triode, the transformer providing a large feedback voltage, and the repetition rate of the current pulses being dependent on the $R_e C_e$ time constant.

Assume that initially C_e is charged negative to the emitter and the transistor is cut off. The capacitor discharges through R_e, and when the emitter voltage reaches zero the emitter current starts. The resultant collector current through the closely coupled transformer induces a voltage which drives the base negative, further increasing the emitter current.

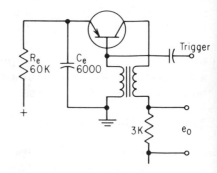

Fig. 16–22. Transistor in a blocking oscillator.

The emitter current charges C_e negatively and as its potential rises, the emitter current delines. When the emitter current is no longer large enough to maintain the collector current at saturation, the collector current starts to fall. This declining collector current induces a positive base voltage through the transformer, driving the transistor back to emitter cutoff. Capacitor C_e is left negatively charged, ready to repeat the cycle after its discharge through R_e.

The repetition rate for short pulses is approximately

$$f_r = \frac{nV_{EE}}{V_{cc}R_e C_e} \tag{16-16}$$

where n is the collector to base transformer ratio, and it is assumed that both emitter and collector swing to saturation.

Intermittent oscillations of this nature may develop in any tuned-circuit oscillator, and are an indication that the RC time constant of the bias circuit is excessive. The phenomenon is occasionally referred to as *squegging.*

16–8. Multivibrators

A number of circuits exist which are capable of almost instantaneous switching or transition from one operating state to a second state. These terminal states or conditions may be stable or semi-stable, and will be separated in terms of voltage or current values, with a region of instability between. These circuits may be classified as

Condition		*Type*
(1)	(2)	
Semi-stable	Semi-stable	Multivibrator
Stable	Semi-stable	Monostable or one-shot
Stable	Stable	Trigger or flip-flop

The name *multivibrator* was originally applied by Abraham and Bloch because of the large number of harmonic frequencies present in its output circuit. The circuit is useful in pulse formation, and may be synchronized to divide frequency or to switch at sub-multiples of an input frequency.

The free-running multivibrator of Fig. 16–23 can be seen as a two-stage RC amplifier with output coupled back to input, and is therefore, basically a feedback oscillator. Operation may be explained by assuming equal plate currents in tubes T_1 and T_2; the potentials at A and B will also be equal. Assume some slight variation which momentarily increases the current in T_2. This effect reduces the voltage at B and lowers the grid

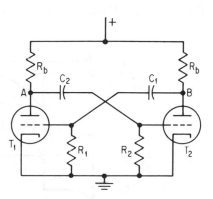

Fig. 16–23. Free-running multivibrator.

potential of T_1 through C_1. This reduction of grid potential of T_1 lowers its current, raises the potential at A, and raises the grid potential of T_2 through C_2; this further increases the current in T_2. This chain of events quickly raises the anode voltage of T_1 up to E_{bb}, and since the voltage across C_2 cannot change suddenly, the grid of T_2 is carried positive. The rise of conduction in T_2 has carried its anode voltage down to saturation level, and through C_1 has driven T_1 below cutoff. With T_2 conducting and T_1 cut off, we have one condition of semi-stability.

As time passes, the charges on C_1 and C_2 readjust and the potential of the grid of T_1 rises above cutoff and conduction begins; this drops the potential at A and reduces the current in T_2 as the capacitor potentials continue to change. The end of the cycle is reached with T_1 conducting and T_2 cut off, and this is the second condition of semi-stability.

The time of transition is very rapid since the capacitor potentials do not change during switching. The delay or dwell time between switching transients is a function of the applicable time constants. The tube with positive grid will have grid current, and the capacitor C_1 or C_2 connected to this tube will charge through the internal grid-cathode path and this charge time will be short. The other capacitor connected to the tube in cutoff will discharge through R_1 and R_b, and this time constant will be controlling and responsible for the exponential rise of grid voltage shown in Fig. 16–24(a). Assuming $R_1 \gg R_b$, as is usual, the end of the dwell or delay time is reached when the grid potential rises to cutoff V_o, and this is

$$V_o = \frac{E_{bb}}{\mu} = (E_{bb} - e_s)\epsilon^{-t_1/R_1C_1} \qquad (16\text{–}17)$$

It is possible to create unequal delay times or unsymmetrical pulses if $R_1C_1 \neq R_2C_2$. Each portion of the full cycle could then be calculated by

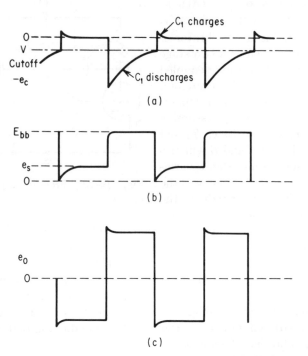

(a)

(b)

(c)

Fig. 16–24. (a) Grid voltage; (b) plate voltage T_1; (c) plate-to-plate voltage.

use of Eq. 16–17, and the period of oscillation of the multivibrator could be determined as

$$T = t_1 + t_2 = (R_1C_1 + R_2C_2) \ln \frac{E_{bb} - e_s}{V_o} \qquad (16\text{--}18)$$

The output wave form of Fig. 16–24 is rich in harmonics of the oscillation frequency. By clipping the plate-to-plate voltage it is possible to obtain square waves or pulses of short rise time. In order that this rise time be really short, it is necessary to minimize stray capacities throughout the circuit, particularly the grid-cathode capacities which should be small with respect to C_1 and C_2.

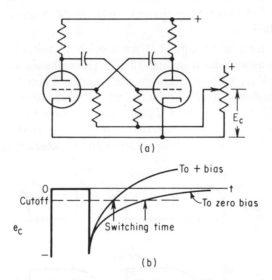

Fig. 16–25. (a) Positive bias on multivibrator; (b) change in switching time due to positive bias.

If the grid resistors are returned to a positive voltage instead of to cathode, as in Fig. 16–25, somewhat more precise operation with less time jitter of the trailing edge of the pulse will be obtained. With positive bias the rising grid-voltage line crosses the cutoff line at a steeper angle, and changes in cutoff voltage will have less effect on the delay time of the multivibrator operation. It is found that there is an almost linear relation between this bias and time delay, and this is an effective method of frequency control. The period of the circuit is then

$$T = (R_1C_1 + R_2C_2) \ln \frac{E_{bb} - e_s + E_c}{V_o + E_c} \qquad (16\text{--}19)$$

A transistor multivibrator is shown in Fig. 16–26. The general theory of operation follows that for the vacuum tube, but some difficulties are created by the loading of the base circuit. Because the transistor is switched into a heavily saturated condition, the base current may be high, and choice of transistors with large h_{fe} will be helpful. This base current also requires a low value of R_{B1} and R_{B2}, and rather large values of C_1 and C_2 if the switching current is to be supplied.

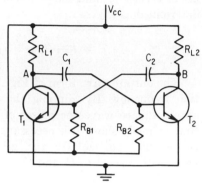

Fig. 16–26. Transistor multivibrator.

Operation may be explained if we assume T_1 initially cut off and T_2 in saturation, as at time t_1 in Fig. 16–27. The collector voltage on T_1 will be V_{CC}, and V_{BE1} will be negative and rising. When V_{BE1} goes slightly positive T_1 conducts, dropping its collector voltage from V_{CC} to $V_{\text{sat}} \cong 0$. Acting through C_1, the base of T_2 is driven negative by V_{CC} volts, and T_2 is cut off. Through C_2 the voltage rise at B is transmitted to the base of T_1, driving it further into saturation. Capacitor C_2 charges quickly through

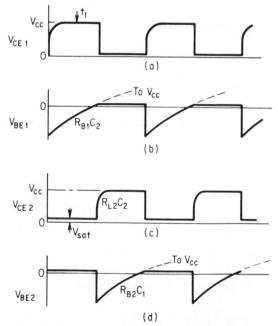

Fig. 16–27. Wave forms in the transistor multivibrator.

R_{L2} and the base of T_1, and the steady base current through R_{B1} holds T_1 in saturation. The charge on C_1 then begins to leak off through R_{B2} and when the base of T_2 goes positive the process is repeated.

The rounding of the leading edge of the collector wave form is due to the charging time of C_2 through the base and R_{L2}. For an accurate square wave this time constant must be short with respect to the $R_B C_1$ or $R_B C_2$ time constants.

The switching transient forced on V_{BE2} drops its potential to approximately $-V_{CC}$ volts. Due to the bias resistor R_{B2} being connected to V_{CC}, the total voltage acting in the $R_{B2} C_1$ circuit is $2V_{CC}$. Then the time variation of V_{BE2} during cutoff for T_2 is

$$V_{BE2}(t) = 2V_{CC}(1 - \epsilon^{-t/R_{B2}C_1}) - V_{CC}$$

and the total period of the multivibrator, allowing for unsymmetrical time constants, is

$$T = (R_{B2}C_1 + R_{B1}C_2) \ln 2 = 1.386(R_{B2}C_1 + R_{B1}C_2) \quad (16\text{–}19)$$

It is possible for the capacitors to be initially charged in such a way that both transistors will saturate, and triggering will not start. The addition of a resistor in the common emitter lead will usually provide a remedy.

Output from these circuits is usually taken at points A or B, or both, through amplifiers which will not appreciably distort the circuit potentials by loading effects.

16–9. Synchronization of the multivibrator

It is possible to cause a multivibrator to synchronize with a driving signal having a frequency n times as great as that at which the multivibrator is operating. If the driving signal then changes frequency over a small range, the multivibrator frequency will stay locked or synchronized. The multivibrator output wave form is independent of this driving signal, only the frequency being determined.

The object of synchronization is to produce an output that is a subharmonic of the input frequency, or to make a *frequency divider*. The ratio of division is usually a small integer, the factor 10 being convenient. In this way the frequency of a highly stable 100-kilocycle crystal oscillator can be subdivided in steps to 10 kc, 1 kc, and finally 100 cycles. This last frequency can be amplified and made to operate a synchronous clock motor, indicating time by the *quartz-crystal clock*. By comparison with time measurements of the rotation of the earth, very accurate primary standards for frequency are possible.

Usually the synchronizing signal is a sine wave although a pulse input is more accurate. The signal is inserted into a grid circuit of the multi-

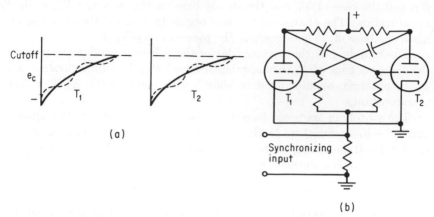

Fig. 16–28. (a) Synchronization of a multivibrator; (b) circuit of a synchronized multivibrator.

vibrator, adding this small-amplitude driving signal to the already present exponentially rising voltage, as in Fig. 16–28. A means of introducing the synchronizing signal is also shown.

Stable operation requires that the grid voltage reach the triggering point at a time when the synchronizing voltage is going positive. Thus, if the circuit, without synchronization, tends to trigger somewhat early, the superimposed negative synchronizing voltage of that moment will hold off the triggering action until the zero of the wave is reached. For the case shown, the count-down factor would be controlled exactly at 4.

16–10. The one-shot or monostable trigger

If the basic multivibrator circuit be modified by changing one of the switching capacitors to a resistor, the circuit becomes a *monostable* or *one-shot* multivibrator. This change makes one of the operating points stable, the second remaining semi-stable, whereas the free-running multivibrator oscillated between two semi-stable end points.

In the circuit of Fig. 16–29, tube T_2 has no bias and is normally conducting, with T_1 cut off. Application of a short positive trigger pulse to the grid of T_1 causes that tube to conduct, abruptly lowering the potential at A. Through C, the grid of T_2 drops an equal number of volts, and is driven considerably below cutoff, as indicated in Fig. 16–30. As C discharges through R_g the grid of T_2 rises in potential and T_2 conducts when cutoff voltage is passed. This conduction lowers the potential at B and the grid of T_1. As the grid of T_2 approaches zero volts, the grid of T_1 reaches

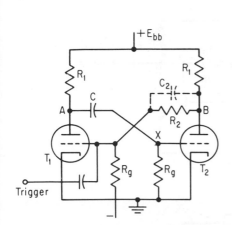

Fig. 16–29. One-shot or monostable multivibrator.

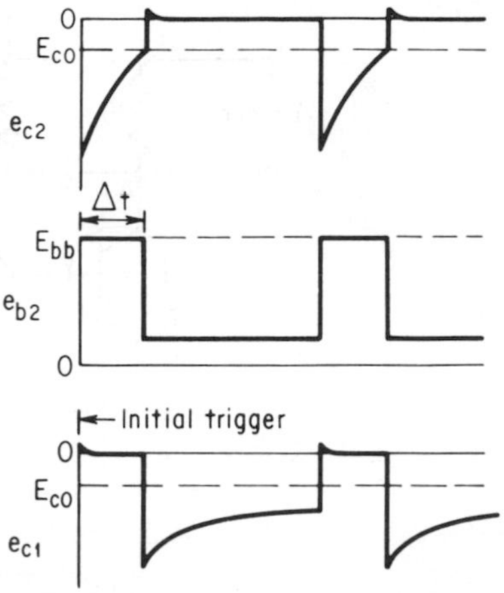

Fig. 16–30. Wave forms in monostable circuit.

cutoff, and the original stable condition of T_2 conducting, T_1 cut off, is restored. For each pulse applied to T_1 the circuit will transfer conduction to T_1 and back to T_2, the length of time Δt for the switch depending on the $R_g C$ time constant.

If the grid resistor of T_2 is returned to a positive voltage instead of cathode, there will be more precise determination of the end of the pulse, as indicated in Fig. 16–25. In fact, variation of the positive bias may be used as a control on the length of pulse produced at B.

Capacitor C_2, indicated by dashed lines in Fig. 16–29, is not a coupling capacitor, but serves to speed up the operation of switching from T_2 to T_1. The grid-cathode capacitance of T_1, which must be charged through R_2, prevents the grid voltage from changing rapidly. Likewise C_{gp} opposes any change in grid voltage. Capacitor C_2, of the order of 50 pf when used, charges these capacitances rapidly; it also overcomes the voltage-divider action of R_g and R_2 and applies the full value of any *change* in voltage to the grid of T_1.

The time duration of the output pulse can be written as

$$T = R_g C \ln \frac{E_{bb} - e_s + E_c}{V_o + E_c} \tag{16–20}$$

when a positive bias E_c is used on T_2.

A transistor monostable circuit appears in Fig. 16–31, and shows its family relationship to the vacuum-tube circuit. A negative trigger pulse is applied to the base of T_2 through C and cuts off this transistor. As before, the change of voltage at B drives T_1 into saturation, but after a time Δt

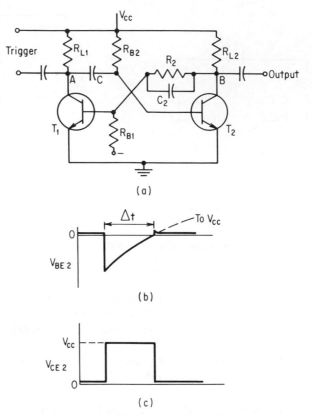

Fig. 16–31. Transistor monostable.

the capacitor C has discharged and raised the base of T_2 back to zero, when the circuit returns to its initial stable state of T_1 off, T_2 on. The period may be shown to be

$$T = R_{B2}C \ln 2 = 0.693 R_{B2}C \qquad (16\text{--}21)$$

following the reasoning applied to Fig. 16–26.

By taking an output from B in either circuit, an accurate square wave of adjustable pulse length may be obtained. The circuit may also be used to reshape or delay the pulses used to trigger it. This is done by differentiation of the voltage at B, producing a positive pulse at time of triggering, and a negative pulse Δt seconds later. The delay may be changed by adjustment of R_{B2} in the transistor circuit, or R_g or the positive bias E_c in vacuum-tube usage.

The output of T_2 may also be used as a *gating* voltage, to turn on or off some other circuit for a predetermined interval after arrival of the initial pulse.

16–11. Flip-flops or bistable circuits

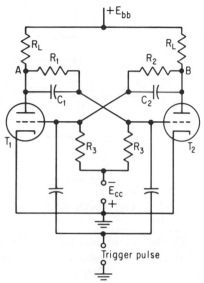

The third of the general class of trigger circuits is the *flip-flop* or *bistable* circuit, in which there are found to be two stable operating states separated by an unstable region. The most famous circuit of this class is the Eccles-Jordan, one form of which is shown in Fig. 16–32. The circuit is formed by replacing both switching capacitors of the multivibrator with resistors, R_1 and R_2 of the figure, and biasing both tubes below cutoff. Capacitors C_1 and C_2 are added to furnish a speed-up function, as for the monostable circuit.

One stable point exists with T_1 off, T_2 on, the other with T_1 on, T_2 off. For analysis assume the condition of T_1 on, T_2 cut off, in which case the

Fig. 16–32. Eccles–Jordan bistable circuit.

grid voltage will be clamped at approximately zero on T_1, with the grid of T_2 below cutoff. If a positive trigger pulse is then applied to both grids simultaneously, it will not alter the current in T_1 which is already conducting, but it will drive T_2 into conduction. This reduces the potential at B and at the grid of T_1, reducing the tube current and raising the potential at A. This action further turns on T_2, and the process continues until T_1 is cut off and T_2 is fully conducting; this is a stable condition. Another positive pulse will cause the circuit to revert to its original stable condition.

Negative pulses might also be used, but it is then the conducting tube which is turned off, with the regenerative action causing the other tube to be turned on. The only requirement on the triggering pulses is that they be of sufficient amplitude to drive the tubes slightly past the unstable equal-current condition, after which the cumulative action completes the current transfer.

Another form of the flip-flop employs pentodes with the suppressor grids used for switching, as in Fig. 16–33. The normal control grids are then available for triggering. Application of positive pulses to the grid of the nonconducting tube will not cause conduction because of the negative suppressor grid, but the use of a negative pulse on the control grid of the conducting tube reduces its anode current and triggers the circuit.

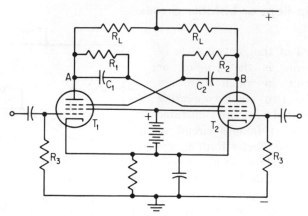

Fig. 16–33. Eccles–Jordan circuit employing pentodes.

The time required to transfer conduction from one tube to the other is known as the *resolving time*; this indicates the needed time separation of two pulses if both are to be resolved or indicated. The resolving time suffers if the speed-up capacitors C_1 and C_2 are made too large, and usual values approximate 50 pf for triode tubes. The time constants R_1C_1 and R_2C_2 should be large with respect to the time required for transition but short with respect to the expected time between pulses.

Figure 16–34 illustrates *NPN* transistors in a similar flip-flop. If it is assumed that T_1 is off, and T_2 conducting, then a positive pulse to T_1 will

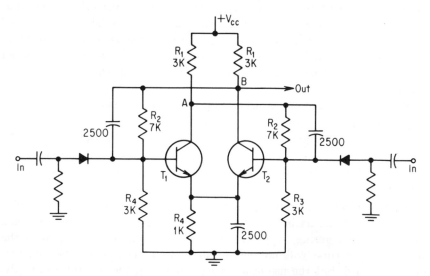

Fig. 16–34. Transistor flip-flop.

reverse the bias and the circuit will trigger. A positive pulse to T_2 will cause the circuit to transfer again. The parameters given in the figure should allow operation up to 100 kc rates with transistors of suitable f_α.

Since one transistor will always be in saturation the emitter voltage in Fig. 16–34 will be

$$V_E = \frac{R_4}{R_1 + R_4} V_{CC}$$

The capacitor will smooth over the transient during the switching operation.

Base triggering as shown will be the most sensitive form, since only a fraction of a volt will usually be required to switch a base into conduction. Such circuits may also be switched at the collector with a larger pulse. By so doing it is possible to utilize a single input to switch a bistable circuit alternately between two states. As shown in Fig. 16–35, a short negative pulse will be transmitted or steered by the diode only to the transistor which is off or has a collector voltage equal to V_{CC}. This is a useful device in counter circuits.

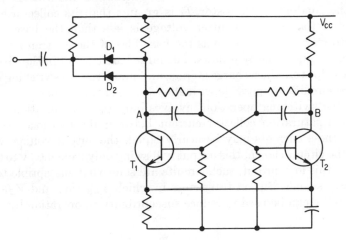

Fig. 16–35. Use of steering diodes for guiding switching pulses.

16–12. Saturation in flip-flops

There has been frequent reference to transistors being operated in the saturated state. This implies heavy collector current which reduces the collector voltage below the value of base voltage, resulting in forward biasing for both transistor diodes, making the collector an emitter.

In the study of transistors it was mentioned that charges are stored in remote base regions while a transistor is in saturation, due to the inability of the low collector voltage to sweep out these charges in the base. When a transistor is switched from saturation to cutoff, these charges come out of storage slowly and delay the switching time. This reduction in switching speed is undesirable.

The collector-emitter saturation voltage $V_{CE}(\text{sat})$ is low, and less than V_{BE}. Both voltages being less than about 0.5 v permits the assumption that all electrode voltages are zero or negligible with respect to supply levels. This stability of saturated voltage levels gives good temperature stability and makes circuit design simple, because it is not necessary to check the actual electrode potentials in detail. Saturated operation also reduces the transistor dissipation during the conducting interval, since the collector-emitter voltage is low; however it requires large trigger power to reverse a saturated transistor.

A very simple circuit, which takes advantage of the stability inherent in the saturated design, is the DCTL or *direct-coupled transistor logic* flip-flop of Fig. 16–36. The bases and collectors are cross-connected without switching resistors or capacitors. The voltages, as indicated, are to be expected with germanium transistors. In saturation the voltage on the base of the conducting transistor T_1 is greater than its collector-emitter voltage, and the collector-emitter voltage is less than the base voltage required to start conduction; thus the base bias of the off transistor T_2 is so low that negligible current flows. The large base current in the saturated transistor helps to reduce charge storage and improves the switching speed; high speed circuits are possible with alloy-diffused transistors.

Since the switching operation involves only the commutation of base current and saturation collector current between the two load resistors, and since these currents may be nearly equal, the output voltage will be low. For the circuit shown, this output will swing only from 0.02 v to 0.50 v. Because of this low output, such circuits are somewhat susceptible to turn off by stray signals. Silicon transistors in which $V_{CE}(\text{sat})$ and V_{BE} differ by about 0.7 v can be used to reduce susceptibility to operation by strays.

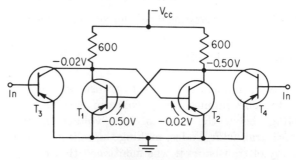

Fig. 16–36. DCTL flip-flop.

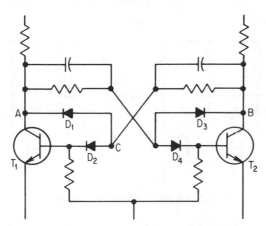

Fig. 16–37. Non-saturating diodes added to bistable circuit.

The circuit can be triggered by transistors T_3 and T_4, connected between collector and ground of the switches. Turning on T_4, connected to the nonconducting transistor T_2, reduces the base bias of T_1, its collector voltage rises and T_2 is switched.

In an attempt to improve the switching speed of transistor switches, various techniques based on clamping of the collector voltage just above saturation level have evolved; one such *non-saturating* method appears in Fig. 16–37. Diode D_1 is germanium and D_2 is silicon. As transistor T_1 turns on and the voltage at A falls below the voltage at C, diode D_1 conducts and shunts some of the base driving current into the collector, preventing further rise in base current. Since the silicon diode D_2 has a forward voltage drop of about 0.7 v over a considerable current range, it acts as a voltage regulator, holding V_{CE} at about 0.7 v, above saturation level and above V_{BE}. Thus, saturation is approached but not reached, and the time delay produced by base storage in saturated circuits is reduced.

16–13. Scalers or counting circuits

It can be seen that at point B in the flip-flop of Fig. 16–34, a positive pulse is obtained as output when T_2 cuts off, and a negative pulse appears when T_2 turns on. Confining our attention to the negative pulses, then one negative pulse is obtained as output for each *pair* of input pulses to T_1, and the circuit is given the name of a *scale-of-two* circuit.

A second flip-flop may be cascaded with the first as in Fig. 16–38. If it is arranged that T_2 and T_4, or the even-numbered devices, are initially turned on, then a negative output pulse will be given from T_4 of the second

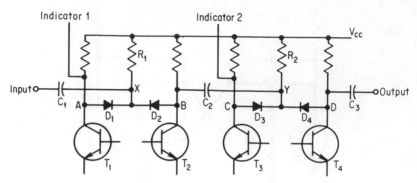

Fig. 16–38. Scale-of-four circuit.

bistable circuit for every four or 2^2 input pulses. With n bistables in cascade, the circuit will scale down the number of input pulses by a factor 2^n.

The basic circuit of Fig. 16–38 will be provided with an auxiliary reset switch so that the even stages are initially conducting. Since the indicators operate only when the point to which they are connected is below V_{CC}, the indicators will be off. The negative-going input pulse is differentiated or sharpened by the R_1C_1 combination, and will turn on T_1, through steering diode D_1, as in Fig. 16–35. Diode D_2 does not conduct because point B is essentially at zero potential, or negative to X, for the conducting transistor T_2. Since the potential at A drops, the indicator at A shows a 1.

A second negative pulse is transmitted through D_2 and turns T_2 on, T_1 off. At the same time, the fall in potential at B is differentiated by R_2C_2 and transmitted as a negative pulse to the second scaling circuit, causing transfer of conduction from T_4 to T_3. Indicator light 1 goes out and 2 turns on. A third pulse returns conduction to T_1 from T_2, and since this results in a positive pulse at B, the circuit of T_3, T_4 is not affected; indicator lights 1 and 2 are now both on, and their sum indicates a 3 count. On the arrival of the fourth pulse T_2 is switched on, a pulse is transmitted to the second switch which turns on T_4; both indicator lights are out and the circuit has returned to its initial condition. However, when T_4 turns on, it transmits a negative pulse to the output through C_3, this is an indication of the arrival of the fourth count, and the circuit is a scale-of-four. Additional switches or *binaries* may be cascaded, utilizing the output pulses at C_3 as input, to extend the counting range.

To make a scaler which would count in the decimal system or register one decade would require four binary switches, but these would have a potential counting range of $2^4 = 16$ before recycling. By use of feedback of pulses it is possible to add or subtract m synthetic pulses to the actual count n so that the scaler will recycle after $n + m$ synthetic total counts.

If the even-numbered transistors or tubes are set to be conducting for a zero or initial count, and if 1 represents conduction and 0 the off condition, then after six input pulses, the counter binary conditions would follow as

Pulses	T_1	T_2	T_3	T_4	T_5	T_6	T_7	T_8	Count indicated
7	1	0	1	0	1	0	0	1	$1 + 2 + 4$
8	0	1	0	1	0	1	1	0	8
9	1	0	0	1	0	1	1	0	$1 + 8$

It is desired that the counter recycle on the tenth pulse, or appear as

10	0	1	0	1	0	1	0	1

which is the condition it would normally have after 16 counts.

The circuit can operate normally through 9 counts, but on the tenth pulse a forward feed will be made to occur through directional diodes from T_2 to turn on T_8, and from T_7 to inhibit the turning off of T_4. These events can happen only on the tenth count, since previous changes of T_2 to *on* have occurred with T_8 off.

Essentially, we have placed T_8 in the condition it would have after 16 normal counts, or we have added 8 counts. Transistor T_4 is in the condition it had two counts earlier, or we have subtracted 2 counts. Thus, the counter has been reset after the needed $10 + 8 - 2 = 16$ pulses. Other feedback connections could have been used to achieve the same result, or to make a scale-of-5 or to produce other scale factors.

16–14. Switching diode matrices

It is frequently necessary to translate the binary output information of a counter into decimal number form, or to change the input information from a serial string of pulses to a set of parallel output circuits. These switching operations can be accomplished by use of variously-connected diode matrices, a binary-decimal translation form being shown in Fig. 16–39.

Inputs $T_1 \cdots T_5$ are bistable pairs, the two possible conducting states being shown as a and b. Polarities of supply voltages are so arranged that when any a or b is conducting, zero output will appear on any vertical bus to which a conducting state is connected by a diode. Thus, an output of $-V$ volts will appear *only* on a vertical bus which is *not* connected by diodes to a conducting binary state.

Correlation of the data in Fig. 16–39 with the indicated diode connections will show that when an input has switched the bistables $T_1 \cdots T_5$ into the indicated condition, the only vertical bus not connected to a conducting state will be that bus representing the corresponding decimal number.

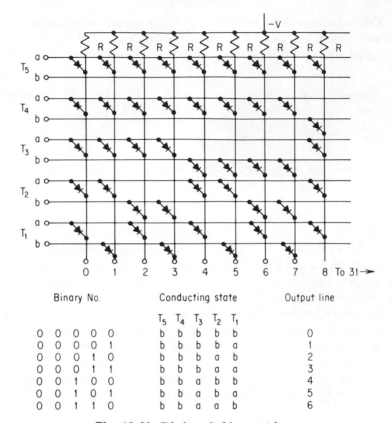

Binary No.					Conducting state					Output line
					T_5	T_4	T_3	T_2	T_1	
0	0	0	0	0	b	b	b	b	b	0
0	0	0	0	1	b	b	b	b	a	1
0	0	0	1	0	b	b	b	a	b	2
0	0	0	1	1	b	b	b	a	a	3
0	0	1	0	0	b	b	a	b	b	4
0	0	1	0	1	b	b	a	b	a	5
0	0	1	1	0	b	b	a	a	b	6

Fig. 16–39. Diode switching matrix.

As shown, the matrix could be extended to translate up to 2^5 or 32 binary numbers to decimal digits. If it be noted that a 0 for a particular binary digit calls for connection of a diode at a, and a 1 will place a diode at b, then a switching matrix can be readily designed to handle any number of inputs and outgoing lines.

Since the control circuits are connected to many diodes in parallel, it is desirable that the diodes have a high reverse resistance. To make the switching precise, the forward resistance should be low.

16–15. Gates

Many electronic switching circuits are required to transfer signals from inputs to desired outputs, under control from a third circuit. These switching circuits are common in multiplex operation and in computer control circuitry, and are known as *coincidence gates* or simply as *gates*. Several simple circuits appear in Fig. 16–40.

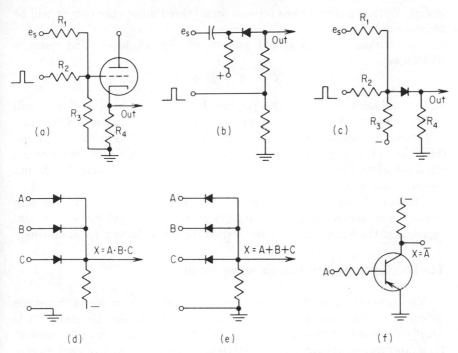

Fig. 16–40. (a), (b), (c) Simple gating circuits; (d), (e), (f) and, or, not gates.

In Fig. 16–40(a), R_4 is large, the tube is heavily biased, and a signal e_s produces no appreciable output. During the period when the positive gating pulse is applied, the bias is reduced, the gain approaches unity and the signal appears in the output.

At Fig. 16–40(b) and (c) are two circuits using diodes with reverse bias; the diodes are therefore nonconductive. During the period of the gating pulse the bias is overridden and the signal e_s is transferred to the output.

In computer circuits it is necessary to carry out certain operations in *logic*, involving the thought processes of *and, or, not,* and *nor.* Circuits to combine signals in these specified relationships are gates in a general sense. The circuit of Fig. 16–40(d) is an *and* gate which performs the operation

$$X = A \cdot B \cdot C$$

where the result is read as *A and B and C*; this means that a 1 is required at all inputs to read a 1 output. Zero volts is taken as a 0, and a large negative voltage as a 1. With zero input or a short on all inputs the output of the circuit is a zero, and will remain in that condition as long as any one input is zero. With negative pulses present on all three inputs the output will be negative or a 1.

An example of an *or* circuit appears at Fig. 16–40(e). The result is written as

$$X = A + B + C$$

and is read as *A or B or C*; this implies that a 1 input at *A* or *B* or *C* will yield a 1 output. With the diodes as shown a negative input on any terminal will yield a negative output and the desired result is achieved. A *not* circuit as in Fig. 16–40(f) implies a negation, therefore, if a 1 appears at the input the output will be a 0 and vice versa. The result is obtainable through the inversion characteristics of the transistor.

Monostable multivibrators are often employed to develop these gating pulses, since the pulse may be readily started or timed by an external signal, and the length of the pulse varied by a bias to suit requirements.

16–16. Cathode-ray sweep wave forms

The generation of the *time-base* or *sweep* wave form for electrostatic deflection of the cathode-ray beam has received considerable study. It is usually desired that the spot move across the screen as a linear function of time, and return abruptly to the starting point at the end of each sweep. This requires a wave of sawtooth form, with linear rise time and abrupt return to zero.

The potential across a capacitor without initial charge is

$$e_C = \frac{1}{C} \int_0^t i \, dt$$

If means can be found for supplying a constant charging current i, then e_C will be the desired linear function of time. Means must also be found for discharging the capacitor rapidly when some maximum potential V_2 is reached, thus giving the wave form of Fig. 16–41(b).

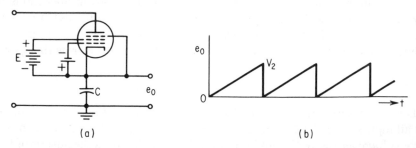

Fig. 16–41. (a) Constant-current charging circuit; (b) sweep wave form.

The anode current of a pentode is substantially independent of anode voltage over a wide range; a pentode becomes a means of supplying a constant charging current to a capacitor, as in Fig. 16–41(a). Although this circuit is occasionally employed, there are difficulties in supplying potentials above ground, since one side of C ordinarily must be grounded.

More usually the simple sweep circuits are based on a compromise with linearity, and use the rise of potential when C is charged from a constant voltage through a series resistor R, as in Fig. 16–42(a). It is still necessary to discharge the capacity when some potential e_1 is reached. The successive wave forms might then appear as at Fig. 16–42(b). The output voltage across the capacity C varies as

$$e = E(1 - \epsilon^{-t/RC}) \tag{16–22}$$

Replacing the exponential with the first few terms of its series gives

$$e = E\left(\frac{t}{RC} - \frac{t^2}{2R^2C^2} + \frac{t^3}{6R^3C^3} - \cdots\right) \tag{16–23}$$

Thus if t/RC is sufficiently small,

$$e \simeq \frac{Et}{RC} = Kt \tag{16–24}$$

with constant supply voltage assumed. If reasonable linearity is to be obtained with this circuit, then t_1/RC must be small, where t_1 is the time of the sweep, or at which the voltage e reaches value e_1. Equation 16–24 then implies that e_1/E must also be small, and it is necessary to amplify the usual small peak output to provide sufficient sweep voltage for deflection of the cathode-ray beam.

If the discharge time is assumed negligible, an expression for the frequency of the sweep can be found from Eq. 16–22 as

$$f = \frac{1}{t} = \frac{1}{RC \ln E/(E - e_1)} \tag{16–25}$$

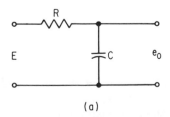

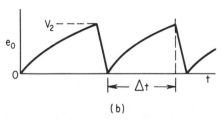

(a)   (b)

Fig. 16–42. (a) RC charging circuit; (b) sweep voltage.

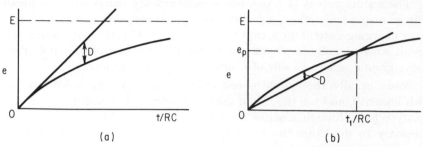

Fig. 16–43. Comparison of exponential with straight line approximations.

The frequency is usually controlled by variation of the RC product of the circuit.

The variation of the sweep voltage with time for the circuit of Fig. 16–42 can never be exactly linear, and a measure of departure from linearity is desirable. One method compares the exponential output with a straight line having the same initial slope, as in Fig. 16–43(a). The first term of Eq. 16–23 gives this linear relation as

$$e = \frac{t}{RC} E \tag{16-26}$$

The difference D between the straight line and the exponential is

$$D = E\left[\frac{t}{RC} - (1 - \epsilon^{-t/RC})\right]$$

and when expressed as a percentage of the linear output e predicted by the straight line, is

$$\text{Per cent } D = \left(1 - \frac{1 - \epsilon^{-t/RC}}{t/RC}\right) \times 100\% \tag{16-27}$$

The maximum percentage deviation occurs at the end of the sweep, or at $e = e_1$, $t = t_1$, so that

$$\text{Max per cent } D = \frac{D_1}{e_1} \times 100\% = 1 - \frac{1 - \epsilon^{-e_1/E}}{e_1/E} \times 100\% \tag{16-28}$$

This expression again indicates the desirability of keeping the ratio e_1/E small if reasonable linearity is to be obtained. Another view of this requirement shows that E and R are to be large, thus approximating an ideal constant-current charging source.

Several other straight lines might be used for comparison; one form is shown in Fig. 16–43(b), chosen to pass through the origin and the point of desired maximum output voltage e_1. Since the latter is usually specified, this line provides a more realistic appraisal of linearity. The equation of such a line is

$$\frac{e - e_1}{t/RC - t_1/RC} = \frac{e_1}{t_1/RC}$$

giving

$$e = \frac{E(1 - \epsilon^{-t_1/RC})}{t_1/RC} \frac{t}{RC} \qquad (16\text{–}29)$$

The difference D between this line and the exponential given by Eq. 16–22 is

$$D = E(1 - \epsilon^{-t/RC}) - \frac{E(1 - \epsilon^{-t_1/RC})}{t_1/RC} \frac{t}{RC} \qquad (16\text{–}30)$$

Obviously, this difference is zero at $t = t_1$ or the end of the sweep, whereas the previous straight line predicted a constantly increasing deviation. The point of maximum departure from linearity will lie near the middle of the sweep, and for small values of t_1/RC may be chosen at the midpoint where $t = t_1/2$ with small error.

The exponential curve has a value e_{mid} at this midpoint, given as

$$e_{\text{mid}} = E(1 - \epsilon^{-t_1/2RC})$$

and the approximate maximum departure from the linear curve in per cent of e_{mid} is then

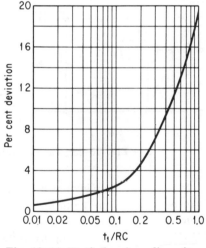

Fig. 16–44. Deviation from linearity as given by Eq. 16–31.

$$\frac{D}{e_{\text{mid}}} \times 100\% = \left[1 - \frac{(1 - \epsilon^{-t_1/RC})}{2(1 - \epsilon^{-t_1/2RC})}\right] \times 100\% \qquad (16\text{–}31)$$

This percentage departure from the linear curve is plotted in terms of t_1/RC in Fig. 16–44. Again, it is noted that small values of t_1/RC must be used to secure good linearity of the sweep, and that it is difficult to secure accuracies better than one per cent with this form of circuit.

16–17. Triggered sweeps

The RC sweep circuit is often used to generate recurrent sweep voltages, at a frequency determined by the RC constants, and with a gas tube to discharge the capacitor at the end of the sweep. To overcome the upper-frequency limit of about 50,000 cycles imposed by the gas tube, vacuum tube circuits have been developed which also permit triggering or initiation of the sweep wave by the voltages to be observed.

The vacuum-tube sweep of Fig. 16–45(a) is supplied with an input rectangular or pulse wave, as might be derived from the input signal by use of a monostable multivibrator. The $R_g C_g$ input circuit clamps the positive swings at zero. This arrangement causes the anode voltage to be low, owing to the Ri_b drop. When the grid is driven past cutoff at t_1, the capacity C begins to charge toward E_{bb}, giving a near linear exponentially rising sweep voltage between t_1 and t_2. At t_2 the grid voltage again becomes zero and C discharges quickly down to its original potential, through the low resistance plate circuit.

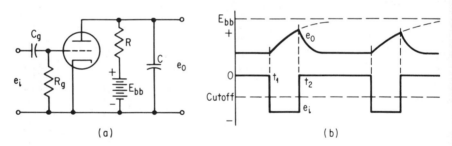

Fig. 16–45. Vacuum tube sweep with RC charging.

It may be assumed that a 100 μsec sweep voltage is desired, and that a 3 per cent departure from linearity may be tolerated. From Eq. 16–31 the value of t_1/RC can be found as 0.13. If the tube chosen is one-half of a 12AU7 operated at 250 supply volts, and with $R = 25,000$ ohms, then the zero-bias current will be 7 ma, with 75 anode volts. This fixes E at $E_{bb} - E_{min} = 175$ v. Equation 16–22, with $t_1/RC = 0.13$ and $E = 175$ v, gives for e_1 at the end of the sweep a value of 21.3 v. Since $t_1 = 100 \times 10^{-6}$ and $t_1/RC = 0.13$, then $RC = 10^{-4}$; with $R = 25,000$ ohms the value of C is found as 0.031 μf, and the design is completed.

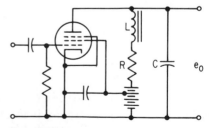

Fig. 16–46. Use of inductor to improve sweep linearity.

An improved version of the circuit appears in Fig. 16–46. An inductor L is in series with R, and if L is large it may be assumed that its current after the tube is cut off continues at the same value as when the tube was carrying current, and thus the capacitor C will be charged at constant current which is the ideal situation.

16–18. The Miller integrating sweep

The previously discussed RC circuits are not sufficiently precise for accurate timing of cathode-ray sweeps, and several methods are available by which improved performance can be obtained. The *Miller integrator* of Fig. 16–47 utilizes a linear voltage developed by integration of a square wave input. The suppressor grid is normally maintained negative, cutting off the plate, with the cathode current going to the positive screen. The control grid is connected to E_{bb} through a large resistor R_2, placing most of E_{bb} across C, since the grid resistance r_c is usually small.

When a positive-going square wave is applied to the suppressor, the tube current largely transfers to the anode, and the anode potential starts to fall. It cannot fall rapidly because if it did so the potential across C would force the grid negative and cause the plate current to decrease and the plate potential to rise. Only a slow linear fall of plate potential results, shown from t_1 to t_2 in Fig. 16–47(b) terminating when the suppressor goes negative at the end of the input pulse at t_2.

The grid current is given by

$$i_c = \frac{(E_{bb} - e_c)}{R_2}$$

and is assumed small. Also, if the gain is A, then $e_b = Ae_c$ and

$$e_c - e_b = \frac{1}{C} \int i_c \, dt = \frac{1}{pC} \tag{16–32}$$

Combining these basic relations leads to

$$e_b \left(1 - \frac{1}{A} - \frac{1}{ApCR_2} \right) = -\frac{E_{bb}}{pCR_2} \tag{16–33}$$

If A be considered large, then

$$e_b = \frac{-AE_{bb}CR_2}{p - (1/ACR_2)} \tag{16–34}$$

The appearance of p in the denominator of this equation justifies the integrating action implied in the name of the circuit.

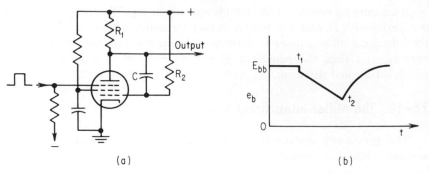

Fig. 16–47. (a) The Miller circuit; (b) output wave form.

Subject to conditions $e_b = E_{bb}$ at $t = 0$, the solution of Eq. 16–34 is

$$e_b = E_{bb} + AE_{bb}(1 - \epsilon^{-t/ACR_2}). \tag{16-35}$$

Using the series for the exponential

$$e_b = E_{bb}\left[1 + A\left(1 - 1 - \frac{t}{ACR_2} + \frac{t^2}{2!(ACR_2)^2} - \cdots\right)\right] \tag{16-36}$$

For usual circuit values the higher order terms may be dropped, giving

$$e_b = E_{bb}\left(1 - \frac{t}{CR_2}\right) \tag{16-37}$$

This equation predicts the linear drop in potential from t_1 to t_2 in Fig. 16–47 (b). The initial step is not included because it is due to charging of circuit stray and tube capacities.

The error introduced by neglecting the higher-order terms is always less than the first neglected term in the alternating series, so that

$$\text{per cent error} = \frac{\dfrac{t^2}{2(ACR_2)^2}}{\dfrac{t}{ACR_2}} \times 100 \text{ per cent} = \frac{50t}{ACR_2} \tag{16-38}$$

For a 200-microsecond sweep with $R_2 = 2$ megohms, $C = 200$ pf, $g_m = 2500$ μmho, $R_1 = 0.1$ megohm, the gain is

$$A = g_m R_1 = 250$$

and the error will be less than 0.2 per cent. This is satisfactory for much precision timing.

16–19. The bootstrap sweep

Feedback may be employed to linearize the rise of potential across the capacitor in an RC sweep circuit. For the RC circuit of Fig. 16–48(a)

$$e_i = iR + \frac{1}{C} \int_0^t i \, dt + V_o$$

where V_o is the potential on C at $t = 0$. If E_o is the charging voltage and I_o the current at $t = 0$, then

$$V_o = E_o - I_o R$$

so that

$$e_i = (i - I_o) R + E_o + \frac{1}{C} \int_0^t i \, dt \tag{16-39}$$

It has been shown that if the potential across the sweep capacitor is to be truly linear with time, then the charging current must be constant. This requires that i at any instant be equal to I_o at the beginning of the sweep, so that

$$i - I_o = 0$$

If this requirement is fulfilled, then

$$e_i = E_o + \frac{1}{C} \int_0^t I_o \, dt \tag{16-40}$$

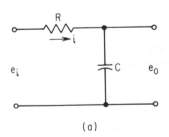
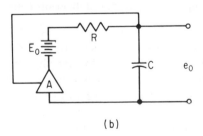

Fig. 16–48. Basis of the bootstrap sweep.

In other words, if the charging voltage is caused to vary by an amount exactly equal to the output voltage, then i will be constant and the output voltage linear. Such an unusual requirement can be met with a circuit as in Fig. 16–48(b), where the amplifier is employed to feed back the output voltage in series with the charging voltage E_o. To meet the requirements properly, the amplifier must have a gain of unity, which can be closely approximated by a cathode follower. In effect, this operation makes the output of the circuit lift the input by its own bootstraps, which supplies the circuit name.

A practical circuit appears in Fig. 16–49. As the sweep voltage across C rises, the cathode follower T_2 raises the input potential by adding the drop across R_k to

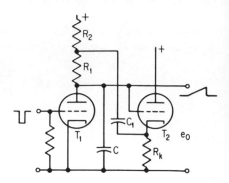

Fig. 16–49. A form of bootstrap sweep circuit.

E_o. Since no cathode follower can have a gain of unity, the theoretical linearity of the circuit is not quite achieved, but with a possible gain of 0.95 in the cathode follower an improvement over the straight RC sweep by a factor of three or four may be obtained.

16–20. Magnetic deflection of cathode-ray tubes

It is occasionally necessary to produce cathode-ray deflection by a magnetic field, and sweep wave forms are needed for this service. It was shown that the magnetic deflection of a cathode-ray beam is very nearly proportional to B, the magnetic flux density. In air-core coils, or in iron-core coils below saturation, the value of B is proportional to i, and so the sweep current in the deflection coils must have the value

$$i = Kt$$

It is therefore necessary to determine the applied voltage which will cause a Kt current to flow through the coil inductance and resistance. Distributed capacity will be neglected here.

It is possible to again depend on transients in RL circuits as first approximations to linearity. The circuit of Fig. 16–50 may be considered, with the resistor R_d added to damp undesired transient oscillations, since the circuit is of second-order form. It is then necessary to find the grid voltage wave form which will produce a uniform change in current in L.

The circuit may be replaced with its equivalents at Fig. 16–50 (b), and (c), where

$$R' = \frac{r_p R_d}{r_p + R_d} \tag{16–41}$$

$$E' = g_m E_g R' \tag{16–42}$$

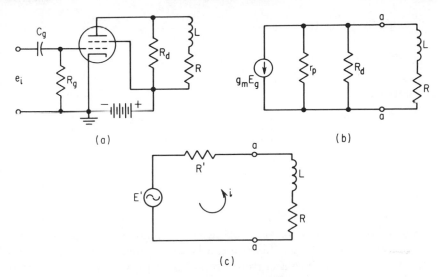

(a)

(b)

(c)

Fig. 16–50. (a) Circuit for generating sweep voltage; (b), (c) equivalent circuits.

A voltage expression may be written around (c) as

$$E' = i(R' + R) + L \frac{di}{dt}$$

However $i = Kt$, and so

$$E' = Kt(R' + R) + KL \qquad (16\text{–}43)$$

The resistance of the deflecting coil will ordinarily be negligible with respect to R', if pentodes are used. It is then possible to write the required grid voltage as

$$E_g = \frac{1}{g_m R'} (KtR' + KL) = \frac{Kt}{g_m} + \frac{KL}{\mu} \left(\frac{r_p + R_d}{R_d} \right) \qquad (16\text{–}44)$$

This indicates a requirement for an input signal of form

$$E_g = K_1 t + K_2 \qquad (16\text{–}45)$$

during the desired sweep duration.

It can be shown that such a wave form can be generated by the circuit of Fig. 16–51, if this circuit is driven by a rectangular wave. When the grid is suddenly driven negative beyond cutoff, the output voltage

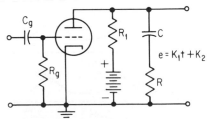

Fig. 16–51. Generating the wave form to drive the circuit of Fig. 16–50.

will suddenly jump from

$$e_o = \frac{E_{bb}r_b}{R_1 + r_b}$$

to a new value

$$e_o' = \frac{E_{bb}r_b}{R_1 + r_b} + E_{bb}\left[\frac{R}{R_1 + R} - \frac{r_b R}{(R_1 + R)(R_1 + r_b)}\right]$$

$$= \frac{E_{bb}}{R_1 + r_b}\left(r_b + \frac{R_1 R}{R_1 + R}\right) \tag{16--46}$$

After this initial jump, which will give a voltage proportional to K_2 the voltage e_o will continue to rise exponentially; and if the time constant $C(R_1 + R)$ is made large, this rise can be approximately linear, giving a voltage that will produce a current proportional to $K_1 t$. Wave forms that may be expected are shown in Fig. 16--52, where (a) represents the input to the voltage-forming tube of Fig. 16--51, (b), the output wave form of that tube which serves as input to the sweep tube of Fig. 16--50, and (c) the current in the deflection coil in the output sweep tube.

A magnetic sweep analogous to the RC voltage-sweep generator is shown in Fig. 16--53. This circuit is driven by a rectangular wave, but the sweep output occurs on the portion of the wave during which the tube conducts, and the length of this period fixes the length of the sweep.

At the instant the grid is driven up from cutoff, the plate current is zero, but it will increase according to

$$i = \frac{E_{bb}}{R + r_b}(1 - \epsilon^{-(R+r_b)t/L}) \tag{16--47}$$

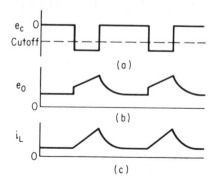

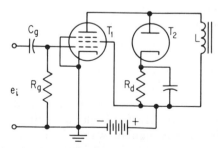

Fig. 16--52. Current and voltage waves in circuit of Fig. 16--50.

Fig. 16--53. Simple generator for magnetic sweep.

If L is very large, and it may be increased over L of the deflection coil alone by use of a series inductor, the time constant of the circuit may be made very large with respect to the time of a sweep and the sweep current will be essentially linear. The departure from linearity may be investigated as it was for the RC case.

During the conduction interval the polarity of the $L\,di/dt$ voltage in the inductance is in such a direction that the diode, T_2, is maintained non-conducting. When the positive input pulse ends and T_1 is cut off, the $L\,di/dt$ voltage reverses and T_2 conducts, dissipating the stored magnetic energy in the diode and R_d. The latter resistor is usually chosen to prevent the circuit from becoming oscillatory, and the transient is quickly damped.

Problems

16-1. For the circuit of Fig. 16–54 plot to scale the waves of e_1 and e_2 for a period of 0.5 sec after switch s_1 is closed.

16-2. In Fig. 16–54 switch s_1 is closed at $t = 0$, and 0.3 sec later switch s_2 is closed. Plot to scale waves of e_1 and e_2 for the period from $t = 0$ to $t = 0.7$ sec.

16-3. The circuit of Fig. 16–55(a) is supplied with a rectangular wave input of zero volts for 200 μsec and -50 v for 100 μsec. The tube has $\mu = 20$, $r_b = 7000$ ohms. Plot the wave form of e_0 to scale over one cycle of the input. Figure 16–2 will be helpful.

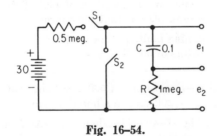

Fig. 16–54.

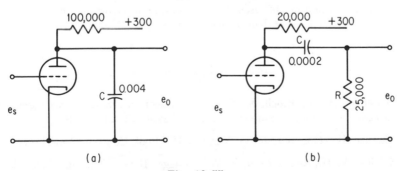

(a)   (b)

Fig. 16–55.

16-4. The circuit of Fig. 16–55(b) has a square-wave input of 200-μsec period, swinging from zero to -100 v. With $\mu = 5$, $r_b = 1000$ ohms, plot e_0 to scale over one cycle of the input.

16-5. (a) A sine wave of 60 v rms is applied to the circuit of Fig. 16–10 (b), with $R = 10,000$ ohms, diode resistance constant at 1000 ohms, and $E = 25$ v, positive grounded. Plot e_o to scale over one cycle.

(b) Repeat (a) with $R = 200,000$ ohms.

16-6. Determine the frequency of oscillation of the multivibrator of Fig. 16–56, if $C_1 = C_2 = 0.003$ μf. Plot a wave form of grid voltage on T_1 during a complete cycle.

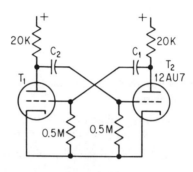

Fig. 16–56.

16-7. Calculate the frequency of oscillation of Fig. 16–56 if $C_1 = 0.015$ and $C_2 = 0.02$ μf. Plot the plate-to-plate output wave form.

16-8. Design a free-running multivibrator to operate at 500 cycles, using plate resistors of 20 K, grid resistors of 500 K, $E_{bb} = 300$ v, and a 12AU7 double-triode tube.

16-9. Design a Miller sweep to give a 500 μsec linear output using a pentode with $g_m = 2500$ μmho, $E_{bb} = 300$ v, with a linearity error of only 0.1 per cent.

16-10. The circuit of Fig. 16–45 utilizes half of a 12AU7 tube with $R = 75,000$ ohms, $C = 0.0075$ μf, $E_{bb} = 300$ v. The input negative pulse has an amplitude of 50 v and a duration of 200 μsec. Plot the output waveform as in Fig. 16–45(b), and determine the per cent departure from linearity.

References

1. Abraham, H., and Bloch, E., "Mesure en valeur absolvé des periods oscillations electriques de haute frequence," *Ann. d. Physik*, **12,** 237 (1909).

2. Chance, B., *et al.*, *Waveforms*. McGraw-Hill Book Co., Inc., New York, 1949.

3. Eccles, W. H., and Jordan, F. W., "Trigger Relay Utilizing Three Element Thermionic Vacuum Tubes," *Radio Rev.*, **1,** 143 (1919).

4. Hull, L. M., and Clapp, J. K., "A Convenient Method for Referring Secondary Frequency Standards to a Standard Time Interval," *Proc. I.R.E.*, **17,** 252 (1929).

5. McDuffie, G. E., Jr., "Pulse Duration and Repetition Rate of a Transistor Multivibrator," *Proc. I.R.E.*, **40,** 1487 (1952).

6. Moffat, D., "Comparison of RC Sweep and Ideal Sawtooth," *Electronic Ind.* 17, 64 (September), (1958).

7. Puckle, O. S., *Time Bases*. John Wiley and Sons, Inc., New York, 1943.

8. Schultheiss, P. M., and Reich, H. J., "Some Transistor Trigger Circuits," *Proc. I.R.E.*, **39,** 627 (1951).

9. Soller, J. T., Starr, M. A., and Valley, G. E., Jr., *Cathode Ray Tube Displays*. McGraw-Hill Book Co., Inc., New York, 1948.

10. Watanabe, Y., "Some Remarks on the Multivibrator," *Proc. I.R.E.*, **18,** 327 (1930).

Conduction In Gases | 17

When a gas is confined at low pressure and excited by a sufficient voltage applied to associated electrodes, very complex phenomena may take place. A current will be carried between the electrodes, and may be accompanied by a visible glow in the gas. The color of the discharge will depend on the nature of the confined gas.

No complete explanation of the phenomena was available until the introduction, in 1913, of the Bohr atom theory, which accounted for the visible glow and the line spectra exhibited by the gases in the discharge. Some knowledge of gaseous conduction is important as a foundation for an understanding of certain gaseous electron tubes, as well as other electronic devices.

17–1. The Bohr atom

Early theories described the atom as composed of a central nucleus of positive charge, around which were scattered negative electrons of equal total charge. The difference between the various chemical elements was due to changes in the number of positive charges, or *protons*, carried by the nucleus. This number of positive charges is equal to the atomic number, and also determines the number of electrons in the normal or unionized state.

The atomic theory developed by Bohr required that the electrons rotate in fixed orbital paths about the central nucleus. In suggesting this structure, Bohr proposed postulates that were not in accord with classical theory but which could permit explanation of line spectra and other points on which understanding had been lacking. By further disregard of classical methods, a whole new field called *wave mechanics*, has been set up to apply specifically to particles of subatomic dimensions. Wave mechanics, although explaining much of the unknown, has led to a less clear physical model of the atom than that given by the original Bohr theory. For the understanding of gaseous conduction, however, the Bohr atom picture is wholly adequate; and when a change is made to the wave mechanical viewpoint, a good approximation can be had by replacing the statement "The electron *is* at such a place" with the phrase "It is *probable* that the electron is at such a place."

Bohr specified that an electron could exist in an atom only if it were in one of the fixed orbits. Since the electron was in the field of the positive nucleus, the electron was required to have sufficient energy of rotation to maintain itself in that orbit, the force of attraction by the nucleus being balanced by outward centrifugal force due to rotation. However, circular motion implies a continuous acceleration toward the center, and classical electrodynamic theory requires radiation of energy by an accelerated charge. If the electron were to give up the energy needed for this acceleration, it would move progressively nearer the nucleus, eventually falling into it. Matter as we know it has existed for a long time and this has not happened. Classical electrodynamics, therefore, provides an unsatisfactory answer, and Bohr avoided the difficulty by arbitrarily setting up as postulates:

1. *An electron does not radiate or give up energy when in a stable orbit.*

2. *The angular momentum of the electron in the orbit is quantized, or can have only values given by $nh/2\pi$,* where n may have only integer values 1, 2, 3, $\cdots$

3. *The energy given up when an electron jumps to an orbit of lower energy is radiated as a single quantum, or bundle of radiant energy (photon).*

With these assumptions Bohr was able to establish an atom model as in Fig. 17–1, supported by experiment and which gave a satisfactory explanation of the origin of line spectra.

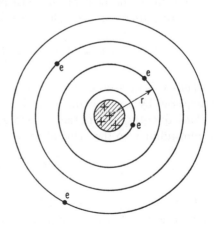

Fig. 17–1. The Bohr atom model.

17–2. Energy associated with an orbit

It is easy to calculate the energy that an electron must possess to maintain its position in any particular orbit in the field of the nucleus of the simple hydrogen atom H^1, having one electron of mass m and one positive electronic charge on the nucleus, the nucleus having a mass M. The electron revolves in an orbit about the central nucleus. Since $M \gg m$, the nucleus may be assumed at rest and unaffected by the motion of the electron. By Coulomb's law, the force between the positive nucleus and the negative electron is

$$f_a = \frac{e(-e)}{4\pi\epsilon_v r^2} = \frac{-e^2}{4\pi\epsilon_v r^2} \qquad (17\text{--}1)$$

The system will be in equilibrium and the motion will be circular if f_a is balanced by a centrifugal force $f_c = mv^2/r$, or

$$mv^2 = \frac{e^2}{4\pi\epsilon_v r} \qquad (17\text{--}2)$$

Due to velocity v in the orbit, the kinetic energy of the electron is

$$\text{K.E.} = \frac{mv^2}{2} = \frac{e^2}{8\pi\epsilon_v r} \qquad (17\text{--}3)$$

after use of Eq. 17–2. The potential at any point in the field of a charge is the work per unit charge required to move a positive charge from infinity to the point under study. If the potential at infinity is taken as the zero reference in the field of the positive nuclear charge, the potential of the orbit of radius r in the field of $+e$ on the hydrogen nucleus is

$$V = \int_\infty^r \frac{f}{q}\, dr = \int_\infty^r \frac{-e}{4\pi\epsilon_v r^2}\, dr = \frac{e}{4\pi\epsilon_v r}$$

where V is measured from infinity to the orbit. From Chapter 2, the energy acquired by an electron moved through a potential V is $V(-e)$ joules. Consequently, the potential energy acquired by the electron in moving from infinity to the orbit of radius r is

$$\text{P.E.} = \frac{e(-e)}{4\pi\epsilon_v r} = \frac{-e^2}{4\pi\epsilon_v r} \qquad (17\text{--}4)$$

The total energy possessed by the electron in the orbit is the sum of the potential and kinetic energies,

$$W = \frac{-e^2}{4\pi\epsilon_v r} + \frac{e^2}{8\pi\epsilon_v r} = \frac{-e^2}{8\pi\epsilon_v r} \qquad (17\text{--}5)$$

The negative sign indicates an energy less than that possessed by the electron at infinity. This is equivalent to stating that the potential energy of a book on the floor is negative, or less than the zero energy of a book at a reference level on the table top.

Although Eq. 17–5 was derived for the hydrogen atom, it holds in principle for atoms of higher atomic number and nuclear charge, despite the fact that the presence of additional negative electrons in other orbits alters the fields and prevents a simple extension of the theory.

17-3. The quantum requirement

Influenced by earlier work of Planck on thermal radiation, Bohr was led to the assumption that the angular momentum of the electron in an orbit could have only integral values given by the relation $nh/2\pi$. In 1924 de Broglie proposed that even though electrons appeared to be particles, or corpuscles, they might also have wave properties. The wave length λ associated with the electron was assumed to be

$$\lambda = \frac{h}{mv} \tag{17-6}$$

where h is Planck's constant, v the velocity, and m the relativistic mass of the electron; this result shows that the wavelength is less for high velocity electrons. In 1928, Davisson and Germer experimentally proved de Broglie's assumption, by measurement of diffraction of electron beams from crystals.

Using $\omega = v/r$ in Eq. 17–6 gives

$$mr^2\omega = \frac{hr}{\lambda} \tag{17-7}$$

If the wave length of the electron in the orbit is required to have the value

$$\lambda = \frac{2\pi r}{n} \tag{17-8}$$

then the orbit of the electron must have a circumference equal to an integral number of wavelengths. It is possible to combine these relations and obtain Bohr's postulated quantum requirement as

$$mr^2\omega = I\omega = \frac{nh}{2\pi} \tag{17-9}$$

Thus the Davisson-Germer experiment which proved the de Broglie assumption also gave experimental support for the Bohr assumption of quantized orbital momentum.

For the hydrogen atom, the kinetic energy may be written in terms of angular velocity as

$$\frac{mr^2\omega^2}{2} = \frac{e^2}{8\pi\epsilon_v r} \tag{17-10}$$

Upon substitution of ω^2 from Eq. 17–9, an expression for the radius of an orbit of the hydrogen atom can be written as

$$r_n = \frac{n^2 h^2 \epsilon_v}{\pi m e^2} \qquad (17\text{–}11)$$

For hydrogen, the first orbit has a radius of 0.53×10^{-10} meter. The radii of the successive permitted orbits are proportional to the squares of integers, 1, 2, 3, $\cdots$; these integers are called the *quantum* numbers of the various orbits. For elements of higher nuclear charge and additional electrons, exact solutions are not possible, but by analogy the Bohr theory provides qualitative results for the heavier atoms.

From Eq. 17–5 the energy associated with an electron's occupancy of an orbit in the hydrogen atom can be found as

$$W_n = -\frac{m e^4}{8 n^2 h^2 \epsilon_v^2} \qquad (17\text{–}12)$$

The energy values of the first four orbits of the hydrogen atom are

Orbit	Energy in Joules
First	-2.17×10^{-18}
Second	-0.54×10^{-18}
Third	-0.24×10^{-18}
Fourth	-0.13×10^{-18}

These values, and the previous theory, are confirmed by spectroscopic observation, utilizing the Bohr radiation postulate of Section 17–4.

The lowest value of energy is that of the first orbit. Consequently, this orbit is the most stable and is the one occupied by the electron when the hydrogen atom is in its *normal state*. From this premise the general definition can be drawn that *an atom is in its normal state when the electrons are in their lowest energy condition.*

Although circular orbits have been assumed, it is known that in the general case of motion of an electron around a heavy nucleus, or of a planet around the sun, the path is an ellipse with the central mass at one of the foci. Further analysis demonstrates that some of the orbits are elliptical, some circular. Interesting phenomena occur in the elliptical orbits: the velocity varies around the path, since the angular momentum $m r^2 \omega$ must be constant, and the mass also varies with the velocity, so that the elliptical orbits themselves rotate slowly about the nucleus. For an engineering discussion, the important fact is that a very definite value of energy is associated with each orbit, regardless of shape.

To describe all the conditions under which an electron exists in an atom, a *set* of quantum numbers has been developed. The number n, used above, is known as the *total quantum number* and designates the orbit of the electron. A number l, called the *azimuthal quantum number*, designates the eccentricity of the elliptical orbits; s is the *spin* of the electron; and m describes the *orientation* of the spinning electron when the atom is in a magnetic field. The Pauli exclusion principle then states that in any atom no two electrons can have an identical *set* of quantum numbers. This might be paraphrased to say that at any instant no two electrons in an atom can exist under exactly identical conditions. The arrangement of electrons dictated by the Pauli exclusion principle can be used to build up the periodic table of the elements on a logical basis.

17-4. Radiation from the atom

We have not yet discussed electromagnetic radiation (light) from the atom, and the spectrograph shows that atoms do radiate. For large quantum numbers (values of n) the radius is large, and associated with the large radii orbits are larger values of energy W_n of the electron. If an electron, initially in an outer orbit of energy W_2, falls, as a result of an atomic disturbance or instability, to an inner orbit of lower energy W_1, energy in the amount given by $W = W_2 - W_1$ must be accounted for. Since reliance may be placed in the conservation of energy, it may be assumed that this energy, W, has been radiated.

Earlier work by Planck on the relation of a quantum of energy to the frequency of radiation had given

$$W = hf \qquad \text{joules.} \qquad (17\text{--}13)$$

This equation states that a quantum, or single bundle of radiant energy called the *photon*, has a definite size for every frequency, or color, of the radiation.

It is then reasonable to surmise that the energy radiated by the electron will appear as electromagnetic radiation of frequency

$$f = \frac{W_2 - W_1}{h} \qquad \text{cycles/sec} \qquad (17\text{--}14)$$

In terms of wavelength, Eq. 17-14 becomes

$$\lambda = \frac{hc}{W_2 - W_1} \text{ m.} = \frac{10^{10}hc}{W_2 - W_1} \text{ A.} \qquad (17\text{--}15)$$

where $c = 3 \times 10^8$ m per sec, the velocity of light in space.

Equation 17-15 predicts that photons of wavelengths 4340, 4861, and 6563 A should be radiated when electrons fall from the fifth, fourth and third orbits of the hydrogen atom to the second orbit. These wavelengths represent colors in the violet, blue, and orange portions of the visible spectrum, and are actually found in the spectrum of hydrogen as the *Balmer series* of lines. Transitions are possible between outer orbits to other lower levels, and electrons may come from outside the atom to enter any of the orbits, giving rise to other series of high-energy and short-wavelength lines. In all cases the Bohr theory predicts the wave length of the line, and experiment yields a check which establishes the validity of the Bohr assumptions.

An electron can, at any instant, make only one jump and emit only one frequency. A discharge, as in a neon tube, is the integrated result of jumps occurring in a very large number of atoms. The number of atoms involved is so large, and so many transitions of each kind occur per second, that the light appears as if it were produced continuously and were constant in intensity. If a discharge due to only a few atoms could be observed, it would appear as intermittent flashes of the various colors. The differences in intensity observed for the various lines of the spectrum are due to the fact that certain jumps are more probable than others and that more electrons make these jumps per second, producing a greater integrated light intensity.

17–5. Excitation, ionization, recombination

When an atom in the normal state receives external energy sufficient to raise one of its electrons to a higher than normal orbit or energy state, the atom is said to be *excited,* and the quantities of energy required for the transitions from the normal to the excited levels are called *energies of excitation.* These amounts of energy are exactly equal to the quanta radiated when the electron falls back to lower orbits. Since an electron in an orbit has no capability for storing surplus energy, the energy taken up by an electron when it is raised to an excited level can be only the exact amount corresponding to the differences in energy of the levels. An atom remains in an excited state for about 10^{-8} sec or less; then the electron falls back to a normal orbit, and the atom returns to the normal state. The fall back to a normal orbit may occur directly, or the electron may make the transit by jumps to several intermediate orbits on the way. Each jump is, of course, accompanied by emission of a photon of appropriate frequency or color, to radiate the energy.

If the atom is given sufficient energy, an electron may be transported from a normal or excited orbit to a point a great distance from the atom—in brief, the electron is removed from the atom. The atom is said to be *ionized* and the process is known as *ionization.* The electron becomes a free electron, and the atom is then an ion with one positive electronic charge. The minimum energy required to remove an electron from a normal atom is called the *ionization energy,* or the *ionization potential.* By supplying greater amounts of energy, it is possible to remove additional electrons from a positive ion, resulting in a multicharged ion. Since such action involves removal of a negative electron from a positively charged body, the energy required for removal becomes progressively greater for each additional electron removed. Ions with more than one charge are not common.

After ionization, the ion is free to move under any electric fields acting in the space and will obey the ballistic laws, provided that consideration is given to its great mass and the positive sign of its charge. It is possible for an electron in a normal orbit to take up energy in excess of the amount required for ionization; this excess energy appears as kinetic energy of the free electron after the release.

A list of ionization potentials for a few common gases is given in Table 25.

The energy required for excitation or ionization can be imparted to a gas atom in a number of different ways:

By collision of a high-energy electron with the gas atom.
By capture of a photon of proper energy by the atom.
By collision of positive ions with gas atoms.
By transfer of thermal energy to the atom, or collision between atoms.

The least energy required to produce excitation, or the energy needed for the jump from a normal orbit to the next orbit above, is called the *first critical potential* when expressed in electron volts. An electron moving in a gas with energy less than the first critical potential of the gas will, upon collision with an atom, rebound elastically without appreciable exchange of energy. If the electron has an energy equal to or greater than the critical energy, it may upon collision excite the atom and give up the energy needed to raise an electron from a normal to an excited orbit, or from a

TABLE 25. IONIZATION POTENTIALS OF CERTAIN COMMON GASES AND VAPORS

Element	Ionization Potential (ev)
Argon	15.69
Helium	24.48
Hydrogen	13.6
Krypton	13.3
Mercury	10.39
Neon	21.47
Sodium	5.1
Xenon	11.5

lower excited state to a higher one. Any excess of energy over that exactly needed remains with the first electron as kinetic energy.

If the original electron has a kinetic energy equal to or greater than the ionization energy, it may upon collision give up energy to cause excitation to any level, or it may supply enough energy to remove an electron completely from the atom and produce ionization. In the latter case, energy is transferred to overcome the ionizing forces, and any remaining energy of the original electron will be shared with the electron removed from the atom.

If a photon of radiant energy strikes the atom, the atom may be excited or ionized. A photon carries an amount of energy dependent on the frequency, and this energy cannot be subdivided, so that the frequency of the photon needed to raise an electron to a particular orbit is exactly the frequency that will be emitted by the electron when it returns to the original orbit. If a photon possesses energy greater than ionization energy, the atom may be ionized by the photon, and the excess energy of the photon will appear as kinetic energy of the emitted electron. In every case of excitation or ionization of atoms by photons, the photon is totally absorbed and disappears.

Recombination of ions with free electrons to form neutral atoms occurs most readily on surfaces existing in the discharge. The surface of an anode, grid, cathode, or tube wall holds charges of one sign, and charges of opposite sign are attracted to the surface, combine, and form neutral gas atoms or molecules.

17-6. Metastable states

Spectral data indicates that certain levels exist, by showing jumps *to* those levels, but there is infrequent indication of jumps *from* those levels to lower ones in the spectral lines. These energy levels or orbits from which it is improbable for electrons to drop to lower levels are called *metastable levels*.

Electron release from a metastable state occurs usually by giving the electron additional energy, thereby raising it to a higher level from which a drop to a lower or normal level then may take place. It is found that one or more such levels exist in many atoms.

The period during which an atom may exist in a metastable state may be of the order of 10^{-4} sec, much longer than it can exist as an excited atom. During this relatively long time, there is a high probability of an additional collision with an electron having sufficient energy to complete the ionization process. That is, owing to the metastable state, ionization may take place in two steps, permitting ionization by electrons with energy much

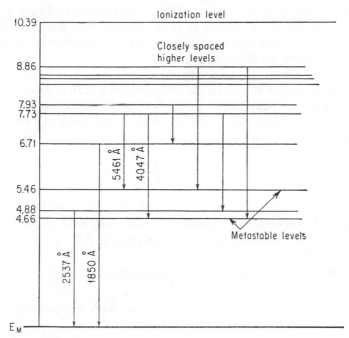

Fig. 17–2. Energy-level diagram of the mercury atom.

below the ionization energy for the gas. For instance, in mercury the ionization potential is 10.39 v, and the first metastable state is at 4.66 v. An electron with only 5 ev energy may collide with this atom, furnishing the energy to raise an electron to the first metastable state. Owing to the long life of the electron in this state, probabilities are excellent that a collision may occur with another electron having 5.73 or more volts energy, thereby ionizing the atom with individual collision energies well below the ionizing potential.

As an aid to understanding the transitions possible in one of the heavier atoms, an energy-level diagram for mercury is given in Fig. 17–2. This shows some of the energy levels most important in producing the mercury spectrum. The 2537 A line is the one contributing most to the properties of the fluorescent lamp and the germicidal lamps; other lines are in the visible region, giving the discharge its characteristic greenish hue.

17–7. Mean free paths

As an electron and an atom approach each other, they experience forces due to the fields of the electrons and nucleus of the atom and to the electric field of the electron. A collision between electron and atom is more in the nature of a mutual deflection of paths due to these forces. As far as the results are concerned, however, collisions may continue to be considered as occurring between elastic spheres.

The distance that an electron moves between successive collisions with atoms in a gas is called the *free path*. The average length of the free paths is called the *mean free path*. For electrons moving through a gas of molecular radius σ, with N molecules per cubic centimeter, the mean free path of an electron can be calculated from the equation

$$\text{M.F.P.} = \frac{1}{\pi N \sigma^2} \tag{17--16}$$

The factor N is Avogadro's number, 2.69×10^{19} molecules per cc at 0°C and 760 mm Hg pressure. This value of N varies directly as the pressure and inversely as the temperature, so that in general

$$N = 2.69 \times 10^{19} \frac{P T_o}{P_o T} \text{ molecules/cm}^3 \tag{17--17}$$

where P_o and T_o are the standard conditions, with temperature in °K. The mean free path in various gases is given in Table 26.

TABLE 26. THEORETICAL MEAN FREE PATHS OF ELECTRONS IN GASES AT 25°C

Gas	M.F.P. (cm) Pressure = 0.001 mm Hg	M.F.P. (cm) Presure = 1 mm Hg
Mercury.................	14.9	0.0149
Argon..................	45.0	0.0450
Neon...................	78.7	0.0787
Hydrogen..............	81.7	0.0817

When gas pressures are high, the mean free path is short, and an electron can acquire ionizing energy during transit of distances commensurate with the mean free path only if the field intensity is high. As the pressure is reduced, the mean free path lengthens, making it possible to ionize, or break down, the gas with a lower field intensity. However, when the gas pressure is further reduced, it is found that the field intensity needed for breakdown becomes high again, since there are then so few gas atoms that the probability of an electron's colliding with a gas atom during flight from cathode to anode becomes small; that is, the mean free path at very low pressure may be much longer than the cathode-anode distance.

A curve of breakdown potential plotted against gas pressure for an electrode distance of 1 mm is shown in Fig. 17–3. The curve is for air, but similar curves would be obtained for other gases.

At atmospheric pressure there are about 10^{19} gas molecules per cubic centimeter. When the pressure is reduced to that referred to as *high vacuum*, where the pressure is of the order of 0.001 micron or about 10^{-9} atm, there are still about 10^{10} molecules of gas per cubic centimeter. Yet the molecules are so small and the spaces between them so great that electrons can travel over 10^4 cm on the average before colliding with even one molecule.

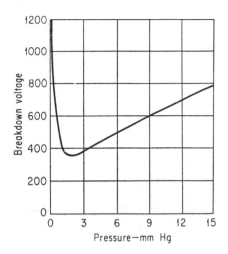

Fig. 17–3. Breakdown potential between electrodes spaced 1 mm in air.

In vacuum tubes having electrode spacings of 1 mm, the probability that an electron will collide with gas atoms during cathode-anode transit is negligible. With gas tubes which depend upon collisions for their operation, it is necessary to ensure gas pressures of the order of 0.001 to 0.1 mm of mercury so that electronic mean free paths are less than interelectrode distances, and the collision probabilities are thereby increased.

17–8. The gas discharge

The gas enclosed at low pressure between the electrodes of the tube in Fig. 17–4 (a) will always have a few ions and electrons present owing to cosmic ray or ultraviolet radiation. If a small potential E be applied, a few of these ions and electrons will be attracted to the electrodes. As the potential is raised, an increasing number of the free charges being formed by the radiation will be attracted to the electrodes, and the current will increase linearly, as in the region OA in Fig. 17–4(b). The constant-current region AB indicates that saturation has been reached, and that ions and electrons are drifting to the electrodes as rapidly as they are created by the radiation. Upon removal of the radiation source, the current would cease, however, since there would be no continuing charge source, and the discharge would be *non-self-maintaining*.

Further increase in potential raises the electric field, and as B is passed, a few of the electrons gain energy sufficient to ionize gas atoms. For every

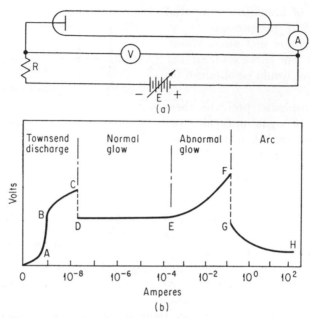

Fig. 17–4. (a) Circuit for obtaining volt-ampere characteristic; (b) the volt-ampere curve.

electron ionizing by collision, two electrons and an additional positive ion are then free in the discharge. Further increase in potential may provide the second pair of electrons with ionizing energy, and then four electrons and associated ions reach the electrodes for each single electron liberated by the radiation. Higher potentials will cause an exponential increase in current with voltage, as shown in the region BC of the curve. The non-self-maintaining region of the volt-ampere curve from O to C is called the *Townsend discharge*, for J. S. Townsend, who investigated it in 1901.

At some potential C, the energy accumulated by the heavy ions in traveling through the gas is sufficient to cause secondary emission by bombardment of the cathode. The emitted secondary electrons in turn ionize by collision, creating further ions to bombard the cathode, so that the discharge regenerates itself, or becomes *self-maintaining*. It is then independent of any radiation source for its electrons and ions. When the discharge becomes self-maintaining, the gas is said to *break down*, and the value of potential at which this happens is the *breakdown potential*.

Upon breakdown, the potential across the tube falls to D, and a visible glow appears in the gas and on the cathode. The constant voltage drop in this region is employed in forms of voltage-regulator tubes. As the current is increased, the *normal glow* on the cathode covers more cathode area, keeping approximately a constant current density at the cathode. When the whole cathode is covered with glow, further increases in current require the current density to rise, and the tube voltage increases, as in region *EF*.

As the current is further increased, the bombardment of the cathode by positive ions become more intense. A transition occurs at *F*, and the cathode current density further increases, as a result of current concentration at some point on the cathode. The tube voltage falls, and the discharge is then an *arc* operating in the region *GH*. The metal surface of the cathode may be sputtered off by ionic bombardment, and the cathode may become so hot as to melt. In the arc region the voltage drop will be of the same order as the ionizing potential, or even less, indicating ionization by means of the metastable states.

An arc discharge ordinarily shows the downward slope of the volt ampere curve from *G* to *H*, indicating negative resistance properties. The current is then determined largely by the value of resistor *R* in the circuit. Without *R*, the current would continue to rise indefinitely until limited by some tube or circuit failure.

17–9. The plasma

Positive ions are relatively heavy, and for a given amount of energy their velocity is low. The ions remain in the space in the tube much longer than the high-velocity electrons; consequently there may be more positive ions in the space at a given instant than there are electrons. These positive ions then produce a positive space charge which successfully *neutralizes* the negative space charge due to the electrons. An electron near the cathode then is accelerated, rather than opposed, by the space charge.

In arc discharges the slow-moving positive ions congregate at the cathode in great density, setting up a positive space charge which limits the ion current flowing to the cathode. The gathering of positive ions near the cathode is called the *cathode sheath*. Because of the shielding of the cathode from the anode by the sheath, electric force lines from the cathode terminate on positive ions close by. Since no electric field can exist between two like charges, the field between the anode and the positive ions is zero. Consequently, an intense electric field exists in a very narrow region near the cathode, with a large potential drop in this region. Only a small field intensity occurs over the remainder of the tube length, and the potential drop is low; hence almost the entire voltage drop across the tube occurs in the cathode sheath.

Between the sheath and the anode, the electrons are accelerated only sufficiently to produce enough ions to neutralize the electron space charge.

This region is called the *plasma*. An equilibrium is reached at about equal numbers of positive ions and negative electrons, all moving slowly and in somewhat random directions owing to the low value of electric field present. If insufficient ions are produced, the current reaching the anode falls because of increase of negative space charge. The lower current reduces the voltage drop in R, resulting in a higher potential across the tube. A higher anode potential accelerates the electrons in the plasma and they produce more ionizing collisions, returning the space-charge conditions to near zero. Overproduction of positive ions produces a converse effect, and equilibrium is again reached at nearly neutral conditions in the plasma.

Problems

17-1. A doubly ionized helium atom is equivalent to a bare hydrogen nucleus except for charge and mass.

(a) With atomic weight of helium equal to 4.002, calculate the radii of the first four orbits.

(b) Determine the energy of the above four orbits.

(c) Find the spectral wave lengths to be emitted by an electron in coming from infinity to each of the four orbits.

(d) Compute the wave lengths radiated from jumps from each orbit to the normal ($n = 1$) orbit.

17-2. Brackett has observed lines in the hydrogen spectrum of wave lengths, 40,500 Å and 26,300 Å, representing jumps from the fifth and sixth orbits, respectively, to the fourth. Determine the wave lengths of lines to be expected for jumps from the fifth and sixth orbits to the first.

17-3. (a) Find the minimum velocity needed by an electron to ionize a neon atom.

(b) How far would the electron have to travel to acquire this velocity in a field of 100 v per centimeter?

17-4. A mercury atom has an electron in the first metastable level with 4.66 ev energy.

(a) What is the wave length of a photon of light needed to raise this electron to the next, or 4.88-ev, level?

(b) If the atom then emits a flash of light of wave length 2537 Å, what has happened?

17-5. A sodium atom is ionized by a photon, and the electron has 1.0 ev energy upon being freed.

(a) Find the wave length and frequency required for the photon.

(b) If the ion recombines with an electron that reaches the normal state by passing first to a level of 2.11 ev above the normal, what will be the wave lengths of the photons emitted?

17-6. (a) Find the velocity needed by an electron to excite the ultraviolet mercury-vapor line at 2537 Å.

(b) What would be the minimum frequency of a photon capable of ionizing mercury vapor?

17-7. An X-ray diode is operated with a potential of 250,000 v between anode and cathode. What is the wave length of the electrons in the beam as they reach the anode? Consider relativistic corrections.

17-8. Compute the wave length of an electron in the third circular orbit of a hydrogen atom. Show that the requirement that the orbit be an integral number of wave lengths is met.

17-9. An electron, after falling through 8 v potential, collides with a mercury atom having an electron in a metastable state of 5.46 ev energy. If the atom is ionized, what will be the velocities of the two electrons after the collision, assuming the energy to be equally shared? Also neglect energy given to the ion.

17-10. Plot a curve of M.F.P. of an electron in mercury vapor for the range of pressures 0.01 to 10 mm Hg and standard temperature conditions. The radius of the mercury atom is 1.82×10^{-8} cm. The curve may best be plotted on semilogarithmic paper.

17-11. Find the minimum field intensity required for electrons to produce ionization in each of the following gases:

Mercury, at 0.15 mm mercury pressure,	$0°C$, $\sigma = 1.82 \times 10^{-8}$ cm.
Argon, at 1.2 mm mercury pressure,	$30°C$, $\sigma = 1.43 \times 10^{-8}$ cm.
Neon, at 0.70 mm mercury pressure,	$30°C$, $\sigma = 1.17 \times 10^{-8}$ cm.

17-12. If the cathode-anode spacing of a diode is 0.5 mm, and the gas is argon at 0.1 mm mercury pressure, 20°C temperature, what is the probability of any particular electron having a collision with a gas atom during its transit through the tube?

References

1. Cobine, J. D., *Gaseous Conductors*. McGraw-Hill Book Co., Inc., New York, 1941.

2. Crowther, J. A., *Ions, Electrons and Ionizing Radiations*, 7th ed. Longmans, Green & Co., New York, 1939.

3. Jeans, J. H., *An Introduction to the Kinetic Theory of Gases*, 4th ed. Cambridge University Press, London, 1940.

4. Richtmyer, F. K., and Kennard, E. H., *Introduction to Modern Physics*, 4th ed. McGraw-Hill Book Co., Inc., New York, 1947.

Power Rectification | 18

The first electronic rectifiers capable of handling large currents were gas diodes, ordinarily employing mercury vapor. While they are still extensively utilized in industry, heavy-current silicon diodes are replacing them because the efficiency of the semiconductor devices is still higher than the already high efficiency of the gaseous diodes, and they are more rugged and long-lived.

In application both types may be used in the same basic circuits, and design need differ only because of the reduced voltage drop of the silicon diodes. There will be other differences in application, however, relating to ambient operating conditions and susceptibility to damage by voltage and current surges.

18–1. Semiconductor high-current rectifiers

By increasing the junction area of the fused alloy type of diode, it is possible for both germanium and silicon diodes to handle many kilowatts of power at d-c voltages up to 600 at the present time. Current densities as high as 100 amp per

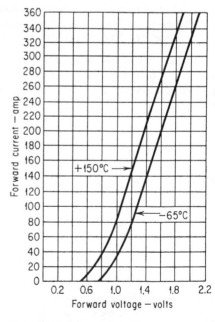

Fig. 18–1. Forward volt-ampere curve for silicon power diode.

sq cm are used, with forward drops of about a volt, as shown in Fig. 18–1. Forced cooling may be necessary to maintain the junction temperature within limits.

For the usual ambient temperature ranges, the combined radiation and liquid or air convection losses per unit area can be expressed as a linear function of the local temperature drop through the thermal contact to the ambient level. Thus a thermal resistance in terms of degrees centigrade per watt of heat transferred is usually given for a diode, under stated conditions of mounting on a large heat sink or heat storage capacity. A typical mounting by screwing into a large plate is suggested by Fig. 18-2. Diodes are made with either cathode or anode connected to the base screw, so that various circuit requirements for the common electrode connection can be met.

Internal losses are the sum of forward power dissipation and reverse losses. The forward dissipation is a result of load current and an internal drop of the order of one volt, whereas reverse currents are dependent on reverse voltage, and on operating temperature. For silicon units having forward ratings of several hundred amperes at one volt drop, reverse currents of 50 to 100 ma may be expected. Reverse voltages as high as 500 to 600 v for germanium and 1000 v for silicon can be allowed. Current surges up to 500 per cent of forward value may be carried for a second or two, assuming good heat transfer to a heat sink. Operating temper-

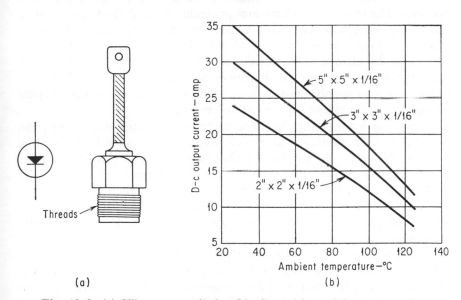

(a)   (b)

Fig. 18–2. (a) Silicon power diode; (b) effect of heat sinks on operating temperature.

atures of 90°C for germanium and 190° to 200°C for silicon are maximums at present. The effect of aluminum mounting plates on operating temperature is shown in Fig. 18–2(b).

In reverse voltage ratings, an allowance must be made for transients encountered in any particular circuit, since the heat loss on the reverse cycle is of equal importance to that of the forward cycle in determining operating temperatures.

Because the internal voltage drop is so small compared to other circuit voltages, it can be neglected in almost all circuit analysis. Thus in the following sections the ideal conditions developed for zero internal drop are applicable to semiconductor diode use.

18–2. Gas diodes

A gas diode or *phanotron* (tube with visible glow) consists of an anode and thermionic cathode sealed into an evacuated envelope, into which has been introduced a gas, such as mercury vapor, argon, or xenon, at pressures from 10^{-6} mm to several mm of mercury. Anodes are of nickel or graphite, depending on the severity of the anticipated service.

With electron emission from the hot cathode, the surrounding space will be filled with a negative space charge. There will be negligible current until an anode voltage somewhat above ionization potential is applied. A few electrons will then obtain sufficient energy to ionize gas atoms upon collision. The resultant positive ions neutralize part of the negative space charge, allowing more electrons to gain ionizing energy, and the process culminates in an arc discharge, with a positive space charge around the cathode and a plasma in the space near the anode. The process from first ionization to formation of the arc may occur in 10 μsecs. The chief function of the gas is to supply positive ions which neutralize the negative space charge, permitting large currents at low voltage drop.

The breakdown voltage for mercury vapor may approximate 15 volts, but after the arc is established the *tube drop* or *arc drop* will be of the order of 10 to 15 volts, or near the ionizing potential. This drop will remain essentially constant for all currents in the rated range.

Upon reversal of applied potential the positive ions in the space will migrate to the anode and the walls, recombining with electrons available there, and the space is said to be *deionized*. Such diodes are inherently rectifiers.

The gas pressure corresponds to that of mercury vapor at the temperature of the point of mercury condensation. The pressure being dependent on temperature, the characteristics of mercury-vapor tubes are functions of temperature. For critical applications the gas used may be argon or xenon, where the gas pressure changes only slightly with temperature.

18–3. Cathodes in gas diodes

If the tube drop is sufficiently great, the positive-ion energies may be great enough to destroy the coating of an oxide cathode by bombardment. Hull discovered that if the energies of the positive ions were kept below a certain threshold value, or the tube drop was less than 24 v for mercury vapor, the rate of loss of cathode material by bombardment was low enough that efficient oxide-coated cathodes could be designed with long life. With tube drops of the order of the ionizing potential of 10.4 v in mercury vapor, a reasonable factor of safety is available. Safe operating voltages in other gases may be higher owing to the lower ion masses.

If the drop is kept under the safe limit, the energies of the ions will also be less than the value at which secondary emission by bombardment may occur at the cathode. Consequently, no dependence can be placed on secondary emission as a source of electrons, and the cathode must be designed to normally emit all the electrons needed to maintain the rated maximum anode current.

A cathode should be brought to operating temperature before connecting the anode circuit. At low temperatures there are few mercury atoms in the space, and the probability of ionization is reduced, the negative space charge is not neutralized, the tube drop rises and may reach the destructive level. To avoid such damage, mercury temperatures should be above 20°C.

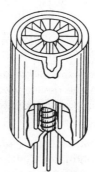

Fig. 18–3. Heat-shielded indirectly-heated cathode.

Concentrations of negative space charge in confined spaces will be neutralized by the ions, and it is possible to employ heat shields or reflecting thermal insulators around oxide cathodes without raising the tube drop. These shields increase the emission per watt of heating power, and are constructed as shown in Fig. 18–3.

Certain gas rectifiers employ a mercury pool as a cathode. Electron emission occurs when a *cathode spot* is formed on the mercury surface; the spot can be initiated by a small spark which produces the first electrons and ions. The electrons then travel to the positive anode, producing additional ions by collision, neutralizing the space charge, and forming an arc to the anode. The theory of the pool cathode is not well established, although Langmuir theorized that the arc is maintained by a form of high-field emission. The positive-ion sheath is very close to the mercury surface, and the electric field intensity is sufficient for large emission densities.

Bombardment of the cathode by ions can do no damage, and peak currents are not limited by cathode damage, but by heat or magnetic stresses. Methods of establishing the initiating spark will be discussed for the ignitron in Section 19–8.

18–4. Diode ratings

Because of the nonsinusoidal wave forms present in diode circuits, the methods of rating differ from those for other electrical devices.

Average current. In the gas diode with constant tube drop of 10-15 v, or in the semiconductor diode with constant drop of about one volt, the internal heating or the average power lost internally is proportional to the average value of current. Thus the diode is rated in maximum average current, instead of in rms values.

Peak current. This is the maximum limit imposed by instantaneous heating in the semiconductor, or by available emission in the gas diode.

Forward drop. Also called *tube drop* for gaseous devices, this is the voltage across the device during the conducting interval.

Peak inverse voltage. This is defined as the maximum allowable voltage across the device when nonconducting or with anode negative. The limit must be imposed because of the potentiality of voltage breakdown in the reverse direction.

Temperature limits. To prevent excessive reverse saturation current, semiconductor devices of germanium and silicon are presently limited to about 85° and 190°C respectively. In mercury-vapor devices the limits are usually placed at an ambient in the range of 20° to 80°C.

An occasional reverse breakdown may occur in gas diodes even though operated within ratings, and is known as *arc back*, or *flash back*. Haphazard in occurrence, high gas pressure due to high operating temperature is contributory, and gas diodes applied in high-voltage service must be protected by high-speed circuit breakers.

18–5. Half-wave rectifier

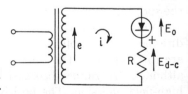

The half-wave circuit of Fig. 18–4 will be studied as the basic building block for most power rectifiers. Analysis in Chapter 5

Fig. 18–4. Half-wave rectifier.

showed that for a lossless diode

$$I_{d-c} = \frac{E_m}{\pi R}, \qquad E_{d-c} = \frac{E_m}{\pi},$$

$$I_m = \frac{E_m}{R}, \qquad \text{P.I.V.} = E_m,$$

$$P_{a-c} = \frac{E_m^2}{4R}$$

where the load is resistive, and of value equal to R.

For semiconductor diodes the internal voltage drop will approximate one volt; this will usually be small with respect to E_m, and therefore the above relations apply. For gas tubes, with internal drop of 10 to 15 volts, the above relations also apply if $E_m \gg E_o$, where E_o is the internal tube drop.

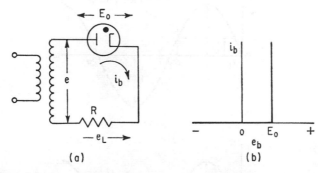

Fig. 18–5. (a) Gas diode rectifier; the dot inside the symbol indicates a gas-filled device; (b) ideal gas diode volt-ampere curve.

Referring to Fig. 18–5(b), the constant voltage drop of the gas diode may be represented by the straight line of the volt-ampere curve. When the anode voltage increases from zero, the arc does not start until the tube voltage reaches the ionization value. Since the ionization point is usually only slightly above the tube drop, no great error is introduced by assuming that breakdown and tube drop E_o are equal.

If $e = E_m \sin \omega t$, the current in Fig. 18–5(a) may be written as

$$i_b = \frac{E_m \sin \omega t - E_o}{R} \qquad (18\text{–}1)$$

The current i_b must be zero for all negative values of the above. Setting the numerator to zero to obtain the starting angle for conduction gives

$$\alpha_1 = \sin^{-1} \frac{E_o}{E_m} \tag{18-2}$$

The cutoff or stopping angle, α_2, is

$$\alpha_2 = 180° - \alpha_1 \tag{18-3}$$

The conduction angle is then $\alpha_c = \alpha_2 - \alpha_1$.

Gas-tube rectifier circuits may be employed to operate d-c motor armature circuits from a-c supply circuits, or to charge a battery. The counter emf will add to the tube-drop term in the equation, and the term $E_m \sin \omega t$ will have to rise to a higher value before conduction can start. The proper emf values must be introduced into the circuit equations, and will alter the values of α_1 and α_2.

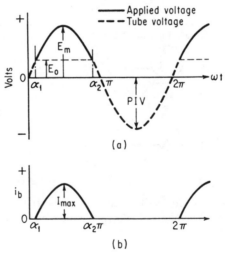

Fig. 18–6. (a) Voltage wave forms in a half-wave gas-diode rectifier; (b) current wave form.

From Fig. 18–6(b) the wave form can be seen as the top of a sinusoid, E_o/R units being sliced horizontally from the base. The dashed curve in Fig. 18–6(a) is the voltage across the tube. Starting at zero, the voltage rises until the discharge starts at α_1 and then remains constant during conduction at the value E_o. At α_2, the circuit voltage becomes less than the tube drop, and conduction ceases. During the negative half cycle, the entire circuit voltage appears across the tube. The maximum value of this negative voltage is the peak inverse voltage of the circuit.

The average current I_{d-c} may be obtained as

$$I_{d-c} = \frac{1}{2\pi} \int_0^{2\pi} i_b \, d\omega t = \frac{1}{2\pi} \int_{\alpha_1}^{\alpha_2} \frac{(E_m \sin \omega t - E_o)}{R} \, d\omega t \qquad (18\text{–}4)$$

By use of trigonometric identities, the result may be simplified to

$$I_{d-c} = \frac{E_m}{\pi R} \left[\cos \alpha_1 - \left(\frac{\pi}{2} - \alpha_1 \right) \sin \alpha_1 \right] \qquad (18\text{–}5)$$

and the output d-c voltage is obtained by $E_{d-c} = I_{d-c}R$. As α_1 becomes small, or $E_o \ll E_m$, the bracketed term approaches unity, and $I_{d-c} = E_m/\pi R$ as given above for the ideal diode.

As the conduction angle becomes smaller with a decreasing ratio of E_m/E_o, the peak anode current increases for a given I_{d-c} value. The peak anode current is an important gas tube limitation, and can be written

$$I_{\text{peak}} = \frac{E_m - E_o}{R} = \frac{E_m}{R} (1 - \sin \alpha_1) \qquad (18\text{–}6)$$

The average power input from the transformer may be calculated as

$$P_{a-c} = \frac{1}{2\pi} \int_0^{2\pi} ei_b \, d\omega t = \frac{1}{2\pi} \int_{\alpha_1}^{\alpha_2} E_m \sin \omega t \, \frac{(E_m \sin \omega t - E_o)}{R} \, d\omega t$$

After integration and use of the definitions of α_1 and α_2

$$P_{a-c} = \frac{E_m^2}{2\pi R} \left[\frac{\pi}{2} - \alpha_1 - \cos \alpha_1 \sin \alpha_1 \right] \qquad (18\text{–}7)$$

which approaches $E_m^2/4R$ for small α_1 values.

The diode loss can be found as

$$P_d = \frac{1}{2\pi} \int_0^{2\pi} e_b i_b \, d\omega t = \frac{1}{2\pi} \int_{\alpha_1}^{\alpha_2} E_o \, \frac{(E_m \sin \omega t - E_o)}{R} \, d\omega t$$

The factor E_o has been assumed constant and may be taken outside the integral sign. The remaining integral can be recognized as that which leads to the average current I_{d-c}, so

$$P_d = E_o I_{d-c} \qquad (18\text{–}8)$$

independent of current wave form.

The value of R serves to limit the current in the circuit; if R were zero the current would increase until diode damage occurred. Consequently, arc-discharge tubes must be operated with sufficient series resistance to limit the current to a safe value.

The d-c component of current impresses a d-c magnetomotive force on the transformer core; saturation may result, with consequent large primary current. Because of this and other factors, the half-wave circuit is little used for heavy currents; its use as a building block justifies its study, however.

18–6. Full-wave rectifier

The full-wave circuit employs two half-wave diodes to supply a common resistance load. It has been previously analyzed for the ideal diode in Chapter 5, leading to the following relations:

$$I_{d-c} = \frac{2E_m}{\pi R} \qquad E_{d-c} = \frac{2E_m}{\pi}$$

$$\text{P.I.V.} = 2E_m$$

and a power input twice that of one diode. These results are directly applicable when semiconductor diodes are employed, or when $E_o \ll E_m$ for gas diodes.

When E_o is not negligible with respect to E_m, further analysis becomes necessary and may be carried out by writing the mesh equations during the conduction intervals, as

$$\left. \begin{array}{l} i_{b1} = \dfrac{E_m \sin \omega t - E_o}{R} \\[2ex] i_{b2} = 0 \end{array} \right\} \qquad \alpha_1 < \omega t < \alpha_2 \qquad (18\text{–}9)$$

$$\left. \begin{array}{l} i_{b1} = 0 \\[2ex] i_{b2} = \dfrac{-E_m \sin \omega t - E_o}{R} \end{array} \right\} \qquad (\pi + \alpha_1) < \omega t < (\pi + \alpha_2) \qquad (18\text{–}10)$$

where $E_m \sin \omega t$ is the instantaneous voltage e for each half of the transformer. The current pulses through the load are drawn in Fig. 18–7(b). The angles α_1 and α_2 are given by the same expressions as for the half-wave rectifier.

By use of the fact that there are two pulses of current per cycle, instead of one as in the half-wave rectifier, an analysis for the d-c current may be made in a manner similar to that for the half-wave rectifier. Then

$$I_{d-c} = \frac{2E_m}{\pi R} \left[\cos \alpha_1 - \left(\frac{\pi}{2} - \alpha_1 \right) \sin \alpha_1 \right] \qquad (18\text{–}11)$$

In the above it should be noted that E_m is the peak voltage for one-half

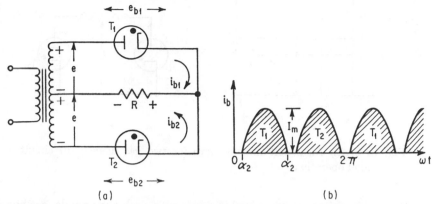

Fig. 18–7 (a) Full-wave gas diode rectifier; (b) load current of (a).

of the transformer secondary. For a given voltage per diode, the d-c voltage of the full-wave circuit is twice that obtained from the half-wave rectifier.

In the full-wave circuit, the d-c components of the diode currents flow through the transformer secondary in opposite directions, each away from the center tap. No saturation of the iron will occur, and ordinary transformer core construction will suffice.

The bridge circuit of Fig. 18–8, discussed as a form of full-wave rectifier in Section 5–11, is also well suited to large d-c current use. The same d-c voltage can be obtained from a transformer in the bridge circuit as from a transformer with twice the turns in the conventional full-wave circuit. However, current flows continuously in the trans-

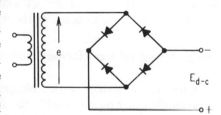

Fig. 18–8. The bridge rectifier.

former when in the bridge circuit, so that the current rating in bridge use is only about two-thirds that for the same transformer in the usual full-wave connection.

18–7. Parallel operation of gas diodes

Assume that two gas diodes have the ideal volt-ampere characteristics shown by the heavy lines of Fig. 18–9(a). If connected in parallel, the voltage at the beginning of a cycle will rise until it reaches E_{o2}, at which tube T_2 will conduct and carry current. Since the voltage of the parallel combination cannot rise above that point, tube T_1 never will conduct, and tube T_2, the tube with the lowest tube drop, will carry all the load.

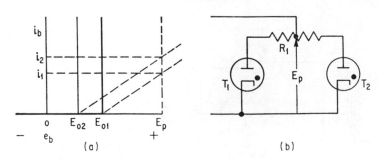

Fig. 18–9. (a) Ideal volt-ampere curve for two gas diodes; (b) circuit for parallel operation.

If a small resistor is connected in series with each tube anode, as shown at Fig. 18–9(b), the individual tube-circuit characteristics will change to the sloping dashed lines of Fig. 18–9(a). If the resistor in series with tube T_2 is large enough that at some current less than full load the voltage E_p across the resistor and tube T_2 becomes greater than the tube drop of T_1, then T_1 will conduct and share the load at a common voltage of E_p, as shown in Fig. 18–9(a).

Tubes may differ in tube drop by as much as 6 or 7 v, and if the resistors can produce a drop of this value at the desired tube current, parallel operation will be satisfactory. To avoid power loss, a small center-tapped reactor may be used in place of the resistor.

18–8. Effect of transformer leakage reactance

A full-wave rectifier, with leakage inductance L_s for each half or phase of the transformer represented in the anode leads, is shown in Fig. 18–10(a). In the analysis of rectifiers with leakage reactance neglected, it has been assumed that the current in one diode ceases before that in the next begins. Actually, owing to the effect of the leakage L_s in maintaining the current, the second diode may start to conduct before the first ceases, with an overlap of the two currents resulting, as shown by the crosshatched overlap region in Fig. 18–10(b). The transfer of current from one diode to another is spoken of as *commutation*.

With the assumption that D_2 has started conducting before D_1 has ceased, an emf equation written through both transformer secondaries and both diodes gives

$$e_1 + e_2 - L_s\frac{di_1}{dt} - L_s\frac{di_2}{dt} + e_{b1} - e_{b2} = 0$$

the negative sign appearing on $L_s(di_1/dt)$ because of the direction of

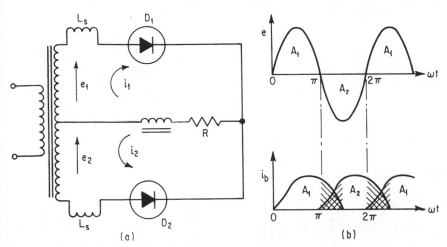

Fig. 18–10. Conditions in the full-wave circuit during current commutation.

current change. If the diode drops may be neglected, then

$$e_1 + e_2 = L_s \frac{di_1}{dt} + L_s \frac{di_2}{dt} \qquad (18\text{–}12)$$

and this equation shows that the whole transformer voltage appears across the leakage inductances during commutation.

During the commutation interval, the voltages across the leakage reactances subtract from the load voltage. Hence a transformer with appreciable leakage will affect the voltage regulation of a rectifier adversely.

The two currents add up to an approximately constant sum during the overlap interval, so that the lag of current behind the voltage may be overlooked insofar as d-c current, and ripple, is concerned. For simplification in analysis, the current may then be assumed as flowing to the most positive anode at any given instant.

18–9. The three-phase half-wave rectifier

A great many circuits are available for rectification of polyphase electric power, but only one example will be given here, followed by a general treatment. In the analysis that follows, the effects of transformer resistance and leakage, current overlap, and internal diode drop are neglected.

The simplest polyphase rectifier is the three-phase half-wave circuit of Fig. 18–11, with star-connected transformer secondary. If D_1 is conducting, then its cathode and the positive end of the load, are at essentially

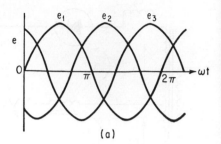

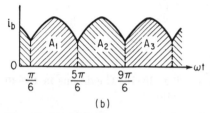

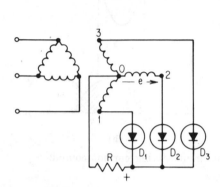

Fig. 18–11. Three-phase half-wave rectifier.

Fig. 18–12. Voltages to neutral, and anode currents of the three-phase half-wave circuit.

the voltage e_{o1}, or e_1 of Fig. 18–12. The cathodes of D_2 and D_3 will be positive with respect to their anodes, and cannot conduct. These potential relationships will change at $\pi/6$, $5\pi/6$, $9\pi/6$, $\cdots$, and these are points of commutation, as in Fig. 18–12. The current to D_1 is then

$$i_b = \frac{E_m \sin \omega t}{R}, \qquad \frac{\pi}{6} < \omega t < \frac{5\pi}{6} \tag{18–13}$$

and the direct load current may be obtained as three times the average current of one diode, or

$$\text{total } I_{\text{d-c}} = \frac{3}{2\pi} \int_{\pi/6}^{5\pi/6} \frac{E_m \sin \omega t}{R} d\omega t = \frac{0.827\, E_m}{R} \tag{18–14}$$

and

$$E_{\text{d-c}} = 0.827\, E_m$$

The power input from the secondary of the transformer is

$$P_{\text{a-c}} = \frac{3}{2\pi} \int_{\pi/6}^{5\pi/6} \frac{E_m^2 \sin^2 \omega t}{R} d\omega t = \frac{0.706 E_m}{R} \tag{18–15}$$

Since the diode losses are neglected, the theoretical value for the efficiency of rectification is readily obtained as

$$\max \eta_R = \frac{(0.827 E_m)^2/R}{0.706 E_m^2/R} \times 100\% = 96.5\% \qquad (18\text{–}16)$$

The peak inverse voltage between anode A_1 and the cathode K occurs when $\omega t = 4\pi/3$, and is

$$\text{P.I.V.} = \sqrt{3}\,E_m = 2.09 E_{d\text{–}c} \qquad (18\text{–}17)$$

The ripple will be due to three pulses per cycle, so that its lowest frequency is 180 cycles for 60-cycle input. Its magnitude may be computed by finding I_{rms}, the effective value of the load current:

$$I_{\text{rms}} = \sqrt{\frac{3}{2\pi} \int_{\pi/6}^{5\pi/6} \frac{E_m^2 \sin^2 \omega t}{R^2}\, d\omega t} = \frac{0.838 E_m}{R} \qquad (18\text{–}18)$$

The ripple is then 17 per cent, as computed by

$$r = \sqrt{(I_{\text{rms}}/I_{d\text{–}c})^2 - 1} = \sqrt{(1.014)^2 - 1} = 0.17 \qquad (18\text{–}19)$$

The direct current of each anode appears in the secondary phase windings and may cause transformer saturation, with its attendant large primary current. The circuit may be modified to the *zigzag* form, of Fig. 18–13, to avoid this. Windings on the same core are drawn parallel to each other, so that on each core are two coils which carry d-c components I_o in opposite directions, thereby neutralizing the d-c magnetomotive force on the core. The anode voltage e must be derived as the sum of two coil voltages at 60°, or each coil must supply $0.575e$.

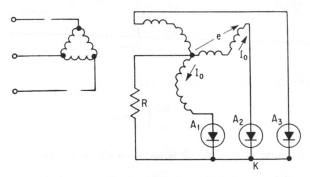

Fig. 18–13. Three-phase zig-zag circuit, showing d-c cancellation.

18–10. m-phase rectifiers

Rectifiers are built with a large number of phases (6, 12, 18, or more) using star-connected transformers, and involving branched or zigzag windings to eliminate d-c core saturation. A general analysis may be undertaken by studying the rectification of m phases, using m diodes, each of which conducts for $2\pi/m$ radians per cycle; the load current appears in Fig. 18–14. This definition of m requires continuous load current, and this analysis does not apply to the single-phase half-wave circuit.

Neglecting losses, the d-c load current of an m-phase rectifier is

$$I_{\text{d-c}} = \frac{m}{2\pi} \int_{\pi/2-\pi/m}^{\pi/2+\pi/m} \frac{E_m \sin \omega t}{R} \, d\omega t = \frac{E_m}{R} \frac{m}{\pi} \sin \frac{\pi}{m} \tag{18–20}$$

Since $E_{\text{d-c}} = I_{\text{d-c}}R$, it is possible to write

$$\frac{E_{\text{d-c}}}{E_m} = \frac{m}{\pi} \sin \frac{\pi}{m} \tag{18–21}$$

as a dimensionless ratio to show the effect of variation of m on the d-c voltage. The ratio as plotted in Fig. 18–15 shows that there is little gain in d-c voltage above six phases.

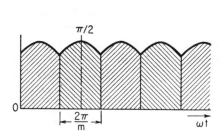

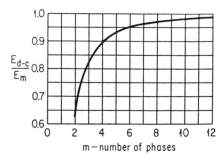

Fig. 18–14. Current pulses in the m-phase rectifier.

Fig. 18–15. D-c output voltage as function of m.

The d-c power output can be written as

$$P_{\text{d-c}} = \frac{E_m^2}{R} \left(\frac{m}{\pi} \sin \frac{\pi}{m} \right)^2$$

The rms value of current flowing through each diode can be found as

$$I_{\text{rms}} = \sqrt{\frac{1}{2\pi} \int_{\pi/2-\pi/m}^{\pi/2+\pi/m} \frac{E_m^2 \sin^2 \omega t}{R^2} \, d\omega t} = \frac{E_m}{R} \sqrt{\frac{1}{2\pi} \left(\frac{\pi}{m} + \sin \frac{\pi}{m} \cos \frac{\pi}{m} \right)}$$

and the a-c power input from the transformer is obtainable as $mI_{\text{rms}}^2 R$, or

$$P_{\text{in}} = \frac{m}{2\pi} \frac{E_m^2}{R} \left(\frac{\pi}{m} + \sin \frac{\pi}{m} \cos \frac{\pi}{m} \right) \qquad (18\text{–}22)$$

The maximum theoretical efficiency then becomes

$$\max \eta_R = \frac{(2m/\pi) \sin^2 (\pi/m)}{\pi/m + \sin (\pi/m) \cos (\pi/m)} \times 100\% \qquad (18\text{–}23)$$

The theoretical efficiency is 81.2 per cent for $m = 2$, and reaches 99.8 per cent for $m = 6$.

The ripple percentage can be calculated by use of $I_{\text{d–c}}$ and I_{rms}. The resultant curve of Fig. 18–16 shows that the ripple decreases rapidly with an increase in the number of phases. This factor, plus the increase in the lowest frequency present in the ripple, makes the distortion of the primary-current wave form much less with rectifiers having m large. This is important because harmonics introduced into the primary power circuit may cause telephone interference.

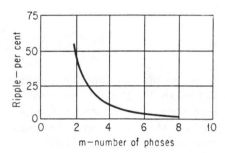

Fig. 18–16. Ripple percentage vs number of phases.

18–11. Transformer utilization factor

Transformers for power use are designed for sinusoidal current, but transformers supplying rectifiers do not always have sinusoidal current waves, and the larger the number of star-connected phases, the shorter is the time of current conduction per cycle in a given winding. The distorted current waves indicate the presence of harmonics, and the harmonic currents cause transformer heating, yet produce no useful d-c output. To provide for these harmonic currents, a transformer rated at more than the d-c power output is required. A measure of the ability of a transformer in a given rectifier circuit to supply d-c power is called the *utilization factor* of the transformer, defined as

$$\text{U.F.} = \frac{P_{\text{d–c}}}{\text{volt-amperes}} \qquad (18\text{–}24)$$

Because of the harmonic volt-amperes, the utilization factor is always less than unity.

The volt-ampere ratings of primary and secondary may differ, due to wave form variations. The total secondary volt-amperes are $mE_m/\sqrt{2}$ times the rms current so that

$$\text{Total Sec. V.A.} = m\,\frac{E_m}{\sqrt{2}}\,\frac{E_m}{R}\,\sqrt{\frac{1}{2\pi}\left(\frac{\pi}{m} + \sin\frac{\pi}{m}\cos\frac{\pi}{m}\right)} \quad (18\text{--}25)$$

The d-c power output is

$$P_{\text{d--c}} = \frac{E_m^2}{R}\left(\frac{m}{\pi}\sin\frac{\pi}{m}\right)^2$$

and the secondary utilization factor for an m-phase rectifier transformer is

$$\text{Sec. U.F.} = \frac{(2m/\pi)\,\sin^2\,(\pi/m)}{\sqrt{\pi[(\pi/m) + \sin\,(\pi/m)\,\cos\,(\pi/m)]}} \quad (18\text{--}26)$$

A curve of this function appears in Fig. 18–17. It can be seen that a maximum occurs near $m = 3$, which implies that the most economic conduction angle is near 120°.

The two opposite star-connected secondary windings are supplied by a single primary phase. The current in a primary winding is the effective value of two current pulses so that

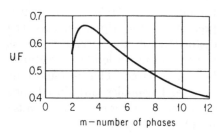

Fig. 18–17. Secondary utilization factor of the m-phase rectifier.

$$\text{Pri. } I_{\text{rms}} = \sqrt{2}\,\frac{E_m}{R}\,\sqrt{\frac{1}{2\pi}\left(\frac{\pi}{m} + \sin\frac{\pi}{m}\cos\frac{\pi}{m}\right)}$$

assuming 1:1 voltage transformation. If the circuit has p primary phases,

$$\text{Pri. V.A.} = \frac{pE_m^2}{R}\,\sqrt{\frac{1}{2\pi}\left(\frac{\pi}{m} + \sin\frac{\pi}{m}\cos\frac{\pi}{m}\right)} \quad (18\text{--}27)$$

The primary utilization factor is then

$$\text{Pri. U.F.} = \frac{(m/\pi)^2\,\sin^2\,(\pi/m)}{p\sqrt{(1/2\pi)[(\pi/m) + \sin\,(\pi/m)\,\cos\,(\pi/m)]}} \quad (18\text{--}28)$$

$$= \frac{m}{p\sqrt{2}}\,\text{Sec. U.F.} \quad (18\text{--}29)$$

TABLE 27. THEORETICAL* DESIGN DATA—RECTIFIERS WITH RESISTANCE LOAD

| | Single-Phase | | Three-Phase | | Six-Phase |
	Full-Wave	Bridge	Half-Wave	Full-Wave	Half-Wave
Value of m	2	2	3	6	6
Avg load current, I_{d-c}	$0.636E_m$†$/R$‡	$0.636E_m/R$	$0.827E_m/R$	$1.65E_m/R$	$0.955E_m/R$
Avg current/tube	$I_{d-c}/2$‡	$I_{d-c}/2$	$I_{d-c}/3$	$I_{d-c}/3$	$I_{d-c}/6$
Peak current/tube	$1.57I_{d-c}$	$1.57I_{d-c}$	$1.21I_{d-c}$	$1.21I_{d-c}$	$1.047I_{d-c}$
E_{d-c}	$0.636E_m$	$0.636E_m$	$0.827E_m$	$1.65E_m$	$0.955E_m$
Lowest ripple frequency	$2f_1$	$2f_1$	$3f_1$	$6f_1$	$6f_1$
Ripple	47%	47%	17%	4%	4%
Transformer V.A. rating:					
Secondary	$1.75P_{d-c}$	$1.23P_{d-c}$	$1.50P_{d-c}$	$1.047P_{d-c}$	$1.82P_{d-c}$
Primary	$1.23P_{d-c}$	$1.23P_{d-c}$	$1.23P_{d-c}$	$1.047P_{d-c}$	$1.28P_{d-c}$
Maximum theoretical efficiency	81.2%	81.2%	96.5%	99.8%	99.8%
P.I.V.	$3.14E_{d-c}$	$1.57E_{d-c}$	$2.09E_{d-c}$	$1.045E_{d-c}$	$2.09E_{d-c}$

* Assuming tube drop and transformer leakage reactance both negligible in effect.

† E_m is the peak value of voltage to neutral of one phase of the transformer (see circuit diagrams)

‡ I_{d-c} is defined as the average current in the load.

Values of primary and secondary volt-ampere ratings for other rectifier circuits are given in Table 27. Computations for circuits in which the d-c components neutralize in a given transformer secondary follow the method outlined. Circuits such as the three-phase half-wave, which produce an unbalanced d-c component in a transformer secondary, cannot be analyzed without further knowledge of primary-current wave forms. This phase of the subject is beyond the scope of the treatment given here.

18–12. Polyphase rectifiers with inductance filters

Although the ripple present in the output of polyphase rectifiers is small, it is undesirable in many applications, and an inductance may be connected in series with the d-c load as a filter. Because of the small ripple value and the ripple frequency, nominal inductance values may give substantially constant load current, resulting in diode currents as illustrated in Fig. 18–18 for an m-phase rectifier.

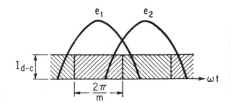

Fig. 18–18. Current in an m-phase rectifier with series inductor.

In such a general m-phase rectifier having an inductance in the load, it can be seen by analogy that

$$E_{d-c} = \frac{m}{2\pi} \int_{\pi/2-\pi/m}^{\pi/2+\pi/m} E_m \sin \omega t \, d\omega t = E_m \frac{m}{\pi} \sin \frac{\pi}{m} \quad (18\text{–}30)$$

Since the diode current is $I_{d-c} = I_{rms}$, the power input from the transformer secondaries is

$$P_{a-c} = \frac{m}{2\pi} \int_{\pi/2-\pi/m}^{\pi/2+\pi/m} I_{d-c} E_m \sin \omega t \, d\omega t = I_{d-c} E_m \frac{m}{\pi} \sin \frac{\pi}{m} \quad (18\text{–}31)$$

This is also the value of $P_{d-c} = E_{d-c}I_{d-c}$, and thus the theoretical rectification efficiency has been raised to 100 per cent. This result should be expected, since with constant current, no harmonic currents are present to give power output not usable as d-c power.

The effective current per diode for this rectifier is

$$I_{rms} = \sqrt{\frac{1}{2\pi} \int_{\pi/2-\pi/m}^{\pi/2+\pi/m} I_{d-c}^2 \, d\omega t} = \frac{I_{d-c}}{\sqrt{m}} \quad (18\text{–}32)$$

The a-c volt-ampere input for all secondaries is

$$\text{Sec. V.A.} = \frac{E_m}{\sqrt{2}} \frac{I_{d-c}}{\sqrt{m}} m = \sqrt{\frac{m}{2}} E_m I_{d-c}$$

and the secondary utilization factor is

$$\text{Sec. U.F.} = \frac{I_{\text{d–c}} E_m \dfrac{m}{\pi} \sin \dfrac{\pi}{m}}{\sqrt{\dfrac{m}{2}}\, E_m I_{\text{d–c}}} = \frac{\sqrt{2m}}{\pi} \sin \frac{\pi}{m} \tag{18–33}$$

This expression may be readily maximized, showing that the secondary U.F. is a maximum at $m = 2.7$, or between the two-phase and three-phase conditions. For circuits in which the d-c components cancel in a transformer secondary, the primary effective current per phase consists of two pulses leading to a value of

$$\text{Pri. } I_{\text{eff}} = \frac{\sqrt{2}\,I_{\text{d–c}}}{\sqrt{m}}$$

The total primary volt-amperes are

$$\text{Pri. V.A.} = \frac{E_m}{\sqrt{2}} \frac{\sqrt{2}\,I_{\text{d–c}}}{\sqrt{m}} \frac{m}{2} = \frac{\sqrt{m}}{2} E_m I_{\text{d–c}}$$

and the primary utilization factor is

$$\text{Pri. U.F.} = \frac{I_{\text{d–c}} E_m \dfrac{m}{\pi} \sin \dfrac{\pi}{m}}{\dfrac{\sqrt{m}}{2} E_m I_{\text{d–c}}} = \frac{2\sqrt{m}}{\pi} \sin \frac{\pi}{m} \tag{18–34}$$

Calculated ratings for rectifiers with rectangular current pulses are given in Table 28. For rectifiers having values of $m = 3$ or higher, there

TABLE 28. TRANSFORMER UTILIZATION FACTOR—RECTIFIERS WITH INDUCTIVE FILTER*

	Single-Phase		Three-Phase		
	Full-Wave	Bridge	Half-Wave	Full-Wave	Six-Phase
m.................	2	2	3	6	6
Primary U.F........	0.90	0.90	0.827	0.955	0.780
Primary V.A. rating..	$1.11 P_{\text{d–c}}$	$1.11 P_{\text{d–c}}$	$1.21 P_{\text{d–c}}$	$1.047 P_{\text{d–c}}$	$1.28 P_{\text{d–c}}$
Secondary U.F.......	0.636	0.90	0.675	0.955	0.552
Secondary V.A. rating	$1.57 P_{\text{d–c}}$	$1.11 P_{\text{d–c}}$	$1.48 P_{\text{d–c}}$	$1.047 P_{\text{d–c}}$	$1.82 P_{\text{d–c}}$

* Based on theoretically infinite inductance.

is negligible difference in performance and in transformer ratings between rectifiers with and without inductance filters, since the current wave forms are close approximations to the rectangular form without any filter present.

18–13. Rectifier circuit design

The major factors in determining the circuit to be used are usually ripple and transformer utilization. Transformers are large items in the cost of a rectifier installation. Avoidance of d-c saturation through some form of zigzag winding increases the transformer cost. Large numbers of phases increase the cost but decrease the ripple. A complete cost analysis of various circuits is needed to provide the economic factors, which may then be balanced against engineering performance.

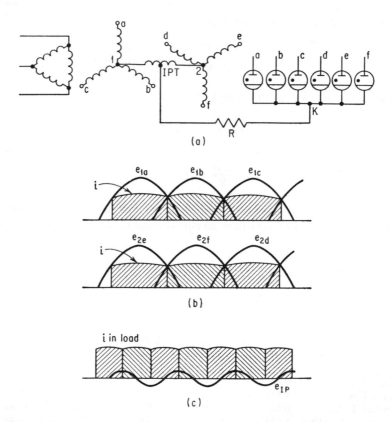

Fig. 18–19. (a) Three-phase double-Y circuit; (b) current wave forms; (c) interphase reactor voltage wave.

In general, three major diode ratings must be individually checked to make certain that a given type of rectifier service exceeds none of them. These ratings are the average current per diode, the peak current per diode, and the peak inverse-voltage rating of the diode. Any one of the three may provide a limit to the amount of power obtainable from a given rectifier.

Of the circuits discussed, the single-phase circuits suffer from high ripple percentage and low ripple frequency, and low secondary utilization. The three-phase half-wave circuit has poor transformer utilization, and to avoid saturation must make use of the zigzag winding, thereby increasing transformer cost.

While the six-phase circuit is not often used because of low utilization, various modifications of the circuit are available to improve the transformer utilization through lengthening the conduction angle. A circuit demonstrating this principle appears in Fig. 18–19, and employs six secondary windings connected in two stars, the neutrals interconnected by an interphase reactor. At any instant there are two anodes carrying current, one in each group, and each anode conducts for 120°, or near the optimum for best utilization. In effect, the two transformer banks constitute two rectifiers which are connected in parallel by the interphase reactor. Point-by-point addition of the two current waves shows that the load current will have a ripple frequency which is six times that of the supply.

By reason of the unequal instantaneous currents flowing in the two halves of the reactor, a three-phase voltage of amplitude $E_m\sqrt{2}$ will appear across the reactor, as shown in Fig. 18–19(c).

18–14. Voltage regulator (VR) tubes

The normal glow region of the cold-cathode gaseous-discharge characteristic of Fig. 17–4 is employed in certain two-element tubes for voltage regulation. After the breakdown voltage is reached, the voltage across the discharge becomes constant over a considerable range of current, with currents of milliampere order flowing. The voltage across the tube is determined by the material of the cathode and the gas used, such as neon, argon, or helium. Tube voltages with various gas mixtures are in the range of 75 to 150 v.

A typical voltage regulator has a cylindrical cathode and central wire anode. A short wire stub extends from the cathode to a point close to the anode, raising the value of the electric field and lowering the voltage required for initial breakdown which is from 50 to 100 per cent above the rated operating voltage. A circuit for operation of such a tube is shown in Fig. 18–20(b). The sum of the load and regulator current will be sufficient to provide a voltage drop in R equal to the difference in supply and tube

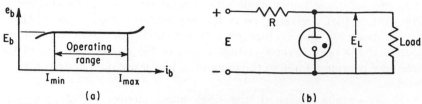

Fig. 18–20. (a) Volt-ampere curve of a VR tube; (b) circuit for a VR tube.

voltages. A decrease in load current will cause a corresponding increase in tube current to maintain the drop in R and voltage E_L constant. If E is the d-c supply voltage and I_{max} the maximum rated tube current, the resistor R may be calculated as

$$R = \frac{E - E_L}{I_{max}}$$

The tube has some rated minimum current I_{min}, and the load may draw any current from zero to a value $(I_{max} - I_{min})$ without passing outside the operating range of the regulator tube.

Voltage-regulator tubes may be connected in series for higher controlled voltage. Since the action of the regulator is quite rapid, fast voltage changes are wiped out, and a glow tube is quite efficient as a filter.

Problems

18-1. A silicon diode having an average voltage drop of 0.5 v is used to supply a d-c load of 12 v and 5.0 amp. Find:

(a) The input a-c volts.
(b) The peak anode current.
(c) The power loss in the diode.
(d) The non-d-c power loss in the load.

18-2. A mercury-vapor diode is used in a single-phase half-wave circuit to supply a 50-ohm resistive load from a 30-v rms a-c supply. Assume the tube drop is 12 v. Find:

(a) The direct current.
(b) The peak anode current.
(c) The d-c load voltage.
(d) The power loss in the tube.
(e) The non-d-c power loss in the load.
(f) Plot to scale the wave forms of anode current, supply voltage, and tube voltage.

18-3. For the previous problem, calculate the reading obtained on a d-c voltmeter connected directly across the tube. Can the tube drop be measured in this way?

18-4. A single-phase full-wave rectifier uses two silicon diodes rated at 1.5 amp peak current and 0.225 amp average current. The transformer voltage to center tap is 250 v rms and the load is 3000 ohms. If the diode drop is 1.0 v, find:

(a) D-c load current.
(b) D-c power output.
(c) Total diode loss.
(d) Peak inverse voltage.
(e) A-c power input from the transformer.

18-5. A mercury-vapor rectifier rated at 5 amp peak current, 1.5 amp average current, is used in a single-phase half-wave circuit to charge a 12-v storage battery having 0.035-ohm internal resistance. The a-c supply is an 18-v rms source. Assume that the breakdown and tube-drop voltages are equal at 10.

(a) What value of resistor will be needed in the circuit to prevent exceeding the peak current rating?

(b) What is the value of battery-charging current with this resistor in the circuit?

18-6. The 866 mercury-vapor diode is rated as follows:

10,000 v P.I.V.	15 v tube drop
1.0 amp peak plate current	2.5 filament volts
0.25 amp average plate current	5.0 filament amp

(a) What is the maximum d-c power which two of these tubes might supply to a resistance load in a full-wave rectifier circuit, a very large inductance being in series with the load?

(b) What is the over-all efficiency while this load is being rectified, if the power and filament transformers are 96 per cent efficient?

18-7. A silicon diode is used in a half-wave circuit to supply direct current to a 15-ohm load. The source has a voltage of 12 rms. If diode drop is negligible, find:

(a) The peak diode current.
(b) The average diode current.
(c) The a-c load current (rms).

18-8. An FG-104 mercury-vapor phanotron, rated 3000 v peak inverse, 40 amp peak anode current, and 6.4 amp average anode current, is used in a single-phase half-wave circuit. Neglecting tube voltage drop, find:

(a) The maximum possible d-c current, without exceeding ratings.
(b) The maximum possible d-c voltage.
(c) The a-c transformer voltage (rms) required for (b).
(d) The a-c input power, if (a) and (b) occur simultaneously.

18-9. Two mercury-vapor diodes, rated at 5 amp peak current each, are used in a full-wave single-phase circuit to supply a total of 6 amp direct current at 750 v to a resistance load. If tube drop is negligible, find:

(a) Rms a-c voltage required for each half of the transformer secondary.
(b) Direct current per tube.
(c) Whether tubes are operated within the peak rating.

18-10. Starting with Eqs. 18-9 and 18-10, develop Eq. 18-11 for the d-c output current.

18-11. A rectifier using six silicon diodes rated 35 amp average, 150 amp peak each, has a 230-v delta-connected primary and star-connected secondary. The load is 200 amp at 600 v d-c. Assuming negligible leakage reactance, find:

(a) Current and voltage ratings of all transformer windings.
(b) If the transformer is 97 per cent efficient, what is the over-all efficiency? Assume 0.5 v drop in each diode.

18-12. A 440-v delta-connected primary and 2200-v star-connected three-phase secondary supply three hot-cathode mercury-vapor diodes rated at:

$$12.5 \text{ amp avg} \quad\quad 5 - E_f \text{ v}$$
$$75 \text{ amp peak} \quad\quad 20 - I_f \text{ amp}$$
$$3500 \text{ P.I.V.} \quad\quad 12 \text{ v tube drop}$$

If the efficiency of both anode and filament transformers is 94.5 per cent, find:

(a) D-c current supplied to a 50-ohm load.
(b) D-c output power.
(c) Kva rating of anode transformer secondaries (total).
(d) P.I.V.
(e) Over-all rectifier efficiency.

18-13. A six-phase half-wave rectifier is to use a mercury-vapor tube rated as follows:

$$75 \text{ amp avg} \quad\quad 5 \text{ filament volts}$$
$$450 \text{ amp peak} \quad\quad 65 \text{ filament amp}$$
$$16,000 \text{ P.I.V.} \quad\quad 10 \text{ v tube drop}$$

(a) Without exceeding any rating, find the maximum direct current, voltage, and power which may be obtained from this rectifier.
(b) State primary- and secondary-transformer ratings for voltage and volt-amperes. Primary service is to be 440 v, three-phase.

18-14. Design a 500-kw, 1500-v d-c rectifier system using the three-phase half-wave, zigzag connection. Calculate:

(a) Transformer secondary voltage for all windings.
(b) Direct current through each diode.
(c) The kva rating of the transformer primary and secondary. Assume the load has a large inductance or a filter.

18-15. A transformer having a 3000-v center-trapped secondary is used to supply either a single-phase full-wave or bridge rectifier. Find the ratio of the d-c power output in full wave to that in the bridge circuit for equal volt-ampere loading of the transformer.

18-16. For the m-phase rectifier without filter, derive the general expression for the ripple.

18-17. You have a number of silicon power diodes rated as follows:

$$250 \text{ P.I.V.} \qquad \text{Drop} = \text{negligible}$$
$$I_{\text{peak}} = 15 \text{ amp} \qquad I_{\text{av}} = 5 \text{ amp}$$

(a) Find the maximum d-c power available in the following service to a resistance load: one-phase, full-wave; three-phase, half-wave; six-phase, half-wave.

(b) The diodes cost $125 each and transformers cost $20 per kva. Find the total cost per d-c kw output for each of the three circuits.

(c) The transformers are 94 per cent efficient. If a return of 12 per cent must be paid for depreciation and interest on investment in equipment, and the rectifiers are used 5000 hours per year, find the cost of d-c power per kilowatt-hour from each rectifier, if the input a-c power costs 1.5¢ per kilowatt-hour.

References

1. Chin, P. T., "Gaseous Rectifier Circuits," *Electronics*, **18,** 138 (April 1945), 132 (May 1945).

2. Henkels, H. W., "Germanium and Silicon Rectifiers," *Proc. I.R.E.*, **46,** 1086 (1958).

3. Hull, A. W., "Gas-Filled Thermionic Tubes," *Trans. A.I.E.E.*, **47,** 753 (1928).

4. Koller, L. R., "Cathode Sputtering in Arc Discharges," *Physics*, **7,** 225 (1936).

Power Control | 19

Addition of a grid to the gas diode, and of an electrical starter to the mercury-pool tube, allows control of considerable electrical power at high efficiency. These gas devices are now being superseded by the silicon control rectifier and other semiconductor devices, with characteristics similar to the controlled gas tubes, but with even higher efficiency and longer life. These devices permit the control of heavy alternating and rectified currents as required in welding, lighting, motor control, and regulation of rectifiers.

19–1. The thyratron

The first large power device was the *thyratron* (door tube), developed from the gas diode by insertion of a grid to form an electrostatic shield between cathode and anode. With a highly negative grid, electrons emitted from the cathode face a repelling field and are unable to pass through the grid openings. As the grid is made less negative, a few electrons pass through the grid holes, are accelerated toward the anode and receive enough energy to ionize upon collision with gas atoms. The resulting positive ions neutralize the negative field near the grid, more electrons are accelerated; the process is cumulative and an arc discharge forms from cathode to anode. The discharge therefore *starts* at the critical grid potential which permits the first electron to ionize.

The ionization process takes only 10 to 20 μsec. A positive ion sheath then forms around the grid, and this sheath is so complete that the grid is completely shielded from the discharge. Therefore, *after start of the discharge, the grid potential has no effect on the current*, the current value being dependent on the external anode circuit resistance. The arc can only be extinguished by removal of the positive anode potential.

Before breakdown, the grid current is small and due to a few electrons with emission energies sufficient to overcome the negative grid field. After ionization, the grid current reverses, because positive ions flow to the grid; this current may be large and must be limited by external resistance.

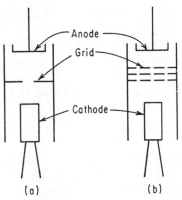

(a)   (b)

Fig. 19-1. Cross section of (a) negative-grid thyratron; (b) positive-grid thyratron.

Cross sections of thyratrons appear in Fig. 19-1. The cathodes are heat-shielded and the anodes are of nickel or graphite; the grid is a perforated metal cylinder.

The value of grid voltage which just prevents ignition of the arc is called the *critical grid potential*, and a curve may be drawn as in Fig. 19-2, relating the critical grid potential and the anode potential. Those in Fig. 19-2(a) represent characteristics for a *negative-grid* design, in which a negative grid voltage must always be present to *prevent* the discharge. In Fig. 19-2(b) appear the curves for a positive-grid tube, in which a positive voltage must be present to *cause* conduction. The grid characteristics in mercury vapor are functions of temperature, and argon or neon types are available for temperature-sensitive or critical applications.

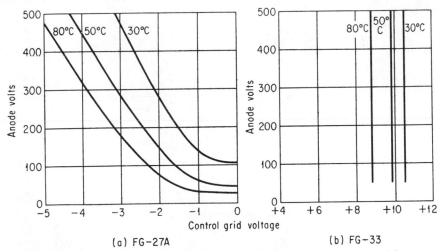

(a) FG-27A   (b) FG-33

Fig. 19-2. Critical grid curves for (a) negative-grid tube; (b) positive grid tube.

It is desired that the grid control the starting of the arc in each half cycle of an alternating anode voltage. Thus the time of deionization of the grid sheath must be less than the time of the negative half-cycle. This requirement places an upper frequency limit on thyratron application, since deionization times from 10 to 1000 μsecs are usual.

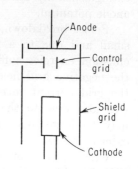

Fig. 19–3. Shield-grid thyratron.

Even with usual small grid currents, an appreciable drop may occur before ignition in high-impedance grid circuits, making the grid more negative and tending to delay breakdown. To reduce grid current a *shield grid* may be introduced, as in Fig. 19–3. Electrons strike the shield instead of the control grid, and raise the grid impedance so that 100 megohms or more may be used in the control circuits.

19–2. Silicon control rectifiers

Several semiconductor devices, built with PNPN or NPNP configurations, as in Fig. 19–4, have trigger functions and handle large currents, as does the thyratron. In the device of the figure, on the operating half cycle forward bias is placed on junctions J_1 and J_3, and only the usual small forward voltages appear across these junctions. This leaves junction J_2 with reverse bias, and the behavior is determined by the action of this junction.

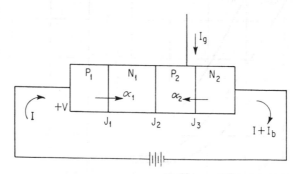

Fig. 19–4. A silicon-controlled rectifier (SCR).

For the first part of this discussion I_g may be assumed zero. The total current I across J_2 will be composed of three components, $\alpha_1 I$ of holes from the P_1 region, $\alpha_2 I$ of electrons from the N_2 region, and the leakage current I_{C0}. Thus

$$I = \alpha_1 I + \alpha_2 I + I_{C0} = \frac{I_{C0}}{1 - (\alpha_1 + \alpha_2)} \tag{19-1}$$

The leakage current in silicon is very small, and at low emitter currents the value of α in a silicon transistor is also small. Because of these conditions the current given by Eq. 19–1 is low.

However, the value of α increases rapidly as the emitter current of a junction is increased, and Eq. 19–1 shows that as the sum of α_1 and α_2 approaches unity, the current I will become very large.

These controlling factors may now be correlated with the volt-ampere diagram of Fig. 19–5. At low currents in the region OA of the curve, the value of $(\alpha_1 + \alpha_2) < 1$, and junction J_2 behaves as a PN junction with reverse bias. In the region AB the value of $(\alpha_1 + \alpha_2)$ increases and at B $(\alpha_1 + \alpha_2) = 1$, with the so-called breakover or triggering value of voltage V_T, and current I_H. As the alphas further increase with current the junction J_2 is found to be forward biased, and the whole device then behaves as if it were a single PN junction biased in the forward direction. Operation is in the CD region of the volt-ampere curve, with high current and low voltage drop.

Because of the negative resistance properties of the BC region, conduction can be stopped only by reducing the current below the value I_H, the holding current. When the current is driven below this value, conduction ceases and the operating point goes from C to O as indicated.

It is possible to increase α_2 independently by supplying a current I_g to P_2, and this is the principle of the silicon control rectifier (SCR). By

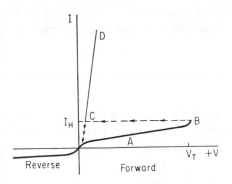

Fig. 19–5. Typical volt-ampere characteristic of a silicon control rectifier.

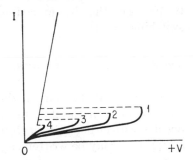

Fig. 19–6. Volt-ampere curves for varying values of I_g; $I_{g4} > I_{g1}$.

use of an external circuit, the current I_g is driven in the same direction as I across junction J_3. This additional base current is effective in raising α_2 independently of the applied voltage V. By this means the condition of $(\alpha_1 + \alpha_2) = 1$ can be reached at lower values of breakover voltage, with only small values of gate electrode current I_g.

In this mode of operation, using a triggering current to the gate electrode or P_2, the volt-ampere curves become as in Fig. 19–6. The higher the value of triggering current, the lower is the value of applied voltage V at which breakover occurs. With sufficiently high values of I_g, as for 4, the device will turn on at very small voltages and behaves as a simple PN junction in the forward direction. When the current falls below the holding value I_H, conduction ceases and on the reverse half-cycle the device appears as two reverse-biased junctions in series.

In usual operation with a–c input, the control rectifier is operated with a peak a-c voltage well below the breakover value, and triggering is accomplished at the desired time in the cycle by supplying a triggering current to the gate electrode. Once the device has been triggered into conduction, the gate no longer has any control, similar to the grid in the thyratron. The only method of stopping conduction is to reduce the main current I below the holding value I_H.

The silicon control rectifier is thus triggered by a current pulse, as opposed to a voltage pulse for the gas thyratron. Much lower source impedance must be used for turning on the SCR, but otherwise many of the triggering circuits will be fundamentally the same for the two types of control rectifiers.

Mounting, cooling, and temperature considerations for the SCR will follow those indicated for the semiconductor power diode. Ratings available at present approximate those of thyratrons, with gate currents of one ampere peak controlling operating currents as high as 50 amperes. Turn-on time approximates one μsec and turn-off is accomplished in 5 to 10 μsec, thereby exceeding the capabilities of usual thyratrons in switching speeds.

19–3. Control rectification

Variation of the time in the cycle at which triggering or firing occurs allows control of the d-c output voltage of a rectifier, and this control is possible with either SCR or thyratron. The current in the half-wave circuits of Fig. 19–7 may be written as

$$i_l = \frac{E_m \sin \omega t}{R}, \qquad 0 < \omega t < \pi \tag{19–2}$$

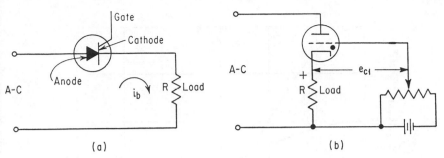

Fig. 19-7. (a) Silicon control rectifier; (b) thyratron rectifier.

neglecting internal drop for both rectifier types.

Circuits will be discussed later which permit control of the triggering or firing angle θ_1, usually by applying a pulse to the gate or grid at the desired instant in the anode cycle. The direct-current output will be the average of the wave form of Fig. 19-8, given by

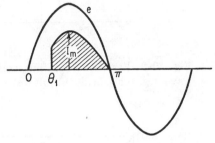

Fig. 19-8. Control rectifier current wave form.

$$I_{\text{d-c}} = \frac{1}{2\pi} \int_0^{2\pi} i_b \, d\omega t = \frac{1}{2\pi} \int_{\theta_1}^{\pi} \frac{E_m \sin \omega t}{R} \, d\omega t = \frac{E_m}{2\pi R} \ (1 + \cos \ \theta_1)$$

$$(19\text{-}3)$$

This shows that the direct-current output may be controlled by variation of the angle θ_1 at which the rectifier is turned on in each cycle. Fig. 19-9 is a dimensionless plot of Eq. 19-3, and illustrates the smoothness of control obtainable. An additional advantage is the fact that this control of output is possible with negligible power loss, because of the high efficiency of the rectifiers.

When used with inductive loads a more complex analysis, similar to that for the R-L filter on the half-wave rectifier, is required. It is possible to determine the cutoff angle of current flow, ωt_2 for each value of θ_1 and ratio $\omega L/R$ of the load by graphical means, after deriving the usual transcendental equation. The values obtained for ωt_2 are plotted in Fig. 19-10. Then it can be found that average voltage output will be

$$E_{\text{d-c}} = I_{\text{d-c}}R = \frac{E_m}{2\pi} \ (\cos \theta_1 - \cos \omega t_2) \qquad (19\text{-}4)$$

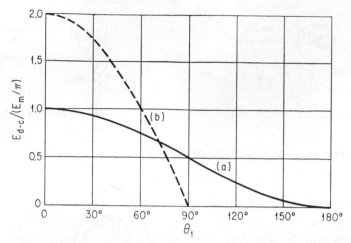

Fig. 19–9. Variation of output voltage with triggering angle: (a) half-wave, resistance load; (b) full-wave, inductive load.

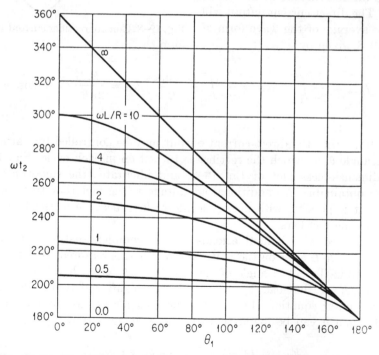

Fig. 19–10. Variation of cutoff angle ωt_2 with delay angle for values of $\omega L/R$.

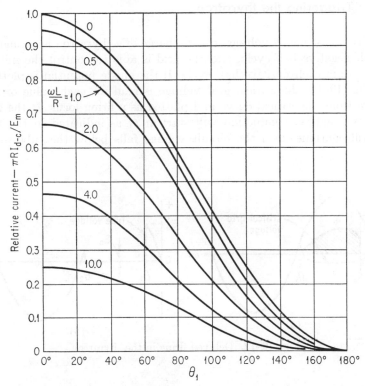

Fig. 19–11. Relative current with inductive load as function of delay θ_1 and load $\omega L/R$ ratio; half-wave circuit.

It can be seen that the average voltage is reduced by later triggering angles, θ_1, as well as being a function of the load impedance angle. A plot of Eq. 19–4 appears in Fig. 19–11, in terms of the load parameter $\omega L/R$ and the delay angle θ_1.

When a full-wave rectifier is used with an inductive load the current is usually continuous, and the effect of the inductance is largely that of producing this continuity of current. The results may again be derived, with proper attention to limits and to the fact that the current value at angle θ_1 is equal to that at angle $\theta_1 + \pi$. The direct voltage will then be found as

$$E_{\text{d-c}} = I_{\text{d-c}}R = \frac{2E_m}{\pi} \cos \theta_1 \tag{19–5}$$

if the load current is continuous. A plot of the above equation appears as the dashed curve of Fig. 19–9, showing good control characteristics.

19–4. Triggering the thyratron

With an a-c anode voltage, the discharge in a thyratron is extinguished in each negative half-cycle, and the grid is able to control the initiation of the arc in each positive half cycle. If the anode potential is plotted as e in Fig. 19–12, the critical grid voltage is read for each value of anode voltage from the critical curve and plotted as a firing locus. If the grid is e_{c1} volts negative, conduction will start at θ_1, as indicated in the figure, and will continue until the circuit voltage falls below the tube drop at θ_2.

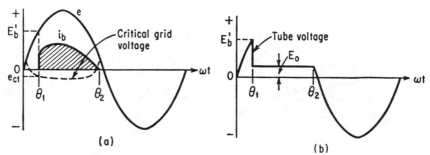

Fig. 19–12. Delayed firing in the thyratron.

If E'_b is the anode voltage at which the tube discharge begins, then

$$\theta_1 = \sin^{-1} \frac{E'_b}{E_m} \tag{19–6}$$

As shown in Fig. 19–12(b), at breakdown the tube voltage drops abruptly to E_o, and the current rises if no inductance is present. The current wave form for a thyratron with resistance load is non-sinusoidal, being a sinusoid with E_o/R units sliced off the bottom, and with the left side cut off to angle θ_1.

A variable d-c bias may be used to control a thyratron, as in Fig. 19–12(a). Firing will occur at the instant the bias becomes more positive than the value given by the critical locus. By necessity this must occur in the first 90° of the anode wave, so that the output current is controllable only from 100 per cent to 50 per cent, and this is not usually a sufficient control range. Also, the critical locus is temperature sensitive in mercury tubes, and the method is employed only where on-off control is desired. A considerable excess of grid voltage is used and this insures positive turn-on and turn-off.

A more desirable form of control is by a variable phase a-c grid voltage, as in Fig. 19–13. The grid voltage is made to lag by a variable angle θ, and if e_g is large, it can be seen that θ will approximate θ_1, the firing angle, and is usually so assumed. By varying the phase of the grid voltage, the discharge may be started at any angle between 0° and 180°, with the output voltage varying in accordance with Eq.

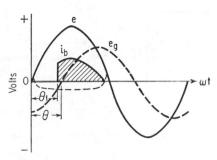

Fig. 19–13. Phase shift control.

19–3, plotted in Fig. 19–9(a). Leading grid voltage will always fire the tube at 0° and thus will provide no control.

For large grid voltage magnitude, the grid wave will cross the critical locus at a steep angle, and variations of the locus due to temperature will have small effect. Circuits for providing a convenient phase shift, or for shaping the grid voltage into phased pulses will be discussed later.

The previous methods may be combined where a variable d-c voltage is the control variable. In this *bias-phase* method, the variable d-c bias is applied in series with an a-c voltage lagging in phase by a fixed angle, usually between 45° and 90°, as in Fig. 19–14. If the d-c bias is made more negative, the a-c grid wave is moved downward, firing the tube at later angles. The d-c bias may also be positive, moving the firing angle forward in the cycle as at Fig. 19–14(b). The circuit affords the freedom from temperature variations also possible with the phase-shift form of control.

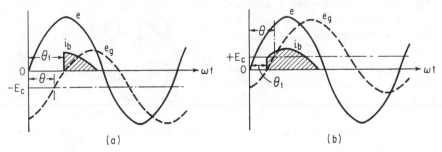

Fig. 19–14. Bias-phase control: (a) with $\theta = 60°$ and negative bias; (b) same with positive bias.

19–5. Triggering the silicon control rectifier

The silicon control rectifier is adaptable to many of the firing circuits used for the thyratron. In Fig. 19–15(a), a simple switching action is

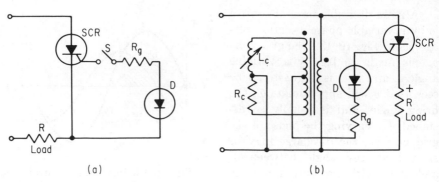

Fig. 19–15. Firing circuits for the SCR.

demonstrated, with gate circuit requirements taken from the a-c supply. If switch S is closed, the gate rectifier D will conduct when the upper lead is positive, thus triggering the SCR. At the instant the SCR conducts, its voltage drops to the low conduction value, and the gate current drops to essentially zero. Resistor R_g is present to limit the gate current, and its resistance is determined by E_m/I_g. The diode D prevents the inverse voltage from being applied between cathode and gate electrode on the inverse half cycle. Opening switch S will cause conduction to cease at the end of the next half cycle.

In Fig. 19–15(b) a phase-shift bridge, described in the next section, is adapted to the silicon control rectifier. In Fig. 19–16 appears a controlled bridge rectifier, with control pulses derived from a voltage-sensing circuit, which can shift the phase of the gating pulses as required to regulate the d-c output.

Transistor circuits have been developed to supply triggering wave forms for the silicon control rectifier, but an especially useful device for this purpose is the *unijunction switching transistor*. As in Fig. 19–17(a),

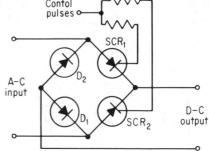

Fig. 19–16. Gated control rectifier.

the device is made on a slab of N silicon having two base contacts, and an alloyed P silicon emitter electrode. Between base B_1 and B_2 the material represents a resistance of a few thousand ohms. In operation, base B_2 will be positive with respect to base B_1, and some fraction η of the applied voltage V_{BB} will appear at the emitter. If the applied emitter potential V_E is less than V_{BB}, then the emitter will be reverse biased and only leakage current will flow. If V_E becomes greater than ηV_{BB}, the

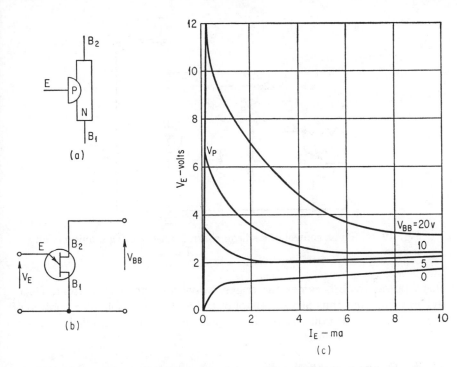

Fig. 19–17. The unijunction transistor: (a) construction; (b) circuit symbol; (c) characteristic curves.

junction becomes forward biased and a large emitter current flows with a low forward voltage drop between the emitter and B_1.

A family of volt-ampere curves is shown in Fig. 19–17(c), indicating large negative resistance regions well suited to fast switching action. The value of the peak voltage V_P can be computed from

$$V_P = \eta V_{BB} + 0.7$$

the 0.7 v factor being present as an approximation to the inherent emitter-base forward voltage drop. From the curves it can be seen that $\eta \cong 0.6$ for the measured unit.

The use of a unijunction transistor to develop a trigger input for a phase-controlled silicon control rectifier is schematically shown in Fig. 19–18. Diode D is incorporated to synchronize the gate signal with the rectifier anode voltage. When terminal A and the anode of SCR are positive, diode D blocks current and the transistor T is cut off. This allows capacitor C to charge through variable resistor R_x, introducing a time delay before the emitter of the unijunction transistor U reaches its voltage peak and triggers. The current through U to base 1 discharges C through R_2 in a

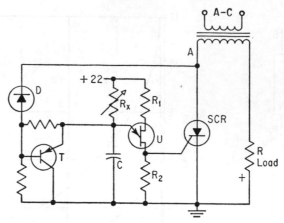

Fig. 19–18. Phase control of a silicon control rectifier using a unijunction trigger.

sharp pulse which becomes the trigger wave form for the rectifier. Delay in triggering, and thus phase control of the SCR, is possible by variation of the $R_x C$ time constant. These basic principles may be applied to many other control functions.

19–6. The phase-shift bridge

A variable phase, constant amplitude voltage is obtainable from the circuit of Fig. 19–19(a). Either Z_1 or Z_2 may be varied to shift the phase of the output, obtained between B and D. If A is in phase with the voltage at 1, then CA may be drawn as a phasor with B as the midpoint, as in Fig. 19–19(b). Voltage drops $IZ_1 = IR$ and $IZ_2 = IX_c$ must add to voltage CA, and must also be mutually at right angles so that the locus of D must be a semicircle with CA as the diameter. The phasor BD is

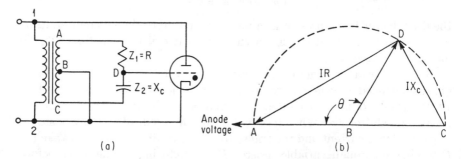

Fig. 19–19. (a) phase shift bridge; (b) circle diagram for phase-shift bridge.

then a variable-phase, constant-amplitude voltage, and the angle θ is its angle of lag behind the voltage at 1, which connects to the anode of the control rectifier.

The lag angle may be computed from the circuit constants and geometry as

$$\tan \theta/2 = \frac{Z_1}{Z_2} = \omega C R \qquad (19\text{–}7)$$

If R and X_c are interchanged, the circle of Fig. 19–19 would be thrown below the axis, making θ an angle of lead, and firing the tube for all values of angle.

Variable inductors may also be used, making Z_1 inductive and Z_2 resistive. The angle can then be obtained as before,

$$\tan \theta/2 = \frac{Z_1}{Z_2} = \frac{\omega L}{R} \qquad (19\text{–}8)$$

A saturable reactor is a convenient device for the variable inductor element of a phase-shift bridge, since the inductance may be varied by a small d-c current. The circuit appears in Fig. 19–20. Alternating current flows through coils 1 and 2 of the reactor, so connected that their a-c fluxes add in the outside core path and oppose in the center leg 3. Since these coils are on a closed iron core, their reactance is high and the phase angle will be that given with a high L value.

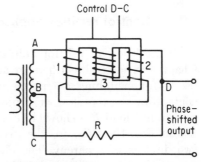

Fig. 19–20. Saturable reactor in phase-shift bridge.

As the controlling small direct current is supplied to coil 3, d-c fluxes are set up in the outer legs of the core. The operating point on the magnetization curve is moved toward the saturation region, or a point of lower slope on this curve. Since reactance is proportional to the slope of the magnetization curve, the reactance of the a-c coils is reduced by the direct current, and the phase of the bridge output will shift as the direct current is varied.

To distort the output wave to precise firing pulses, a saturated transformer is often inserted in the BD connection of the bridge. Such a transformer is operated in series with a resistor or designed for sufficient internal reactance to give an equivalent effect. A highly peaked magnetizing current is drawn, driving the iron into the saturation region. The peaked magnetizing current produces an IR drop in the series resistor, flattening the peak of the voltage wave applied to the transformer and giving a

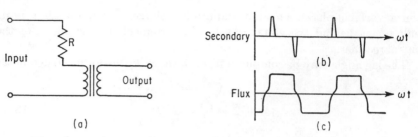

Fig. 19–21. Flux and secondary voltage of a saturating transformer.

primary flux wave as in Fig. 19–21(c). The flux changes appreciably only at the beginning and end of the half cycles, and the secondary emf consists of peaks occurring at each 180° of the cycle. Shifting of the phase of the primary voltage with the bridge causes these peaks to occur at any point in the cycle. The sharp peak of voltage produces precision firing of the control rectifier.

19–7. Control rectifier applications

In addition to use for voltage control of rectifiers in the circuits of Chapter 18, control rectifiers are adaptable to other services. One important use is for switching a-c power loads at high speeds, where mechanical contactors are too slow or subject to undue wear. A typical circuit for switching a load R is shown in Fig. 19–22(a) for the silicon control rectifier, and in Fig. 19–22(b) for the thyratron. The similarity of circuits for the two devices is apparent. The circuit is an *inverse-parallel* connection of two rectifiers, so that one handles each half wave, and alternating current is transmitted when the rectifiers are turned on by closure of switch S. Resistor R_g and the diodes provide protection of the gate electrode or the grid, as previously described. Switch S may be replaced with circuits deriving signals from light, voltage, current, temperature, or other inputs.

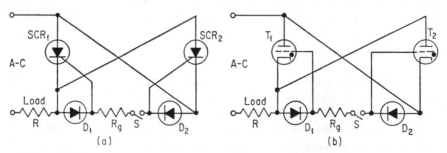

Fig. 19–22. A-c switch (a) using silicon control rectifiers; (b) with thyratrons.

A second form of switching circuit is shown in Fig. 19–23, as applied to thyratrons. Control of loads having a current rating greater than that of the control rectifier is then possible. The load is a welding transformer T_1, connected in series with a control transformer T_2 having a primary rated for line voltage and a step-up turns ratio such that with normal primary welding current, full-rated thyratron current will flow in the secondary. With rectifiers off, the reactance of the primary of T_2 as an unloaded transformer is high, and negligible voltage appears across T_1. When the control switch is closed, the thyratrons conduct, one on each half cycle, short-circuiting the series transformer and placing full voltage across the welding transformer. By arranging

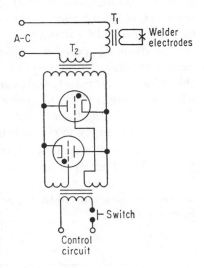

Fig. 19–23. Series transformer control of a welder.

the gate so that the control rectifiers may fire only on full half cycles, exact values of welding heat may be obtained with any total number of half-cycle intervals desired.

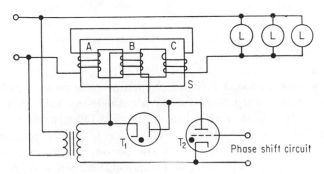

Fig. 19–24. Thyratron light-dimming circuit with saturable reactor.

The control rectifier has also been applied to supply the direct current for saturable reactors, to monitor heavy a-c loads, as in control of illumination or the temperature control of large electric furnaces. Such an application is shown for the thyratron in Fig. 19–24. The load current flows through coils A and C of the reactor, so arranged that their reactance is high with no direct current flowing, and the lamp brilliance is low. As the rectifier triggering voltage is made less lagging, direct current from

T_2 passes through coil B, tending to saturate the iron, and reducing the reactance of the a-c coils. If the control rectifier is turned full on, the lamp currents reach the rated value, and lamp brilliancy is normal.

The diode T_1 is used to approximate full-wave action without a second control rectifier. In each cycle, while the current in coil B is increasing, the anode of T_1 is maintained negative by the $L di/dt$ voltage of the reactor; when the current decreases, the sign of the inductive voltage reverses, and T_1 conducts during the negative half cycle when T_2 is inoperative, or until the magnetic energy in coil B is dissipated.

Control of alternating current with thyratrons and saturable reactors permits handling large amounts of a-c power with expenditure of only 1 or 2 per cent in the control circuit. Disadvantages are poor power factor of the a-c circuit at light loads and distortion of the a-c voltage wave form on the load.

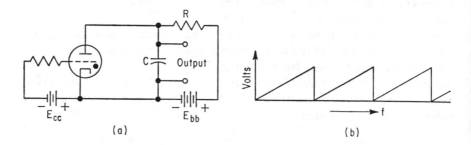

Fig. 19–25. Thyratron triggered sweep circuit.

In the wave-generating field for thyratrons, a common application is that of the simple sweep oscillator for a cathode-ray tube shown in Fig. 19–25. A thyratron is set with a bias so that it will fire at some low anode voltage that is also the voltage on capacitor C. The capacitor charges through a high resistance R from a d-c source, the voltage across the capacitor being given by the usual exponential. When e_c reaches the thyratron breakdown voltage, the tube fires and the capacitor discharges through the thyratron. When the voltage e_c falls below the arc-maintaining voltage, the thyratron ceases conduction because R is large and is unable to recharge the capacitor rapidly. The tube deionizes, the grid regains control, and the capacitor charges again until the action is repeated.

The charging voltage across the capacitor is suited to use as a time base for the cathode-ray oscillograph, under the limitations discussed in Chapter 16.

The unijunction transistor may also be employed in a sawtooth generator, as in Fig. 19–26. Frequency is determined by the C, R_2, R_3, combination, with Q_1 serving as the element to discharge the capacitor when its potential reaches the peak point voltage. Feedback is provided through R_1 and C_1, and integration through R_2, C_2, both serving to linearize the sweep. With high h_{fe} for T_1, the linearity can be within 0.3 per cent.

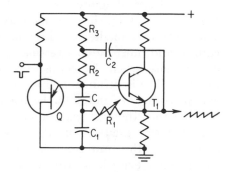

Fig. 19–26. Unijunction sawtooth generator.

19–8. The ignitron

A cathode spot can be initiated on a mercury-pool cathode by use of a semiconductor ignitor electrode. From this has developed the *ignitron* (ig-nī′tron) class of mercury-vapor tubes, suited to service requiring very high current ratings, and illustrated in Fig. 19–27.

Fig. 19–27. Cut-away view of an ignitron. (Courtesy of the General Electric Co.).

The electrical ignitor is shaped as in Fig. 19–28, and dips into the mercury pool. The starter is made of silicon or boron carbide and must be non-wetting, or form a meniscus when in contact with the mercury. The ignitron is fired by passing a current from the ignitor to the pool. It is believed that the first spark appears when the potential gradient in the gas layer surrounding the unwetted starter rod in the mercury exceeds a critical value. The small spark developed at the junction of the rod and mercury grows into a full cathode spot capable of emitting many amperes in only a few microseconds.

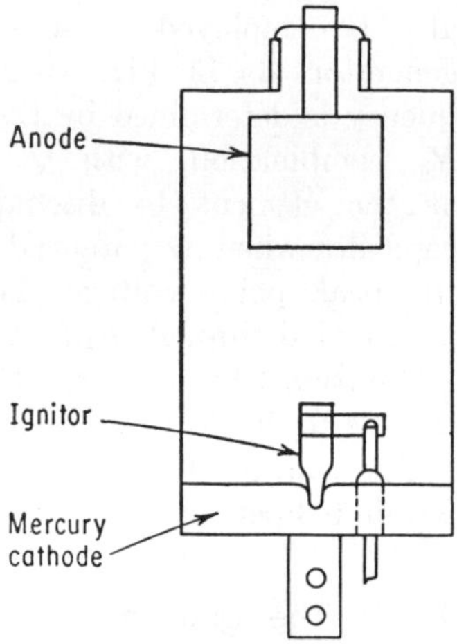

The current required to operate the ignitor may be 10 to 30 amp at 50 to 200 v. Although the instantaneous power is large, circuits are usually designed so

Fig. 19–28. Internal construction of an ignitron.

that the current flows for a very short interval, and the average power requirements are then small.

The cathode spot on a pool cathode may become unstable if the current falls below 3 amp. An auxiliary anode, supplied from a separate a-c source, is provided in many ignitrons to furnish a minimum load on the cathode spot.

19–9. Ignitron circuits

The ignitron has been developed for two main applications: as a synchronous a-c contactor in resistance welding and as a rectifier, using two types of ignitor firing circuits. Self-excitation is used in most welding applications, whereas separate excitation is preferred for rectifier service; both are shown in Fig. 19–29.

A diode is used in series with the ignitor to prevent damaging reverse currents in the ignitor on the negative half cycle. If it is desired to control the firing angle, the rectifier diode is changed to a thyratron which, by means of grid control, can fire the ignitron at the selected angle. The control circuit fires a thyratron T_2 or an SCR, usually through a saturating transformer from a phase-shift bridge. The triggering device conducts and passes its load current through the ignitor to the mercury-pool cathode. This fires the ignitron, and its cathode-anode voltage becomes the arc drop of 10 to 20 v. The arc-drop voltage is across the trigger and ignitor, and thus the thyratron fires the ignitron and is itself almost instantaneously

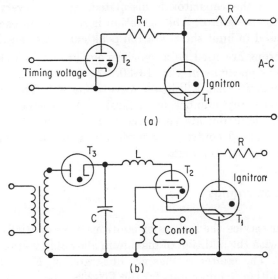

Fig. 19–29. (a) Self-excitation; (b) separate excitation.

extinguished. The ignitor current flows only long enough in each cycle for the ignition process to take place, usually less than 100 μsec, and the average ignitor power is low.

In Fig. 19–29(b), the capacitor C is charged by the rectifier T_3 during the half cycle in which the ignitron anode is negative. At the desired instant in the next half cycle, the thyratron grid is excited, usually by a pulse, and the capacitor discharges through thyratron T_2 and the ignitor, firing the ignitron. The thyratron and ignitor cease conduction as soon

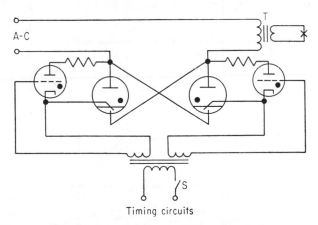

Fig. 19–30. Ignitron synchronous switch.

as the energy in the capacitor is dissipated, giving a very short, high current pulse to the ignitor. The operation is repeated in each cycle. The inductor L is used to limit the thyratron peak current to a safe value.

When ignitrons are used as a synchronous switch in welding service, the circuit may appear as in Fig. 19–30. The ignitrons are connected in parallel opposing, so that a full a-c wave is passed. The tubes may be controlled to pass any number of integral cycles desired. The circuit is also of use when ignitrons are employed to replace switches or contactors in duty such as *on-off* control of electric furnaces where maintenance of ordinary contactors is very high.

19–10. Ignitron ratings

For rectifier service the ratings of ignitrons are essentially the same as for gas diodes, with the addition of maximum allowable voltage and current for the ignitor. The ignitor ratings are illustrated in Fig. 19–31, a curve of minimum ignition requirements for the FG-238 tube.

When ignitrons are used in welding-contactor or other highly inter-mittent service, they are rated in terms of maximum average anode current and maximum a-c kilovolt-ampere demand, with the time of averaging the anode current specified. The kilovolt-ampere demand is determined by the rating of the load or welder controlled. The average current per

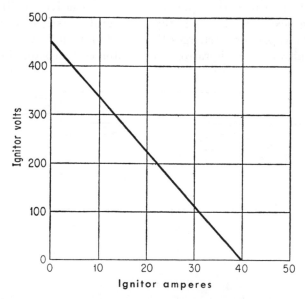

Fig. 19–31. Minimum ignitor requirements for the FG–238.

cycle can be calculated from the demand a-c kilovolt-amperes and the supply voltage:

$$I_{\text{line}} = \frac{\text{V.A.}}{E_{\text{line}}}; \quad \text{average tube current per cycle} = \frac{\sqrt{2}\, I_{\text{line}}}{\pi} \quad (19\text{–}9)$$

The rated ampere-second capacity of the tube is the rated average current, max $I_{\text{d–c}}$, times the averaging time, t_a, or

$$\text{rated ampere-seconds} = \max i_{\text{d–c}} t_a \quad (19\text{–}10)$$

The permitted time of conduction t_c for a particular load may then be found from

$$\max I_{\text{d–c}} t_a = \frac{\sqrt{2}\, I_{\text{line}}}{\pi} t_c$$

or

$$t_c = \frac{\pi \times \max I_{\text{d–c}} t_a}{\sqrt{2}\, I_{\text{line}}} \quad (19\text{–}11)$$

and the allowable duty in per cent is

$$\text{per cent duty} = \frac{t_c}{t_a} \times 100\% = \frac{\pi \times \max I_{\text{d–c}}}{\sqrt{2}\, I_{\text{line}}} \times 100\% \quad (15\text{–}12)$$

This determines the allowable percentage of *on* time during any given averaging period, to avoid tube overload and overheating.

19–11. Inverters

A circuit that will change direct current to alternating current is called an *inverter*. Inverter operation of gas control tubes is with d-c anode potential, and circuits must develop transients capable of driving the anode voltage to zero or negative values long enough for the space to deionize and allow the grid to regain control. A capacitor-and-resistor network may be used to set up the desired transient, as in Fig. 19–32. Suppose switch S_1 to be closed to start current flow in the thyratron, S_2 being open. The voltage drop across R_1 charges the capacitor C to a voltage equal to the d-c supply voltage minus the tube drop, and of polarity as indicated.

For illustration, assume the d-c supply to be 600 v and the tube drop 10 v; then, when the steady state is established, there will be 590 v across R_1 and 590 v across C, since no current will flow in R_2. The left plate Y of the capacitor C is then 590 v negative with respect to the right plate X. If switch S_2 is closed and S_1 opened, the potential of plate X is changed

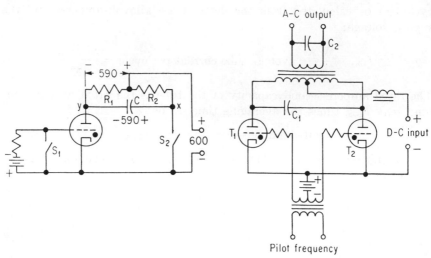

Fig. 19–32. Switching a thyratron with d-c anode potential.

Fig. 19–33. Separately excited parallel inverter.

from +600 v to zero instantaneously. The potential on C cannot change instantaneously, so that plate Y must still be 590 v negative with respect to plate X. Plate X is at zero, however, so that plate Y and the anode must instantaneously be at -590 v. Since a finite time is required for the potential of the left plate Y to become positive, the anode may be negative a sufficient time to deionize the space and allow the grid to regain control.

The parallel inverter, as drawn in Fig. 19–33, replaces switch S_2 with another thyratron. If T_1 is turned on by a positive grid pulse, capacitor C_1 charges, and current proceeds through the transformer to T_1. The grid of T_2 is negative; but on the next half cycle the pilot frequency fires T_2 and lowers the right end of C_1 to near zero potential, driving T_1 off. The transient currents in the output transformer alternate, inducing an a-c wave in the secondary. Capacitor C_2 is present to smooth the output wave to near sinusoidal shape.

A valuable form of d-c to a-c or d-c to d-c inverter or voltage changer is shown in Fig. 19–34, employing switching transistors. The circuit is a feedback oscillator, operating at a medium frequency dependent on coils 1 and 3, the maximum flux density, and V_{CC}. Low-voltage d-c, as from a storage battery, is supplied to the transistors, and feedback is provided by coils 1 and 4. Output is taken from 5 as a-c, or may be rectified for d-c output at the desired voltage.

The transistors operate from cut off, with a positive bias voltage, to saturation with negative base and almost the entire V_{CC} voltage appearing across the inductive load, usually less than 0.5 v being across the collector-

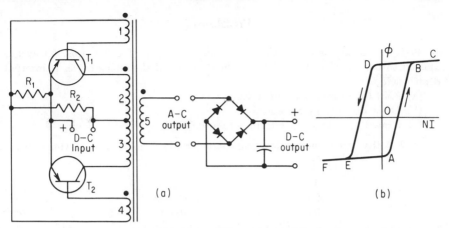

Fig. 19–34. Transistor d-c inverter.

emitter circuit of the transistor. The power dissipated is small in saturation, and while appreciable instantaneous power may be expended in the transistor during the switching interval, the switching time is so short that there is low average dissipation, and efficiencies exceed 90 per cent.

To consider the operation, let the core flux be at A on the hysteresis loop for the iron in Fig. 19–34(b), with the current in T_1 exceeding that in T_2. The flux will then begin to change toward B, inducing voltages in coils 1 and 4 which make the base of T_1 negative and that of T_2 positive, as indicated by the polarity dots. Then T_1 saturates and T_2 cuts off. The flux in the core continues toward positive saturation, almost the entire d-c supply voltage appearing across coil 2. At B, the rate of change of flux decreases, the voltage on T_1 rises and the increased current drives the core to C. However, $d\varphi/dt$ has fallen, the voltage in coil 1 drops, transistor T_1 goes toward cut off, taking the operating point on the hysteresis loop toward zero NI near D. This change in flux induces an opposite voltage in coils 1 and 4, cutting off T_1 and making the base of T_2 negative and T_2 conducts. There is current in coil 3 and the core flux begins to build toward negative saturation at E. When this point is reached, the induced voltages again reverse and the switching process repeats.

The secondary a-c output is of square form, since the cycle time is largely occupied in flux change from A to B, or D to E on the flux loop, switching time of the wave being small. Thus the output is easily rectified and filtered if d-c is desired. It is found that the frequency of switching is given by

$$f \cong \frac{V_{CC}}{4N_2\varphi_m}$$

where N_2 is the number of turns on coils 2 or 3.

Problems

19-1. A silicon control rectifier with anode supply of 200 v rms, 60 cycles, applied through a 100-ohm resistor, is fired at 60° of the anode cycle. If internal drop is zero,

(a) Find the average current flowing.
(b) Draw the current wave form.
(c) Draw the voltage wave form across the SCR.

19-2. A thyratron has a critical grid characteristic given by the following data:

E_b (v)	E_c (v)		E_b (v)	E_c (v)
500	+4		3,800	−3
1000	+2		6,400	−4
1800	0		10,000	−5

(a) Plot the critical grid characteristic.

(b) Plot the critical grid locus as a function of time for an anode voltage of 600 v rms, showing also the anode voltage to a different scale.

(c) Graphically determine the time of firing if a grid voltage of 10 v rms lagging 90° is used.

19-3. The drop in a control rectifier is zero. If the anode supply is 120 v rms and the load a resistance of 10 ohms, find:

(a) The average current when the diode fires at 135°.
(b) The average current when the diode fires at 0°.

19-4. A thyratron is rated at 75 amp peak, 12.5 amp average. What is the greatest possible delay in the firing angle, if direct current is at rated value?

19-5. Find the needed value of series resistor to limit the average current to 0.6 amp, if 120 v rms is applied to an SCR, with firing angle at 75° of the anode cycle.

19-6. (a) Using the characteristics of the FG-27A thyratron in Fig. 19–2, at 50°C condensed mercury temperature, for what percentage of the time of a cycle will current flow through such a tube if it is operated at 500 peak sinusoidal anode volts and grid volts of −4? Assume that tube drop is 15 v.

(b) With the 15-v tube drop, what value of direct current will flow through a 250-ohm load resistor in the anode circuit?

(c) What is the power loss in the anode in part (b)?

19-7. A certain 30-kw, 300-v rectifier may operate at 20 per cent load for 14 hr and at 75 per cent load for 10 hr each day. Three thyratrons to handle the load have heaters taking 5 v, 20 amp each, and tube drops at all currents of 12 v. Three ignitrons capable of handling the load have tube drops of 20 v each with negligible ignitor losses. The circuit is three-phase half-wave.

(a) If power costs 2 cents a kilowatt-hour, which type of tube will be the cheapest to operate in this rectifier over the time of one year?

(b) How much is the saving?

19-8. A thyratron is rated 12.5 amp average anode current, 75 amp peak, and 10,000 v peak inverse voltage. The time of averaging current is 30 sec. A certain application is operated on 20 sec and off 10 sec.

(a) Using the circuit of Fig. 19–23, with a supply a-c voltage of 440 v rms, and assuming that full line voltage is across the primary of T_2 during the off period, find the maximum kilovolt-ampere welder rating which can be controlled without exceeding any tube rating.

(b) What rating in volts and kilovolt-amperes should the series transformer T_2 have, assuming its primary is wound for 550-v service?

19-9. Two ignitrons are used in the circuit of Fig. 19–30 to supply a resistance-welder load demand of 500 kva at 250 v rms, 60 cycles. The tubes to be used are rated at 40 amp average current each, with an averaging time of 20 sec.

(a) Find the total number of cycles of conduction time permissible in any averaging period.

(b) How much would the average current rating of an ignitron have to be increased to permit two *on* periods of 5 sec each in any averaging period?

(c) If the tube voltage drop is taken as 16 v and cooling water at 15°C is supplied to each tube at the rate of 2 gpm, what temperature rise will occur in the water for continued operation under (a), above? Tubes may be considered as firing at 0° of the cycle.

19-10. A spot welder is rated at 300 kva, 440 v single phase, 60 cycles. An ignitron contactor for this welder has a duty cycle of four 12-cycle *on* periods, separated by 20-cycle *off* periods, ending with a 72-cycle rest period. Total time of the duty cycle is 180 cycles, or 3 sec.

(a) What must be the average current rating of the two tubes in the contactor, if they are rated for a 5-sec averaging period?

(b) What should be the maximum average current rating of each tube?

References

1. Aldrich, R. W., and Holonyak, N., "Multiterminal *PNPN* Switches," *Proc. I.R.E.*, **46,** 1236 (1958).

2. Hull, A. W., "Gas-Filled Thermionic Tubes," *Trans. A.I.E.E.*, **47,** 753 (1928).

3. ——., "Hot Cathode Thyratrons," *G. E. Rev.*, **32,** 213, 390 (1929).

4. Mackintosh, I. M., "The Electrical Characteristics of Silicon *PNPN* Triodes," *Proc. I.R.E.*, **46,** 1229 (1958).

5. Moll, J. L., Tanenbaum, M., and Holonyak, N., "*PNPN* Transistor Switches," *Proc. I.R.E.*, **44,** 1174 (1956).

6. Schmidt, P. L., "Voltage Conversion with Transistor Switches," *Bell Lab. Record,* **36,** (1958).

7. Shea, R. F., *Principles of Transistor Circuits.* John Wiley and Sons, Inc., New York, 1953.

8. Slepian, J., and Ludwig, L. R., "A New Method of Initiating the Cathode of an Arc," *Trans. A.I.E.E.*, **52,** 693 (1933).

Light-Sensitive Devices | 20

The first photosensitive cells employed selenium, which varied in resistance with light or was photoconductive. There followed cells employing electron emission, and we have now returned again to semiconductive devices with their advantages of size and sensitivity. Applications in counting, control of position, printing registration, television, and color measurement are now common.

20–1. Photo-sensitive device classification

All photo-sensitive devices convert light or radiant energy into electrical energy. Various methods of conversion are employed and the cell types are classified accordingly.

Photoemissive cells. In photoemissive cells the energy of the light beam causes emission of electrons from a metal surface enclosed in an evacuated or gas-filled glass bulb, or quartz for ultraviolet light transmission.

Photovoltaic cells. In the photovoltaic cell the radiant energy causes generation of an emf. The current resulting may be made proportional to the radiant energy. These cells consist of oxides or semiconducting layers on metal base plates, and need not be evacuated.

Photoconductive cells. These cells vary their electrical resistance in accordance with the radiant energy received. Formerly made of selenium deposited on a glass plate, modern forms employ a semiconductor junction.

Photoemissive and photovoltaic cells are also classified as high and low impedance, respectively. The difference in internal impedance restricts the choice of instruments and circuits employed with them.

20–2. Sensitivity definitions

The sensitivity of a photoelectric cell is stated in terms of current per unit of radiant power striking the cell surface. This is usually given in terms of microamperes per microwatt of incident power at a certain specified color or wave length of light. The latter specification must be added because of the changes in emission efficiency at different wave lengths of incident light. The standard source is frequently a tungsten-filament lamp operating at a temperature such that its spectrum of radiant energy is that of a black body operating at 2870°K. The relative distribution of energy at different wave lengths for a tungsten filament operating at this *color temperature* is shown in Fig. 20–1. For a photocell having most of its sensitive region in the visible or ultraviolet, sensitivity would mean little without such an exact specification of a standard source.

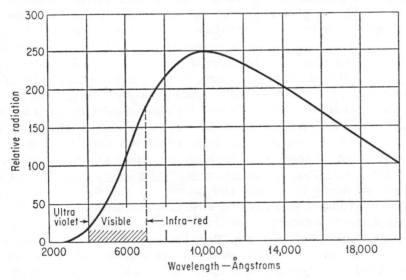

Fig. 20–1. Relative radiation from tungsten at a color temperature of 2870°K.

Sensitivity may also be stated in terms of visible light only, when it is called *luminous sensitivity* and is stated in terms of microamperes per lumen of incident light. The *lumen* is a measure of the *visible stimulus* given to the human eye by the incident radiation. Because of the color selectivity of photosensitive surfaces, specification of luminous sensitivity should be accompanied by a statement of the source used.

To convert the candle power rating of a point source to lumens, the following relation may be used:

$$L = \frac{CA}{d^2} \tag{20-1}$$

where L is the intensity in lumens on A sq ft from a point source of candle power C at a distance of d ft.

20-3. Photoemissive cathodes

From the Einstein equation for photoelectric emission,

$$hf = eE_w + \frac{mv^2}{2} \tag{20-2}$$

it might be assumed that the value of the emitted current would depend on the number of photons striking the surface per second. For constant total energy per unit area of surface, the number of photons decreases linearly with increase in frequency, since the energy per photon increases. Actually, no surface emits numbers of electrons varying in this manner, and variation with frequency approaches the threshold asymptotically, not abruptly. The reason for these variations is as yet unexplained.

The most common materials used for photoemissive cathodes are the alkali metals because their threshold frequencies lie in, or at frequencies below, the visible spectrum. The preparation of surfaces of these materials usually involves evaporation of the metal in vacuum to produce condensation of the very thin, usually monatomic, film on the cathode. Cesium, potassium, rubidium, sodium, and lithium, in combination with either oxygen or hydrogen, are frequently used. Choice of material makes possible phototubes with a variety of spectral sensitivity responses, and curves for typical surfaces are given in Fig. 20-2. The S-2 surface is a cesium-cesium oxide surface with reasonable sensitivity throughout the visible region (4000-7000 Å). A comparison of the S-2 curve with that of the radiation from a tungsten filament at 2870°K is given, and it can be seen that the S-2 surface is well adapted for use with a tungsten source. The S-3 surface employs rubidium, with its greatest sensitivity in the blue end of the spectrum. The S-4 surface of cesium is highly sensitive, having a peak response 20 times greater than the peak of the S-3 surface. The peak occurs at 3750 Å, in the near ultraviolet, making such a surface useful for measurements with blue light sources. In application, it is important to select a cell having a high response in the spectral region in which the source has high output. The S-4 surface would be of little use with a tungsten-filament source, for example.

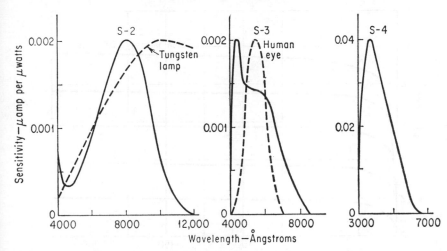

Fig. 20–2. Color sensitivity of several photoemissive surfaces.

20–4. The vacuum photoemissive cell

A photoemissive cell consists of a light-sensitive cathode, and an anode to collect the emitted electrons. The anode may be a wire so mounted as to not cast a shadow on the cathode. The whole is assembled in a glass or quartz bulb, as in Fig. 20–3.

With light of appropriate color striking the cathode, a small voltage causes a small current. As the voltage is increased, the current rises rapidly, but is limited by space charge at very small anode potentials. Further increase in potential causes the value of current obtained to level off, as is shown in Fig. 20–4. This indicates saturation, or that all the electrons emitted are being attracted to the anode. For a

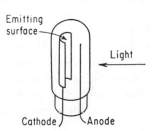

Fig. 20–3. Photoemissive cell.

higher light intensity, saturation occurs at a higher current. Owing to saturation, the current is almost entirely independent of the applied emf above values of 20 v. The very slight slope of the characteristic curves is due to the Schottky effect, which reduces the work function at higher potentials. The output current of a vacuum photocell, operated in the saturation region, is linear with light intensity, and this confirms the Einstein equation.

The slope of the volt-ampere curve is the conductance of the photocell. The low slope indicates that the vacuum cell has a very low conductance or a very high resistance of hundreds of megohms. The parallel form of

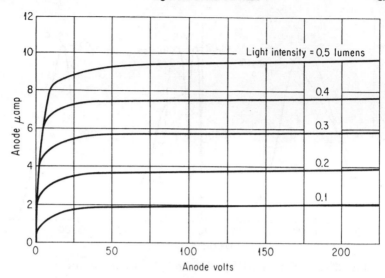

Fig. 20–4. Plate characteristics of 922 photoemissive cell.

equivalent circuit may be applied for the cell, the value of internal resistance being so large with respect to any practical load that the internal resistance may be neglected. Consequently, the equivalent circuit is that of a constant-current generator connected to a load resistor.

It would seem that a larger load should result in a higher output voltage, but indefinite increase of the load resistor becomes impractical owing to leakage currents. If a load of hundreds of megohms were used, it would be found that the leakage-current paths in parallel with the load, over the phototube surface and insulation, would reduce the effective load resistance to a much lower value. In practice the upper limit for the load resistance is usually considered 10 to 20 megohms.

20–5. The gas-filled photoemissive cell

By introduction of a small amount of argon or other gas into a photoemissive tube, a considerable increase in current output can be achieved. The emitted electrons, in moving to the anode, collide with gas atoms and produce ionization. The electrons freed from the atoms join in the electron flow to the anode, and the positive ions may add to the emitted current by causing secondary emission from the cathode surface. In this manner the anode current may be increased four to seven times over that in an equivalent vacuum cell, and this increase in current is called the *gas amplification factor*. Attempts to increase this factor above about 10 usually result in excessive bombardment of the cathode by the positive ions and damage to the surface. Such damage is prevented by operation of gas cells below about 90 v.

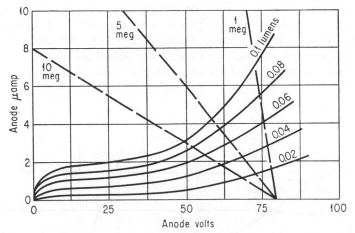

Fig. 20–5. Plate characteristics for 921 gas photoemissive cell.

Volt-ampere characteristics of a gas-filled photocell are drawn in Fig. 20–5. The curves are of the same shape as for the vacuum cell up to the ionization potential of the gas at about 20 v. The current for the gas tube then rises, owing to the electrons added by ionization and secondary emission. For all anode potentials above 20 v, the gas-filled cell is seen to have a sensitivity exceeding that of the vacuum cell. Since the cells of Figs. 20–4 and 20–5 are identical in type of surface and cathode area of 0.4 sq in., the gas-amplification factor at any desired voltage may be computed. For 75 v and 0.1 lumen per square foot applied to the cell, the gas amplification can be obtained as 4.2.

The variable spacing of the volt-ampere curves shows that the current output of the cell is not linear with light intensity. This is a disadvantage of the gas-filled cell, although it is not serious for small variations in light intensity. An additional difficulty encountered when the gas cell is used in sound reproduction is a loss of sensitivity for high-frequency light variations. This loss is due to the time lag between a change in light intensity and the corresponding change in current, caused by the slow speeds of the positive ions.

20–6. Calculation of output

A load line for the load-circuit equation

$$i_b = \frac{E_{bb}}{R_L} - \frac{e_b}{R_L} \qquad (20\text{–}3)$$

may be drawn on the volt-ampere characteristics of a photocell, as was done for the diode and triode. When drawn through the intercept $e_b = E_{bb}$

and with slope of $-1/R_L$, it allows prediction of performance of the photocell with a load R_L. Figure 20–6(a) shows load lines for 5 and 20 megohms drawn on the volt-ampere characteristics of the Type 922 cell for $E_{bb} = 200$ v. The current in the load for a particular light flux input can be found from the intersection of the load line with the volt-ampere curve for that light input.

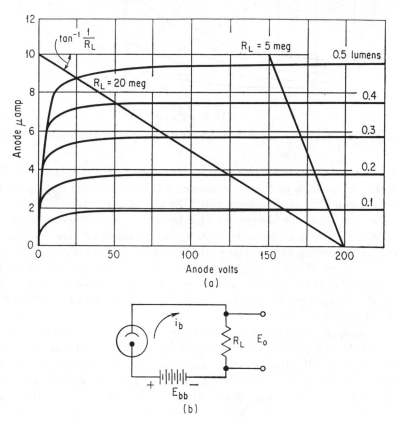

Fig. 20–6. (a) Use of load line; (b) photoemissive cell circuit.

Sinusoidal or other variations of intensity from a quiescent value can be analyzed by considering the quiescent light value as fixing a Q point. For instance, with the cell of Fig. 20–6, with 20-megohm load and a Q point at 0.3 lumen per square foot, a sinusoidal variation with peak-to-peak light variation of 0.2 lumen will produce 95 v peak-to-peak across the load.

The load-line method is also applicable to the gas-filled cell.

20–7. Photoemissive cell applications

The photoemissive cell, either gas or vacuum, has a high internal resistance and provides a high voltage and low current output. This property makes it unsuited to the direct operation of circuits of low impedance, but since the grid circuit of a vacuum tube is of high impedance, the vacuum-tube amplifier is a satisfactory relay and impedance reducer for the photocell.

A typical combination is shown in Fig. 20–7. Choice of R_L for such a circuit may be limited somewhat by grid current produced by stray electrons in the triode. Medium-μ triodes are the most satisfactory and permit grid resistors as high as 10 to 15 megohms. The potentiometer in the grid circuit may be used to adjust the plate current to a minimum, with zero light. Then, when light strikes the cell, the grid of the triode becomes positive owing to the drop across R_L. As a result of the change in the grid bias, the plate current increases and operates the relay. For applications in which the light is modulated, the relay may be replaced by a conventional RC-coupled a-c amplifier.

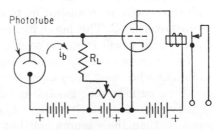

Fig. 20–7. Circuit of photoelectric relay.

A circuit of high sensitivity is shown in Fig. 20–8(a), and utilizes two photocells so that one becomes the load for the other. The curve for T_1 in (b) is that of the usual vacuum photocell for some particular light intensity. The load is T_2; and although it does not have a linear volt-ampere characteristic as a resistor, it has a volt-ampere curve like T_1 (at equal light intensities), and this curve is drawn in (b) in exactly the manner a normal linear load line would be drawn. With the indicated load line the operating point is at A, where the two solid curves intersect.

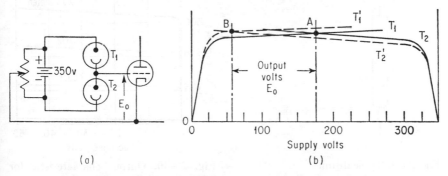

Fig. 20–8. (a) Highly sensitive circuit; (b) load lines for (a).

If the light beam is arranged to shift in such a way that an increase on T_1 causes a decrease on T_2, then after a small change of light intensity in this manner the two cells will have characteristics given by the dashed curves for T'_1 and T'_2. The point of intersection and operation is now at B, giving an output voltage change of 118 v. This is much larger than could be obtained across any reasonable value of external resistance load for a similar change in light intensity.

All types of photoemissive cells, except those having S-4 surfaces, are limited in operating temperature to about 100°C. The S-4 surface must not be used over 50°C. This figure includes any temperature rise of the cathode due to radiant heat from the source.

The vacuum cell is linear with light and independent of applied voltage variations when used at voltages over 20. It is relatively stable in sensitivity over long periods. The gas cell is less linear, less stable, and is dependent of the value of applied voltage. The gas cell is four to seven times more sensitive than the vacuum cell but cannot be used at full sensitivity at frequencies above 2000 cycles. The decision as to which cell should be used, therefore, hinges largely on the sensitivity required, at least for the lower frequencies.

20–8. Photodiodes and phototransistors

Semiconductor units in which light falls upon a back-biased PN junction also have photoelectric properties. The light falling on the junction creates electron-hole pairs which are then swept out by the applied potentials as a photocurrent. Such a unit is illustrated in Fig. 20–9, with performance given in Fig. 20–10, as a function of polarizing voltage. Good linearity with light is obtained. The cell has excellent infrared sensitivity, with the threshold at about 17,000 Angstroms.

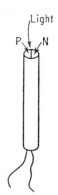

Fig. 20–9. Typical junction photodiode.

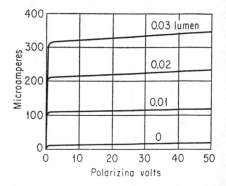

Fig. 20–10. Output characteristic for 7223 photodiode.

It is to be expected that some electrons from the impurity atoms would exist in the conduction band at normal temperatures, and in darkness.

These have been raised to the conduction band from donor impurities by thermal energies, and produce conductivity in the dark or "dark current." If there is a high impurity percentage, the dark current may be so large as to mask the photocurrent.

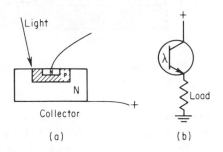

Semiconductor elements of transistor form logically follow from the above photodiode; the combination adds transistor gain to the diode, and is shown in Fig. 20–11. The collector

Fig. 20–11. (a) Phototransistor; (b) Circuit and symbol.

is normally back-biased, and radiation on the emitter-base junction injects carriers into the base, setting up the usual transistor action. Spectral response and collector characteristics appear in Fig. 20–12.

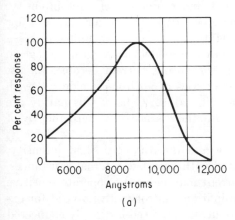

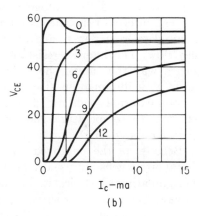

Fig. 20–12. (a) Frequency response of LS–400 phototransistor; (b) collector characteristics; light radiation as mw/cm^2.

20–9. Photovoltaic cells

The mechanism discussed in Section 20–8 is also found to explain the *generation of an emf* under the illumination of a barrier layer. By reason of reception of light energy, electrons may be raised to the conduction band, and when the semiconductor is placed in contact with a metal, these high-energy electrons flow over into the metal from the semiconductor. A reverse flow from the metal is prevented by the surface barrier set up in

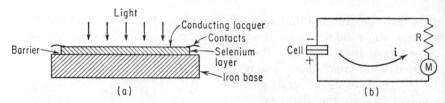

Fig. 20–13. (a) Photovoltaic iron-selenide cell; (b) circuit for measurement of light flux.

the semiconductor. As long as the illumination *exists* there is a supply of electrons and the current into the metal continues.

Two types of self-generating, or *photovoltaic* cells using the barrier layer principle are the copper-copper oxide and the iron-selenium cells. The iron-selenium cell consists of an iron base plate, covered by a thin film of iron selenide. This arrangement is diagrammed in Fig. 20–13. At Fig. 20–13(b) is shown the operating circuit of the cell. The copper-copper oxide cell is similar.

The voltage generated is of the order of a few hundred millivolts in bright light, and the voltage is not a linear function of light intensity. The cell internal resistance is found to be small, so that currents of a few hundred microamperes—and in sunlight currents of a few milliamperes—may flow. The internal resistance varies proportionately with voltage in such a way that under short circuit the output current becomes almost linear with illumination. The characteristics of an iron-selenide cell with various external loads are shown in Fig. 20–14. Cells of this nature are sensitive to temperature and will lose their sensitivity permanently if operated above 55°C.

Because of the improved stability and linearity with light intensity, photovoltaic cells are usually operated with very low external resistances, approximating short circuit. The current may be used to operate sensitive relays directly, forming simple illumination controls with no need for external voltage sources. In another application the cell is directly connected to a low-resistance portable microammeter, calibrated directly in light intensity, to make a photographic exposure meter.

The semiconductor film between the electrodes is quite thin, and the internal capacity of photovoltaic cells is high. This capacity appears in shunt with the cell, and short-circuits alternating current developed by the use of modulated light. Even at a 60-cycle frequency the response is less than one-half the output for a steady light source.

Photovoltaic cells may be connected in parallel to increase the current output when working into low-resistance loads, and in series when working into high-resistance loads. The short-circuit current is approximately proportional to the area of surface exposed to the light.

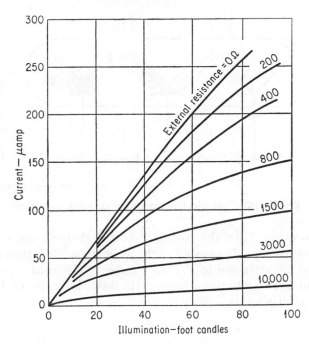

Fig. 20–14. Current vs illumination for photovoltaic cell. Area $= 1.1$ in^2.

20–10. Electron multipliers

The currents expected in photoemissive cells under low light conditions are extremely small, and difficult of amplification. The amplification problem has been overcome by application of principles of secondary emission in a device known as the *secondary-emission multiplier*.

If the secondary-emission coefficient is greater than unity, it is possible to achieve amplification of the original beam current, or *multiplication* of the electrons. For example, if on the average the secondary-emission coefficient is 5, or each primary electron releases 5 secondaries, then if a beam current of 1 μamp strikes the surface, a current of 5 μamp may be attracted from the surface as secondary electrons. The original input electron current may originate from any source, but usually it will be a photoelectric current. The design of a tube to use this amplification may take the form of a multistage multiplier, with the total amplification due to a number of surfaces in cascade.

Figure 20–15 shows the basic design of all multistage multipliers, in which a series of electrodes, all treated with secondary-emitting materials, are operated at successively higher positive potentials. For each electron leaving the source S, δ electrons are emitted from target T_1. These are

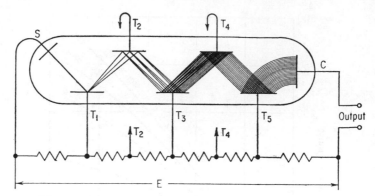

Fig 20–15. Photoelectric secondary emission multiplier.

attracted to target T_2 by the positive potential thereon, and since each of the electrons reaching T_2 causes δ electrons to be emitted, then δ^2 electrons leave T_2 and are attracted to T_3. The number of electrons leaving T_3 is δ^3, and the number of electrons leaving the nth electrode, or the current gain of the multiplier, is

$$\text{gain} = \delta^n \qquad\qquad (20\text{--}4)$$

where n is the number of electrodes on which secondary emission is employed. With δ frequently in the range of 9 to 10, and as many as 10 stages used, gains of several million are possible in a single tube.

Although in theory the multiplier of Fig. 20–15 would operate satisfactorily, actually many electrons would pass straight down the tube under the attraction of the potential on the collector C, reducing the gain. As a result, development has been directed to multipliers in which the electrons are focused successively on one target after another, thus preventing spreading of the beam. The targets, called *dynodes*, are so shaped as to provide electric fields which give a focusing effect for electrons proceeding from one target to the next.

Problems

20-1. Plot a current-vs.-illumination characteristic for the 921 photocell of Fig. 20–5 with a load of 1 megohm if the voltage supply is 80 v.

20-2. A photocell receives a change in intensity from 0.12 to 0.32 lumen per sq ft. If the tube is a 922 of Fig. 20–4, and has a load of 10 megohms and applied voltage of 150, find the change in voltage across the load.

20-3. An illumination control for a schoolroom employs the circuit of Fig. 20–7 with a 922 photocell and a 6J5 tube. The photocell operates at 150 v with $R_L = 3$ megohms; the 6J5 tube has the grid bias adjusted for a plate current of 0.2 ma at $E_{bb} = 250$ v, with the resistance of the relay being 10,000 ohms. If the relay opens its contacts and turns off certain lamps at 4 ma coil current and closes the contacts at 1.8 ma, find the limits between which the room illumination will be allowed to vary. (*Hint*: the 922 cell is linear, so its characteristics may be interpolated.)

20-4. (a) A 922 cell is used with a 10-megohm load and applied voltage of 100. Light striking the photocell changes sinusoidally from 0.07 to 0.11 lumen per sq ft. What is the rms voltage across the load?

(b) If this voltage is now applied to the grid of a 6J5 triode with $\mu = 20$, $r_p = 10,000$, and load of 12,000 ohms, what rms voltage will be developed across the load?

20-5. Draw the circuit and discuss the changes needed in the circuit of Fig. 20-7 to make the relay open its contact for minimum light and close for maximum light. Describe the adjustment of the slider on the bias-control potentiometer.

20-6. A tetrode having g_m of 1500 μmho is followed by four stages of current multiplication having $\delta = 3.4$. Find the output-current change expected because of a 1-v rms signal on the tetrode grid.

20-7. A conventional photocell produces a change in output of 1 μa for a given change in light intensity. If a nine-stage multiplier having $\delta = 8$ follows this photocell, what is the change in output current of the multiplier?

20-8. A 50-cp lamp is used as a point source for a 921 cell in a circuit with a 5-megohm load and 80 v applied. How far away can the source be and still produce a current of 4 μa in the load? The area of the cell surface is 0.4 sq in.

20-9. For the photodiode of Fig. 20-10, determine the load which will give maximum power output.

20-10. An 8000-ohm relay is used with the phototransistor of Fig. 20-12. It drops out at 1 ma and picks up at 3 ma. If 40 v is applied, find the light levels at which the relay will operate.

References

1. Bartlett, C. H., "Comparative Characteristics of the Copper Oxide and Photronic Cells," *Rev. Sci. Instruments*, **3,** 543 (1932).

2. Goodwin, W. N., Jr., "The Photronic Photographic Exposure Meter," *Jour. S.M.P.T.E.*, **20,** 95 (1933).

3. Metcalf, G. F., "Operating Characteristics of Photoelectric Tubes," *Proc. I.R.E.*, **17,** 2064 (1929).

4. Pierce, J. R., "Electron-Multiplier Design," *Bell Lab. Record*, **16,** 305 (1938).

5. Sawyer, D. E., and Rediker, R. H., "Narrow Base Germanium Photodiodes," *Proc. I.R.E.*, **46,** 1122 (1958).

6. Shepard, F. H., "Some Unconventional Vacuum Tube Applications," *R. C. A. Rev.* **2,** 149 (1937).

7. Zworykin, V. K., Morton, G. A., and Malter, L., "The Secondary-Emission Multiplier," *Proc. I.R.E.*, **24,** 351 (1936).

Microwave Devices 21

The triode vacuum tube is inherently limited in upper frequency by the transit time of an electron between cathode and anode, and when this time becomes an appreciable part of a cycle, the possible gain becomes small.

Various efforts have lead to a series of devices which overcome the transit-time limitation, and to other totally new forms using solid-state and quantum techniques, by which the frequency spectrum of electrical wave generation has now been expanded into the optical region.

This chapter will present material on the present state of the art in these devices.

21–1. Velocity modulation of an electron beam

In the first major step beyond the triode, the time of transit was utilized to allow electrons with cyclically varying velocities to catch up with preceding slower electrons, or to form *bunches*. These bunches then excited an output circuit as pulses of current. This principle has become known as *velocity modulation*, and the device as the *klystron*.

The general arrangement of a klystron is shown in Fig. 21–1, with a beam of electrons from the cathode passing through holes in the *buncher* into a drift region of length L, relatively free of electric fields. The beam then passes through a *catcher* to reach a positive collector. The beam is assumed to remain well focussed, or the mutual repulsion between electrons is here neglected.

The buncher and catcher are resonant cavities which will sustain an alternating electric field between their left and right faces in the figure, and have properties similar to a parallel resonant circuit at a wave length

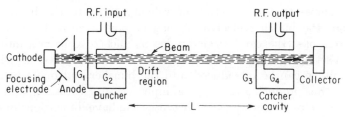

Fig. 21–1. Two cavity klystron amplifier.

commensurate with their mechanical dimensions. The cyclic voltage existing between the G_1 and G_2 electrodes in the first cavity gives the electrons a small cyclic velocity variation

$$v = v_o(1 + \alpha \sin \omega t)$$

as they leave G_2. If the current passing through G_2 is i_1, then the charge entering the drift space in an increment of time dt is $i_1 dt$. Since there can be no accumulation of charge in the drift region, this same charge will pass through electrodes G_3 and G_4 of the catcher cavity at some later time increment $d(t + t_d)$, where t_d is the time of transit in the drift space. If the outward current is i_2, then by necessity

$$i_1 dt = i_2 \, d(t + t_d) \qquad (21\text{–}1)$$

The time of transit t_d can be obtained as

$$t_d = \frac{L}{v} = \frac{L}{v_o(1 + \alpha \sin \omega t)}$$

If $\alpha \ll 1$, then

$$\frac{1}{1 + \alpha \sin \omega t} \cong 1 - \alpha \sin \omega t$$

so that

$$t_d \cong \frac{L}{v_o} (1 - \alpha \sin \omega t) \qquad (21\text{–}2)$$

Rewriting Eq. 21–1

$$i_1 \cong i_2 \frac{d\left[t + \dfrac{L}{v_o} (1 - \alpha \sin \omega t)\right]}{dt} \cong i_2 \left(1 - \frac{L\alpha\omega}{v_o} \cos \omega t\right) \qquad (21\text{–}3)$$

If the tube is designed such that $(L\alpha\omega/v_o) \ll 1$, then

$$i_2 \cong i_1 \left(1 + \frac{L\alpha\omega}{v_o} \cos \omega t\right) \qquad (21\text{–}4)$$

which shows that a variation of velocity given to the beam in passing
through the buncher electrodes, has become a current variation as the
electrons pass the catcher electrodes G_3 and G_4. Currents induced in G_3
and G_4 set up voltages and fields in the catcher cavity. By proper feedback
this voltage can be introduced into the buncher and made to excite that
cavity, thus producing the original input-velocity variation, and the device
becomes an oscillator. Since the cavities can have dimensions of centimeter
order, the klystron frequency range is capable of being carried down to
such wave lengths.

Figure 21–2 further illustrates the action, if the slopes of the electron
paths in the drift space are considered as representing the individual
velocities contributed by the indicated voltage wave across the buncher
electrodes.

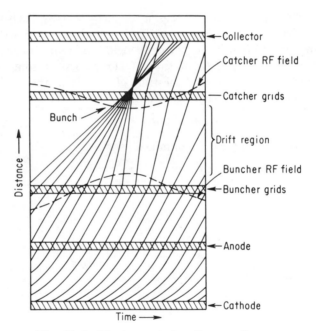

Fig. 21–2. Klystron velocity-distance diagram.

21–2. The klystron oscillator or amplifier

One form of klystron is shown in Fig. 21–3(a). An electrical equivalent
at (b) shows resonant circuits replacing the resonant cavities of (a). The
cavities resonate electrically when a beam of electrons passes through
them, much as a bottle develops an acoustical tone when air is blown across
its mouth.

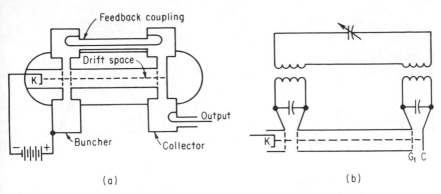

Fig. 21–3. The klystron and its equivalent circuit.

In the buncher gap, the flow of electrons is uniform throughout the cycle. As many electrons are speeded up as are slowed down, and the net energy interchange is zero. As the closely-bunched group of electrons pass through the catcher cavity, a strong a-c field is induced whose polarity is such as to slow down the bunch, or to extract energy from it. Half a cycle later the direction of the electric field across the gap has reversed, but this aiding field then acts on only the low-density or non-bunched portion of the beam. Thus many more electrons are slowed down than are speeded up, and there is a net exchange of energy from the beam to the radio-frequency circuit.

Since transit time is employed to aid in bunching of the electrons in the drift space, it is not a deterrent in high-frequency operation, as it is in conventional triodes. Klystron tubes of this type are useful to 30 gigacycles, with power outputs from kilowatts at the lower frequencies to a few milliwatts at the higher end of the range.

A more usual form of high-frequency klystron is the *reflex* type, of Fig. 21–4. In this device the output resonant circuit is eliminated and the collector is replaced with a *repeller*, maintained at a negative potential. In effect the reflex klystron utilizes an electron feedback which causes one resonant circuit to serve for both input and output. In passing through the two grids of the resonant cavity, the electron beam is given a velocity variation, as before. Faced by the negative repeller, the electrons are then repelled back into the region of the two grids. Sufficient transit time has been available during this slowing down and reversal action for the electrons to have become bunched, so that in passing through the resonant cavity in the reverse direction, they pass as bunches, inducing current in the resonant circuits as discussed previously.

The bunching action is illustrated in Fig. 21–5. Consider path *a*, plotted in distance and time, as that of an electron which passed through the input circuit at a time the potential was zero and becoming negative.

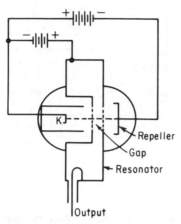

Fig. 21–4. The reflex klystron.

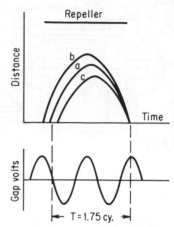

Fig. 21–5. Production of bunches in the reflex klystron.

It proceeds toward the repeller, but is slowed down, reversed, and returned to the gap. A second electron, as at b, passes through the gap at the time of a positive voltage and is given a velocity higher than that of a. It travels further against'the repelling field than the first electron, but it travels at a higher average velocity, and so it returns to the gap at the same instant as the first electron. A third electron, as at c, goes through the gap at a negative potential time, and is slowed down. It does not travel as far against the repelling field but travels more slowly, so that c is also able to return to the gap at the same time as a.

The action as these bunches return through the cavity gap is like that previously discussed, the phase conditions being such that energy is delivered from the bunched beam to the resonant cavity. The phasing of the bunches is controlled by the repeller voltage, while the frequency of operation is determined by the dimensions of the resonant circuit or cavity. The time of travel in the repeller or drift space must be $T = n + \frac{3}{4}$ cycles and is usually set at $1\frac{3}{4}$ or $2\frac{3}{4}$ cycles. Several modes or frequencies of operation are possible with one adjustment, with the cavity fixing the operation at one frequency. Broad tuning is possible through changing the dimensions of the resonant cavity, and fine tuning over about a one per cent range is possible with the repeller voltage.

21–3. Ballistics of the magnetron

A magnetic field was combined with a radial electric field by A. W. Hull, to produce the basic form of *magnetron*, another efficient oscillator at microwave frequencies. As in Fig. 21–6, a cylindrical anode A has a

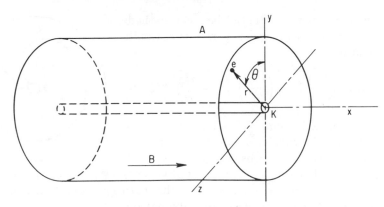

Fig. 21–6. Geometry of the basic magnetron.

cathode or electron source at K. The magnetic field is established longitudinally by a strong permanent magnet.

In polar coordinates the position vector $\bar{r}$ of the electron e is

$$\bar{r} = r(\cos\theta + j\sin\theta)$$

By differentiation it can be found that

$$\frac{d^2\bar{r}}{dt^2} = \left[\frac{d^2r}{dt^2} - r\left(\frac{d\theta}{dt}\right)^2 + j\frac{1}{r}\frac{d}{dt}\left(r^2\frac{d\theta}{dt}\right)\right](\cos\theta + j\sin\theta) \qquad (21\text{–}5)$$

from which it is seen that the motion may be described by two accelerations at right angles, a_r and a_θ, as

$$a_r = \frac{d^2r}{dt^2} - r\left(\frac{d\theta}{dt}\right)^2, \qquad a_\theta = \frac{1}{r}\frac{d}{dt}\left(r^2\frac{d\theta}{dt}\right)$$

These are analogous to a_x and a_y in rectangular coordinates. The accelerations will produce two electron velocity components, radial or v_r, and tangential or ω_θ. The total energy of the electron at any point in the region may be computed, and will be found wholly due to the radial electric field ϵ_r, since no work can be done by a magnetic field.

The energy relations give

$$\frac{m}{2}\left(v_r^2 + r^2\omega_\theta^2\right) = \int_{r_k}^{r} e\mathcal{E}_r\, dr \qquad (21\text{–}6)$$

Evaluation in terms of the parameters of the problem, with r_k as the cathode radius, and with radial electron emission assumed or $d\theta/dt = 0$ at the cathode surface, leads to

$$\frac{m}{2}\left[v_r^2 + \left(\frac{rBe}{2m}\right)^2\left(1 - \frac{r_k^2}{r^2}\right)^2\right] = -e\int_{r_k}^{r}\mathcal{E}_r\, dr = V_{kr} \qquad (21\text{–}7)$$

where V_{kr} is the potential between cathode and a point in the space at radius r. Consequently

$$v_r = \sqrt{\frac{2eV_{kr}}{m} - \left(\frac{rBe}{2m}\right)^2 \left(1 - \frac{r_k^2}{r^2}\right)^2} \quad (21\text{-}8)$$

For a fixed value of B, a large value of V on the anode will give a large radial velocity, and the electron paths will be as at (1), Fig. 21–7. For smaller V, the radial velocity will go to zero at some r, and the path becomes that at (2), with the tube cut off.

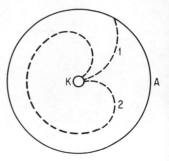

Fig. 21–7. Possible electron paths in the magnetron.

21–4. Magnetron oscillators

The modern magnetron tube was developed during World War II, from the above basic principles; it became a major source of power for radar in the centimeter wave length range.

The anodes are usually of the multicavity type, as in Figs. 21–8 and 21–9, although the exact cavity shape varies. The magnetic field is perpendicular to the plane of the page in Fig. 21–9(b), and a radial electric field is established between anode and cathode, with the anode positive. The magnetic field is sufficient for the tube to be in the cutoff condition with no a-c excitation present.

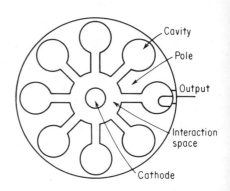

Fig. 21–8. One form of multi-cavity anode.

As in the klystron, the cavities serve as resonant circuits, and alternate poles become instantaneously positive and negative because of high-frequency voltages, although the whole anode structure is at positive d-c potential to the cathode. The effect is that of a number of resonant circuits in series around the periphery for which the circuit of Fig. 21–9(a) is an approximate equivalent. The circuit capacitance (electric field) is essentially concentrated across the gap, and the circuit inductance (magnetic field) is formed by the inner part of the cavity. The capacitances C_2 constitute the gap capacitances, whereas those marked C_1 are the capacitances between pole faces and cathode.

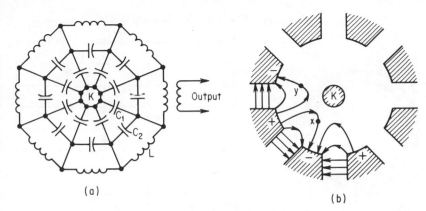

Fig. 21–9. (a) Equivalent circuit for the multi-cavity magnetron; (b) the electric fields.

Since the circuit returns upon itself, it can be seen that for a steady state to exist,

$$\beta = \frac{2\pi n}{N}$$

where

β = phase shift per section, in radians,
N = number of sections or pole faces,
n = number of cycles around cathode.

When $n = N/2$, the phase shift is π radians per section, and the pole faces alternate in polarity. This state, called the π *mode*, results in electric fields as in Fig. 21–9(b), and these fields rotate at a velocity such that two poles are passed per cycle.

Other modes of oscillation in which n takes on values of N, $N/3$, $N/4$, . . . , are also possible. They operate with field distributions different from the π mode, and at slightly different frequencies. To avoid the possibility of slight changes in current or field intensity causing a shift in mode and in frequency, it is desirable to accentuate the probability that the system will operate on the π mode, or to separate the frequencies of the other modes further from that of the π mode.

This may be done by *strapping* the anode with two small end rings, one connected to the even-numbered poles, the other to the odd-numbered poles. For the π mode the rings will be opposite in potential and will add capacity to the system, thereby *lowering* the resonant frequency. For other modes the phase differences between alternate poles cause currents to flow in the rings, thus placing the ring inductance in shunt with that of the anode and *raising* the frequency of the other modes. The desired

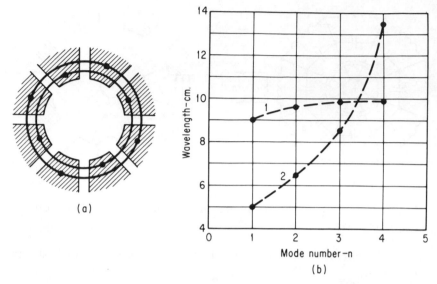

Fig. 21-10. (a) Strapped anode; (b) variation of wavelength with mode number for (1) unstrapped, and (2) the strapped magnetron.

result, a frequency separation of the π mode from the other modes, is obtained as indicated in Fig. 21-10(b).

With a-c fields such as are shown in Fig. 21-9(b) established, consider a single electron following a curved trajectory in the steady d-c electric and magnetic fields. If it has a clockwise tangential component of velocity and is at X, the electric field due to the a-c poles will be such as to increase its energy and its tangential velocity. An increase in tangential velocity will increase the magnetic force (f_m = Bev) tending to accelerate the electron toward the cathode. This increase in magnetic force will tend to neutralize the radial force due to the positive potential on the anode and cause the electron to be rather quickly returned to the cathode and re-removed from further action.

An electron at y is in a field in which the tangential electric field will slow it down, or extract energy from it. This process reduces the inward-directed magnetic force and allows the outward radial force due to the positive anode potential to accelerate the electron in an outward direction. Motion in an outward direction causes a magnetic force to redirect the electron with a tangential component. But tangential motion is opposed by the a-c electric field, which again extracts energy and slows down the electron. Electrons in the region of point y eventually reach the anode, having transferred energy from the static electric field to the dynamic electric field during their transit.

Electrons in positions such as x are quickly removed; electrons in positions near y are slowed down, redirected and accelerated, and again slowed down, with the process repeated until they reach the anode, so that a set of electron spokes are formed which rotate in synchronism with the fields produced by the poles, as shown in Fig. 21–11.

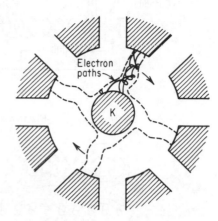

The electrons which are returned to the cathode absorb only a small amount of energy from the fields, whereas those rotating in the spoke efficiently convert energy from the static electric field to the dynamic electric fields set up by the resonant circuits.

The all-electronic translation of energy in the magnetron accounts for the high efficiencies reached, which

Fig. 21–11. Individual electron paths and the rotating electron "spokes."

are in the range of 30 to 60 per cent. The frequencies reached are above 30,000 megacycles.

Magnetrons are tunable over limited ranges by changing cavity volumes with plungers: by inserting plungers near the back ends of the slots, thereby lowering inductance and raising frequency; or by inserting plung-ers near the forward ends of the slots, these increasing the capacity and lowering frequency.

21–5. Traveling-wave-tubes (TWT's)

As in the several preceding types, the *traveling-wave-tube* employs a process which converts the d-c energy supplied to an electron beam into a-c energy by interaction of the beam and an electric or magnetic field; the result is amplification of an applied signal.

An electron beam is formed and focussed, caused to pass down a long interaction region, and finally arrives at a collector, as in Fig. 21–12(a). In the interaction region the electrons are held together or prevented from dispersing in transverse directions, by a strong longitudinal magnetic field supplied by a coaxially located focussing coil.

A common form of TWT applies the signal to a small diameter helix or coil which closely surrounds the electron beam, and the wave will travel essentially at the velocity of light along the wire from which the helix is wound. Because of the helical path, the actual forward progress of the wave along the axis of the helix is a fraction of the velocity of light,

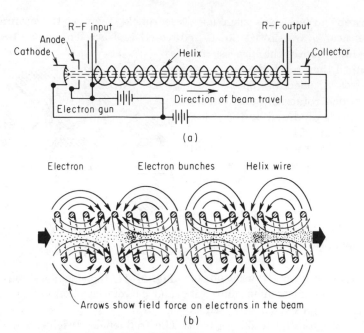

Fig. 21–12. Principle of the traveling-wave tube.

and is called the *phase velocity*. This velocity is comparable to the velocities achieved by the electrons in the beam under moderate accelerating voltages, and adjustment of the accelerating voltage permits reaching a condition where the phase velocity of the wave and the electron velocity in the wave approach equality.

The radio-frequency field of the helix may now exert a continuing force on the electrons of the beam, as indicated in Fig. 21–12(b); even though the signal fields are weak, the interaction distance may be many centimeters. The electrons which are in a retarding field region are slowed down, and the electrons in an accelerating field region are speeded up. The result is velocity modulation, and due to the length of the interaction region the beam will become bunched. As the beam travels down the helix, the electrons that are slowed down add energy to the circuit at the expense of beam energy, or induce a radio-frequency current in the helix. Both the density of the electrons in the bunch and the amplitude of the signal wave progressively increase as they travel together down the tube. At the collector end, the amplifier signal is transferred to an output circuit or waveguide under matched conditions.

In this process, those electrons that are accelerated extract energy from the circuit. If the beam voltage is so adjusted that the velocity of the beam is slightly higher than the phase velocity of the circuit wave, then more electrons are decelerated than are accelerated, and a net transfer of energy from the beam to the circuit occurs. There will be a maximum in the gain versus beam-voltage curve as a result.

Actually, the bunches induce a backward wave as well as the forward wave. Under the conditions described above, the phase relations and velocity of the backward wave components are such as to lead to ineffective coupling to the beam, and the effect may be neglected. In some forms of *TWT*'s the backward wave can be developed, and the forward wave then becomes negligible in effect.

In the klystron, the interaction between beam and circuit occurs over only a short distance, and to obtain a high unit field and transfer of energy a sharply-resonant, high-impedance circuit is needed, but this implies narrow-band frequency response. In the *TWT* the helix is a non-resonant circuit and the beam-circuit interaction occurs over a considerable distance at low field intensity. As a result, the *TWT* will amplify all signals which produce essentially the same phase velocity, and practical band widths of operation may approximate an octave of frequency.

At the long-wave limit of gain, the helix becomes electrically short, and there is insufficient interaction distance to transfer the required energy; at the short-wave limit the interaction becomes poor because the circuit wave concentrates close to the helix wires and does not enter the beam region.

21-6. The maser

In discussion of the parametric amplifier in Chapter 15, it was mentioned that usual amplifier noise was due to the inherent particle nature of current, and in devices not employing current phenomena the inherent noise could be low, allowing amplification of very weak signals. The *maser* (Microwave Amplification by Stimulated Emission of Radiation) and its optical offspring the *laser*, operate by reason of quantum mechanical release of energy from excited atoms or molecules, thus without conventional current, and do provide very small noise levels in amplification.

The ammonia maser was the first such device. Its operation is dependent on the fact that the nitrogen atom in the ammonia molecule may occupy either of two energy levels or positions with respect to the three hydrogen atoms, and that there is a certain probability of the atom being at either level at a given time. The difference in energy between the two levels is small and equal to the energy of a photon with a frequency of 24 gigacycles $(f = W/h)$.

In ammonia molecules the two levels can be separated by an electric field, the low energy molecules being dispersed and those in the higher level being concentrated and passed to a resonant cavity, tuned to the critical frequency. Here we must remember that our microwave signal introduced into the cavity field as a wave has a dual—it may also be thought of as a photon of suitable energy given by $W = hf$. If a microwave signal is introduced having a frequency exactly equal to the photon frequency which will be emitted by the molecule in its jump to the lower level, it can trigger or stimulate this jump. The ammonia molecules then fall back to their lower energy states, and emit the energy difference as photons. Where we introduced one photon, we now have two. If these photons each trigger other molecules, the chain reaction can be self-sustaining or the discharge can supply its own input. The amplifier turns into an oscillator, generating an output at the frequency of the photons emitted by the ammonia energy jump, as long as a supply of excited ammonia molecules is maintained.

The ammonia maser is at its best as an oscillator; to use it as an amplifier requires that the input signal be an almost exact frequency. The band width accepted is so narrow as to make this difficult, whereas for oscillator purposes the narrow band width or precision of frequency emitted is highly desirable. Such devices are now being employed as very stable frequency standards, expected to maintain frequency within 1 part in 10^{10} over long time periods.

It can be seen that the success of the ammonia maser was dependent on achieving a medium in which there was an abnormal population density of high-energy states, and stimulating them by a trigger input of appropriate frequency to emit photons as the atoms fall back to their lower energy states.

In the ammonia maser the over-population of high-energy states was achieved somewhat mechanically by electric-field sorting. In the next step, which led to development of solid-state masers, the desired high population density in a particular energy state was obtained by *pumping* or raising atoms in their normal or ground energy state, to a higher energy level by supply of energy.

The various energy levels used depend on differences in the electron spin in the atom, rather than on atomic energy jumps in molecules. In most atoms which are non-magnetic or unaffected by a magnetic field, the electrons are paired off with their spins or magnetism cancelled. There are a few atoms, however, in which some electrons have unpaired spins, and the material is then affected by a magnetic field or is paramagnetic; in particular those materials having more than one unpaired electron are used. In such atoms there will be one more energy level than there are unpaired electrons; chromium has three unpaired electrons and four energy levels, and ruby with chromium as one of its constituents is a particularly suitable maser material.

The value of using electrons having the spin as the level differentiating factor is that the exact energy difference between these levels can be varied somewhat by the magnetic field to which the crystal is exposed. Also, these electrons are to some extent affected by the magnetic effects of neighboring atoms, so that not all the electrons will be subjected to exactly the same field. As a result the energy levels differ very slightly, or jumps from these levels will yield slightly differing frequencies, which gives the solid devices a greater band width than the ammonia maser, and the frequency of response can be tuned over a wide range of frequencies by variation of the applied magnetic field.

Two basic requirements must be met if amplification is to be achieved. First, the emission of radiation by spontaneous transition of electrons between the two working levels must be very much less probable, than the emission of radiation when the jump between the same levels is triggered or stimulated by a small input of microwave energy of the correct frequency. This is a situation inherent in the metastable levels of atoms. Second, some mechanism must be provided to change or invert the normal population density of the several energy levels employed.

The probability that a transition from a state n to a state m of lower energy will take place is of the form

$$P_{n,m} = A_{n,m} + uB_{n,m}$$

where $A_{n,m}$ is the spontaneous transition probability, u is the introduced radiation (photon) density at the position of the atomic system, and $B_{n,m}$ is the probability of stimulated emission. Einstein showed that

$$A_{n,m} = \frac{8\pi hf^3}{c^3} B_{n,m} \qquad (21\text{–}9)$$

so that spontaneous emission increases as the cube of the frequency. Fortunately, in the microwave region, the probability of spontaneous transition for the energy levels under consideration is very small, so that stimulated emission by input signal energy makes microwave amplification possible.

For the second requirement, we might first note that if there are equal numbers of atoms in states n and m, the probability of jumps upward, absorbing energy or photons, is equal to the probability of jumps downward which emit photons. A net gain in outward radiation, or amplification, is possible only if there are more electrons in the upper energy state than in the lower one. Normally the ratio of population densities of atoms in the several states is such that $N_1 > N_2 > N_3$. If we can pump or excite atoms by introducing energy of frequency f_{13}, it may be possible to make $N_3 > N_1$. Amplification might then be possible by stimulated transitions from level 3 to level 2, at a frequency f_{32}. Another scheme, called a three-level maser, raises atoms to the 3 level with rapid spontaneous transitions following to the 2 level. If spontaneous transition from 2 to 1 is not very probable, a high density of electrons can be maintained at the 2 level, for stimulation by an input signal. This system allows simultaneous and continuous supply of energy or pumping of electrons from level 1 to 3, at frequency f_{13}, without interfering with the amplified output of stimulated emission at frequency f_{21}.

A number of materials, with small percentages of impurity elements, and having the required transitory electron levels are available. One is ruby, with chromium the active impurity which also gives ruby its color, another is lanthanum ethyl sulfate with gadolinium as the active impurity, or iron-doped titanium dioxide.

Masers are thus well suited to microwave amplification, even to the millimeter region. Inherent noise is a result of spontaneous emission, and this is related to a noise temperature as $T \geqq hf/k = 5 \times 10^{-11}f$. This is equivalent to a noise temperature of 5°K at 100 gigacycles. Another limit is imposed by the pumping energy, which must be supplied at a frequency higher than signal frequency, since the energy input per electron must be in one jump instead of in two as for the emission. Band width is dependent on the variation in energy level of the several states as between the individual atoms, due to slight magnetic intensity differences, or to line width from the spectral viewpoint, and approximates one per cent. Noise figures at present operating frequencies, when cooled to liquid nitrogen temperatures, are near zero.

Applications have been made as first-stage amplifiers for radio astronomy, space communications, and long-distance radar reception.

21–7. The optical maser or laser

In the laser (Light Amplification by Stimulated Emission of Radiation) the maser principle has been extended to optical or visible light frequencies of 10^{14} or 10^{15} cycles per second. In the past, light sources of high intensity utilized heated filaments or arcs, or an aggregate of tiny light sources operating independently of each other. The emission was a continuous spectrum of incoherent light. The laser provides the first opportunity to generate high intensity coherent or truly monochromatic light; the radiation will produce interference patterns and can be readily focussed in a small neighborhood.

The principle has been applied to generate light pulses in ruby, in which certain energy levels of the chromium atoms have been found to provide suitable output frequencies. The situation is illustrated in Fig. 21–13 where the pumping transitions occur in the green and yellow spectral region at 5600 A and 4100 A. This energy is supplied by repeated flashes of intense white light from a xenon flash tube wrapped around the ruby rod, as in Fig. 21–14. Spontaneous transition with emanation of heat then occurs in the crystal, and electrons drop from level 3 to the split metastable state 2. The population density of electrons at this level grows because of the long life time of about 10^{-3} seconds in this state.

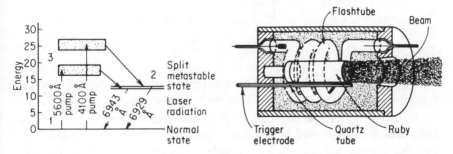

Fig. 21–13. Energy levels in the ruby laser.

Fig. 21–14. Ruby laser design.

When the population of electrons in state 2 exceeds that in 1 due to the pumping process, it is possible for laser action to begin. A spontaneous transition at 6943 A, or a triggering coherent beam of light at this wave length, will stimulate other atoms to emit radiation in step or coherency. This stimulated emission builds up very rapidly in an avalanche effect, until the stimulated downward transitions exceed the rate of production of excited atoms at 2 by the pumping process. The population excess is reduced below the maintaining level and the radiation dies, until pumping again establishes an excess population in the upper state and the radiation is again triggered. The result is a pulsed radiation, with repetition rate dependent on the amount of energy being supplied by the pump.

To increase the intensity of the triggering action, the ends of the ruby rod are optically flat and coated as partially reflecting mirrors. The mirrors turn part of the coherent beam back into the active volume, and the resulting feedback makes the ruby a regenerative oscillator. Only the modes which are reflected normal to the end mirrors will stimulate radiation, other modes ultimately being lost through the side surfaces of the rod, and the result is a very sharply parallel output beam. Output is obtained through the semi-reflecting mirror surfaces at the rod ends. It is found

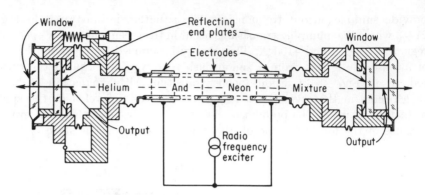

Fig. 21–15. Gas-phase continuous laser.

that output and band width are temperature dependent, and operation is usually at the temperature of liquid nitrogen or below.

It has been found possible to generate continuous output in a gas phase laser, as indicated in Fig. 21–15, using a helium-neon mixture. The two electrons of helium can have parallel or anti-parallel spins; in the first case the energy level is higher than in the second or net zero spin condition. Unexcited helium will have electrons in both levels, although the normal or ground state is that of the lowest energy spin. The higher energy level for the parallel-spin case is considerably above the normal state and is metastable, and a certain number of electrons are trapped in these levels.

Neon has an energy level very close to that of the helium metastable energy level. Collisions between metastable helium atoms and unexcited neon atoms have a high probability of energy transfer to the neon, and the neon population density in the excited level will increase. When these excited neon atoms return to their normal or ground state, they do so by several transitions which lead to output in the optical range.

Pumping is accomplished by establishing an electrical discharge in the gas by radio-frequency excitation. When the ionized helium atoms recombine, a fair percentage recombine as parallel-spin atoms and so the supply of metastable electrons is continually maintained.

While the process leads to continuous radiation, the gas-phase device is a low output device, due to the continuous output, whereas the ruby laser is capable of large peak power output, as the summation of the pumping energy supplied continuously. The line width of the gas laser appears to be very narrow, perhaps only a few hundred cycles.

Solid-state continuous output lasers are also in development.

References

1. Bloembergen, N., "Proposal for a New Type of Solid-State Maser," *Phys. Rev.*, **104,** 324 (1956).

2. Chodorow, M., Ginzton, E. L., Neilsen, I. R., and S. Sonkin, "Design and Performance of a High-Powered Pulsed Klystron," *Proc. I.R.E.*, **41,** 1584 (1953).

3. Collins, G. B., *Microwave Magnetrons.* MIT Radiation Lab Series, vol **6.,** McGraw-Hill Book Co, Inc., New York, 1948.

4. Fisk, J. B., Hagstrum, H. O., and Hartman, P. L., "The Magnetron as a Generator of Centimeter Waves," *Bell Syst. Tech. Jour.*, **25,** 167 (1946).

5. Gordon, J. P., Zeiger, H. J., and C. H. Townes, "Molecular Microwave Oscillator and New Hyperfine Structure in the Microwave Spectrum of NH_3," *Phys. Rev.*, **95,** 282 (1954).

6. ——, "The Maser—New Type of Microwave Amplifier, Frequency Standard, and Spectrometer," *Phys. Rev.* **99,** 1264, (1955).

7. Gordon, J. P., and White, L. D.," Noise in Maser Amplifiers," *Proc. I.R.E*, **46,** 1599 (1958).

8. Hull, A. W., "The Magnetron," *Jour. A.I.E.E.*, **40,** 715 (1921).

9. Kompfner, R., "The Traveling-Wave Tube as an Amplifier at Microwaves," *Proc. I.R.E.*, 35, 124 (1947).

10. Maiman, T. H., "Optical Maser Action in Ruby," *Nature*, 187, 493 (1960).

11. Pierce, J. R., "Reflex Oscillators," *Proc. I.R.E.*, **33,** 112 (1945).

12. ——., *Traveling-Wave Tubes.*, D. Van Nostrand Co., Inc., New York, 1950.

13. Pierce, J. R., and Field, L. M., "Traveling-Wave Tubes," *Proc. I.R.E.*, **35,** 108 (1947).

14. *Proceedings of the I.E.E.E.* Special issue on Quantum Electronics. **51,** 1–294 (1963).

15. Varian, R., and Varian, S., "A High-Frequency Oscillator and Amplifier," *Jour. App. Phys.*, **10,** 321 (1939).

Appendices

Selected Vacuum-Tube and Transistor Characteristic Curves and Data

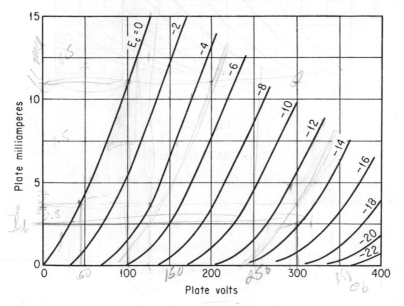

Fig. A–1. Type 12AU7 triode.

$$C_{gp} = 3.8 \text{ pf}; \quad C_{gk} = 4.2 \text{ pf}; \quad C_{pk} = 5.0 \text{ pf}$$
$$\text{Maximum anode dissipation} = 2.5 \text{ w}$$

At recommended Q point:

$$E_b = 250 \text{ v} \qquad \mu = 20$$
$$E_c = -8 \text{ v} \qquad r_p = 7700 \text{ ohms}$$
$$I_b = 9 \text{ ma} \qquad g_m = 2600 \text{ } \mu\text{mho}$$

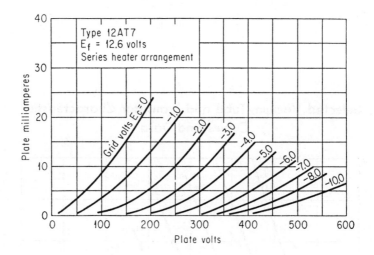

Fig. A–2.

Type 12AT7 (one unit)

$$C_{gp} = 1.5 \text{ pf} \qquad C_{gk} = 2.2 \text{ pf} \qquad C_{pk} = 0.5 \text{ pf}$$

At recommended Q point:

$$E_b = 250 \text{ v} \qquad \mu = 60$$

$$I_b = 10 \text{ ma} \qquad r_p = 10,900 \text{ ohms}$$

$$g_m = 5500 \text{ } \mu\text{mhos}$$

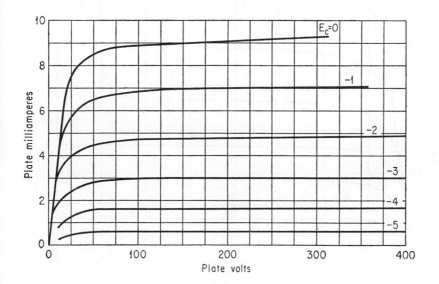

Fig. A–3.

Type 6AU6 pentode

$C_{gp} = 0.0005$ pf $C_{gk} = 6$ pf $C_{pk} = 7$ pf

Maximum anode dissipation = 2.5 w.

Maximum screen dissipation = 0.3 w.

At recommended Q point:

$E_b = 250$ v $I_b = 3$ ma

$E_{c1} = -3$v $I_{c2} = 0.8$ ma

$E_{c2} = 100$ v $r_p = 1$ megohm

$E_{c3} = 0$ v $g_m = 1650$ μmho

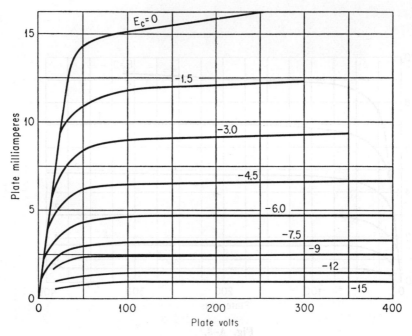

Fig. A–4.

Type 6BD6 pentode (variable μ)

$C_{gp} = 0.004$ pf $\qquad C_{gk} = 4.3$ pf $\qquad C_{pk} = 5$ pf

Maximum anode dissipation $= 3$ w.

Maximum screen dissipation $= 0.4$ w.

At recommended Q point:

$E_b = 250$ v $\qquad\qquad I_b = 9.0$ ma

$E_{c1} = -3$ v $\qquad\qquad I_{c2} = 3.0$ ma

$E_{c2} = 100$ v $\qquad\qquad r_p = 0.8$ megohm

$E_{c3} = 0$ v. $\qquad\qquad g_m = 2000$ μmho at -3 v bias.

$\qquad\qquad\qquad\qquad\quad = 10$ μmho at -35 v bias.

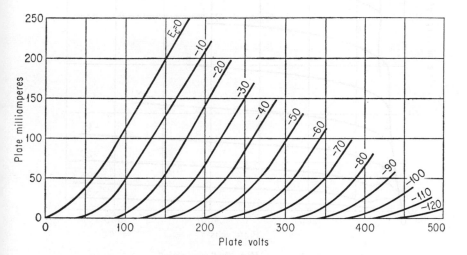

Fig. A–5. Type 2A3 power triode. $C_{gp} = 16.5$ pf; $C_{gk} = 7.5$ pf; $C_{pk} = 5.5$ pf. Maximum anode dissipation $= 15$ w. At recommended Q point (Class A): $E_b = 250$ v; $E_c = -45$ v; $I_b = 60$ ma; $\mu = 4.2$; $r_p = 800$ ohms; $g_m = 5250$ μmho.

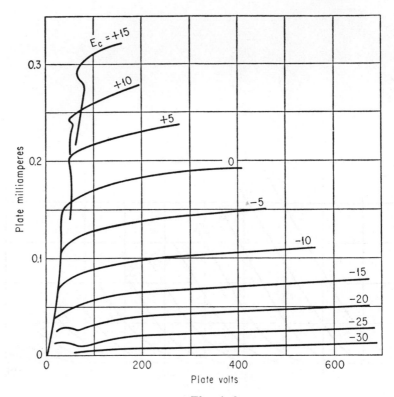

Fig. A–6.

Type 6L6 beam tetrode.

$$C_{gp} = 0.9 \text{ pf} \qquad C_{gk} = 11.5 \text{ pf} \qquad C_{pk} = 9.5 \text{ pf}$$

Maximum anode dissipation = 19 w.

Maximum screen dissipation = 2.5 w.

At recommended Q point (Class A):

$$E_b = 350 \text{ v} \qquad I_b = 54 \text{ ma}$$

$$E_{c1} = -18 \text{ v} \qquad I_{c2} = 2.5 \text{ ma}$$

$$E_{c2} = 250 \text{ v} \qquad r_p = 33{,}000 \text{ ohms}$$

$$g_m = 5200 \text{ } \mu\text{mho.}$$

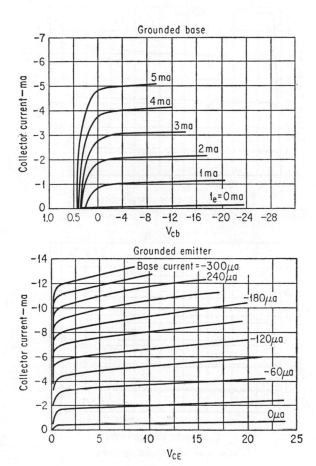

Fig. A-7.

Type 2N64 germanium transistor

$h_{fe} = 45$	$V_{CB} = 22$ v max
$h_{ie} = 1500$ ohms	$I_C = 10$ ma max
$h_{oe} = 2.0$ megohms	$I_E = 10$ ma max

Collector dissipation $= 33$ mw.

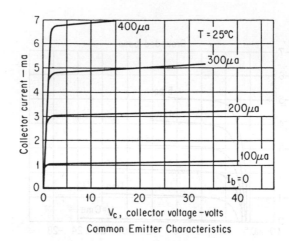

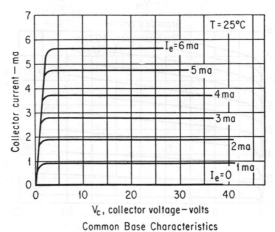

Fig. A–8.

Type 2N160 silicon transistor

$h_{fb} = 0.90$ (at $V_E = 5$ v, $I_E = 1$ ma) $C_c = 7$ pf

$h_{ib} = 100$ ohms $V_{CB} = 40$ v max

$h_{rb} = 400 \times 10^{-6}$ $V_{EB} = 1$ v max

$h_{ob} = 0.5$ μmho $I_C = 25$ ma max

$f_{ab} = 2$ mc $I_B = 5$ ma max

Selected Bessel-Function Values

x	$J_0(x)$	$J_1(x)$	$J_2(x)$	$J_3(x)$	$J_4(x)$	$J_5(x)$	$J_6(x)$	$J_7(x)$	$J_8(x)$	$J_9(x)$	$J_{10}(x)$
0	1.0000	0.0000	0.0000	0.0000	0.0000	0.0000	0.0000	0.0000	0.0000	0.0000	0.0000
1	0.7652	0.4401	0.1149	0.0196	0.0025	0.0003	0.0000	0.0000	0.0000	0.0000	0.0000
2	0.2239	0.5767	0.3528	0.1289	0.0340	0.0070	0.0012	0.0002	0.0000	0.0000	0.0000
3	−0.2601	0.3391	0.4861	0.3091	0.1320	0.0430	0.0114	0.0026	0.0005	0.0000	0.0000
4	−0.3971	−0.0660	0.3641	0.4302	0.2811	0.1321	0.0491	0.0152	0.0040	0.0009	0.0002
5	−0.1776	−0.3276	0.0466	0.3648	0.3912	0.2611	0.1310	0.0534	0.0184	0.0055	0.0015
6	0.1506	−0.2767	−0.2429	0.1148	0.3576	0.3621	0.2458	0.1296	0.0565	0.0212	0.0070
7	0.3001	−0.0047	−0.3014	−0.1676	0.1578	0.3479	0.3392	0.2336	0.1280	0.0589	0.0235
8	0.1717	0.2346	−0.1130	−0.2911	−0.1054	0.1858	0.3376	0.3206	0.2235	0.1263	0.0608
9	−0.0903	0.2453	0.1448	−0.1809	−0.2655	−0.0550	0.2043	0.3275	0.3051	0.2149	0.1247
10	−0.2459	0.0453	0.2546	−0.0584	−0.2196	−0.2341	−0.0145	0.2167	0.3179	0.2919	0.2075
11	−0.1712	−0.1768	0.1390	0.2273	−0.0150	−0.2383	−0.2016	0.0184	0.2250	0.3089	0.2804
12	0.0477	−0.2234	−0.0849	0.1951	0.1825	−0.0735	−0.2437	−0.1703	0.0451	0.2304	0.3005
13	0.2069	−0.0703	−0.2177	0.0023	0.2193	0.1316	−0.1180	−0.2406	−0.1410	0.0670	0.2338
14	0.1711	0.1334	−0.1520	−0.1768	0.0762	0.2204	0.0812	−0.1508	−0.2320	−0.1143	0.0850

Index